D1032503

Genetics & Human Heredity

QH
431
.H49

Genetics &

HUMAN HEREDITY

J. BEN HILL Professor Emeritus of Botany
The Pennsylvania State University
State College, Pennsylvania

HELEN D. HILL Assistant Geneticist
U.S. Regional Pasture Research Laboratory
Forage Crops and Diseases Section
Field Crops Research Branch
Agricultural Research Service
U.S.D.A.

McGRAW-HILL BOOK COMPANY, INC.

New York   Toronto   London

575.1
H553

59963

COPYRIGHT © 1955 BY THE McGRAW-HILL BOOK COMPANY, INC.

This book is fully protected by copyright, and no part of it, with the exception of short quotations for review may be reproduced without the written permission of the publisher

Library of Congress Catalog Card Number: 55–6857

PRINTED IN THE UNITED STATES OF AMERICA
BY THE MAPLE PRESS COMPANY, YORK, PA.

Preface

The preparation of this text designed for students in elementary genetics grew from the experience of teaching the subject over a number of years and has been written with the interest of the student in mind. The objectives of having the students understand the basic principles and the difficulties they encountered have been fundamental in the endeavor to present the subject with clarity and in logical sequence. The purpose has been to emphasize the long-accepted genetic concepts as well as to present more recent advances in the field.

The aspects of genetics may perhaps be considered under the following headings:

I. The Physical Basis or Cytogenetics in the Transmission of Hereditary Units or Genes, and

II. The Nature and Actions of the Genes in the Development of Characteristics.

The first of these categories, often referred to as "Classical Genetics" includes studies of Chromosomal Behavior concerned with the transmission of the genes from one generation to another. While some of this material is relatively old, dating from the first decade of the 20th century, much is comparatively recent. The newer parts of the physical basis, often called Cytogenetics, include studies in heteroploidy, involving the influence of varying chromosomal numbers in the development of characteristics in living organisms, chromosome structure, and chromosomal aberrations and possibly mutations, involving the nature of the gene.

Actually, all chromosomal behavior in heredity is properly included in cytogenetics. Even consideration of the separation of the two members of a pair of homologous chromosomes leading to the segregation of allelic genes may be considered as cytogenetics. These topics are fundamental and are still the subject of active research. The information gained in the broad aspects of cytogenetical research constitutes a great accumulation of knowledge in genetics. Regardless of how old or how "classical" this material may be it is basic to any discussion of genetics and is especially important in a textbook written for beginning students.

Although most of the highly important but still meager information on the nature and action of genes is new, the problem of gene action is as old or even older than the science of genetics. Darwin and Weismann were concerned with the topic. Even in the simplest cases of inheritance the idea of dominant and recessive characters was encountered. Very early the question arose of how one gene can act to develop a dominant trait and its allele to determine the recessive character. Another question long in the minds of biologists is that of the relationship of a gene transmitted to the zygote through one of the gametes and the subsequent appearance of the trait it determines in the organism. These matters were and still are part of the topic of the nature of the gene and the question of how genes act. In answer to these questions almost nothing has been known until recently, when, in response to intensive research, certain features of gene action have come to light. Some of these facts have to do with the development of structures and organs in plants and animals; these aspects of the subject from the material of "Developmental Genetics."

In other cases, the facts have to do with the relationship of genes to specific chemical reactions or to a series of reactions. Some of the gene actions are related to the chemical reactions involved in the production of colors in plants and the coats of animals, others to the development of specific proteins, enzymes, vitamines, or antigens. This material forms the aspects of the subject currently referred to as "Physiological" and "Biochemical Genetics." Regardless of the designation this is all part of the more comprehensive topic of the Nature and Action of the Gene in Heredity and Development.

As with the chromosome basis of heredity and cytogenetics, gene action must also be considered in any general discussion of genetics and references to both occur throughout the volume. Whereas the physical basis of heredity and cytogenetics and gene action constitute two aspects of genetics they are not mutually exclusive; they are complementary and both are essential to the development of knowledge of heredity.

Organization of a manuscript often is the result of compromise between a number of different sequences, each of which has some reasonable justification. The order followed here has been adopted with the hope of furnishing the reader with a foundation for a relationship between known cytological structures and the physiological processes leading to genetic consequences. The attempt has been made to present the major treatment of a topic in one place, though there may be and often are repeated references to it elsewhere.

For students adequately grounded in biology, the whole of Section 1, The Biological Background of Genetics may be omitted from class consideration and used only for reference. In the experience of the senior author there were few students sufficiently well prepared to omit this material. Some instructors may prefer to consider the topics, gene action and interaction, immediately following mendelian heredity. In such cases, since the sections are largely units, Section 3, Linkage and Crossing Over may be interchanged with Section 4 or even follow Section 5, Influence of Multiple Genes in

Development of Heritable Characters. With this changed sequence, modified ratios will follow immediately after the discussion of mendelism. Other changes in the order of presentation may occur to individual instructors, while some may prefer to omit certain sections or chapters. Teachers of purely agricultural courses might wish to dispense with Section 10, Twins and Human Heredity, while in courses for students interested in the human animal, this section would have considerable interest.

The illustrations have all been designed or selected to amplify the discussion and to aid the student in visualizing the subject matter. Examples in the text as well as the illustrations have been chosen to clarify the principles of heredity.

The examples and illustrations used in the text as well as the problems and questions are about equally balanced between the plant and animal kingdoms. Research has obviously been conducted either from the plant or animal standpoint, but the problems it was designed to solve are not restricted to one or the other. Nevertheless, attempts have been made to appeal to the interests of students in both fields by including discussions of applicability to both plants and animals.

In the preparation of the manuscript the authors have received generous assistance from others. Drafting for illustrations 33, 45, 47, 49, 51 to 58, 63, 85, 87, 92, 96, 97, 102, 111, 114, and 119 was done by Paul Blasingame; drawing for figures 30, 31, 46, 64, 65, 75, 76, 77, 174, 175 and 181 was done by Philip Bogatin; for figures 24, 26, and 118 by Albert Hildebrandt; for figures 32, 43, 116 and 120 by Elsie McDougle; and for figures 29 44, 50, 108, 109, and 171 by Kathryn Popp. For assistance with photography thanks are due to H. W. Thurston, Jr. and Homer I. Grove, The source of other photographs is acknowledged in the legends. For assistance with the manuscript we wish to express our gratitude to Virginia Penrod and Kathryn Popp. For frequent consultation our thanks go to James P. Kelly. Among those who have read portions of the manuscript we should like to mention with appreciation W. G. Donaldson, Julia M. Haber, Mary Hawthorne, Charles Rick, and Martha Overholts Rick. The suggestions of R. E. Dengler, J. Burne Helme, H. W. Popp, and Karl Sax on matters of terminology have been incorporated in various portions of the text. And especially we wish to acknowledge the constructive criticism and helpful advice of the following in connection with some of the chapters in their special fields: A. K. Anderson, S. S. Atwood, A. F. Blakeslee, Kenneth G. Brown, M. A. Farrell, R. J. Garber, Martha Jayne, D. F. Jones, James P. Kelly, Harold J. Miller, W. M. Myers, H. H. Newman, E. L. Nixon, John R. Shuman, H. W. Thurston, Jr., H. A. Wahl, and A. S. Wiener. The chapter on Population Genetics was written by Henry R. Fortmann.

Fall 1953   *J. Ben Hill*
State College, Pennsylvania   *Helen D. Hill*

Contents

section 3   Linkage and Crossing Over

section 4   Actions and Interactions of Genes in Development of Heritable Characters

section 8   Development of Heritable Characters

section 9   Sex Determination and Sexual Types

section 10   Twins and Human Heredity

The Biological Background of Genetics

The term **genetics,** applied to one of the biological sciences, is derived from the Greek language and means the science of being born or coming into being. It is concerned with heredity and deals with inheritance in the human race as well as in plants and the lower animals. Genetics has aesthetic and economic as well as personal and scientific appeal. Besides having an interest in inheritance in one's own family, many persons as amateurs or professionals are interested in growing plants and rearing animals, and some of them are keenly aware of the role of heredity in the success of their efforts.

Heredity in a restricted aspect is generally understood to be the tendency of offspring to be like their parents. But many variations and divergences as well as resemblances among related organisms are likewise inherited. Genetics, involving the study of descent and relationships of individuals, seeks, therefore, to account for all inherited characteristics that living organisms show.

It is emphasized throughout this discussion that genetics has been developed as a result of the use of the experimental method. One aspect is the analysis of breeding data resulting from self-fertilization, cross-fertilization, and selection in living organisms. Another is a study of cells, chromosomes, and nuclear divisions revealing the physical basis of heredity. In this phase, techniques and methods of genetics and its related biological science, cytology, have been combined into a very productive science called **cytogenetics.** Recently investigations have been directed toward the solution of the problem of gene action in the development of heredity traits. Attempts are being made to learn how genes, individually and collectively, exert their influence.

Although most students undertaking the formal consideration of genetics have already made some study of cell structure and life histories of plants and animals in other biological subjects, the facts and principles are often remembered only vaguely or perhaps completely forgotten. Material in Chapters 1 and 2 has been assembled to provide a background of biological facts for students beginning the study of genetics. For students with adequate preparation in biology, perhaps this material may be omitted from immediate consideration.

chapter 1

Cells, Chromosomes, and Genes

Early studies in heredity were undertaken without adequate knowledge of the cell with its nucleus, chromosomes, and the all-important hereditary units, or genes, contained in them. Extended investigations of cell structure more recently undertaken have yielded invaluable data on the nature of the cell and its parts. The following pages contain a brief outline of cell structure.

The Cell

Small individual units called **cells** are generally recognizable in plant and animal tissues. Although most cells are of microscopic proportions, some plant cells are large enough to be seen without magnification. Certain specialized structures such as the eggs of birds are extremely large, single cells. A typical cell consists of the living **protoplast**, the nonliving **vacuome** or system of vacuoles, and the surrounding protective membrane or cell wall (Fig. 1).*

THE PROTOPLAST. The **protoplast,** composed of the living material, **protoplasm,** is the organized working unit or protoplasmic system. Protoplasts are structurally differentiated into **nucleus** or **karyosome** and **cytosome** or **cytoplast.** The protoplasmic materials composing these structures may be regarded as **nucleoplasm** and **cytoplasm.**

---

* A consideration of cell structure and cell activities involves difficulties associated with the controversial interpretations of many topics which have been presented by various investigators during the last century. Factors leading to these controversies are: (1) the small size of the cell and its parts, many of which are near the limits of microscopic visibility, and (2) difficulties in reconciling the true nature of living structures with their appearance in permanent, stained preparations. Among controversial topics may be mentioned the structure and nature of protoplasm, including that within the nucleus; the presence or absence of a nuclear membrane; the ultimate structures of the chromosomes with chromonemata and postulated matrix; the reality of spindle fibers as seen in stained preparations of dividing nuclei; and the presence or absence of cell walls in animal cells. With these difficulties in mind, the following brief description of the cell has been undertaken. Within the limitations of a genetics text, it is manifestly impossible and undesirable to enter to any considerable degree into the discussion of many divergent views and theories. In order to have a brief, consecutive discussion, the most generally accepted viewpoint or theory is adopted. For more detailed accounts of these topics, the reader is referred to general discussions of cytology as cited in the literature list.

THE NUCLEUS. The **nucleus,** an essential cell part, is typically a globular structure, centrally located in most young cells, but generally occupying a peripheral position in older vacuolate plant cells. Within the nucleus, stainable material called **chromatin,** during nuclear divisions, appears aggregated into organized bodies, the **chromosomes.** The name *chromatin,* meaning *deep-staining material,* was applied to this important nuclear substance by early biologists on account of its great affinity for stains they used in preparing cells for microscopic observation. The term *chromosome* means, literally,

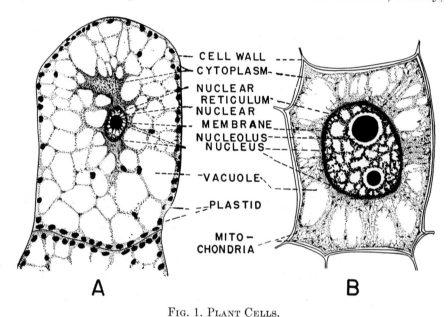

CELL WALL
CYTOPLASM
NUCLEAR RETICULUM
NUCLEAR MEMBRANE
NUCLEOLUS
NUCLEUS
VACUOLE
PLASTID
MITO-CHONDRIA

A   B

FIG. 1. PLANT CELLS.
A, low magnification, cell of one of the brown algae, *Stypocaulon,* showing nucleus, cytoplasm, and plastids. *B,* high magnification, cell from root tip of *Narcissus,* showing large nucleus, cytoplasm, and mitochondria. (Modified after Hill, Overholts, and Popp: "Botany," 2nd ed., New York, McGraw-Hill Book Company, 1950.)

colored body. Although chromosomes are not recognizable as such in all cells at all times, they are regarded as complete entities regardless of their visibility. During stages of nuclear division, they appear as definitely visible bodies of variable size and shape (Fig. 2 and 6). In nuclei that are not actively dividing, it is generally possible to see one or more small, readily stainable, spherical bodies, the **nucleoli** (singular, nucleolus). In stained preparations each nucleolus generally appears surrounded by a clear, unstained region, the *halo.* Besides chromosomes and nucleoli, the nucleus contains a stain-resistant material variously designated as **nuclear sap,** *nuclear gel,* or *karyolymph.* In addition to its physiological importance in the cell, the nucleus plays a major role in heredity.

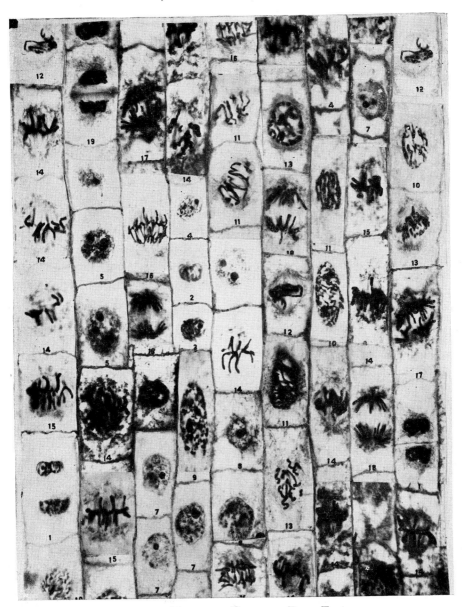

FIG. 2. MITOSIS IN HYACINTH ROOT TIP.
Portion of longitudinal section showing stages in cell and nuclear division.
(Courtesy, Philip F. Jones.)

THE CYTOSOME. Surrounding the nucleus is the largest part of the protoplast, the living material of the **cytosome** or cytoplast. It is designated the cytoplasm or cell material to distinguish it from the nucleoplasm or nuclear material. Structural differentiations in the cytosome which may be recognized are: the plasma membrane, the limiting membrane of the protoplast, and mass of protoplasm composing the cytosome, a group of nonliving vacuoles and canal systems that contain water solutions, oil, and other substances. The term **vacuome** has been applied to the system of vacuoles. Cells, especially plant cells, frequently contain nonliving substances such as mineral crystals, starch grains, food particles, and other by-products of metabolic activities of living protoplasm. These substances are present in the cytoplasm and in the vacuoles as **inclusions**. Also within the cytosomes of both plants and animals are minute, living bodies resembling bacteria in size and shape, the **mitochondria** or chondriosomes. Collectively the mitochondria constitute the **chondriome**. In plant cells, the cytosome also contains microscopic bodies, considerably larger than mitochondria. These are called **plastids**, literally *small bodies*. On the basis of their contained pigments, plastids are designated *leucoplasts*, *chloroplasts*, and *chromoplasts*. Leucoplasts are colorless bodies; chloroplasts develop the green pigment, chlorophyll, that gives plants their characteristic green color; and chromoplasts develop yellow and orange carotenoid pigments. Collectively the plastids constitute the **plasmon** or *plastidome*.

THE CELL WALL. The cell wall is a nonliving, protective structure deposited by the protoplast surrounding the living material. Plant cells characteristically have cellulose cell walls, which may be conspicuous, hard, and thickened. The statement that animal cells do not have walls is often made, but some animal cytologists, as Wilson, have considered walls present in animal cells. Whether they be regarded as walls or not, outer membranes of animal cells are much less conspicuous than those of plant cells.

GROWTH AND MULTIPLICATION OF CELLS AND CELL PARTS. Cells and their component protoplasmic parts, the cytoplasm, plastids, nucleus, chromosomes, and genes, all have capacity for growth and multiplication. In general, division of the cell and its parts accompanies growth (Fig. 2 and 6).

AN OUTLINE OF THE CELL AND ITS PARTS

Protoplast. The living, working unit or protoplasmic system made up of the living material, protoplasm

Nucleus or karyosome. Central organ of the living protoplast composed of protoplasmic material designated nucleoplasm

Nuclear membrane

Nucleoli

Chromatin, chromosomes

Nuclear gel, nuclear sap, or karyolymph

Cytosome or cytoplast. The living protoplast surrounding the nucleus
  Plasma membrane, the external layer of the protoplast
  The principal mass of cytoplasm
  Vacuolar membrane, a cytoplasmic membrane limiting the vacuole
  Plasmon, composed of plastids, especially abundant in plants:
    Leucoplasts
    Chloroplasts
    Chromoplasts
  Chondriome, composed of extremely small, living structures called mitochondria or chondriosomes
  Vacuome or nonliving structures in the cytoplasm, composed of vacuoles and canal systems in the cytoplasm and containing water solutions, oil, and other substances
  Inclusions, numerous nonliving substances such as mineral crystals, starch grains, and other food particles formed by metabolic activities of the living protoplast and deposited in the cytoplasmic mass.
Cell Wall. A nonliving, protective structure formed by activities of the protoplast and deposited outside of the living material

The Chromosomes

The thought that the chromosomes carry the hereditary units or genes and are distributed to the germ cells by the mechanism of nuclear division has come to be called the Chromosome Theory of Heredity. The relationship of chromosomes to heredity makes their study of paramount importance in genetics.

CHROMOSOME FORM AND STRUCTURE. Chromosomes are more complicated structures than was implied in older descriptions of deep-staining, rod-shaped bodies. Instead of being merely granular bodies, chromosomes have definite structural and morphological characteristics. The chromosome consists of a central, differentiated, threadlike portion called the **chromonema,** an enveloping mass of chromatin called the matrix surrounding the central thread, and, according to some investigators, a thin outer sheath or pellicle, the presence of which is generally inferred from behavior rather than demonstrated (Fig. 3). The term *chromonema* (plural, chromonemata) is made up of the Greek words *chroma* and *nema* meaning color and thread, respectively, and was applied because of affinity of the chromonema for certain stains. In favorable preparations, small dense masses, **chromomeres** (Greek *meros*, part, and *chrom*, colored), may be observed at irregular intervals in the chromonemata. Chromomere literally means the deep-staining particle of chromatin in the chromonema. The hereditary units or genes are thought to be located in these chromomeres (pp. 11–14). The chromonemata are regarded as the most important structural features of chromosomes and are sometimes called the **genonemata** or *gene strings,* because the genes are associated with them.

A part of most chromosomes that can be identified as permanent is a small structure in the chromonema called the **centromere.*** Although the term *centromere* means literally the *central body*, its position is variable in different chromosomes. It may be near an end or at any point between the two ends of the chromosome. Since the position is normally constant for any individual chromosome, it becomes an identifying character. Although the centromere is small, its position can frequently be recognized, because it is normally located in a narrow place in the chromosome, called the primary constriction or the centric constriction. The parts of the chromosome

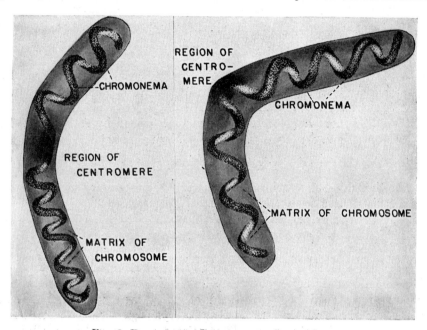

FIG. 3. DIAGRAM OF CHROMOSOME STRUCTURE.

between the centromere and each end are called the *arms* of the chromosome. When these are of unequal length, they may be referred to as the longer and shorter arms.

CHROMOSOME MORPHOLOGY AND INDIVIDUALITY.   Chromosomes are of microscopic size but may be relatively large, intermediate, or small. They may be of various shapes: straight or rod-shaped, twisted or spiral, curved, filamentous, or almost spherical bodies. Long chromosomes may appear in a variety of forms with V, J, L, or O common shapes (Fig. 4).

---

* Numerous other terms have been used to designate this chromosomal structure. Some of them are: insertion region, spindle-fiber attachment, achromite, primary constriction, kinomere, and kinetochore. White, in his recent book on animal cytology, prefers the term *centromere* because of the easy derivation of adjectival forms such as acentric, monocentric, dicentric, polycentric, etc.

They may be of even thickness throughout their length, or they may be narrow or constricted at some regions. The position of the centromere or spindle-fiber attachment, whether near one end of the chromosome or near the middle, is an important morphological feature. Among the minor features used in identifying chromosomes, constrictions, *terminal knobs,* and *satellites* or *trabants* may be mentioned. Satellites are small, spherical bodies, generally attached to the ends of certain chromosomes by a narrow chromatin thread which may be only a very much elongated constriction. Minor

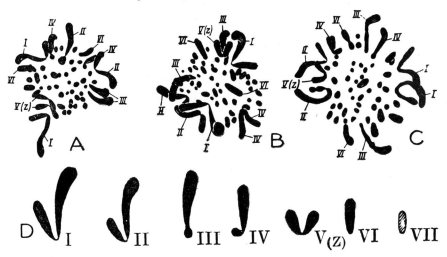

FIG. 4. CHROMOSOMES OF THE FOWL.

A, from an embryonic testis, showing two V-shaped sex chromosomes. *B,* from embryonic ovary, showing one sex chromosome. *C,* from a somatic cell, evidently female. The chromosomes are numbered in descending order of size, with sex chromosomes shown as V$_{(z)}$. Not all the chromosomes are shown in these diagrams. Studies place the diploid number at 80 for this species. *D,* the seven largest chromosomes of the fowl have distinguishing characteristics, including length, point of attachment of the spindle fiber, and relative length of the arms. (Courtesy, F. B. Hutt and W. F. Lamoreux, modified after Sokolow and Troimow, from *J. Heredity.*)

morphological features may be constant structures in some chromosomes and serve to identify them. Their functions are largely unknown. With the above criteria, chromosome morphology has been determined in a number of organisms extensively used in genetical studies. Among them are the fruit fly, *Drosophila;* the Jimson weed, *Datura;* Crepis; Indian corn or maize; and others.

CHROMOSOME NUMBERS. Chromosome numbers are, in general, constant for each species but vary greatly among the many plants and animals and are known to vary even within some species. Chromosome numbers may be used as an index of relationship between and within species. Among well-known mammals, 60 is a common chromosome number, although sheep are reported to have 54 chromosomes and man is known to have 48. Some lower animals as Paramecium and other similar

Table I

CHROMOSOME NUMBERS
ANIMALS

Homo sapiens, man	2N	48
Canis familiaris, the dog	2N	78
Tatu novemicinctum, the armadillo	2N	60
Bos taurus, the ox	2N	60
Capra hircus, the goat	2N	60
Ovis aries, the sheep	2N	60
Ovis aries, the sheep (Count by Berry)	2N	54
Equus caballus, the horse	2N	60
Gormys bursaria, the pocket gopher	2N	84
Cavia, the guinea pig	2N	60–64
Lepus, the rabbit	2N	44
Marsupials	2N	22–28
Fowls{	2N	36
	also 2N	80
Reptiles	2N	48
Frogs	2N	22–26
Drosophila melanogaster, the fruit fly	2N	8
Solenobia triquetrella, one of the moths	2N	120
Ascaris megalocephala, var. *univalens*, one of the nematodes	2N	2
Ascaris megalocephala var. *bivalens*, one of the nematodes	2N	4
Cambaris virillis, one of the Crustaceae estimated,	2N	200
Artemia, in one parthenogenetic species of brine shrimp, estimated	2N	168
Castinidium variable, one of the rhizopods estimated	2N	1500–1600
Aulacantha scalymatha estimated	2N	1600
Paramecium, estimated	2N	several hundreds but less than 1000

PLANTS

Some species of Fungi	2N	4
Sphaerocarpos, one of the liverworts	2N	16
Osmunda regalis, the royal fern	2N	44
Ophioglossum, one of the ferns	2N	344
Morus, the mulberry, of Japanese origin	2N	24 and 48
Morus nigra, mulberry of Chinese origin, estimated	2N	224 and 308
Kalanchoe, a member of the family Crassulaceae, estimated	2N	500
Cannabis sativa, the hemp	2N	20
Humulus japonicus, one of the hops	2N	16
Phlox	2N	14
Pisum, the pea	2N	14
Lycopersicon, the tomato	2N	24
Solanum tuberosum, the potato	2N	48
Datura, the Jimson weed	2N	24
Pyrus malus, the apple	2N	34
Prunus laurocerasus, a cherry	2N	170–180
Crepis capillaris, one of the species of the composites	2N	6
Agave, one of the East African species	2N	150
Ananas, the pineapple, certain hybrid varieties	2N	150
Crocus, certain species	2N	6
Lilium, the lily	2N	24
Zea mays, the cultivated corn	2N	20
Triticum vulgare, the cultivated wheat	2N	42

forms have numerous chromosomes, sometimes estimated to be numbered by the hundreds, while others comparatively low in the scale of evolution as compared with mammals have only a few chromosomes.* For example, the fruit fly, *Drosophila*, has 8, and a nematode worm, *Ascaris*, has 2 and 4 chromosomes. Although the range in chromosome numbers is not quite so great, conditions similar to those in animals are also found in plants. Some plants, low in the scale of evolution, have only a few chromosomes, but small numbers are likewise characteristic of some species in the highest order of plants. Among the lowest numbers of chromosomes known for plants are 4 in certain fungi, belonging to the Agaricaceae, and 6 in *Crepis capillaris*, belonging to the composites, one of the most highly specialized families of the flowering plants. At the other extreme of the range of chromosome numbers in plants is the estimated number of approximately 500 recently reported for an undetermined species of *Kalanchoe*, a member of the family *Crassulaceae*, in the angiosperms. Table I presents a restricted list of chromosome numbers known for representative types of animals and plants.

The Genes

The hereditary units basic to the development of contrasting characteristics, such as tallness or dwarfness in pea plants, red or blue colors in flowers, gray or black coats in mice, are located at definite points or loci in the chromosomes. Mendel's designation of the hereditary unit was the "determiner of a character." Later the terms *hereditary factor* and *gene* were introduced. Of these, gene is now generally preferred. The term **gene** is related to the Greek word *genos* meaning race, stock, or offspring. Emphasizing the genetical and cytological relationships, another term, **allele,** pronounced al-leel', has come into use. Each member of a pair of genes may be referred to as the allele of the other, and the pair termed alleles or allelic genes. Alleles are genes occupying corresponding loci in homologous chromosomes. Allelism is then the condition of being allelic. Allele and an earlier term, *allelomorph*, with similar connotation, are derived from the Greek *allēlōn*, meaning "of one another" or reciprocal. Allelism also carries the idea of being parallel. Thus the terms *allelosomes* and *allelosomic* are applied to the two members of a pair of homologous chromosomes.

THE POSITION AND SIZE OF GENES. Analysis of thousands of carefully planned genetical experiments indicates a linear arrangement of the genes in the chromonemata within the chromosomes. This has often been likened to the arrangement of beads on a string, hence the term genonema or "gene string" sometimes applied to the chromonema. Chromosome maps, based on genetical data, show the relative positions of genes in the chromosomes of Drosophila, of maize or Indian corn, and other organisms (p. 151). Of the many attempts to learn about the internal structure of chromosomes, none has yet revealed an identifiable gene. Dense portions in the chromonema, the chromomeres, are generally thought to be the locations of genes. The giant chromosomes in the *salivary glands* of

---

* Acknowledgments are due to Dr. Theophilus Painter, Dr. T. T. Chen, and Miss Irene H. Corey for suggestions as to the range of chromosome numbers in animals.

Drosophila larvae show series of conspicuous bands or actually discs apparently of complex structure (Fig. 5). One of these giant chromosomes arises as a result of the pairing of two homologues followed by successive longitudinal splittings in the chromonemata without separation of the threads. The bands or discs are, therefore, the chromomeres of several or many chromonemata and probably represent the location of genes. Actual position of the bands on salivary-gland chromosomes and that of the genetically located genes corresponds in many cases.

To determine the approximate size of a gene, some investigators calculated the volume of a chromosome, as for example the **X** chromosome in

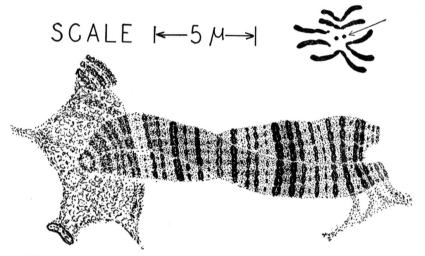

FIG. 5. SALIVARY CHROMOSOME IV OF DROSOPHILA MELANOGASTER AND THE ENTIRE GROUP OF GONIAL CHROMOSOMES AT METAPHASE.

Both are shown on the same scale. In the gonial group the small fourth chromosomes are represented by small black dots in which no structural details can be seen under the highest magnification, in striking contrast to the wealth of detail visible in the salivary chromosomes. (Courtesy, C. B. Bridges, from *J. Heredity*.)

Drosophila, and divided this by the number of genes postulated for it. From these calculations, it was determined that the individual genes must be too small to be seen by the best compound microscope. Pease and Baker in 1949 published results of their studies including micrographs taken with the electron microscope that showed shapes of particles in the bands of the salivary-gland chromosomes of Drosophila. They found spindle-shaped particles that, they say, may *reasonably* be genes. Although the particles were prevailingly flat and spindle-shaped, there were other forms including such as cigar-shaped, globular, and asymmetrical bodies.

THE NUMBER OF GENES.   In organisms which have been the subject of extensive genetic experiments, relatively large numbers of genes are known. The organism best known genetically is the fruit fly or vinegar fly,

Drosophila melanogaster. The effects of several hundred genes have been carefully studied in Drosophila, and considering all the types with their alternate multiple allelic forms, possibly as many as two or three thousand genes are known. About 400 to 500 genes are known in maize or Indian corn, similar numbers in the Jimson weed, *Datura,* and more than 100 are identified in peas.

Since the total number of genes in a highly organized plant or animal must be large, there has been speculation as to the total number of genes in an organism. With the number of chromosomes limited in every organism, each chromosome carries a large number of genes, in some cases probably 1,000 or more. Gowen and Gay have calculated 14,380 as the possible total number of genes in Drosophila. If the fruit fly has this number of genes, what number might be expected in complex organisms such as domesticated animals? Could man possibly have more hereditary units than the fruit fly, *Drosophila?* Estimates of the number in the human being are based on (1) analogy with Drosophila in which the relative lengths and possible numbers of genes of all chromosomes in each organism are compared and (2) knowledge of the relative rates of occurrence of some lethal mutations. Independent approaches by various authors suggest a range of number of gene loci in man from 20,000 to 42,000.

THE PHYSICAL AND CHEMICAL NATURE OF THE GENE. Much thought and research have been devoted to the problem of the physical and chemical nature of the gene. Most investigators regard the gene as a distinct hereditary unit which is relatively, but not absolutely, stable. Genes may undergo *change* or **mutation,** giving rise to alternate or allelic forms (p. 386). Since "normal" genes are known only through the actions and contrasting influences of their alleles, it is generally thought that the actions of only those genes which have mutated are recognizable. There is considerable variation in the frequency of mutation, some genes mutating readily, some very infrequently. Genes which never mutate may remain unknown. Perhaps genes may be subject to constant, though slight change, but only a few of the many mutations produce recognizable somatic or body changes.

There have been various suggestions as to the nature of the genes. They are generally thought to be of molecular order. Some workers postulate that genes are large, single organic molecules, and others that they are groups or configurations of several molecules. Regardless of the number of molecules involved in the structure of genes, it is now generally considered that chemically they are made up of nucleoproteins, possibly of varying complexities. A suggestion, gaining increasingly wide support, is that a gene, although a genetic unit, is not a unitary structure but is possibly of a multiple nature. Huskins has emphasized the multiple thread or polytene nature of chromosomes, and this feature may have a relation to the structure of the gene. According to this theory of gene structure, the gene is actually composed of layers or lamellae, making up a series of platelets. The postulated structure may be likened to a block of plywood. The layers or platelets, while intimately associated, may be more or less independent of each other and individually subject to chemical or physical changes which may result in a mutation.

The action of the gene has been compared to enzymatic action. Although there is evidence in the inheritance of certain characters that some of the primary or secondary products of genes may be enzymatic, at present the tendency is not to regard the gene itself as an enzyme. The data of Mangelsdorf and Fraps from work with the vitamin-A content in the endosperm of yellow corn, a character dependent upon the cumulative action of three pairs of genes, showed that the larger the number of dominant genes the more intense the yellow color and the greater the vitamin-A content. But enzyme activity is seldom closely related to the concentration of the enzyme. Speculating on "what the gene is not," they concluded, therefore, that the gene itself is probably not an enzyme. The topic of gene action is further discussed in Chapters 21 and 22.

REDUPLICATION OF GENES. A fundamental property of genes is their ability to duplicate themselves. One theory of reduplication is that the material composing the gene increases by the assimilation of nonliving material and that the gene divides when the chromonema (or chromonemata) of the chromosome divides. Another possibility is that the materials (molecules or atoms) constituting the gene copy their configuration and thereby make exact duplicates of themselves. Sturtevant suggested that specificity in genes may be more related to shape than to chemical composition and that the new gene is moulded about the old one. He further suggested that the gene may be visualized as a platelet possibly only one layer thick. One face of the gene then acting as a model or templet would automatically fix the other. This structure would lend itself to easy and exact duplication. The duplicated genes would be separated at the following or accompanying division. Some investigators, recognizing the multiple chromonemata or polytene nature of chromosomes and layered structure of genes, consider the possibility of continuous reduplication of genes. The gene duplication may proceed independently of nuclear division, but the final distribution of genes to new cells must be associated with the nuclear divisions of either mitosis or meiosis.

Nuclear Divisions

There are two types of nuclear division. One of these, **mitosis,** is characteristic of all growing tissue in animals and in plants, both somatic and reproductive. The other, **meiosis,** is confined to reproductive tissue and even there is restricted to a limited part of the reproductive cycle.

MITOSIS. The term *mitosis* comes from the Greek words *mitos,* meaning thread, and *ōsis,* meaning condition or process. Mitosis means literally a threadlike condition and refers to the appearance of the long slender chromo-somes, characteristic of the early stages of the dividing nucleus. During mitosis successive stages known as *prophase, metaphase, anaphase,* and *telophase* are recognized (Fig. 6 and 7). These terms come from the Greek word *phasis,* meaning appearance, combined with prefixes also from the

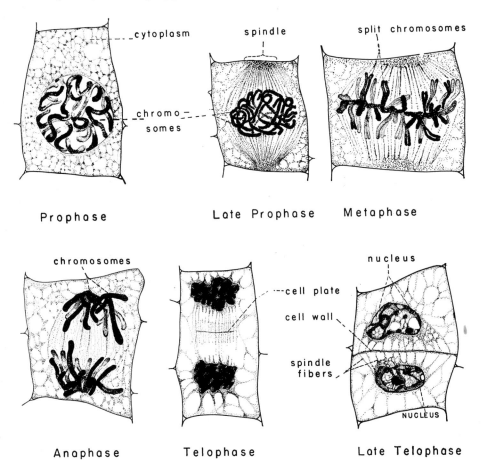

FIG. 6. MITOSIS IN CELLS OF ROOT TIP.
(Modified after Hill, Overholts, and Popp: "Botany," 2nd ed., New York, McGraw-Hill Book Comapny, Inc., 1950.)

Greek language. *Pro* means before. Thus prophase means literally the ap-pearance before division and refers to the early or preliminary events of nuclear division. *Meta* means change or later, and metaphase, the appear-ance of changing or a later appearance. Among several meanings of the prefix *ana,* one is equivalent to back. The term *anaphase* is applied to the movement of the chromosomes as they leave the equator of the division spindle and go back into the newly organized nuclei. *Tel*, meaning last or final, indicates the last or completion stage of nuclear division.

During the early prophase, the chromosomes appear as double, greatly elongated threads uniformly dispersed through the nucleus. Each thread represents the chromonema of a new chromosome. The doubling is the result of the longitudinal splitting of each chromosome which produces two identical halves called **chromatids**.* Cytological observations indicate that the central thread or chromonema of a chromosome is a compound structure of several strands or threads. A chromosome with a multiple central strand is termed a *polytene* structure. During nuclear division, the polytene chromosome splits lengthwise, and each half chromosome or chromatid receives one-half of the central strands. Later in the prophase the chromosomes contract and thicken, and, according to some authors, each of the two threads composing a chromosome begins to accumulate a stainable matrix. Toward the end of the prophase or the prometaphase, as it is sometimes called, the nuclear boundary or membrane disappears, the nucleoli disappear, and a bipolar-division spindle or achromatic figure forms. The spindle figure is apparently formed from the nuclear sap or karyolymph of the nucleus. In some cases, especially in animal cells, cytoplasm may enter into the formation of the division spindle and its *polar asters*. During these developments, the longitudinally split chromosomes, each with two chromatids, move toward the middle or equator of the spindle.

The spindle appears to contain striations or "spindle fibers," some of which have attachments to the chromosomes in the region of the centromere. Again, as with certain other cellular structures, the reality of spindle fibers has been questioned. Schrader, however, after discussing the pros and cons of the reality of spindle fibers, concludes they exist in some form as actual entities.

During the metaphase the chromosomes are grouped midway between the two poles at the equator of the spindle. In early metaphase stages, the two chromatids are often slightly separated at their ends (Fig. 6). At full metaphase the two chromatids of each chromosome lie close together throughout their length with at least the centromere region of each pair directly on the equator. The entire nuclear-chromosome complement is variously disposed, forming the *equatorial plate*. Separation of the two sister chromatids of each chromosome is accomplished during the anaphase. Separation starts in the region of the centromere where, by splitting of the old one, a new centromere becomes part of each chromatid. The chromatid centromeres move apart, possibly under some repulsion force. Gradually,

---

* The ending -*id* of the word *chromatid* has the meaning of derived from or the descendant of, literally the son of. Thus chromatids are derived from chromosomes or are the descendants of chromosomes. The term *chromatid* is properly applied to the half chromosomes so long as they remain attached in the region of the centromere. According to current usage, when the halves are separated during the anaphase of a nuclear division, they are again designated as chromosomes.

the chromatids separate and, with the centromeres leading, the sister chromatids move toward opposite poles of the spindle, in the anaphase.

At the telophase the two groups of new chromosomes round up and form two new nuclei, one at each pole of the nuclear-division spindle. During the telophase a nuclear membrane surrounds each nucleus, and the typical number of nucleoli, developed under the influence of specific nucleolus organizers associated with certain chromosomes, are formed in each of the nuclei. Toward the end of the telophase, the chromosomes assume their threadlike form. The granular appearance characteristic of the metabolic or resting nucleus is interpreted as resulting from the uniform distribution of the attenuated chromosomes. Between the active phases of division, the nucleus is in an interphase, and individual chromosomes are rarely visible. Other evidence, however, indicates that chromosomes although usually not recognizable retain their structural individuality throughout the interphase as well as during the dividing stages of the nucleus. **Cytokinesis,** the division of the cytosome, frequently but not always accompanies mitosis.

SUMMARY OF MITOSIS. Mitosis, the ordinary type of nuclear division with its prophase, metaphase, anaphase, and telophase, occurs in growing tissue, both somatic and reproductive. During the process *each chromosome of the nuclear complement is split once longitudinally;* this is *followed by a single complete nuclear division.* The result of mitosis is the formation of two nuclei each with identical halves of all the chromosomes of the original nucleus. During mitosis each gene is duplicated, and the new genes also pass into the new nuclei. Mitosis is, therefore, a cellular process which results in the passing of chromosomes *without change of number* or gene content from old into new nuclei.

MEIOSIS. During reproduction certain cells in the last stages of their development undergo a distinctive type of nuclear division called meiosis (Fig. 8, 10, 11, and 20). The term **meiosis** comes from the Greek word *meioō*, to make less, combined with *ōsis*, a condition or process. Meiosis, then, actually is a lessening or reducing process referring specifically to *reduction in the number of chromosomes.* Although there may be differences in details, the characteristic stages of prophase to telophase described for mitosis are also recognized in the meiotic divisions. Actually, the *process of meiosis consists of two nuclear divisions* which occur in quick succession. Meiosis takes place only in the reproductive cells, that is, in the 2N sporangia of plants and in the 2N sex glands or gonads of animals.* Any plant or animal cell capable of undergoing meiosis may be referred to as a **meiocyte.** *General uniformity in the processes of meiosis with the compensating phenome-*

---

* Huskins and associates have found that meristematic cells of onion-root tips treated from 5 to 19 hours with 4 to 6 per cent solutions of sodium ribose nucleate showed chromosome pairing and reduction divisions similar in essentials to the divisions seen in germ cells. They concluded that the treatment only increased the frequency of phenomena that occur naturally.

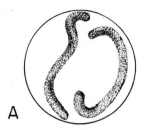

A

**Nucleus with one Pair of
Chromosomes**

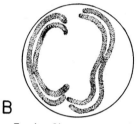

B

**Each Chromosome Split
Forming two Chromatids**

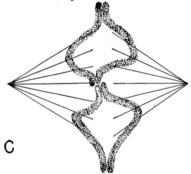

C

**The Division Spindle
and Separation of Chromatids**

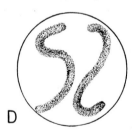 

D   **E**

**The two new Nuclei Resulting from Mitosis
No Change in Chromosome Number**

Fig. 7. Diagram of Mitosis.

There is no pairing of chromosomes and no change in chromosome number.
Compare with Fig. 8.

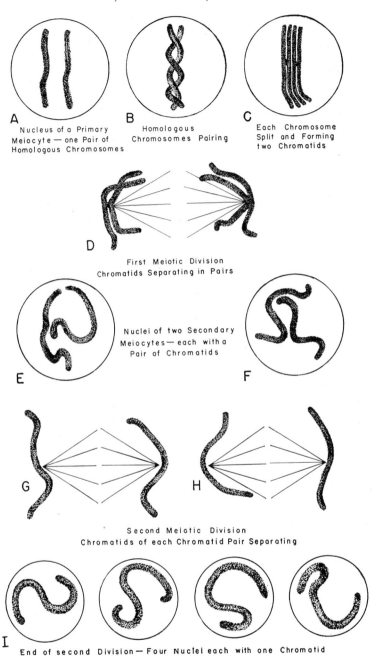

A. Nucleus of a Primary Meiocyte — one Pair of Homologous Chromosomes

B. Homologous Chromosomes Pairing

C. Each Chromosome Split and Forming two Chromatids

D. First Meiotic Division Chromatids Separating in Pairs

E. / F. Nuclei of two Secondary Meiocytes — each with a Pair of Chromatids

G. / H. Second Meiotic Division Chromatids of each Chromatid Pair Separating

I. End of second Division — Four Nuclei each with one Chromatid

FIG. 8. DIAGRAM OF MEIOSIS.
Result of meiosis is reduction of number of chromosomes to one-half the original number as shown at *I*. Compare with Fig. 7.

non, the union of gametes at syngamy or fertilization, *makes the fundamental principles based upon them equally applicable to all sexually reproducing organisms.* The behavior of chromosomes during meiosis and syngamy constitutes the physical basis of such fundamental principles of heredity as Mendel's laws of inheritance, sex determination, and the inheritance of linked genes.

BEHAVIOR OF HOMOLOGOUS CHROMOSOMES DURING THE PROPHASE OF THE FIRST MEIOTIC DIVISION.   In the nuclei of all diploid or 2N organisms, the chromosomes occur in pairs (Fig. 9). The two members of each pair are essentially alike in size, form, and general features and since they carry allelic genes, may or may not differ in their genetic qualities. Because of

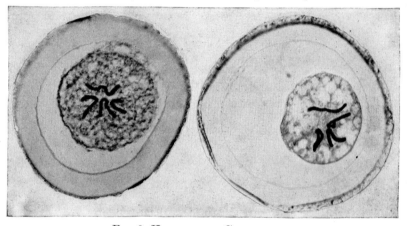

FIG. 9. HOMOLOGOUS CHROMOSOMES.
Photomicrograph of two pairs of homologous chromosomes in each nucleus of zygotes of the parasitic worm *Ascaris.* (Courtesy, Mervin Reines.)

their resemblance, these essentially duplicate chromosomes are termed **homologous** *chromosomes,* which literally means chromosomes that are alike. The occurrence of homologous chromosomes in pairs is related to the origin of every organism from the fusion of two gametes, one from the male parent and the other from the female parent. Each of the gametes has the haploid or 1N number of chromosomes characteristic of the species, and each chromosome of such a "set" may be distinctive in size, shape, and other morphological characters. The chromosomes in the two sets are morphological duplicates provided with similar or contrasting allelic genes. When the gametes fuse, the nucleus of the resulting fertilized egg or zygote has a complement of 2N chromosomes from the chromosome sets of each of the two gametes. The zygote develops into a new 2N or diploid individual potentially able to grow into a sexually mature adult. (See details of reproduction, pp. 30–42.)

During the prophase of the first meiotic division in the meiocytes, the *two members of each pair of homologous chromosomes come together* in **synapsis,** that is, they make longitudinal contact throughout their length, although they do not actually fuse (Fig. 8). The pairing homologues are sometimes called *synaptic mates.* They are also referred to as bivalent chromosomes.* Actually, the pairing is between the allelic genes at corresponding points or loci in the two members of each pair of homologous chromosomes. This feature is brought out when a small section has accidentally been lost from one of the homologues of a pair of chromosomes (Fig. 154). Under these conditions a bend forms in the intact chromosome opposite the deleted portion of its homologous mate, while the alleles of the unaffected portions normally come together.

During the prophase of the first nuclear division of meiosis, each member of the homologous chromosomes splits longitudinally throughout most of its length, forming two chromatids much as occurs in mitosis. Since the homologues are together, longitudinal splitting of the two synaptic mates produces the "chromosome tetrad" or, more properly, the *chromatid tetrad,* a four-partite structure or tetrad of four chromatids (Fig. 8). This condition is also referred to as the "four strand stage" (p. 19). Again, as in mitosis, each chromatid carries duplicates of all genes in the original chromosome. The meiotic longitudinal splits are complete throughout the length of each member of the pair of chromosomes except in the region of the centromere which remains intact through the first meiotic division. Thus, the two chromatids formed from each original chromosome are held together at the centromere, and they *move together as a unit* through the first meiotic division.

SEPARATION OF HOMOLOGUES AND REDUCTION IN CHROMOSOME NUMBER. During metaphase of the *first* meiotic division, the chromosome tetrads of all homologous pairs are at the equator of the division spindle.† As division progresses to anaphase, the two original chromosomes of each pair separate. *Each member of the pair, with its two sister chromatids, moves to an opposing pole* of the division spindle and becomes part of a different nucleus. Rounding up of the group of chromosomes at each pole of the division spindle is accomplished during the telophase of the first meiotic division. Division of the cytoplasm which normally accompanies or follows the nuclear division forms the *secondary* meiocytes (Fig. 11 and 20). Each secondary meiocyte nucleus formed as a result of the first division has two chromatid members derived from a single member of a pair of homologous chromosomes. Reduction of the original 2N chromosomes to the 1N number is actually completed at the end of the first meiotic division. Separation of the chromatids into pairs, each pair representing an original member of a pair of homologous chromosomes, reduces the number of chromosomes in each secondary meiocyte.

---

* The term *univalent* and *bivalent* are pronounced uni-valent and bi-valent by many Americans but univ'alent and biv'alent by the English and some Americans. *Trivalent, quadrivalent,* and other terms are subject to similar diversity of pronunciation.

† The effects of crossing over, omitted at this point, are discussed later (p. 139).

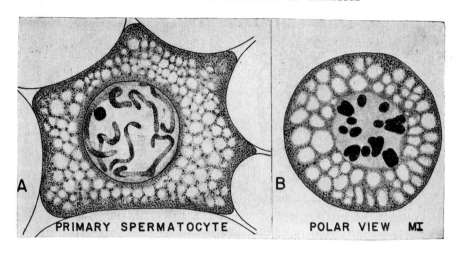

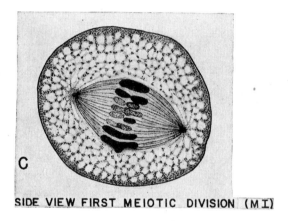

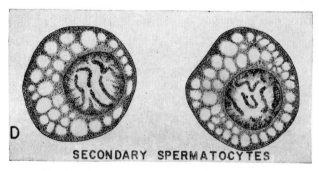

FIG. 10. SPERMATOGENESIS IN GRASSHOPPER.

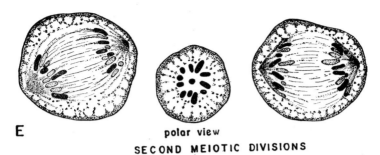

E

polar view

SECOND MEIOTIC DIVISIONS

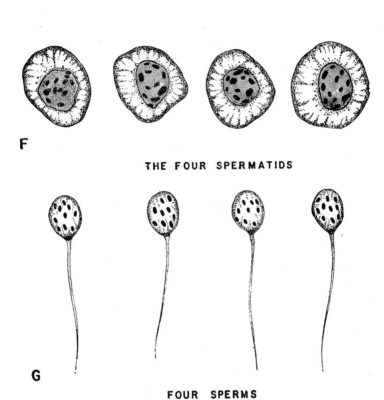

F

THE FOUR SPERMATIDS

G

FOUR SPERMS

PRODUCT OF MEIOSIS IN A

PRIMARY SPERMATOCYTE

FIG. 11. SPERMATOGENESIS IN GRASSHOPPER.

Final Separation of the Chromatids. The *second* meiotic divisions promptly follow the first, and one division occurs in each of the two secondary meiocytes. There is apparently no further pairing or splitting of chromosomes in connection with the second division. This is an important feature, because it constitutes a fundamental difference between the first and second meiotic divisions. During the second meiotic division, in each of the two secondary meiocytes, the centromeres of the original chromosomes, holding the two sister chromatids together, split at anaphase, and the members of each pair of chromatids are separated, one chromatid from a pair passing into one of the four new nuclei formed by the division of the two secondary meiocytes. *During the two divisions constituting meiosis,* therefore, *the four chromatids are separated* and eventually are distributed into the four nuclei that result from the two meiotic divisions (Fig. 8). The 1N or haploid nuclei formed during meiosis become the nuclei of the four meiospores in plants or of the gametes in animals. Besides the reduction in chromosome number and separation of the two members of a pair of homologous chromosomes, the separation or disjunction of the four chromatids of the chromosome tetrad also effects a segregation of the members of each pair of allelic genes to different gametes. This is of fundamental importance in genetics. Meiosis in reducing the chromosome number compensates for the doubling of the chromosome number which occurred in the zygote when the gametes united at fertilization (p. 30). With the segregation of allelic genes during meiosis, the compensation is complete. Syngamy, the union of gametes at fertilization, and meiosis keep the alternating number of chromosomes in equilibrium through successive generations. *Meiosis and fertilization* with all of their physiological and genetic significance *may be properly contrasted.*

Table II

COMPARISON OF MITOSIS AND MEIOSIS

	Prophase	*Splitting of Chromosomes*	*Division of Nucleus*	*Number of New Nuclei*	*Chromosome Number*
Mitosis	No pairing of chromosomes. Longitudinal splitting of 1N or 2N chromosomes observable early.	One longitudinal splitting of individual chromosomes.	One division of nucleus.	Two new nuclei formed.	No change in chromosome number.
Meiosis	Early pairing of the 2N chromosomes to form bivalents. Formation of chromatid tetrads.	One longitudinal splitting of homologous chromosomes.	Two divisions of nuclei.	Four new nuclei formed.	Chromosome numbers reduced to one-half.

The high points of meiosis are:

1. Pairing of the homologous chromosomes in the nucleus of the primary meiocytes

2. Subsequent reduction of the 2N or diploid chromosome number to the haploid or 1N number during the first meiotic division
3. Separation of the synaptic mates or members of a pair of homologous chromosomes
4. Final separation of the chromatids during the second meiotic division provides the material basis for the segregation of allelic genes to the gametes
5. Formation of four nuclei, each with the haploid number of chromosomes.

SUMMARY OF SIMILARITIES AND DIFFERENCES BETWEEN MITOSIS AND MEIOSIS. While there are similarities in mitosis and meiosis, there are also important differences between them (Fig. 7 and 8). The principal similarity of mitosis and meiosis is the *presence of the nuclear spindle* in both types of division. In *mitosis there is one longitudinal splitting of the chromosomes followed by a single division of the nucleus* separating the two new chromosomes into two different nuclei. Thus, the net result of mitosis is the production of two new nuclei with no change in the number of chromosomes. Similarly, preceding the first meiotic division, *there is a single longitudinal splitting of the chromosomes* as in mitosis. *However, this splitting of the chromosomes in meiosis is followed by two nuclear divisions.* The action of the cellular mechanism in meiosis is such that there is a reduction in the number of chromosomes from the 2N to the 1N number and the production of four new nuclei each with one-half the original number of chromosomes.

Questions and Problems

1. What is a cell? What are its parts? Are cells large or small? How do they vary in size?
2. What is chromatin? What are chromosomes? Where are they found?
3. Describe the structure of a chromosome. Are individual chromosomes recognizable in the chromosome complement of an organism? How?
4. What is the chromosome theory of heredity?
5. Why are chromosomes important in genetical studies?
6. Discuss the range of chromosome numbers in plants. In animals.
7. What numbers of chromosomes are found in most of the domesticated animals? In man?
8. To what is the term *gene* applied? What are alleles?
9. How many genes are there estimated to be in an organism? What is the proportion of the numbers of genes to the number of chromosomes?
10. Discuss the size and nature of genes.
11. How do genes pass from one generation to the next one?
12. What two types of cell division are recognized?
13. Describe mitosis. Describe meiosis.
14. Compare mitosis and meiosis. Which is more important in genetical studies? Why?

References

Cold Spring Harbor Symposia on Quantitative Biology, Vol. IX. *Genes and Chromosomes. Structure and Organization*, Cold Spring Harbor, Long Island, New York, The Biological Laboratory, 1941.

———, Vol. XI. *Heredity and Variation in Microorganisms*, Cold Spring Harbor, Long Island, New York, The Biological Laboratory, 1946.

DARLINGTON, C. D.: *Recent Advances in Cytology*, Philadelphia, P. Blakiston's Son & Co., Inc., 1937, Chapters II, III, IV.

DE ROBERTIS, E. D. P., W. W. NOWINSKI, and FRANCISCO A. SAEZ: *General Cytology*, Philadelphia and London, W. B. Saunders Company, 1948.

MORGAN, T. H.: *The Physical Basis of Heredity*, Philadelphia, J. B. Lippincott Company, 1919, Chapter XVI.

———: *The Theory of the Gene*, 2nd ed. New Haven, Yale University Press, 1928.

SCHRADER, FRANZ: *Mitosis*, New York, Columbia University Press, 1944.

SHARP, L. W.: *Fundamentals of Cytology*, New York and London, McGraw-Hill Book Company, Inc., 1943.

———: *Introduction to Cytology*, 3rd ed. New York, McGraw-Hill Book Company, Inc., 1934, Chapters VIII, IX, X, XVI, XVII.

WADDINGTON, C. H.: *An Introduction to Modern Genetics*, New York, The Macmillan Company, 1939.

WHITE, M. J. D.: *Animal Cytology and Evolution*, Cambridge, England, Cambridge University Press, 1945.

WILSON, E. B.: *The Cell in Development and Heredity*, New York, The Macmillan Company, 1925, Chapter VI.

chapter 2

Reproduction in Plants and Animals

Living organisms reproduce by either or both of two methods, **asexual** or nonsexual and **sexual** reproduction. Asexual methods of reproduction or of multiplication are found in both the plant and animal kingdoms. In animals asexual reproduction is confined to the lower forms in which such types as the amoeba and paramecium reproduce by simple division. Most plants, regardless of their evolutionary level, may be multiplied by vegetative or asexual methods. Algae and fungi regularly multiply by means of purely vegetative cells called spores. Multiplication by buds and fragmentation is common among higher plants. Twigs and small branches of the willow and other plants which are easily broken off may frequently grow into independent plants. Stolons, runners, tillers, and branching underground stems are commonly observed structures of multiplication. Nursery practices of making cuttings, budding, grafting, and layering in the propagation of fruit and ornamental plants involve various methods of multiplying individual plants by asexual methods. Commercial production of potatoes, sugar cane, strawberries, and other crops is based upon vegetative multiplication. The essential feature of asexual types of reproduction is separation of parts of an organism and their subsequent growth into a complete organism. New individuals produced asexually lead an independent existence and are capable of performing all vital functions including further reproduction. Considered genetically, however, no new hereditary combinations are formed by nonsexual methods of multiplication, since each additional organism is merely a piece of the original plant or animal.

CLONES. A group of organisms, either plant or animal, that originated from one individual or from a single spore in plants and that was multiplied by asexual methods is called a **clone.** Although, in general, clones are constant somatically and genetically, mutations may occur in them and give rise to departures from clonal constancy. Propagations of the mutations may establish new clones. Many studies of inheritance in asexually reproducing plants and animals have contributed valuable genetical data.

Sexual Reproduction

Sexual reproduction in both animals and plants involves two essential features, **meiosis** and **syngamy**. With its two nuclear divisions, meiosis reduces the number of chromosomes from the somatic or diploid condition to the gametic or haploid. Syngamy or fertilization involves the union of the haploid male and female gametes and restores the diploid number of chromosomes characteristic of the zygote, embryo, and mature organism. Chromosome behavior during syngamy recombines genes in the new generation. A sexually produced organism is, therefore, a genetically new individual formed by a recombination of hereditary units contributed by two parents. Despite diversities in the various groups, sexual reproduction in animals is less complex and more easily understood than the more complicated cycles in plants. For this reason, a discussion of reproduction in animals will be undertaken first.

Sexual Reproduction in Animals

In animals and in plants, the fundamentally important events in the sexual cycle are the **maturation processes,** with *meiosis* reducing the number of chromosomes, and *syngamy*, with fertilization restoring the chromosome number. Although the maturation processes and methods of accomplishing syngamy differ in plants and animals, they have the same significance in their life cycles.

THE MATURATION PROCESS IN THE MALE, *Spermatogenesis.* In the testes, the male gonads or sex glands of animals, certain cells called the primordial **spermatogonia** undergo repeated mitotic divisions which increase their number enormously. This increase is designated the period of multiplication. Each of the primordial spermatogonia normally contains a nucleus which has the diploid or 2N number of chromosomes, the number characteristic of the body cells of the species. As the animal reaches sexual maturity, the production of sperms begins and in the case of most mammals continues for some time thereafter. Of the total number of spermatogonia, relatively a few at a time enlarge, some as much as twenty times the former size of the cells. The time of increase in size for any group of spermatogonia is called the period of growth. When they have increased to maximum size, the spermatogonia are called *primary spermatocytes*, or cells which will produce sperms. The process during which sperms are formed is called **spermatogenesis;** it includes meiosis which accomplishes reduction in chromosome number from 2N to the 1N number characterizing the sperms (pp. 22–23).

The first of the two meiotic divisions occurs in the nucleus of the primary spermatocyte or **meiocyte,** a 2N structure, and the development of two new 1N nuclei follows (Fig. 10). The cytoplasm also divides, and as a final result of the first meiotic division, two new cells are formed. These new cells, the secondary meiocytes, generally called *secondary spermatocytes*, soon undergo the second meiotic division (Fig. 11, 13, and 14). Following this nuclear division, the cytoplasm in each secondary spermatocyte is divided, and two cells also with 1N chromosomes are formed from each of the secondary spermatocytes. These four cells are called **spermatids**. No further divisions occur, but as a final part of the maturation process, each spermatid develops into a **sperm** or a spermatozoon (plural, spermatozoa) with a headpiece, mostly nucleus, a middle section, and a long flagellate tail (Fig. 11). Sperms of animals are generally produced in very large numbers. They are usually motile and swim to the egg cells.

THE MATURATION PROCESS IN THE FEMALE, *Oögenesis.* In many respects the development of the female germ cells parallels that of the male. As the female develops and passes through the juvenile stages, a period of multiplication follows in which the total number of primary oögonia in the ovary, the female sex gland, is greatly increased. Periodically as the animal matures and passes through its reproductive stage, during a period of growth, a few of the total number of oögonia are further enlarged.

Following the period of growth, the enlarged 2N **oögonia**, called *primary* **oöcytes** or meiocytes, undergo meiosis. As a result of the first meiotic division in the primary oöcyte, the chromosome number is reduced from 2N to 1N (Fig. 12). In this division, the spindle is relatively small and generally located near the surface of the oöcyte. The two cells formed by the division are of unequal size. The larger becomes the *secondary* oöcyte, and the smaller one, formed at the outer of the two poles of the spindle, is termed the first polar body or **polocyte**. The polar body is extruded from the oöcyte and may or may not divide again, but in either case it takes no further part in reproduction. The secondary oöcyte promptly undergoes the second meiotic division which again results in the production of two cells unequal in size with reduced number of chromosomes. The larger cell, the **oötid,** develops into the functional female gamete or egg. The smaller cell, called the second polar body, like the first polar body is also extruded and takes no further part in reproduction. Finally the oötid matures into the female gamete termed the ovum or egg. Thus in female animals, the end result of the maturation process called **oögenesis** is the production by each primary oöcyte of one functional gamete or egg and of either two or three nonfunctional polar bodies. In some animals the maturation of the egg and its fertilization, though entirely distinct biological processes, may occur almost simultaneously. There are two general types of maturation in animal eggs. In one of these, of which the whitefish is regarded as an example, maturation and the extrusion of the polar bodies precede the entrance of the sperm (Fig. 14 and 15). In the other type, as seen in *Ascaris*, a worm, the sperm actually penetrates the membrane of the oöcyte before the maturation divisions are completed (Fig. 12).

The meiotic nuclear divisions of the maturation process in plants and animals have also been called the segregation divisions, because the separation of the members of a pair of homologous chromosomes during the divisions constitutes a mechanism for the segregation of the hereditary units or genes located in the chromosomes. An understanding of the behavior of

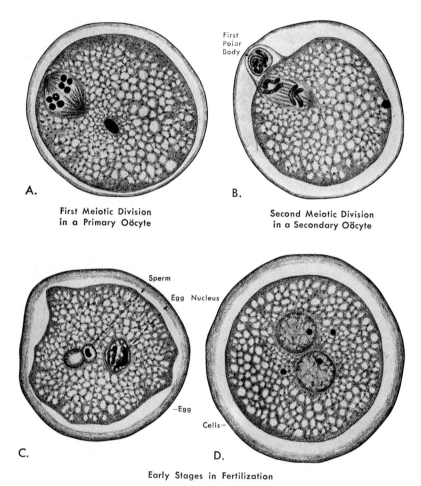

A.

First Meiotic Division
in a Primary Oöcyte

B.

First
Polar
Body

Second Meiotic Division
in a Secondary Oöcyte

Sperm

Egg Nucleus

—Egg

Cells—

C.

D.

Early Stages in Fertilization

FIG. 12. MATURATION IN PARASITIC THREADWORM OF THE HORSE, ASCARIS MEGALO-
CEPHALA VAR. BIVALENS.

the chromosomes during these stages of reproduction is of prime importance, since this behavior is the physical basis for the segregation and assortment of genes, the fundamental principles of Mendelian heredity.

SYNGAMY AND FERTILIZATION.   The process of fertilization, one of the two critical stages in the life cycles of sexually reproducing organisms, consists of the union of the sperm and the egg nuclei. The mechanical means

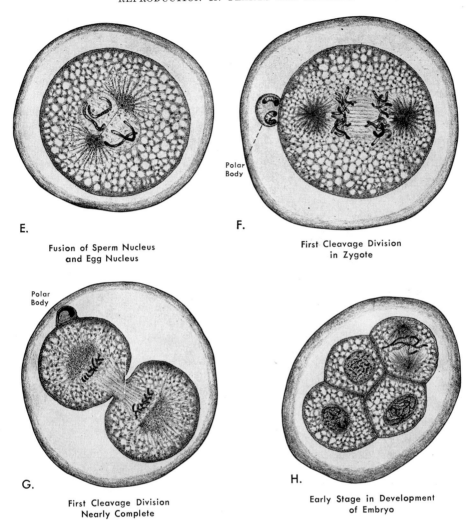

E.

**Fusion of Sperm Nucleus
and Egg Nucleus**

F.

**First Cleavage Division
in Zygote**

Polar
Body

Polar
Body

G.

**First Cleavage Division
Nearly Complete**

H.

**Early Stage in Development
of Embryo**

FIG. 13. FERTILIZATION AND EARLY EMBRYONIC STAGES IN ASCARIS MEGALOCEPHALA VAR, BIVALENS.

E, union of sperm and egg nuclei, each contributing two chromosomes, the haploid number in this species; asters for first mitotic division are forming. F, anaphase of first mitotic or cleavage division of young embryo; G, first cleavage division nearly completed, forming a two-celled embryo. H, later embryonic stage, one cell undergoing mitosis; four chromosomes, the diploid number, are clearly shown.

by which the sperms are brought into the vicinity of the eggs varies with the species of animals. In some of the lower animals as fishes and frogs, the union of the gametes or syngamy takes place entirely outside the bodies of the parents. In other animals, fertilization occurs within the body of the female. In the higher animals, the sperms produced in the male body are

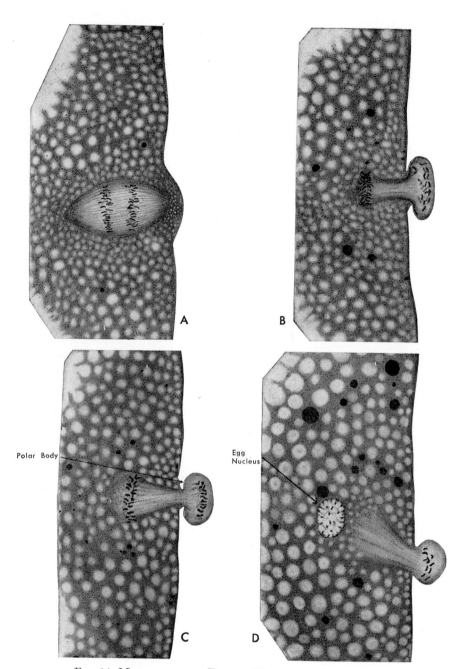

Polar Body

Egg
Nucleus

FIG. 14. MATURATION OF EGGS IN WHITEFISH, COREGONUS.

A, second meiotic division at anaphase; B, telophase of second meiotic division with formation of second polar body. C, later stage in telophase of second meiotic division, nucleus of ovum is beginning to round up. D, second polar body and egg nucleus completely formed.

32

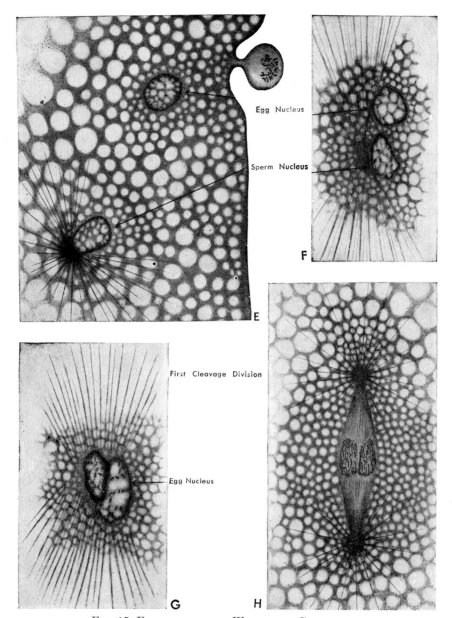

Egg Nucleus

Sperm Nucleus

F

E

First Cleavage Division

Egg Nucleus

G   H

FIG. 15. FERTILIZATION IN WHITEFISH, COREGONUS.

E, sperm nucleus with conspicuous aster is approaching nucleus of egg. *F*, sperm nucleus almost in contact with egg nucleus. *G*, sperm nucleus has made contact with egg nucleus preparatory to fusion. The aster is conspicuous. *H*, prophase of first cleavage division of embryo. The two sets of chromosomes from sperm and egg nuclei, respectively, have retained their identity at center of spindle. Sperm aster has divided and parts have migrated to ends of cleavage spindle, where spindle asters are forming. Development of embryo continues by many rapid mitotic divisions.

33

transferred to the vicinity of the egg within the genital organs of the female by some method of copulation. The motile sperms then swim the remaining distance to the egg. While the very small sperms are produced in enormous numbers in most animals, there are small numbers of the relatively large eggs (Fig. 14 and 15). Normally a single sperm fuses with an egg. As a result of the fusion of the two gametes, each containing a nucleus with the

FIG. 16. TASSEL AND EAR OF CORN.

The tassel, left, is a group of staminate or male flowers. Each branch bears a large number of these imperfect flowers. Anthers and pollen grains are produced in the tassel. The ear, right, is an inflorescence bearing several hundreds of pistillate or female flowers. The silks are protruding stigmas of these imperfect flowers. Each silk is a part of and connects with a single female flower attached to cob inside husks protecting the inflorescence. Tassel and ear are produced on the same plant but in different parts. Corn is thus a monoecious plant.

haploid or 1N number of chromosomes, a single-celled diploid or 2N structure, the fertilized egg or **zygote,** is formed (Fig. 13 and 15). The diploid zygote is the first cell of the new animal produced in sexual reproduction. Undergoing a series of mitotic divisions, which form a large number of somatic cells, the zygote enlarges and divides (Fig. 15). After a definite period of growth and differentiation of parts, it becomes the mature embryo. In mammals at birth, the embryo is separated from its mother and begins an individual existence. It passes through the juvenile stage and eventually attains sexual maturity when it may produce gametes according to its sex.

SEXUAL REPRODUCTION IN PLANTS

Some of the lower plants have served as experimental material in studies of heredity that have yielded significant genetical data.* Until recently, however, most of the genetical investigations in the plant kingdom have been based on the flowering plants, which include many forms of economic importance (Fig. 16 and 17). This brief account of sexual reproduction in plants is confined to the higher forms.

REPRODUCTION IN FLOWERING PLANTS. *Microsporogenesis.* The young anther, morphologically a sporangium, contains masses of cells,

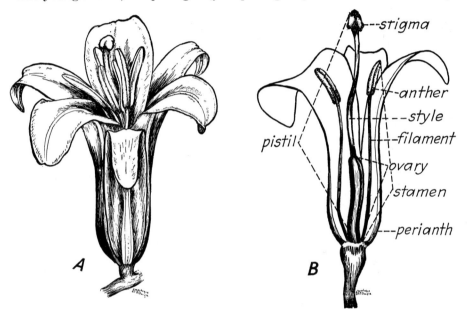

FIG. 17. FLOWERS OF LILY.

A, general view. *B*, longitudinal section showing parts of perianth, stamens, and pistil with its parts. (Courtesy, Hill, Overholts, and Popp: "Botany," 2nd ed., New York, McGraw-Hill Book Company Inc., 1950.)

the sporogenous or spore-generating tissue (Fig. 18 and 19). When the cells attain a certain stage of maturity, they separate slightly, each assuming a spherical shape. These cells are known as the *primary* **microsporocytes** or microspore mother cells. They may also be called **meiocytes,** since each is destined to undergo the process of meiosis (p. 17). The two meiotic divisions result in the production of four meiospores, each with only one-half the number of chromosomes characteristic of the primary meiocyte and the plant that produced it. Not only is the number of chromosomes reduced

---

* Should the reader require a knowledge of reproduction in these lower plants, he is advised to consult textbooks of botany or of biology.

from the diploid or 2N number to the haploid or 1N number, but during meiosis the members of each pair of homologous chromosomes are separated, an important feature in heredity. Generally the four meiospores or microspores may be observed grouped as quartets. There are many thousands of such quartets in an anther.

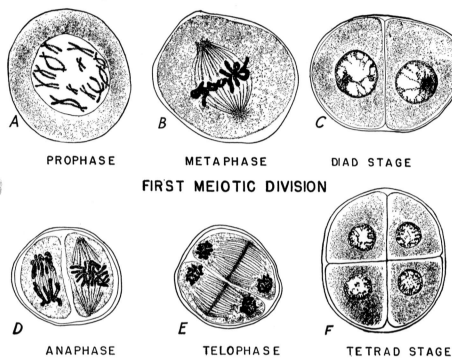

PROPHASE   METAPHASE   DIAD STAGE

FIRST MEIOTIC DIVISION

ANAPHASE   TELOPHASE   TETRAD STAGE

SECOND MEIOTIC DIVISION

Fig. 18. Maturation of Microspores of an Angiosperm.
A, and, B, primary microsporocytes; C, secondary microsporocytes; F, quartet of microspores resulting from the two successive divisions. (Modified after Hill, Overholts, and Popp: "Botany," 2nd ed., New York, McGraw-Hill Book Company, Inc., 1950.)

Development of the Male Gametophyte. The meiospores or microspores formed in the anthers are the first cells of the haploid or 1N phase of the plant. By growth and a short series of mitotic divisions, each microspore may develop into the mature male or **microgametophyte.** Following the first mitotic division in the microspore, two cells of unequal size are formed, a large tube cell and a much smaller one, the generative cell, both enclosed by the original wall of the microspore. At this stage of development, the structures, now called pollen grains, may be shed from the anther (Fig. 19). Transfer of the pollen grains from the anther to the stigma of the flower by means of wind, insects, or water constitutes natural **pollination.**

The pollen grain germinates on the stigma, forming a membranous pollen tube that elongates, penetrating the stigma and style tissues. Either before germination of the pollen grain or afterward, the generative cell divides, forming two male cells or sperms. At maturity the male, or microgametophyte, consists of the pollen tube and its contents, the tube nucleus and the two sperms all floating in the cytoplasm of the pollen tube (Fig. 19).

REPRODUCTION IN FLOWERING PLANTS. *Megasporogenesis.* The ovules or megasporangia are enclosed within the ovary at the base of

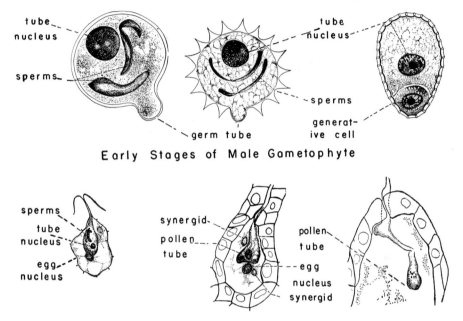

Early Stages of Male Gametophyte

Later Stages of Male Gametophyte

FIG. 19. DEVELOPMENT OF MALE GAMETOPHYTE OF ANGIOSPERMS.
(Modified after Hill, Overholts, and Popp: "Botany," 2nd ed., New York, McGraw-Hill Book Company, Inc., 1950.)

the pistil of the flower. Each ovule contains a large conspicuous cell (sometimes more than one) called the *primary* **megasporocyte** or the megaspore mother cell. This cell, a diploid or 2N structure, is also a meiocyte since it is destined to undergo meiosis (Fig. 20). As a result of the meiotic divisions, four haploid or 1N cells are formed. These are the megaspores, and in many plants they occur in a row, the linear quartet of spores.

DEVELOPMENT OF THE FEMALE GAMETOPHYTE.   Three of the four megaspores are normally functionless, leaving the one located deepest within the tissues to survive and by growth and nuclear divisions to develop into the female gametophyte. The female gametophyte or **megagametophyte,** inappropriately called the "embryo sac," normally develops by a series of three successive mitotic divisions that result in the production of eight nuclei (Fig. 21 and 22). These nuclei, normally four at each end, float in the common cytoplasm of the large embryo sac. Two nuclei, referred to as the polar nuclei because they come from the two ends or poles of the embryo sac,

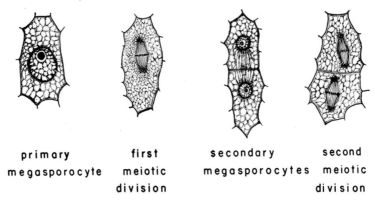

| primary megasporocyte | first meiotic division | secondary megasporocytes | second meiotic division |

Meiosis

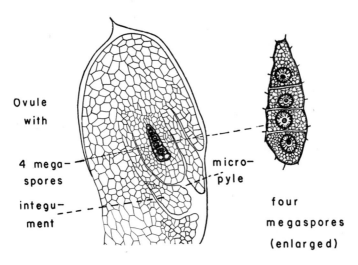

Ovule with

4 mega- spores

micro- pyle

integu- ment

four megaspores (enlarged)

Early Stages of Female Gametophyte

Fig. 20. Maturation Processes in an Angiosperm.
(Modified after Hill, Overholts, and Popp: "Botany," 2nd ed., New York, McGraw-Hill Book Company, Inc., 1950.)

migrate to its center. Three nuclei then remain at each end of the female gametophyte. Those most remote from the micropyle or opening of the ovule are termed antipodal nuclei and are generally functionless. Of the three located in the end of the structure nearest the micropyle, one becomes differentiated into the female gamete or egg, and the other two are called synergids or "helpers." The female gametophyte is now mature (Fig. 21 and 22).

SYNGAMY OR FERTILIZATION AND THE DEVELOPMENT OF THE EMBRYO. While the female gametophytes within the ovules are developing to maturity, hundreds of pollen tubes grow from the stigma down through the style. Upon reaching the ovule, one of the pollen tubes penetrates the micropyle of the ovule. After entering the female gametophyte or embryo sac, the end of the pollen tube becomes greatly swollen and enlarged due to osmotic pressure within it. Soon the tube bursts and discharges the contents of the tube, with the tube nucleus and the two sperms, into the embryo sac. One of the sperms fuses with the egg nucleus. The other sperm fuses with the two polar nuclei in the center of the gametophyte in the so-called "double fertilization" of botanical literature (Fig. 22). The union of the sperm with the egg is called syngamy. Each of the gametes, sperm and egg, is normally a haploid or 1N structure. Fusion of the nuclei constitutes fertilization and results in the production of a diploid or 2N cell called the zygote. The fusion of the second sperm with the two polar nuclei does not signify fertilization at all but is merely the fusion of haploid nuclei. Because three haploid nuclei are involved in this fusion, the resulting nucleus is normally a 3N structure. It is called the *primary* **endosperm nucleus.** Each gamete has a certain number of chromosomes comprising a "set"; their union at fertilization gives a double or 2N number to the zygote. The zygote thus has pairs of homologous chromosomes, matched in size, shape, and genetic qualities, which constitute the synaptic mates so very important in genetical theory. The zygote develops into the embryo of the seed (Fig. 23). Finally upon germination, the embryo develops into the seedling which grows into the young plant and eventually into the mature plant, itself capable of reproduction.

THE DEVELOPMENT OF THE ENDOSPERM. The primary endosperm nucleus formed by fusion of the second sperm with the two polar nuclei soon starts a series of mitotic divisions. The resulting nuclei become separated by walls and form the endosperm or food-storage tissue. Although the endosperm tissue has genetic qualities and develops hereditary characteristics, it is relatively of less importance genetically than the zygote, because it does not reproduce itself while the zygote may develop into a plant capable of perpetuating the species.

APOMIXIS AND RELATED TYPES OF REPRODUCTION. The term **apomixis** refers to nonsexual methods of reproduction in plants which sometimes replace normal sexual reproduction. While several types of reproduction are classified as apomixis, the most important is the development of adventitious embryos in the seed. These embryos may develop as buds from somatic cells of the tissue surrounding the embryo sac. A bud of this kind often assumes the form and structure of a normal embryo. Sometimes this abnormal embryo emerges as a twin embryo with the normal one.

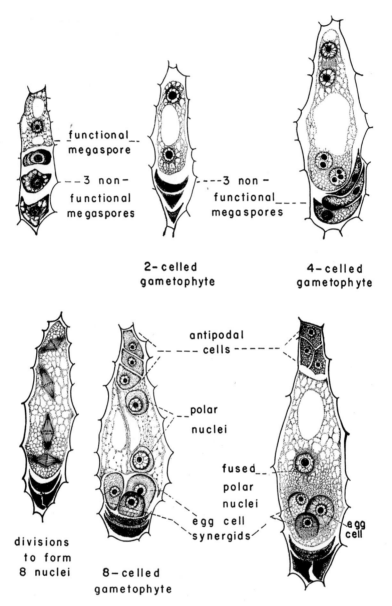

functional megaspore

3 non-functional megaspores

3 non-functional megaspores

2-celled gametophyte

4-celled gametophyte

antipodal cells

polar nuclei

fused polar nuclei

egg cell
synergids

egg cell

divisions to form 8 nuclei

8-celled gametophyte

Stages in Development of Female Gametophyte

Fig. 21. Development of Female Gametophyte in an Angiosperm.
Top left, four megaspores of *Carex*, innermost one enlarging and becoming the functional megaspore with three remaining megaspores disintegrating; successive stages in development of female gametophyte from the functional megaspore. Early development is through three successive mitotic divisions in functional megaspore. Later development is accomplished by organization of nuclei in the gametophyte. (Modified after Hill, Overholts, and Popp: "Botany," 2nd ed., New York, McGraw-Hill Book Company, Inc., 1950.)

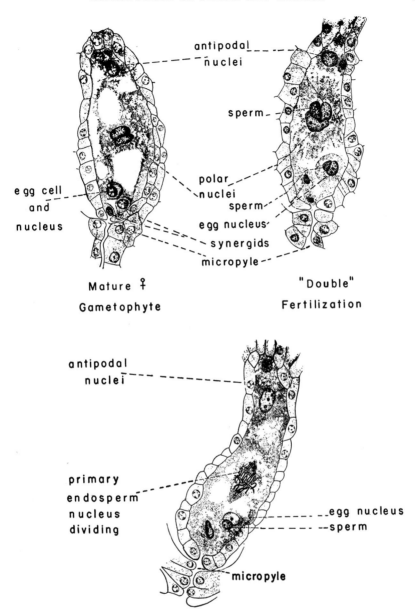

antipodal nuclei

sperm

egg cell and nucleus

polar nuclei

sperm

egg nucleus

synergids

micropyle

Mature ♀ Gametophyte

"Double" Fertilization

antipodal nuclei

primary endosperm nucleus dividing

egg nucleus

sperm

micropyle

Fertilization

FIG. 22. FERTILIZATION IN AN ANGIOSPERM.
Top left, mature female gametophyte of a lily. *Top right*, union of one sperm with egg and second sperm with two polar nuclei in center of embryo sac. *Bottom*, fertilization of egg by sperm in lower end of embryo sac. (Modified after Hill, Overholts, and Popp: "Botany," 2nd ed., New York, McGraw-Hill Book Company, Inc., 1950.)

In other cases when the adventitious embryo is the only one developed in the seed, the seedling and mature plant are like the plant from which they developed. The apomictic embryo, an asexual structure, is genetically like a cutting from the parent plant. Plants which reproduce by apomictic embryos are really clonal. When genetic experiments with some species are

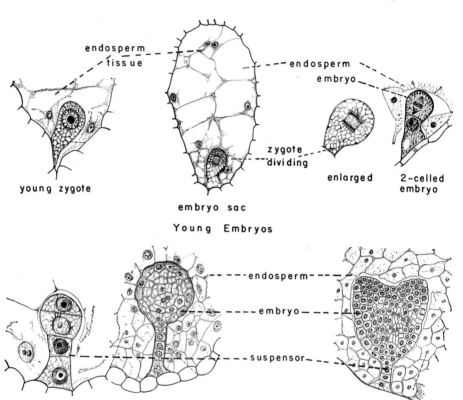

FIG. 23. DEVELOPMENT OF EMBRYO AND ENDOSPERM IN TOBACCO.
Top left, zygote or young embryo, formed following fertilization, surrounded by developing endosperm; right, detail; stages in development of embryo and surrounding endosperm. In later stages the endosperm becomes more compact. Lower right, cotyledons of the embryo are developing. (Courtesy Hill, Overholts, and Popp: "Botany," 2nd ed., New York, McGraw-Hill Book Company, Inc., 1950.)

undertaken, the possibility of apomixis must always be considered as an explanation of aberrant results. Also classified under apomixis are **parthenogenetic** embryos from both reduced and unreduced egg cells or haploid cells such as synergids in the embryo sac. These types of reproduction may be important in genetics when plants with unusual chromosome numbers are developed (pp. 329–359).

Questions and Problems

1. What are the critical stages in the life cycles of animals? Of what importance are these in genetical studies?
2. Name the essential sex glands in animals.
3. Emphasizing the chromosome behavior, diagram and describe spermatogenesis in animals. In which organ of the animal body does spermatogenesis occur? Why is this process important in genetical studies?
4. Emphasizing the chromosome behavior, diagram and describe oögenesis in animals. In which organ of the animal body does oögenesis occur? Of what importance is this process in genetical studies?
5. Describe fertilization in animals. Why is this process important in genetical studies?
6. What two types of reproduction are found in plants? Are these two types also found in the animal kingdom?
7. What is the fundamental feature in asexual reproduction? What is the importance of asexual reproduction in genetical studies?
8. What is the essential feature of sexual reproduction?
9. What are the parts of a typical flower? Which of the parts of a flower are essential to reproduction?
10. What are the critical stages in the life cycles of plants? Why are these critical stages important in genetical studies?
11. Emphasizing the chromosome behavior, diagram and describe microsporogenesis in flowering plants. In which organ does microsporogenesis occur? Why is this process important in genetical studies?
12. Emphasizing chromosome behavior, diagram and describe megasporogenesis in the flowering plants. In which organ does megasporogenesis occur? Why is this process important in genetical studies?
13. Diagram and describe the gametophytes of the flowering plants. Describe gametogenesis, that is, the formation of gametes in flowering plants. In which structures of the plant are the gametes found?
14. Emphasizing the chromosome behavior, describe fertilization in the flowering plants. In which plant structure may fertilization be observed? Why is this process important in genetical studies?
15. Describe briefly the development of the stages zygote, embryo, seedling, and adult plant as these occur in flowering plants.
16. Describe the development of the endosperm in flowering plants. What is the biological function of endosperm?

References

CONKLIN, E. G.: *Heredity and Environment*, 2nd ed. Princeton, Princeton University Press, 1916, Chapter II.

GUYER, F.: *Animal Biology*, 3rd ed. New York, Harper & Brothers, 1941, Chapter XIX.

HILL, J. B., L. O. OVERHOLTS, and H. W. POPP: *Botany*, 2nd ed., New York, McGraw-Hill Book Company, Inc., 1950, Chapter XVIII.

MAXIMOW, A. A., and WILLIAM BLOOM: *A Textbook of Histology*, Philadelphia, W. B. Saunders Company, 1939, Chapters XXIV, XXV.

RICE, V. A.: *Breeding and Improvement of Farm Animals*, 2nd ed. New York, McGraw-Hill Book Company, Inc., 1934, Chapters III, IV.

SHARP, L. W.: *Fundamentals of Cytology*, New York, McGraw-Hill Book Company, Inc., 1943.

———: *Introduction to Cytology*, 3rd ed. New York, McGraw-Hill Book Company, Inc., 1934, Chapter XIV.

WILSON, E. B.: *The Cell in Development and Heredity*, New York, The Macmillan Company, 1925, Chapters III, IV, V.

WINTERS, L. M.: *Animal Breeding*, Part II, New York, John Wiley & Sons, Inc., 1930.

section 2

Mendelian Principles

Underlying the development of genetics, there is a historical background of long duration. Dating back to prehistoric times, man has been cultivating plants and breeding animals, but he accumulated little accurate information about their reproduction and inheritance until modern times. The earliest genetic experiments involved hybridization, that is, mating or "crossing" different types to produce mixed or hybrid offspring. In the latter part of the 18th century, a group of experimenters collectively known as "The Plant Hybridizers" attacked problems of heredity by hybridization of plants. Their techniques were inadequate, but their attempts at solution of these complex problems yielded certain facts important in the development of genetics. One of these was the frequent increase in size and vigor of hybrids over their parents; a second was the general failure of plant hybrids to breed true when self-pollinated or bred together. They referred to this as the "splitting of hybrids." Historically the science of genetics dates from the work of the Austrian monk Gregor Mendel. Although the early investigators had conducted experiments in heredity, they dealt with entire organisms with a diversity of characteristics. The experiments, therefore, had so many variables that a valid explanation of inheritance was not attained. Familiarity with the results of the earlier plant hybridizers enabled Mendel to see some of the reasons for their failures. Following the lead of the earlier workers, he attacked the problem of heredity by means of hybridization of the garden pea, a prolific annual, occurring in many varieties with characteristic differences. Peas are naturally self-pollinated and thus are usually found in pure varieties, an asset in starting genetical studies. Mendel selected as parents plants which differed in a single pair of contrasting characters and studied a number of such traits (pp. 56, 57, Table III). He was able to: (1) determine the number of different forms among the progeny of the hybrids; (2) arrange these forms as to their occurrence in the first, second, or third generations following hybridization; and (3) ascertain the ratios of the distinct forms in the hybrid generations. The use of these methods was the basis of Mendel's success. His approach was statistical. Although the methods were mathematically simple, they were adequate to enable Mendel to offer a scientific explanation of his results.*

---

* After eight years of investigation, Mendel in 1865 presented his results in a paper read before the Naturforscher Verein in the city of Brünn, Austria, now included in Czechoslovakia. This paper entitled *Experiments in Plant Hybridization* was published in the journal of the Brünn society, *Verh. Naturf. Ver. Abhandlungen* **IV**, 1865, which appeared in 1866. The contribution attracted very little attention and remained practically unknown for thirty-five years, when through the publications of De Vries, Correns, and Von Tschermak it was again brought to the attention of the scientific world. William Bateson's translation of Mendel's paper for the Royal Horticultural Society of England in 1901 was a great stimulus to genetical research.

chapter 3

Segregation of Allelic Genes—The First Law of Heredity—Inheritance in Peas

For one of his studies, the inheritance of stature in the garden pea, Mendel used plants five to six feet tall and dwarf plants about one foot in height as parents in a cross. The seeds obtained from hybridizing the tall and dwarf plants grew into plants which uniformly resembled the tall parent but were hybrid for the characters tall and dwarf. Following natural self-pollination of the new hybrid plants, seed from this first hybrid generation was planted for the development of the second hybrid generation. The second generation showed the well-known breaking-up into distinct groups or the "splitting" recorded by earlier plant hybridizers.

THE 3:1 RATIO. It was here that Mendel again went a step further than his predecessors. He classified and counted the plants of the second hybrid generation. His analysis of the 1,064 plants comprising the second generation showed that the plants were of two types, each apparently like one of the parents. There were 787 tall plants and 277 dwarf-type plants, that is about 3/4 or 73.96 per cent tall and 1/4 or 26.04 per cent dwarf, a ratio of 2.84 tall to 1 dwarf or approximately 3:1 (Fig. 24). When Mendel reversed the types of plants used as male and female parents in (reciprocal) crosses, again the first generation all resembled the tall parent, and the second generation had tall and dwarf plants in an approximate ratio of 3:1. For Mendel to have noted the ratio of the types in the second generation was a departure in method. *He measured the results of heredity.* A painstaking worker, he kept detailed pedigree records of his experimental plants, and this also was an innovation. It remains an essential feature of genetical research to the present day. His thorough understanding of the problem, his simplification of procedure, and his careful method of solving it enabled Mendel to make his contribution to biological thought.

Mendel's Explanation of the Results of His Breeding Experiments

Mendel studied the inheritance of seven pairs of characteristics in the garden pea (Table III). In all cases the first-generation hybrids resembled one

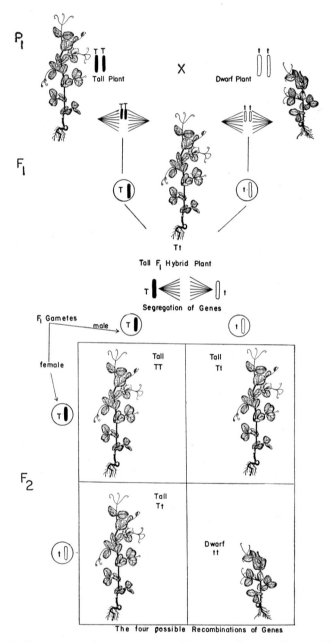

FIG. 24. DIAGRAM OF INHERITANCE IN TALL AND DWARF GARDEN PEAS.

of the parents to the complete exclusion of the other. The character which thus appeared or dominated in the first hybrid generation, he called the *dominant* character. The character which was obscured or receded from view, he called the *recessive* character. He thought of these characters as independent, that is, pure unit characters even in the hybrid generation which could be again recovered as units in the second generation.

Mendel's explanation of the appearance of two classes of individuals in the second generation of a monohybrid is the essence of his contribution to science. Without knowledge of the cell mechanism, Mendel concluded that there must be certain *units* in the germ plasm which *separated* when the reproductive cells were formed. He suggested that these units were **determiners** of the distinct unit characters. Thus, he assumed a determiner for the tall character in peas, which may be represented by T, and another determiner for the dwarf character, t.* Since each plant has two parents, each contributing a single determiner, the hereditary constitution of the tall plants is double and may be represented by two letters, TT, and likewise, the hereditary constitution of the dwarf plants by the corresponding small letters tt.

THE HEREDITARY CONSTITUTION OF THE HYBRID. In production of the hybrid, one determiner or hereditary unit was presumably contributed by each parent.† Thus, the tall parent contributed the unit T, and the dwarf parent, the unit t, which existed as distinct hereditary units in the hybrid plant with a double hereditary constitution Tt.

---

* The need of distinguishing between vast numbers of hereditary units has resulted since Mendel's time in various ways of designating them. The hereditary units occur in organisms in pairs, either of two dominants or two recessives, as in pure-bred plants and animals, or a pair consisting of one dominant and one recessive as in a hybrid. While the practice is not universal, the recessive gene or factor is generally designated by the small-initial letter or by an abbreviation of the name of the character it conditions. The dominant gene is then indicated by the corresponding capital letter or capitalized abbreviation. However, some of the earlier writers did not follow this current practice. In this volume the designation used by the original investigator has frequently been followed, even though it sometimes breaks the above general rule.

Also by common consent among writers on genetical topics, the female parent in a mating or "cross" is written first. The parents concerned in the cross are called the *first parental* generation, which is abbreviated to P_1. The terms P_2 and P_3 indicate earlier parental generations: P_2 the grandparental and P_3 the generation next further removed. The hybrid generations are likewise designated by abbreviated terms, F_1 indicating the hybrid resulting from the mating of the P_1 parents. F_1 means the *first filial* generation. The immediate progeny of a hybrid constitutes the *second filial* generation or the F_2. Later generations are designated as the F_3, F_4, etc.

Another method of designating genes has been used, especially by geneticists working with the fruit fly, *Drosophila*. In this system a plus sign, $+$, is used to designate any "wild-type" or normal gene and a letter, as a, to indicate a mutant gene. Thus, $++$ or $+/+$ may indicate an organism homozygous for any given wild-type or normal gene; $+a$ or $+/a$, an organism heterozygous for these alleles; and aa or a/a, the homozygous recessive-mutant organism. Capital letters, as B, indicate dominant-mutant genes with the plus sign, $+$, again designating the wild-type or normal allele at the same locus.

† Mendel's designation of the hereditary units as *determiners* has been replaced by the terms *factors*, *genes*, and *alleles* (p. 11).

Although Mendel knew nothing of the nature of chromosomes nor of their behavior during cell division, his conclusions, based entirely on the analysis of genetical data and essentially valid, have stood the test of time. Since the genes are carried in the chromosomes (p. 11), the behavior of the chromosomes during the critical stages of meiosis and fertilization is important in the study of heredity. Most organisms have a fairly small number of chromosomes, and all have a very large number of genes (p. 13). In genetical experiments the number of hereditary factors studied is purposely restricted to a small number of the large total. Only the genes primarily concerned in the development of one or a few specific characteristics are considered. All others are temporarily neglected.

The pea plant has 14 chromosomes in the nuclei of the body cells and following meiosis, 7 in the reproductive cells. Thus, when tall and dwarf pea plants are crossed, each of the parents contributes to its respective gametes a "set" of 7 chromosomes. In each case one of the chromosomes in the set carries the genes conditioning the characteristic stature of the parent. In the cross tall $TT \times$ dwarf tt, then, in each egg cell of the set of 7 chromosomes, one will bear the dominant gene T conditioning or, as Mendel said, determining tallness. Likewise in the sperms from the dwarf parent, tt, in the set of 7, one will bear the recessive gene t determining dwarfness. When the sperm unites with the egg at fertilization, these two sets of 7 chromosomes combine, thus restoring the diploid or double number of 14 chromosomes in the zygote or fertilized egg, and as a result of the union of the parental gametes, the zygote will receive the two genes T and t. It is, therefore, hybrid Tt for the characteristics tall and dwarf. The stature of the hybrid plant will depend on the actions of the factors T-t in its genetic constitution. Since the gene T completely dominates the recessive gene t, the plant will be tall, apparently exactly like the tall parent. Though the gene t is present, its action is obscured by the action of the dominant gene T.

The essential feature of the first generation or F_1 of any cross is not that it shows dominance of one character over another or the lack of it but that the F_1 hybrid is a genetic mixture. It has determiners or genes as T and t from each parent. Hybrid organisms of this nature are said to be **heterozygous** as compared with their **homozygous** parents. These terms come from the Greek words *heteros* meaning other or different and *zygon* meaning yoke. Thus, heterozygous carries the meaning of two different things yoked together as the genes T and $t = Tt$. *Homos* means one or the same, and homozygous therefore refers to the joining of two similar things as T with $T = TT$ or t with $t = tt$. Heterozygous organisms are not restricted to the F_1; they may appear in any generation following a cross.

THE SEGREGATION OF GENES. Mendel theorized that the determiners T and t were uncontaminated by their association in the hybrid and that they might again be *separated* and passed pure, each into a different reproductive cell or gamete of the hybrid. Following this assumption of the separation of the dominant and recessive determiners, unit T would be separated from unit t during reproduction in the hybrid, each determiner passing eventually into a different gamete. Therefore, each hybrid from parents differing in one pair of contrasting characters can be expected to produce *two kinds of gametes in equal numbers.*

Since Mendel's time, however, it was found that in the maturation process with the meiotic divisions, the members of a pair of determiners or allelic genes, as they are now called, are separated (p. 52, Fig. 25). This process, therefore, actually accomplishes the *segregation of the genes* or determiners, as Mendel proposed in his basic explanation of the production of two classes of individuals in the offspring of hybrids. When any heterozygous organism, as the F_1 pea plant, hybrid for tallness and dwarfness, produces gametes, there is a separation of genes exactly as Mendel postulated.

As a result of meiosis during which the four chromatids are formed (pp. 19, 21), the chromatids separate in pairs. Chromatids 1 and 2 carrying genes T and T move into one of the two new nuclei formed at the end of the first division, and 3 and 4 carrying the genes t and t pass into the other nucleus.* At the end of the second division, the four chromatids have passed into separate nuclei, and each of the four meiospores contains one member of each pair of homologous chromosomes with one of the allelic genes T or t. Separation of the members of a pair of homologous chromosomes leads to the complete segregation of their allelic genes. The segregation of genes is the fundamental feature of Mendel's theory of heredity and has been quite properly called Mendel's **First Law of Heredity.**

RECOMBINATION OF GENES AND MENDELIAN RATIOS. To account for the occurrence of the different classes of progeny in the second hybrid generation, Mendel assumed that during the process of reproduction of the first-generation hybrid pea plant, half of the male gametes carried the dominant determiner T and half carried the recessive unit t. Likewise, female gametes carrying either T or t occurred in equal numbers. Mendel further assumed that with sufficiently large numbers there would be random or chance union of the two kinds of male and female gametes at fertilization. That is, the male gamete carrying the unit T had equal chances of fertilizing female gametes with T or t. Likewise, a male gamete carrying the unit t had equal chances of fertilizing female gametes with T or t.

Mendel found that following self-pollination of the first-generation plant, the recombination of the pure determiners T and t could be explained by the simple binomial theorem of algebra, $(a + b)^2 = a^2 + 2ab + b^2$. Thus, the possible recombinations of male gametes T and t with female gametes T

---

* It is equally likely that, owing to crossing over, a part of chromatid 1 with gene T and a part of 3 with t may pass into one nucleus while chromatids 2 with T and 4 with t pass into the second; for pedagogical reasons the discussion at the moment will be restricted to the original combinations.

pairing   four chromatids

Homologous Chromosomes of F_1 Hybrid

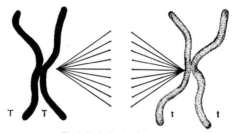

First Meiotic Division

Separation of Chromatids in Pairs

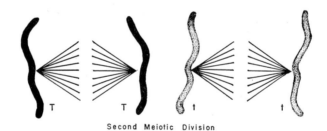

Second Meiotic Division

Separation of Chromosomes

Final Segregation of Genes T and t

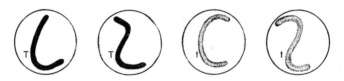

Two Types of Gametes

T and t in Equal Numbers

FIG. 25. DIAGRAM OF SEPARATION OF TWO MEMBERS OF A PAIR OF HOMOLOGOUS CHROMOSOMES.

The chromosomes bear the dominant and recessive determiners T and t.

and t could be represented as $(T + t) \times (T + t) = 1TT + 2Tt + 1tt$. The determiner T, for the dominant trait tallness, occurred in three of the four possible recombinations, in one as homozygous TT and in two as heterozygous Tt. Plants having the combinations containing dominant T would

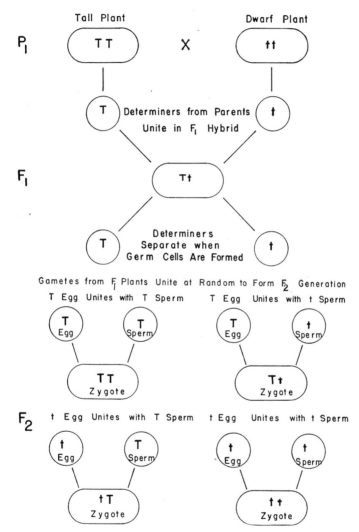

FIG. 26. UNION OF THE DETERMINERS FOR TALLNESS AND DWARFNESS, "T" AND "t," FROM THE TALL AND DWARF PARENTS, RESPECTIVELY.

be tall. Plants with the recessive determiners tt would be dwarf (Fig. 26). This is the genetic basis for the ratio of 3 tall to 1 dwarf in the second hybrid generation. Since recombination is based upon random or chance unions of equal numbers of male and female gametes, the realization of the expected ratio in any case is only a probability and not a certainty (p. 56). For this reason exact Mendelian ratios are obtained only with relatively large F_2 populations.

The use of the binomial theorem of algebra has been largely replaced by various diagrammatic schemes to show the random or chance recombinations of the hereditary factors. One of these schemes, "Punnett's square," commonly called the "checkerboard," is widely used in illustrating the recombination of hereditary units which occurs during fertilization. With the checkerboard the symbols of the genes carried in the female gametes may be written in a horizontal line on the upper side and those in the male gametes, in a vertical row along the left side of the square (or reverse). To illustrate all possible recombinations of genes, the symbols of those in the female gametes are written in all the squares of the checkerboard directly under them. Similarly, the symbols of the genes in the male gametes are written in all squares to their right (Fig. 24). The squares thus contain gene symbols representing the products of the genes in the eggs multiplied by those in the sperms. A checkerboard, therefore, is an empirical or non-mathematical scheme for representing the results of the expansion of $(a + b)^2$ or, in this case, of $(T + t)^2$.

THE 3:1 RATIO. With large numbers involved in a monohybrid, mating $F_1 \times F_1$ always results in gene recombinations of three types in the ratio of 1:2:1. The ratio of individuals in the character classes of the F_2 generation depends, however, on the specific action of the hereditary units involved in the cross. In the case of tall $\times$ dwarf peas in which the gene for tallness completely dominates its allele, the gene for short stature, tall and dwarf plants appear in the approximate ratio of 3:1.

BREEDING BEHAVIOR IN THE F_2 GENERATION. Mendel determined that all dwarf plants of the second generation upon self-pollination bred true for that characteristic, producing only dwarf plants in the third generation. He found also that some, though not all of the tall plants of the second generation, bred true for tallness. These true-breeding tall plants constituted about one-third of the tall forms and approximately one-fourth of the second generation. He concluded that the true-breeding dwarf plants were pure for the recessive determiners tt and that the true-breeding tall plants were pure for the dominant factors TT.

In addition to the true-breeding tall and dwarf plants, Mendel found that many of the tall plants, constituting about one-half of the total F_2 population, continued to split into tall and dwarf classes in the third generation. He presumed that these F_2 plants contained a mixture of the determiners T and t; that is, they were heterozygous Tt plants and therefore actually hybrids genetically like the F_1 hybrid. Throughout his series of experiments, Mendel's conclusions as to the genetic constitution of the F_2 generation were substantiated.

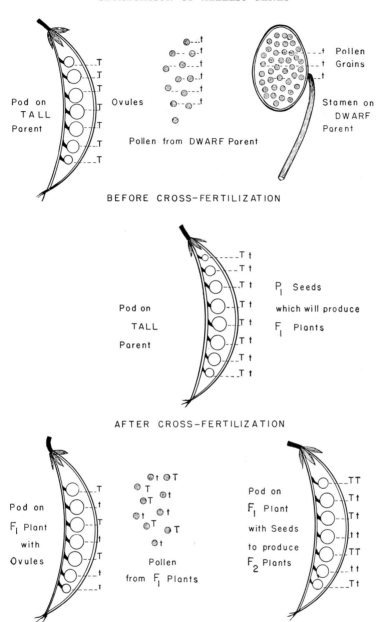

FIG. 27. PRODUCTION OF F_1 AND F_2 GENERATIONS FOLLOWING HYBRIDIZATION OF TALL AND DWARF PEAS.
(Modified after Hill, Overholts, and Popp: "Botany," 2nd ed., New York, McGraw-Hill Book Company, Inc., 1950.)

Table III

SUMMARY OF DATA FROM MENDEL'S EXPERIMENTS WITH PEAS

Characters	Dominants		Recessives		Total	Actual Ratios
	Number	%	Number	%	Number	
Form of Seed, round vs. wrinkled	5,474 round	74.74	1,850 wrinkled	25.26	7,324	2.96:1
Color of Cotyledons, yellow vs. green	6,022 yellow	75.06	2,001 green	24.94	8,023	3.01:1
Color of Seed Coats, gray-brown vs. white	705 gray-brown	75.89	224 white	24.10	929	3.15:1
Form of Pod, inflated vs. constricted	882 inflated	74.68	299 constricted	25.32	1,181	2.95:1
Color of Unripe Pods, green vs. yellow	428 green	73.79	152 yellow	26.21	580	2.82:1
Position of Flowers, in axil of leaf vs. terminal	651 axillary	75.87	207 terminal	24.13	858	3.14:1
Length of Stem, tall vs. short or dwarf	787 tall	73.97	277 short	26.03	1,064	2.84:1

Large Numbers are Necessary in Mendelian Ratios

Since they depend upon probabilities of recombinations in the zygotes and viability of the embryos, even approximations of the characteristic ratios are obtained only with relatively large numbers of individuals. In the experiment involving tall and dwarf types of peas, although Mendel had more than 1,000 second-generation plants, the ratio obtained was only approximately 3:1. In experiments involving other characteristics of the pea plant, Mendel had from fewer than 600 to more than 8,000 individuals in the various second generations obtained. The nearest approximation to a true 3:1 ratio occurred in the cross yielding the most numerous second-generation progeny. In this case with a total of 8,023 individuals, the actual ratio was 3.01:1. From the data in Table III, it will be noted that in general the experiments involving the largest numbers yielded the closest approximations to a true 3:1 ratio. Many of the ratios determined for other material, since Mendel's time, are based upon very much larger numbers than were the classical Mendelian ratios.

Segregation and Recombination of Genes Have Universal Application

Mendelian principles are important in modern genetics, not because of the specific experiments with peas which Mendel performed, but because the laws of inheritance which he formulated have universal application.

Since 1900 there have been thousands of experiments involving the inheritance of hundreds of characteristics of both plants and animals. All indicate segregation and recombination of genes.

INHERITANCE OF COLOR AND ALBINISM IN THE GUINEA PIG. One of the well-known studies which parallels Mendel's investigations in the pea plant has to do with the inheritance of color and albinism* in animals as, for example, black and white or albino in the coat of the guinea pig (Fig. 28). The word *albino* is derived from the Latin word *albus* meaning white and refers to organisms lacking color. The eyes of true albinos are pink, because the tint of the blood vessels shows through the colorless iris tissue of the eye.

In crosses between colored and albino guinea pigs, color, as black, was found to be dominant over the albino. Thus, the dominant gene determining colored coat is C, indicating color, while the recessive gene conditioning lack of color or albinism is the small letter c. Because the guinea pig is a diploid or 2N organism, the genes of a black guinea pig may be represented by CC and those of an albino by cc, with gametes C and c, respectively. As a result of mating the contrasting types, heterozygous black F_1 hybrids with genotypes Cc may be expected (Fig. 28 and 29). Many plants may be self-pollinated, but since animals are monosexual, two individuals must be mated. Animals must therefore be mated F_1 female $\times$ F_1 male to produce the F_2 or second-generation hybrids. The F_2 generation, if numbers are sufficiently large, may be expected to show two classes of color types, black and white. Because of full dominance, the expected ratio will be 3 black to 1 white.

GENOTYPES, BIOTYPES, AND PHENOTYPES. By using the classes of the F_2 generation of the guinea-pig cross as illustrations, the meaning of certain useful terms may be clarified. Among these are genotype, biotype, and phenotype. The suffix *-type* in each of these terms is derived from the Greek word *typos* (Latin *typus*) meaning emblem, symbol, or image. The word **genotype** is a combination of gene and type and means literally the *type of genes* within an individual organism. Every organism has its own genotype. Biotype comes from a combination of the Greek word *bios*, meaning life, and type. Thus, biotype means the *life type*. Several individuals may have similar groups of genes in their genetic constitution, that is, they may be similar genotypically. Such a group of individuals constitutes a **biotype,** that is, a group of organisms with *similar genetic constitution*. Phenotype is formed from the Greek word *phaino*, meaning to display or disclose, and type. It is thus the show type or visible type. The

---

* Various degrees of albinism in other animals are fairly common. Albino coyotes, coons, deer, chickens, and robins have all been reported (Fig. 137). Albinism has been studied in water buffalo. C. O. Levine noted that in some parts of Kwantung, China, 30 per cent of the water buffaloes was albino or at least white. P. Carstens, *et al.*, reported albinism in Brown Swiss cattle. Recently albinism has been reported in the opossum, the bison, and other animals.

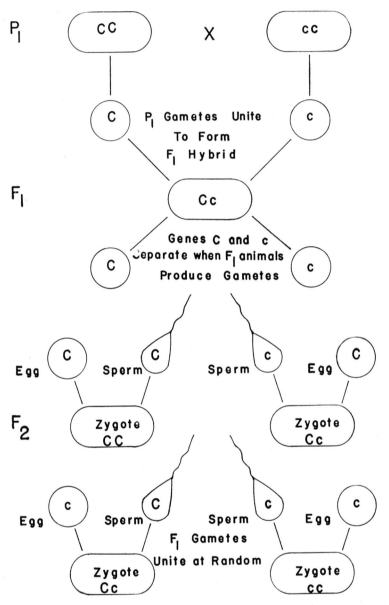

FIG. 28. BEHAVIOR OF THE COLOR GENES "C" AND "c" IN INHERITANCE OF COLORED
AND ALBINO CHARACTERS IN GUINEA PIGS.

term **phenotype** refers to a *group* of individuals having *similar appearance* regardless of their genetic constitution.

The gene make-up of the F_2 individuals is indicated in each square of the checkerboard (Fig. 29). Each recombination of genes, *CC*, *Cc*, and *cc*, represents a distinct *genotype*. All animals with the genetic constitution *CC* belong to a group, a *biotype*. Likewise, all individuals with genotype *Cc* belong to one biotype, and those with *cc* to another. However, all black individuals in the F_2, regardless of homozygous or heterozygous genetic constitution, are grouped on appearance alone into one *phenotype*. Organisms in the same biotype breed alike according to their genetic constitution. Organisms in the same phenotype may not breed alike because they may be genetically dissimilar.

The three terms *genotype*, *biotype*, and *phenotype* are accurate and useful. In actual practice many geneticists make little or no distinction between genotype and biotype, and the term *genotype* is often used to include all organisms genetically alike. All writers, however, make the distinction between genotype and phenotype.

Table IV

GENOTYPES, BIOTYPES, AND PHENOTYPES

CC	*Cc:Cc*	*cc*	Genotypes formed by gene recombination in a monohybrid F_2 generation
1*CC*	2*Cc*	1*cc*	Biotypic ratio of 1:2:1 based on gene recombination
1*CC* 3 black animals	2*Cc*	1*cc* 1 white animal	Phenotypic ratio of 3:1 owing to action of the genes

Two kinds of F_2 ratios are produced in the cross just discussed. The fundamental biotypic or genotypic ratio of 1*CC*:2*Cc*:1*cc* is based on the recombinations of genes in the zygotes. The more superficial phenotypic ratio of 3 black animals to 1 white is based upon the appearance of the individuals in the F_2. The appearance of the animals and hence the visible ratio is the result of the action of the genes. The fundamental genotypic ratio may be thought of as being condensed by gene action into the more evident phenotypic ratio.

INHERITANCE IN FRUIT FLIES. Because of their rapid reproduction and the ease with which they can be cultured, fruit flies, *Drosophila melanogaster*, have been extensively used in studies of heredity. Though the body is a grayish color in the normal fruit fly, among numerous variations in body color one is black. When black- and gray-body colors are brought together in a cross, black is recessive, and the F_1 generation is characteristically gray-bodied. Following the mating of F_1 male and F_1 female, the F_2

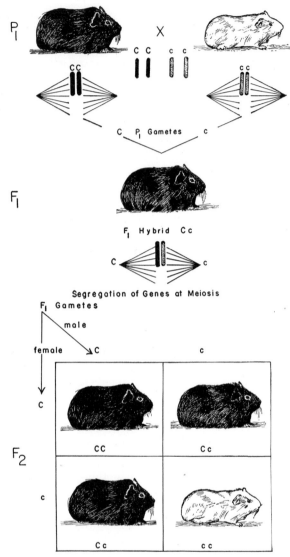

Fig. 29. Inheritance of Contrasting Characters Colored and Albino, in the Guinea Pig.

Theoretically possible recombinations of genes in the F₂ generation are CC, Cc, and cc. Based upon complete dominance of C over c, the F₂ generation will consist of black and white animals in the ratio of 3:1 (bottom). (Redrawn after, W. E. Castle, Carnegie Publication 23, Washington, 1905.)

generation consists of flies with gray bodies and others with black bodies in the ratio of 3:1 (Fig. 30).

Normal fruit flies have long wings. Many wing variations, however, are known. One of these is an extreme abnormality called vestigial wing. Flies with this abnormality have short, narrow wings, in fact, mere stubs or vestiges of normal wings; they are incapable of flight and crawl about like ants. In crosses involving the normal long wing and the vestigial-wing type, vestigial behaves as a recessive. The F_1 generation all have long wings (Fig. 31). Mating male and female F_1 produces an F_2 generation of long-winged and vestigial-winged individuals in the typical Mendelian mono-hybrid ratio of 3:1.

Of the multitude of characters in which the transmission illustrates Mendelian principles, fruit shape in the common summer-squash plants may be mentioned. In hybridization between squash plants producing disk-shaped fruits with those producing spherical-shaped fruits, the disk-shaped proved to be dominant in the F_1 hybrids. F_2 plants bred from these F_1 hybrids showed the segregation into two groups: plants representing three-fourths of the total population produced disk-shaped fruits, and one-fourth produced the recessive spherical-shaped fruits (Fig. 32).

EXTENSION OF MENDELIAN PRINCIPLES TO INHERITANCE IN MAN. The study of the heritable characteristics in man must be made from family histories, and numbers so obtained are of necessity much smaller than those obtained with experimental animals and plants. There are, however, enough data available on the transmission of many of the physical traits, as eye and hair characteristics, and certain of the mental traits, as feeble-mindedness, of man to indicate that the inheritance of these characteristics follows Mendelian principles. Recognition of the universal application of the laws of heredity in the plant and elsewhere in the animal world makes it reasonable to conclude that all of the physical traits of man, too, are subject to the same Mendelian principles.

Among the many physical traits of man which occur in contrasts is that of the normally pigmented skin and albinism (Fig. 191). In man albinism results in a totally white skin and hair almost devoid of pigment. As in other animals the skin and also the eyes of albinos in human beings usually appear pink, because the blood vessels show through the transparent tissues. Albinism in man is a rather rare characteristic, but its appearance in the white race has been sufficiently conspicuous and frequent to suggest that the pigmented condition is genetically dominant over the unpigmented. The mating of two persons apparently normal but heterozygous for the trait would be expected to result in one albino in each four progeny. This proportion is not necessarily obtained from one family in which the total numbers are small but from numbers of individuals in many families. Albinism may occur in all races. It has been described in Negroes and in the American

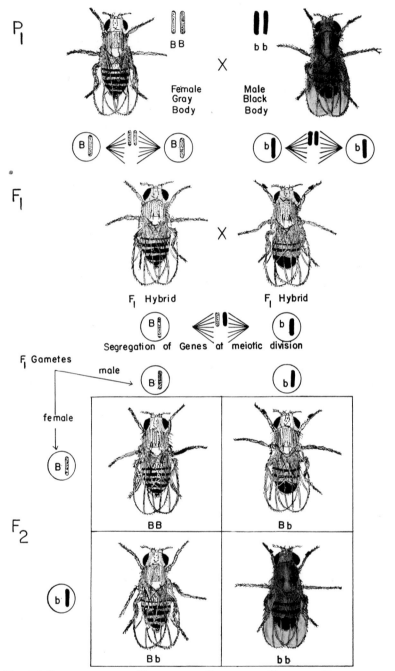

FIG. 30. INHERITANCE OF BLACK- AND GRAY-BODY COLOR IN DROSOPHILA.
Mating the hybrids, $F_1 \times F_1$, results in recombination of genes B and b in four
possible ways and in production of flies of three types of genetic constitution but of
two phenotypic types.

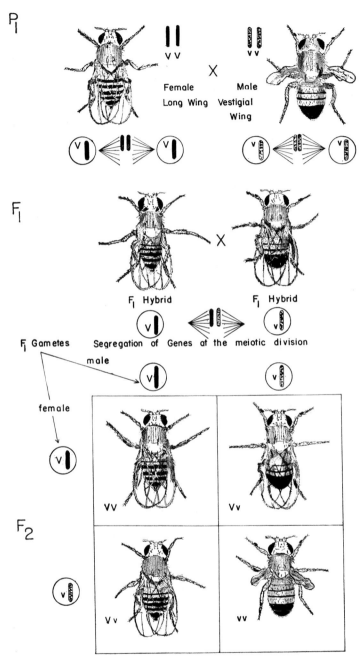

FIG. 31. INHERITANCE OF LONG, "VV," AND VESTIGIAL, "vv," WINGS IN DROSOPHILA.
    Phenotypically there are two types of flies because of dominance of the gene for
long wing over the gene for vestigial wing.

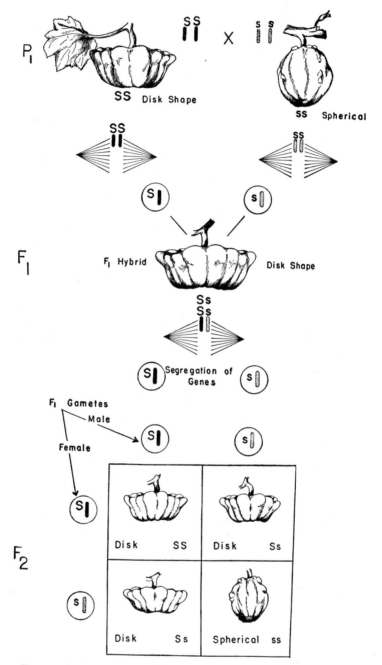

FIG. 32. INHERITANCE OF SHAPE IN FRUIT OF SUMMER SQUASH.
Self-pollination of the F_1 plant (center) results in an F_2 generation producing disk-shaped fruits and spherical fruits in the ratio of 3:1. (Based on plants grown from seeds furnished by E. W. Sinnott.)

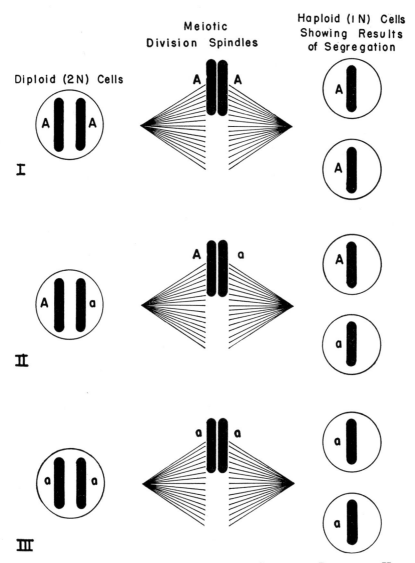

Fig 33. Meiotic Division Spindles of Diploid Cells and Resulting Haploid Cells.

Since segregation of genes depends upon separation of the two members of a pair of homologous chromosomes (or synaptic mates), it occurs regularly during meiotic divisions regardless of whether the genes are in the homozygous-dominant state, AA, the heterozygous, Aa, or the homozygous-recessive state, aa.

I. Diploid cell (left) with homozygous-dominant genes, AA; the spindle (center) showing separation of two members of a pair of homologous chromosomes. This is the physical basis of segregation. Two haploid cells (right) each showing one member of the original pair of homologous chromosomes and the associated gene, A.

II and *III.* The same excepting that the genes are in the heterozygous (Aa) and homozygous-recessive states (aa), respectively.

Indian. White or albino Indians in Panama were the subject of a special study by Harlan (p. 479).

FURTHER EXAMPLES OF MONOHYBRIDS. From the hundreds of recorded examples of Mendelian monohybrid ratios, that is, the occurrence of dominant and recessive characters in the F_2 in a 3:1 ratio, the following limited cases are appended merely as an indication of the diversity of characters analyzed.

Table V

PARTIAL LIST OF DOMINANT AND RECESSIVE TRAITS

Organism	Character		Author	Year
PLANTS	Dominant	Recessive		
Watermelon	Tan seed-coat color	Red		
	Red seed-coat color	Green	McKay	1936
	Green-stripe fruit	White		
Soybean	Tall	Dwarf		
	Dark-colored pods	Light	Woodworth	1923
	Purple-flower color	White		
Cotton	Smooth seed	Fuzzy	Kearney	1927
Barley	Resistance to stem rust	Susceptibility	Powers, et al.	1933
Bean	Resistance to rust	Susceptibility	Wingard	1927
Oats	Resistance to rust	Susceptibility	Garber	1922
Oats	Resistance to smut	Susceptibility	Reed	1934
Corn	Resistance to rust	Susceptibility	Mains	1931
	Teopod	Normal	Lindstrom	1925
Bean	Pole type	Bush type	Emerson	1904
Nasturtium	Doubleness	Singleness	Eyster and	1936
	Superdoubleness	Doubleness	Burpee	
ANIMALS				
Cattle	Black coat	Red	Watson	1921
	Polled or hornless	Horned	Watson	1921
	Dun	Black	Watson	1921
	Black coat	Red	Campbell	1924
Fowl	Leg feathering	Smooth shank	Punnett and Bailey	1918
Man	Various types of allergy* (normal)	Normal	Ritter	1936
	Ear lobe free	Adherent	Powell	1937
	Woolly hair	Normal	Mohr	1932
	Short thumbs	Normal	Hefner	1924

* Allergy, specific sensitivity of some persons to certain proteins.

Incomplete Dominance

In the foregoing crosses, one trait showed complete dominance over the other, yielding an F_2 generation of two phenotypic classes in the approximate ratio of 3 dominants:1 recessive. Not all character pairs, however, show a fully dominant and recessive relationship. In many cases there is incomplete dominance, partial dominance, or lack of dominance. A few of the many recorded cases are mentioned below.

In the Shorthorn breed of cattle, three coat-color types are recognized: red, white, and a mixture or mosaic of red and white hairs, the red-roan

Fig. 34. Inheritance of Red, White, and Roan Colors in Coats of Shorthorn Cattle.

Red bull and white cow may represent P_1 or parental generation. Center, bull and two females represent the intermediate F_1 roan coat. If roan animals are mated, their F_2 progenies will be expected to be of three phenotypic classes as shown below, the red, the white, and the roan. Large numbers of such F_2 individuals will appear in a ratio of 1 red to 2 roan to 1 white. (Upper four photographs courtesy, Cook and Gormley; lower photograph courtesy, Smith, American Shorthorn Breeders Association.)

type. Roan results from mating red and white animals, and the mosaic is the effect of the heterozygous state of the genes for red and white, with neither red nor white dominant. F_1 hybrid animals bred together produce an F_2 generation composed of animals with red, roan, and white coats in the ratio of 1 red:2 roan:1 white (Fig. 34).

In a cross involving these coat colors in cattle, the genes undergo the regular Mendelian type of segregation in the F_1 generation and the expected recombination in the zygotes of the F_2 generation. If the genes conditioning the red color are designated as RR and those conditioning white as rr, the F_1 hybrid has the expected genotype Rr. During the maturation process, the genes R and r segregate, forming two types of gametes for each sex, those bearing the gene R and those bearing the gene r. When F_1 hybrids are mated, the alleles R and r recombine, producing the biotypic ratio of $1RR:2Rr:1rr$ (Fig. 35).*

The currently popular palomino horse of golden color with flaxen mane and tail is genetically a brown, red or chestnut animal heterozygous for an incompletely dominant gene which acts to dilute the brown color. If the dilution alleles are $D\text{-}d$, the genotype of the palomino is Dd. Mating palominos as $Dd \times Dd$ results in the production of chestnut, dd, palomino, Dd, and Cremello, DD, in the approximate ratio of $1:2:1$. The Cremello is a very light-cream color, almost but not quite white, and is sometimes incorrectly referred to as albino. The cream color is the extreme dilution effect of the homozygous dilution gene, DD. The chestnut, an undiluted brown color, results from the effects of the homozygous, dd.

Among incompletely dominant traits in other domestic animals may be mentioned the character "earless" in sheep in which the development of the external ear is suppressed. Crosses between earless, EE, and normal, ee, result in an intermediate condition, small ears in the F_1. Mating $F_1 \times F_1$ yields an F_2 generation consisting of three classes of animals, earless, those with intermediate small ears, and some with normal-sized ears in the phenotypic ratio of $1:2:1$ (Fig. 36).

In the common annual plant *Phlox drummondii*, three types of petal edge or petal form are recognized: the normal or entire petal edge; the cuspidate, an extremely narrow type of petal with a single long tooth on each petal; and an intermediate sort with a fringed edge, called the fimbriate. These three flower forms are the phenotypic expression of a single pair of genes in which dominance is lacking. The parental forms entire, homozygous CC, and cuspidate, homozygous cc, furnish the gametes C and c, respectively, which upon hybridization combine to produce heterozygous Cc in the genotype of the intermediate-fimbriate F_1 hybrid (Fig. 37). Following segregation and recombination of genes, F_2 individuals with genotypes CC, Cc, and cc express themselves in the phenotypic ratio of $1CC$ entire:$2Cc$ fimbriate:$1cc$ cuspidate.

THE GENETIC BASIS OF INCOMPLETE DOMINANCE.   In all monohybrid crosses, the F_2 genotypic ratio is $1:2:1$. The difference between

---

* I. C. Jones suggests that the red, roan, and white colors of shorthorn cattle are dependent upon two pairs of genes, $R\text{-}r$ and $W\text{-}w$. In this interpretation R determines the red color, and W, incompletely dominant, acts to inhibit the production of red. Accordingly, red animals are $RRww$; roan, $RRWw$; and white, $RRWW$.

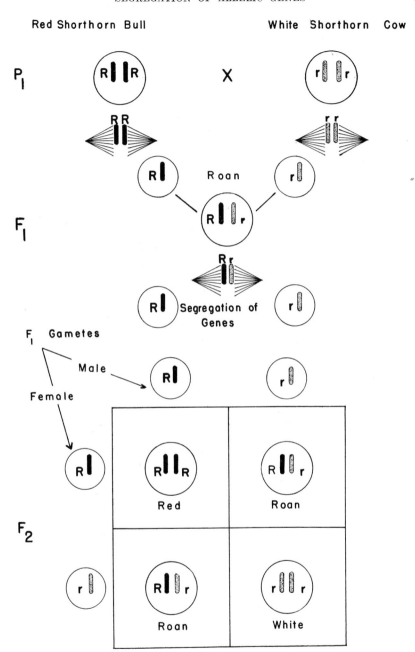

FIG. 35. SEGREGATION AND RECOMBINATIONS OF COLOR GENES "R" AND "r" CONDITIONING RED, ROAN, AND WHITE COATS IN CATTLE.
F_2 generation consists of red, roan, and white animals in the ratio of 1:2:1.

complete and incomplete dominance is in the dominant-recessive action of
the genes and their phenotypic expression. In all cases the genotypic constitution is fundamental.

FIG. 36. SHEEP CHARACTERS, LONG EARS, SHORT EARS, AND EARLESS.
(Courtesy, E. G. Ritzman, from *J. Heredity*.)

The F_2 generation following a cross involving a single pair of alleles
in which there is a lack of complete dominance shows three recognizable
classes of progeny instead of only two as in cases of full dominance. With
incomplete dominance there is an increase in recognizable F_2 phenotypic
classes over cases involving complete dominance, because the heterozygous

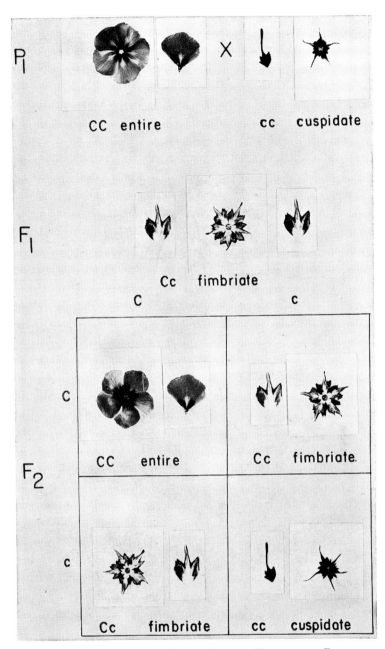

FIG. 37. INHERITANCE OF PETAL FORM IN FLOWERS OF PHLOX.

Table VI

GENES AND PHENOTYPIC RATIOS*

AA	Aa	aA	aa	
AA	$2Aa$		aa	The theoretically possible genotypes in the monohybrid F_2 generation
AA 1 homozygous-dominant individual	$2Aa$ 2 recognizable heterozygous individuals		aa 1 homozygous-recessive individual	The 1:2:1 genotypic ratio in the monohybrid F_2 generation. This normally occurs regardless of the dominant-recessive relationship
AA and $2Aa$ 3 phenotypically dominant individuals, partly homozygous and partly heterozygous			aa 1 homozygous-recessive individual	The 1:2:1 phenotypic ratio in which the members of a pair of allelic genes show incomplete dominance
				The 3:1 phenotypic ratio in which one member of a pair of allelic genes shows complete dominance

* Genotypes of an F_2 monohybrid generation. The phenotypic ratios depend upon the dominant or partially dominant action of the factors.

or hybrid individuals differ visibly from both of the parental types. This is expressed in the 1:2:1 phenotypic ratio with three recognizable classes. The 3:1 ratio, with only two classes, may be considered as a modification or condensation of the basic 1:2:1 ratio because of the dominant action of the factors involved in the cross.

Organisms heterozygous for incompletely dominant factors are often referrred to as "unfixable heterozygotes." They are, however, no more unfixable than any other type of heterozygous plant or animal, for actually all heterozygotes continue to split into two genotypic classes of homozygotes and one heterozygous class. The unique feature of the heterozygotes of incompletely dominant factors is that they are phenotypically recognizable, while those of completely dominant genes are not.

Analysis of Inheritance

Hybridization or "crossing" as used in genetical experiments is really a method of making an analysis of the hereditary units basic to a pair of contrasting characters.* This technique may be roughly compared to the chemical analysis of an unknown chemical mixture or compound. Both techniques seek knowledge about the constituents of the unknown. The systems of mating employed in hybridization are of three general kinds: (1) the direct cross or sibcross, (2) the backcross, and (3) the testcross. In the direct or sibcross, an F_1 individual is "selfed," or F_1 individuals or sibs are mated to obtain the F_2 generation. This method has already been described. The backcross involves mating of F_1 hybrids to one or the other of the immediate parents, generally the recessive. For analytical purposes it is unimportant whether the actual parent or an organism of similar genetic constitution is used in the mating. The term *testcross* is applicable to the technique of mating the F_1 to some individual of appropriate genetic constitution. Generally the testcross is made by mating the heterozygous F_1 individual to another that is homozygous recessive for the genes involved. The progeny resulting from a direct cross or sibcross is referred to as the F_2 generation; that from a backcross, as the backcross generation; and that from the testcross, as the testcross generation.

Generally the purpose in these types of mating is the same, namely, to analyze the product of the original hybridization in order to identify and learn about the actions of the genes involved. Often the three types of crosses are equally good for this purpose. Homozygous organisms produce *only one type of gamete;* those heterozygous for one pair of alleles produce *two types, equally numerous.* Recombination of genes in the monohybrid direct cross yields a genotypic ratio of 1:2:1. Monohybrid backcrosses and testcrosses yield genotypic ratios of 1:1. Phenotypic ratios in all cases depend upon the dominant-recessive action of the genes involved. All types of ratios, genotypic and phenotypic, are readily determined (Fig. 38, 39, and 40).

USES OF THE TYPES OF MATING. The direct cross has been used exten-

---

* Hybridization in animals is accomplished by mating males and females of the desired types. If fertilization occurs, the offspring resulting from the mating will be of a hybrid nature. Hybridization in plants usually involves the removal of the young unopened anthers from a flower, to guard against self-pollination, and the fastening of a suitable bag over the emasculated flower to prevent undesired cross-pollination. After a few days, when the stigma is receptive, pollen from the desired parent flowers is placed on the stigma of the emasculated flower and the bag replaced. If pollination is successful, seeds containing hybrid embryos may be produced. Planted at a suitable season, such seeds may germinate and produce hybrid plants.

sively in genetic analysis. It is effective with experimental material that is inexpensive, when it is feasible to procure large numbers of individuals, and when the organism is readily selfed as in the case of peas, maize or Indian corn, and many other plants. It can be used when sibcrossing is easily accomplished as in the case of an F_1 population of Drosophila. Under conditions of full dominance, backcrossing the

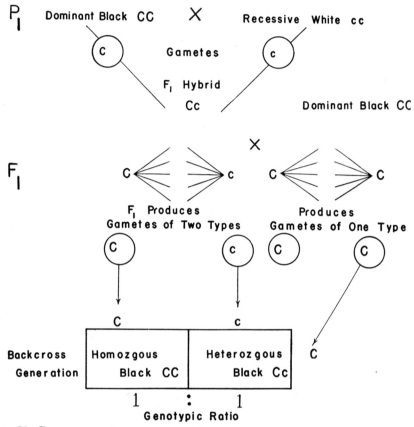

FIG. 38. RESULTS OF BACKCROSSING F_1 TO DOMINANT-PARENTAL TYPE UNDER CONDITIONS OF FULL DOMINANCE AS IN THE GUINEA PIG.

In the backcross F_2 there are heterozygous, Cc, and homozygous-dominant individuals, CC, in a 1:1 ratio. Because of full dominance, these animals are all alike in being black.

heterozygous F_1 to the dominant parent yields a 1:1 genotypic ratio, but the backcross progeny is phenotypically alike and is of little value in genetic analysis. Under conditions of incomplete dominance, backcrossing to either dominant or recessive parent yields a 1:1 phenotypic ratio (Fig. 38, 39, and 40). The testcross heterozygous $F_1 \times$ homozygous recessive yields a testcross progeny both genotypically and phenotypically in a 1:1 ratio. Since significant testcross ratios involve only one-half the numbers required in monohybrid direct crosses and only one-fourth those necessary in the case of dihybrids, the testcross is indicated in problems of inheritance in which it is not feasible to experiment with large numbers. Backcrossing has a tendency to make the progeny homozygous and thus to "fix" certain characters. Genetically the practice of backcrossing tends to make the experimental material homo-

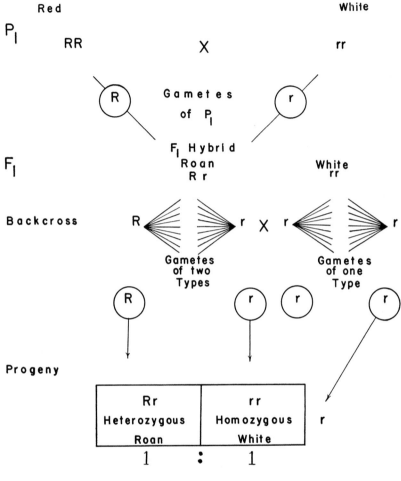

Genotypic and Phenotypic Ratios

Fig. 39. Results of Using Backcross or Testcross under Conditions of Incomplete Dominance.

In cattle if heterozygous roan F_1, Rr, is backcrossed to recessive white, rr, an F_2 will consist of two classes.

zygous for specific traits. For these reasons it is often used in practical breeding programs.

The testcross, however, has its limitations. When the labor involved in mating the F_1 to the recessive stock is an item and the direct cross is easily made, the latter is preferable. An example of this is the phlox plant in which each flower produces a maximum of only three seeds. The phlox plant is, however, very readily self-pol-

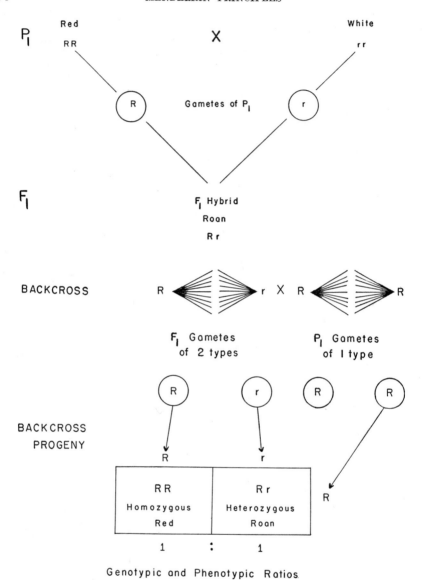

Genotypic and Phenotypic Ratios.

FIG. 40. RESULTS OF BACKCROSSING F_1 TO DOMINANT-PARENTAL STRAIN UNDER CONDITIONS OF INCOMPLETE DOMINANCE.

In cattle if heterozygous roan F_1, Rr, is backcrossed to dominant-red parental strain, two classes will be produced, one class of heterozygous animals, Rr, which will be roan and the other class of homozygous, RR, which will be red. Backcrossing to dominant-parental strain will yield two phenotypic classes only under conditions of incomplete dominance.

linated, and an F_2 generation is easily obtained. In phlox the testcross is seldom used. In inheritance studies in tobacco, corn, foxglove plants, and many others in which hundreds of seeds may be obtained from a single hand-pollination, the use of either the testcross or the direct cross may be equally desirable. The fruit fly, *Drosophila*, is another example of an organism in which either the direct cross or the testcross may be used equally well. Fruit flies are cheap, they cost little to maintain, they produce many offspring from a single mating, and the interval between generations is short. A later section will emphasize the use of the testcross in linkage studies, particularly with Drosophila.

The Probabilities in Mendelian Segregation and Recombination— the "Goodness of Fit" in Monohybrids

The probabilities in Mendelian segregation and recombination have frequently been illustrated by the chance falling of heads or tails in tossing coins. Segregation of the dominant and recessive factors of one pair of alleles may be illustrated by tossing a single coin. With one toss the coin falls either heads or tails. The same situation prevails in the segregation of allelic genes as A-a to gametes. In either male or female, normal segregation of one pair of alleles contributes a dominant A, or a recessive a, to a gamete, normally never both dominant and recessive genes.

THE PROBABILITIES IN RECOMBINATION—*Illustrated by Tossing Two Coins.* The gametes, both male and female, carry either the recessive or the dominant gene of a pair of alleles, and during reproduction in F_1 hybrids, dominant and recessive genes are recombined at random to form the F_2 genotypes. The probabilities of this chance recombination of F_1 gametes to form the $1:2:1$ ratio of F_2 genotypes may be illustrated by simultaneously tossing two coins as a dime and a penny. Heads of one coin, the dime, may represent a male gamete with a dominant gene; tails, a male gamete with the recessive allele. Likewise, the penny may represent a female gamete with heads a dominant and tails a recessive allele.

These two coins may fall in combinations of two heads, corresponding to the double or homozygous-dominant genotype, as AA; one head and one tail, corresponding to the heterozygous genotype, Aa; or two tails, corresponding to the homozygous-recessive genotype, aa. These are the possible combinations of heads and tails in tossing two coins together, but what is the probability or chance of getting one of these combinations in any single toss of the two coins? What are the probabilities of realizing these combinations of two heads, one head and one tail, and two tails in the ratio of $1:2:1$?

A coin has equal chances of falling either heads or tails. The chance of its falling heads in any one toss is then one in two or $1/2$. What then is the chance of both coins falling heads if two are tossed simultaneously? This chance may be determined mathematically by the formula $1/2 \times 1/2 = 1/4$ or one in four. Similarly, the chances for both falling tails is also $1/4$ or one in four. There is a chance of one in four or $1/4$ that one coin, the dime, may fall heads and the other, the penny, tails, and there is an equal chance that the dime may fall tails and the penny heads. The probability that one coin may fall heads and the other tails may be expressed mathematically as $1/4 + 1/4 = 1/2$.

Mathematically, the probabilities of obtaining two heads, one head and one tail, or two tails in tossing coins may be shown in the expansion of $(h + t)^2$ in which h represents heads, t represents tails, and the exponent, 2, indicates the number of coins. Thus, since the chance of a coin, falling heads or tails is one in two, or $1/2$, at any one toss of a coin:

$$
\begin{aligned}
(h + t)^2 &= h^2 &&+ 2ht &&+ t^2 \\
&= (1/2)^2 &&+ 2(1/2)(1/2) &&+ (1/2)^2 \\
&= 1/4 &&+ 2/4 \text{ or } 1/2 &&+ 1/4
\end{aligned}
$$

that is   1 chance   2 chances   1 chance
            in 4 of   in 4, or 1   in 4 of
            getting two   in 2, of getting   getting two
            heads   a head and a   tails
                           tail

From the above it may be seen that in the realm of pure chance, as in tossing two coins, heads and tails may be expected to occur in the ratio of one pair of heads, two pairs with heads and tails, and one pair of tails. With a sufficiently large number of tosses of coins, this ratio may be realized with a statistically unimportant or insignificant error.

By analogy the probabilities, based on pure chance, are that either a homozygous-dominant, as AA, or a homozygous-recessive, as aa, genotype may be found one time in four in an F_2 monohybrid generation. Statistically, the possibilities are that a heterozygote, as Aa, may be found twice in four. Stated otherwise, with large numbers involved, the statistical probabilities are that one-half of any monohybrid F_2 generation will be heterozygotes and that gene recombinations in the genotypes of an F_2 generation of a monohybrid will occur in a $1:2:1$ ratio.

GOODNESS OF FIT. In genetical work only approximations of the expected Mendelian ratios are generally realized. Rarely indeed is a true $3:1$ F_2 ratio or a perfect $1:1$ backcross ratio observed. Even with large numbers of individuals, the phenotypic classes may deviate from their expected value. The geneticist is interested in learning how well the approximate ratios found in experimental work actually fit a true Mendelian ratio. The phrase *goodness of fit* has been applied to studies of relations of observed and theoretical values of Mendelian ratios. Statistical methods devised for testing the significance of the deviations from the true Mendelian ratios make it possible to learn if the deviations are sufficiently great to suggest that the assumption of a $3:1$ or a $1:1$ ratio is not justified.

DETERMINATION OF THE EXPECTED RATIO. In one of Mendel's experiments, he hybridized tall and dwarf pea plants and grew an F_2 generation of 787 tall plants and 277 dwarf plants in a total of 1,064 plants (p. 56). By dividing the number in the larger class, 787, by that in the smaller, 277, an observed ratio of $2.84:1$, not the expected $3:1$, is obtained. The exact $3:1$ ratio in a population of 1,064 can be calculated as $798:266$ or the number of individuals expected in the dominant and recessive classes, respectively. The observed values $787:277$ therefore show a deviation of 11 from the expected ratio of 798 tall : 266 dwarf plants in the F_2 population of 1,064. The population of 1,064 was actually only a sample of the possible recombinations of the thousands of probable gametes produced by the F_1 monohybrids. The question may arise as to the validity of Mendel's $3:1$ ratio. Is a ratio of $787:277$ a good $3:1$ ratio in this sample population? How frequently would such a deviation from the expected ratio occur due to chance, that is, the error of random sampling?

CHI-SQUARE AS AN INDICATION OF THE SIGNIFICANCE OF THE DEVIATION. Statisticians test the importance or significance of deviations from the expected numbers in Mendelian ratios by the **chi-square method.** *Chi*, the lower-case Greek letter χ, is used to indicate the statistical test for goodness of fit of observed data to the theoretically expected ratio.

The capital letters, X_1, X_2, etc., are used to designate the observed values in each class, and the theoretically expected number is indicated by m. The deviations are then $X_1 - m$ and $X_2 - m$. In calculating chi-square, the plus and minus deviations of the observed data from the theoretically expected values are each squared. Each squared value is then divided by the expected number for that class, and the quotients are added together to give χ^2. The deviations are squared to use their relative sizes and not their actual magnitudes in the calculations.

The mathematical formula for calculating chi-square is:

$$\chi^2 = \frac{(X_1 - m)^2}{m} + \frac{(X_2 - m)^2}{m}$$

In Mendel's problem with 787 tall and 277 dwarf as the observed values in a total of 1,064 pea plants in the F_2 generation, a 3:1 ratio is expected. But the expected values in the two classes are 798 tall and 266 dwarf. The deviations are $X_1 - m = 787 - 798 = -11$ and $X_2 - m = 277 - 266 = +11$.

When these values are substituted in the formula for calculating chi-square, it becomes:

$$\chi^2 = \frac{(787 - 798)^2}{m} + \frac{(277 - 266)^2}{m}$$

$$= \frac{(-11)^2}{798} + \frac{(11^2)}{266}$$

$$= {}^{121}\!/_{798} + {}^{121}\!/_{266} = 0.152 + 0.455 = 0.607$$

$$\chi^2 = 0.607$$

Chi-square would be zero if the total observed number in each class were the same as the expected. Thus, the value of chi-square will *increase* as the observed numbers *deviate in increasing amounts* from the expected. Conversely, the value of chi-square will *decrease* as the observed numbers *approach the expected*. The relative magnitude of chi-square is important in biological studies because it indicates the fit of observed data to a hypothetical ratio.

Statisticians use tables for the distribution of chi-square to indicate the relative value and significance of this constant in statistical problems. One of these tables prepared by Snedecor from a study of 400 ratios indicates that a chi-square value of 0.607 is in fact very low. He states that "by a fairly general concurrence of opinion" a value of 3.841 is regarded as large or, as the statistician puts it, significant. The 5-per-cent point is 3.841, which means that only 5 per cent of all samples has a chi-square value greater than 3.841. This also means that there is only one chance in 20 that a sample will have a chi-square value greater than 3.841.

Thus Mendel's observed values of 787 for the tall and 277 for the dwarf plants with a deviation of -11 and $+11$ did not deviate significantly from the expected 798:266 ratio. This conclusion confirmed Mendel's observed ratio of 787 and 277 as actually a good 3:1 ratio.

Questions and Problems

The solution of the following problems in Mendelian heredity requires attention to:

1. Data on the number and kinds of genes involved in the inheritance of the characteristics under consideration
2. Meiotic segregation of the members of the pairs of allelic genes concerned in the determination of the traits (Fig. 9, 10, 11, 14, and 33)
3. Recombination of the members of each pair of genes when the gametes fuse at fertilization (Fig. 13, 15, and 22)
4. Calculation of phenotypic ratios based on the dominant-recessive action of allelic genes.

Data on Monohybrids in Rodents

In rodents such as rats, mice, guinea pigs, and rabbits, full coloration *vs.* albinism is determined by a pair of allelic genes, *C-c*. Full coloration is determined by the dominant member *C* and albinism by the homozygous-recessive *cc*. The distribution of color, the solid or self-coloration *vs.* spotted, as in black and in black with white spotting, is conditioned by an additional pair of alleles, *S-s*. Self-coloration is conditioned by the dominant member *S* and the spotted trait by the homozygous-recessive *ss*. In guinea pigs a third trait, rough coat *vs.* smooth coat, is conditioned by the allelic pair *R-r*, rough being determined by the dominant *R* and smooth by the homozygous-recessive *rr*.

1. What single biological fact (now discovered) was a factor in the slow development of the facts of heredity?
2. Discuss the importance of a recognition of the male and female sexes in animals and plants as a factor in the development of genetics.
3. Are there any evidences that man observed the facts of heredity before the science of genetics was developed?
4. What were the contributions of the plant hybridizers to biological thought?
5. Discuss the relative importance of Mendel's contribution to biological thought.
6. Who were the men associated with the rediscovery of Mendelian principles of heredity?
7. When a black-coated female guinea pig, *CC*, is mated with an albino male guinea pig, *cc*, the F_1 generation, *Cc*, of males and females is all black. Explain the classes and ratio of animals expected in the F_2 generation. What is the biotypic ratio in the F_2 generation? On the basis of F_2 genotypes, what kinds of gametes will be produced by the individuals in the F_2 generation? If mating within each biotypic class of the F_2 is assumed, what ratios may be expected in an F_3 generation?
8. Assume that a pure-bred, solid-color or self black mouse, *SS*, is mated with a black-and-white-spotted male mouse, *ss*. Predict the characteristics of the F_1 generation. If F_1 animals of this type are mated *inter se*, $F_1 \times F_1$, what sorts of animals may be expected in the F_2 generation? Show exactly how Mendelian principles are demonstrated in a cross of this type.
9. Assume that a rough-coated guinea pig, *RR*, is mated with a smooth-coated female guinea pig, *rr*. Carry this hypothetical cross to the F_2 generation. Emphasize the segregation of genes when the F_1 animals produce gametes. By use of the checkerboard, indicate the recombination of genes to obtain the genotypes of the F_2 generation. What ratio of animal types is found in the F_2 generation?

Monohybrids in Drosophila

The fruit fly or vinegar fly, *Drosophila melanogaster*, is the standard experimental animal in laboratory courses in genetics. If these flies are available, it is possible for students to make crosses involving several distinct characteristics which follow Mendel's Laws of Heredity.

Data on dominance and recessiveness of some of the many heritable characteristics in the fruit fly from the chromosome map (Fig. 69, p. 151).

Dominant Wild Type	Recessive Mutant Type
Gray-body color, *BB*	Black-body color, *bb*
Gray-body color, *EE*	Ebony-body color, *ee*
Red-eye color, *PrPr*	Purple-eye color, *prpr*
Red-eye color, *SS*	Sepia-eye color, *ss*
Red-eye color, *ScSc*	Scarlet-eye color, *scsc*
Red-eye color, *PP*	Pink-eye color, *pp*
Long wing, *VV*	Short vestigial wing, *vv*

10. If a normal wild-type female fly with gray body, *BB*, is mated with a mutant black-body type, *bb*, what will be the nature of the F_1 flies? Emphasizing the segregation of genes, diagram to show the types of gametes which the F_1 male and female will produce. Predict the genotypes and the characteristics of the F_2 generation. What ratio may be expected? Which Mendelian principle is involved in the production of the F_2 genotypes?

11. A student made a cross between a wild-type female Drosophila with red eyes, *PrPr*, and a mutant-type male fly with purple eyes, *prpr*. In the F_1 progeny there were 63 females and 55 males all of which had red eyes. F_1 females and F_1 males were mated to obtain the F_2 generation. Examination of the F_2 flies showed that there were 145 flies with red eyes and 55 flies with purple eyes. Explain the biological and genetical features of this cross. What Mendelian principles are involved?

12. Just previous to a vacation period, a student made a Drosophila cross and obtained an F_1 generation of wild-type flies with red eyes. He mated F_1 females to F_1 males and left on his vacation. Upon his return he found an F_2 population of 100 wild-type flies with red eyes and 30 flies with a mutant-eye color which he identified as pink. Failure to find his original notes convinced him that they had been left out of his brief case when he left his home to return to college. How would you explain the nature of the original cross?

13. In problems 11 and 12 above, the two classes of F_2 progeny, 145:55 and 100:30, respectively, are not quite perfect 3:1 ratios. How do you account for the discrepancies? Supposing there had been 1,000 F_2 flies in each case, would the chances of a perfect 3:1 ratio have been increased? What if 10,000 F_2 flies?

14. A student crossed the normal wild-type long-winged Drosophila, *VV*, to the mutant-type vestigial-winged fly, *vv*. The F_1 generation of males and females all had normal long wings. Mating F_1 females and F_1 males yielded an F_2 generation of 520 long-winged flies and 140 flies with vestigial wings. Explain the biological and genetical principles underlying these results.

MONOHYBRIDS IN CORN AND WHEAT

Data on the dominance and recessiveness of the heritable characters in corn and wheat. In the common field corn (maize), the aleurone colors are conditioned by three distinct genes, *A-a* or *C-c* or *R-r*. In each of these, the dominant gene (*A* or *C* or *R*) conditions the character of colored grain (usually red) over the recessive genes (*a* or *c* or *r*) which condition white grains. In a similar manner, purple-grain color is conditioned by *Pr*, a dominant-color factor, and red by the corresponding allelic gene, *pr*, which is recessive.

Likewise, in wheat the gene conditioning red-grain color is dominant over that conditioning the white-grain color. This pair of allelic genes is indicated by *R-r*.

There are several heritable endosperm characters in corn. In the case of sweet corn (garden corn), the sweet character is due to the homozygous-recessive gene *su-su* which conditions the development of sugar, instead of the customary starch, in the endosperm of the grain. Starchy corn is conditioned by the dominant gene *Su*. Another endosperm character is the recessive trait of shrunken grain as contrasted with the normal full grain. The allelic genes *Sh-sh* condition these endosperm characters.

In considering the heritable characteristics of seeds, it is important to remember that many of the seed structures borne on the mother plant actually belong to the following generation (pp. 30, 86). Characters of this nature are the colors and starchy or sugary nature of the cotyledons of peas. Mendel mentioned the fact that the F_2 segregation in pea seeds could be seen in the pods produced on the F_1 plant. F_2 segregation in corn seeds can be seen on the ears produced on the F_1 plants. The endosperm and aleurone structures are produced as a result of a "double fertilization" in the embryo sac of the ovules. Because of this fact, the F_2 classes may be counted on the ears produced by the F_1 corn plant. This fact should be kept in mind in considering the following problems.

15. An experimenter had grown two strains of corn in widely separated fields for a number of years. One of these strains produced only red grains, while the other produced only white grains. In the summer of 1950, he took pollen from the tassels of the white race of corn and applied it to the silks of the red strain of corn. The seeds of this cross were planted in 1951, and at harvest time of that year, the F_1 corn plants had mature ears with both red grains and white grains. One of these ears had 328 red grains and 111 white grains. Explain the biological and genetical principles underlying these results.

16. Assume hybridization between corn plants producing purple grains and those producing red grains. With the use of diagrams, explain the biological and genetical principles involved in accounting for the predicted F_2 generation.

17. An ear of corn has 340 purple grains and 116 red grains. Give an explanation of the ancestry of the plant which produced this ear.

18. Assume hybridization between starchy field corn, *Su-Su*, and one of the garden varieties of sweet corn, *su-su*. Describe what may be expected in succeeding generations. Show where the inheritance follows Mendelian principles.

19. Predict the nature of the F_1 and F_2 generations secured by hybridization between a corn plant producing grains with full endosperm and one producing shrunken endosperm. How do Mendelian principles apply in this case? Explain by diagrams.

MONOHYBRIDS IN PEAS

20. Crossing starchy peas with round seeds, *WW*, with sugary peas producing wrinkled seeds, *ww*, results in the development of an F_1 plant. This F_1 pea plant produces pods which contain both round peas and wrinkled peas. Thus, the segregation of characters may be observed directly without actually growing the F_2 generation.

If tall peas and dwarf peas are hybridized, the F_1 plant is produced as in the cross above. However, in this case it is necessary to plant the seeds produced by the F_1 plant and actually to grow the F_2 plants in order to observe the segregation of the characters tall and dwarf. Explain why this is true. In order to solve this problem, it may be necessary to diagram each of the above crosses, keeping in mind the nature of the characteristics under consideration.

MONOHYBRIDS IN HUMAN BEINGS

21. In man many characteristics are known to be inherited on exactly the same Mendelian basis as the traits of plants and animals. Name some heritable human traits of this nature.

22. Explain in detail how albinism is inherited in man.

23. It is now recognized that Mendel's Laws of Heredity may be universally applied to all plants and animals, including man. What biological phenomena fundamental to Mendelian principles occur in all forms of life, both plant and animal (and man)? How are these phenomena related to Mendelian principles?

INCOMPLETE DOMINANCE IN MONOHYBRIDS

24. Explain in detail the inheritance of the roan character in cattle. (See data, p. 67.)

25. Crosses between certain varieties of phlox produce an intermediate F_1 known as fimbriate. Explain the inheritance in this instance.

26. Compare the genotypic and phenotypic ratios which may be expected under conditions of incomplete and complete dominance.

THE BACKCROSS OR TESTCROSS

Problems in the use of the backcross or testcross may be solved by following the part of the general directions on parental types, F_1, and the segregation of genes in the F_1 (p. 50). It should be noted that mating the heterozygous F_1 to either of the parental types involves the recombination of the two (or more) types of F_1 gametes with the single type of gamete produced by the homozygous or pure-bred parental stock.

27. Crossing the black guinea pig, CC, with the albino results in the production of a heterozygous black F_1 animal, Cc. Assume that the F_1 animals are testcrossed to the dominant-black parental stock. What results, genotypically and phenotypically, may be expected?
28. Assume that the F_1 animals from the black $\times$ white guinea-pig cross are testcrossed to the recessive-albino parental stock. What genotypic and phenotypic results may be expected?
29. With the roan-color characteristic of the heterozygous condition following crosses between red and white animals in the Shorthorn breed of cattle, predict the phenotypic results of testcrossing the roan to the red type. What will be the result of the testcross roan $\times$ white?
30. Compare the results of testcrossing the heterozygous F_1 to the parental types under conditions of full dominance with those obtained under conditions of incomplete dominance. Are there any differences in the genotypic ratios in the two cases? What causes the differences in the results of testcrossing?
31. Definition of terms. What do you understand by the following terms?

homologous chromosomes	genotype
alleles or allelomorphic genes	phenotype
homozygous condition	gamete
heterozygous condition	zygote

References

BATESON, WM.: *Mendel's Principles of Heredity*, Cambridge, England, Cambridge University Press, 1909, 317–361.

CASTLE W. E.: *Genetics and Eugenics*, 2nd ed. Cambridge, Harvard University Press, 1920, 313–353.

COOK, ROBERT F.: "A Chronology of Genetics," in *The Yearbook of Agriculture*, 1937, U. S. Dep. Agr., Washington, D. C., Government Printing Office, 1457–1477.

ILTIS, H.: *Life of Mendel*. Translated by E. and C. Paul. New York, W. W. Norton & Company, Inc., 1932.

ROBERTS, H. F.: *Plant Hybridization before Mendel*, Princeton, Princeton University Press, 1929.

SHARP, L. W.: *Fundamentals of Cytology*, New York, McGraw-Hill Book Company, Inc., 1943, Chapter XII, 168–192.

———: *Introduction to Cytology*, 3rd ed. New York, McGraw-Hill Book Company, Inc., 1934, Chapter XVII, 284–313.

SINNOTT, EDMUND W., L. C. DUNN and DOBZHANSKY, TH.: *Principles of Genetics*, 4th ed. New York, McGraw-Hill Book Company, Inc., 1950, 463–493.

SNEDECOR, GEORGE W.: *Statistical Methods*, 4th ed. Ames, Iowa State College Press, 1946.

WARNER, M. F., M. A. SHERMAN and E. COLVIN: *A Bibliography of Plant Genetics.* (U. S. Dep. Agr. Misc. Publ. #164) Washington, D. C., 1934.

WERKENTHIN, FRED C.: "The Founders of the Art of Breeding," *Proc. Iowa Acad. Sci.* XXIX:291–310 (1922).

WILSON, E. B.: *The Cell,* 3rd ed. New York, The Macmillan Company, 1925, Chapter XII, 916–976.

ZIRKLE, CONWAY: *The Beginnings of Plant Hybridization.* (Morris Arboretum Monograph I) Philadelphia, The University of Pennsylvania Press, 1935.

chapter 4

Assortment of Genes—Mendel's Second Law of Heredity

After proposing the principle of segregation and recombination in mono-hybrids, Mendel stated, "The next task consisted in ascertaining whether the law of development (heredity) discovered in these (monohybrids) ap-plied to each pair of differentiating characters when several diverse char-acters are united in the hybrid by crossing." Consideration of this problem led to his formulation of the *Second* Law Of Heredity, The Free or Independ-ent Assortment of Genes. This law has to do with the grouping of the prod-ucts of the independent segregation of the members of two or more pairs of genes.

Dihybrids

DIHYBRIDS IN PEAS.   The Inheritance of Seed Characters.   Among the several characteristics of pea plants which Mendel studied were the color characters of seeds, yellow and green, the genes or determiners of which may be indicated as Y-y. He combined these color characters with the structural characters, round seeds and wrinkled seeds, the genes of which may be indi-cated R-r. These seed characteristics, he said, "gave results in the simplest and most certain way." For hybridization Mendel selected pea plants which bred true for the dominant characters, yellow round seeds, and others which bred true for the contrasting recessive traits, green wrinkled seeds. These seed characters are developed in the embryo. Yellow and green are the colors of the cotyledons, and the round or wrinkled feature of the seeds is depend-ent upon the nature of the stored carbohydrates in the cotyledons. If carbohydrates are stored in the form of starch, the cotyledons, when dry, are full and consequently the seeds are round. If carbohydrates are stored in the form of sugar, the cotyledons, when dry, are shrunken and the seeds appear wrinkled (Fig. 41). These seed characteristics are developed in accordance with the action of the genes in the genotypes of the embryos, and the embryos as young plants show the characters in the seeds as they mature.*

---

* Inherited characteristics may become visible at definite stages in the development of organisms, and the time of development may vary with the several characters. Char-acteristics such as those of embryos of plants or animals are visible at relatively early

Following hybridization of the two parental varieties of peas, yellow round, $YYRR$, and green wrinkled, $yyrr$, the seeds produced in the pods on the seed parent contained the F_1 embryos with the genotype $YyRr$. Since the cotyledons of these F_1 embryos or young first-generation plants were yellow and starchy, the indications were that the genes Y and R were both completely dominant. When Mendel planted these F_1 seeds, he found that "the plants raised there-from yielded seeds of four sorts which frequently presented themselves all in one pod." In all, 556 seeds were produced by the naturally self-fertilized F_1 plants. They showed four classes of the segregating characters as follows: 315 round yellow seeds, 101 wrinkled yellow seeds, 108 round green seeds, and 32 wrinkled green seeds. These numbers can be arranged into a ratio of approximately 9:3:3:1, about 9 round yellow:3 wrinkled yellow:3 round green:1 wrinkled green seed in the entire population (Fig. 41). When, regardless of color, all round seeds are grouped 315 + 108 and compared with all the wrinkled seeds, 101 + 32, the ratio of the total number, 423:133, is approximately that of 3:1, the typical monohybrid F_2 ratio in cases of full dominance. Likewise, considering color regardless of shape, the total number of all yellow seeds, 315 + 101 = 416, compared with the total number of all green seeds, 108 + 32 = 140, that is, 416:140, also yields approximately a 3:1 ratio. Thus, the 9:3:3:1 phenotypic ratio which Mendel obtained may be thought of as a 3:1 ratio multiplied algebraically by 3:1, that is, $(3 + 1)(3 + 1) = 9 + 3 + 3 + 1$.

MENDEL'S EXPLANATION OF THE 9:3:3:1 RATIO. Though Mendel was unacquainted with the behavior of chromosomes in meiosis, he saw clearly that when the dihybrid plant formed reproductive cells, the members of each of the two pairs of determiners for the two pairs of contrasting characters must have separated independently of the members of the other pair. As a corollary of the independent separation of the determiners, he postulated the grouping of the determiners in the gametes into four possible equally numerous assortments as YR, Yr, yR, and yr. This is the basic feature of his Second Law of Heredity.

SEPARATION OF THE CHROMOSOMES AND ASSORTMENT OF GENES. It is now known that the cell mechanism responsible for the separation of chromosomes, operative during meiosis, leads to the production of spores by the F_1 hybrid plant (Fig. 41). The members of the pair of genes, Y-y, determining

---

stages. Others may be visible in the middle stages of the life span. Still others may not be visible until full maturity of the organism, while some may not show up until old age has been reached. Seed characters which depend on developments of the embryo (and in some cases the endosperm tissues) are visible early in the life span. Flower color, fruit color, fruit size and shape, however, do not develop until the plant is mature. Seed characters of many kinds show segregation expected in the F_2 generation in the seeds produced by the F_1 plant as the seeds form. Since the cotyledons of the seeds produced by the F_1 plant are a part of the early stages of the F_2 generation, they show segregation of embryonic characters. Many of the inherited characteristics of the grains of maize (corn) are likewise segregated in the seeds produced by the F_1 plant.

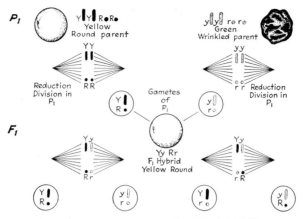

FOUR POSSIBLE ASSORTMENTS OF GENES

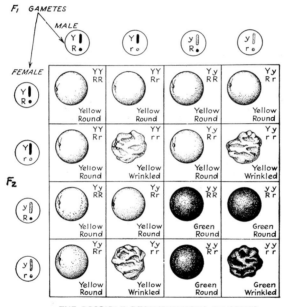

THE POSSIBLE RECOMBINATIONS OF GENES

FIG 41. SIMULTANEOUS INHERITANCE OF TWO PAIRS OF CONTRASTING CHARACTERS, YELLOW ROUND PEAS AND GREEN WRINKLED PEAS.
(Modified after Hill, Overholts, and Popp: "Botany," 2nd ed., New York, McGraw-Hill Book Company, Inc., 1950.)

the cotyledon colors, yellow and green, are located in the two members of one pair of homologous chromosomes, Y in the one and y in the other homologue. The members of the second pair of genes, R-r, determining round and wrinkled seeds, are each similarly located in one chromosome of a second pair of synaptic mates. During the meiotic divisions, the members of these two pairs of synaptic mates with their associated genes are arranged at random on the division spindle. The diagram in Figure 41 illustrating the separation of the members of two pairs of homologous chromosomes and the simultaneous segregation of the two pairs of alleles Y-y and R-r shows that there are equal possibilities that Y may be associated with R or with r in the separation. Likewise, there are equal chances that y may be associated with R or r. As a

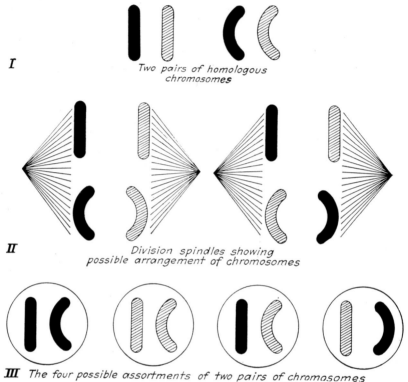

I   Two pairs of homologous chromosomes

II   Division spindles showing possible arrangement of chromosomes

III   The four possible assortments of two pairs of chromosomes

FIG. 42. BEHAVIOR OF CHROMOSOMES DURING MEIOSIS.

I, chromosomes in the nuclei of any diploid organism; *II*, possibilities of chromosome arrangements on division spindles during meiotic divisions; *III*, possible assortments of chromosomes resulting from divisions at *II*. (Courtesy, Hill, Overholts, and Popp: "Botany," 2nd ed., New York, McGraw-Hill Book Company, Inc., 1950.)

result of this independent and random segregation of the two pairs of alleles, they may be assorted into four possible groups, YR, Yr, yR, and yr, in the numerical ratio of approximately $1:1:1:1$. The independent separation of two or more pairs of homologous chromosomes, resulting in the random grouping of the chromosomes with their associated genes, forms the physical basis for Mendel's *second* principle, The Free Assortment of Genes in the gametes (or spores).

RECOMBINATION OF GENES.   The $9:3:3:1$ ratio observed in the F_2 generation may be accounted for on the assumption of chance or random re-combinations of the YR, Yr, yR, and yr assortments when the F_1 gametes united at fertilization following self-pollination of the F_1 plants. With fairly large numbers involved, each of the four types of sperms, YR, yR, Yr, and yr, might be expected to fertilize all of the four types of eggs, YR, Yr, yR, and yr. In other words, each of the four types of eggs, YR, Yr, yR, and yr, has an equal chance of being fertilized by any one of the four types of sperms, YR, Yr, yR, or yr. As a result of this random union of gametes, recombina-tions of the two pairs of genes Y-y and R-r occur to form the 16 theoretically possible genotypes of the F_2 generation as shown in the checkerboard (Fig. 41). Grouping of similar recombinations shows the following genotypic ratio: $1 YYRR : 2 YYRr : 1 YYrr : 2 YyRR : 4 YyRr : 2 Yyrr : 1 yyRR : 2 yyRr : 1 yyrr$. Be-cause of the full dominance of Y and R over their alleles, y and r, these gene combinations yielded the 315 round yellow, 101 wrinkled yellow, 108 round green, and 32 wrinkled green seeds in the F_2 generation, or approximately a $9:3:3:1$ ratio.

In most cases of dihybrids, if sufficiently large numbers are involved, there is mathematical probability that approximately the expected recom-binations will occur in the F_2 generation. Mendel's actual counts for the four classes of the F_2 generation listed above were sufficiently close to the

Table VII

GENOTYPES AND PHENOTYPIC RATIOS OF DIHYBRID GUINEA PIGS

Genotypes	Phenotypes
1 CCRR 2 CCRr CCRr 2 CcRR CcRR 4 CcRr CcRr CcRr CcRr	These 9 genotypes each contain at least one C and one R. Since both of these genes are dominant, individuals with these genotypes will be dominant for both characteristics: 9 phenotypically black, rough-coated animals
1 CCrr 2 Ccrr Ccrr	These 3 genotypes contain at least one C which dominantly conditions color. They will produce colored animals. All genotypes are homozygous reces-sive for r and will therefore condition smooth coats: 3 phenotypically black, smooth-coated animals
2 ccRr ccRr 1 ccRR	These 3 genotypes are all homozygous for c. They will therefore produce the albino type. They do, however, contain at least one R which dominantly conditions rough coat: 3 phenotypically white, rough-coated animals
1 ccrr	This 1 genotype is homozygous for both c and r. Only the recessive charac-ters will be conditioned: 1 phenotypically white, smooth-coated animal

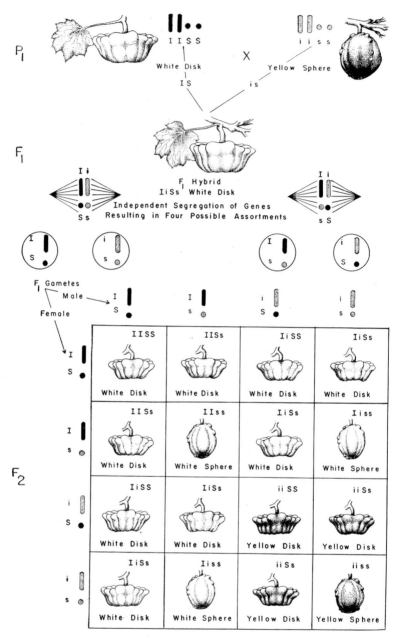

FIG. 43. SIMULTANEOUS INHERITANCE OF TWO PAIRS OF CONTRASTING CHARAC-
TERISTICS IN SUMMER SQUASH.

Because of complete dominance in both pairs of genes, four phenotypic classes
in the ratio of 9:3:3:1 are produced in the F_2 generation. (Based on plants grown
from seeds furnished by E. W. Sinnott.)

9:3:3:1 ratio to indicate that his hypothesis was correct. Two of these four classes resembled the parental forms, while the other two were recombinations of the parental traits. Of the classes resembling the parents, the round yellow type was like the double-dominant parent, and the other, the wrinkled

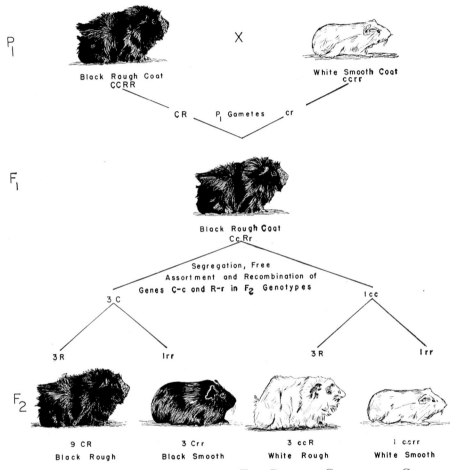

FIG. 44. SIMULTANEOUS INHERITANCE OF TWO PAIRS OF CONTRASTING CHARACTERISTICS IN GUINEA PIG.
(Modified after W. E. Castle, Carnegie Publication #23, Washington, 1905.)

green type, which was the smallest group, resembled the double-recessive parent. The two new classes, the wrinkled yellow type and the round green type, recombined the parental traits entering the cross.

DIHYBRIDS IN GARDEN SQUASH. Among the numerous cases of assortment is the combination of fruit shapes and fruit colors in garden squash. Fruit shapes, spherical and disk, conditioned by the genes $S\text{-}s$ yield an F_2 3:1 ratio when crossed (Fig. 43). White-squash fruits are conditioned

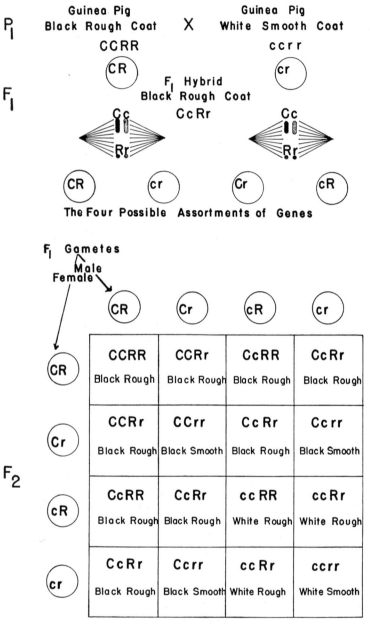

FIG. 45. INDEPENDENT SEGREGATION, ASSORTMENT, AND RECOMBINATIONS FOLLOW-
ING A CROSS INVOLVING TWO PAIRS OF GENES, "CCRR" AND "ccrr."

The genes C-c and R-r are assorted to the gametes CR, Cr, cR, and cr in the
ratio of 1:1:1:1. The checkerboard indicates recombination of genes. Because of
complete dominance of one member of each pair of genes, C-c and R-r, the 16
genotypes condition an F₂ generation of black rough, black smooth, white rough,
and white smooth animals in the phenotypic ratio of 9:3:3:1.

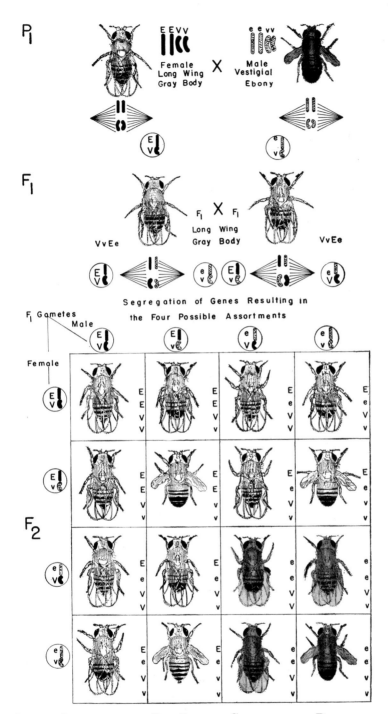

FIG. 46. INHERITANCE OF TWO PAIRS OF CHARACTERS IN DROSOPHILA.

During maturation the genes *VvEe* are assorted to the gametes *VE*, *ve*, *Ve*, and *vE* in the ratio of 1:1:1:1. Because of complete dominance of one member of each pair of genes, *V-v* and *E-e*, the 16 genotypes condition an F_2 generation in the phenotypic ratio of 9:3:3:1.

by the dominant gene I, which inhibits color. Yellow color in squash fruits is conditioned by the homozygous state ii, the recessive allele of I. The genes $IiSs$ segregate, assort, and recombine in a manner exactly as $YyRr$ in peas and yield an F_2 phenotypic ratio of 9 white disk : 3 white spherical : 3 yellow disk : 1 yellow spherical.

DIHYBRIDS IN GUINEA PIGS.   In addition to the many heritable traits of hair color in the guinea pig, there are variations of hair arrangement. Usually the hair of the guinea pig lies flat and smooth over the surface of the body (Fig. 44). These types are called smooth-coated, in contrast with rough-coated, animals. In the rough variation, the hair grows in rosettes. Coat color and albinism are conditioned by the genes C-c. Crosses of colored and albinos yield an F_2 ratio of 3 : 1 (Fig. 28). Rough coat, R, is dominant over smooth, rr, and crosses involving these traits likewise yield 3 : 1 ratios. In dihybrid combinations as black rough, $CCRR$, $\times$ albino smooth, $ccrr$, segregation, assortment, and recombination of genes occur, again resulting in an F_2 ratio of 9 black rough : 3 black smooth : 3 albino rough : 1 albino smooth (Fig. 45).

DIHYBRIDS IN THE FRUIT FLY.   In the section on monohybrids, the heritable variation of the fruit fly, *Drosophila*, black body *vs.* gray body, was cited as an example of a character inherited according to Mendelian principles. The simultaneous inheritance of two pairs of characters in the fruit fly may be illustrated by the cross gray body with long wings, $EEVV$, *vs.* ebony body with vestigial wings, $eevv$. Figure 46 presents the essential features of this cross.

Incomplete Dominance in Dihybrids

There are also dihybrid combinations of incompletely dominant genes. For example in the snapdragon red flowers are determined by the genes RR and white flowers by rr, but because of incomplete dominance the heterozygote Rr produces pink flowers. Leaf form in the snapdragon is similarly determined by incompletely dominant genes. It may be assumed that broad leaves are BB, narrow leaves bb, and intermediate types Bb. Crossing a broad-leaved red-flowered snapdragon plant, $RRBB$, with a white-flowered narrow-leaved plant, $rrbb$, would produce an F_1 with pink flowers and medium

Table VIII

INCOMPLETE DOMINANCE IN A DIHYBRID

1$RRBB$, conditioning red-flowered, broad-leaved plants
2$RRBb$, conditioning red-flowered, medium-broad-leaved plants
1$RRbb$, conditioning red-flowered, narrow-leaved plants
2$RrBB$, conditioning pink-flowered, broad-leaved plants
4$RrBb$, conditioning pink-flowered, medium-broad-leaved plants
2$Rrbb$, conditioning pink-flowered, narrow-leaved plants
1$rrBB$, conditioning white-flowered, broad-leaved plants
2$rrBb$, conditioning white-flowered, medium-broad-leaved plants
1$rrbb$, conditioning white-flowered, narrow-leaved plants

---

leaves, intermediate between the parental types. Self-pollination of F_1 would yield an F_2 generation with a genotypic ratio of $1:2:1:2:4:2:1:2:1$ (Fig. 47). Because of incomplete dominance, the phenotypic ratio is exactly the same as the genotypic ratio, Table VIII.

Considered separately, each pair of allelic genes conditions a $1:2:1$ ratio. As to flower color alone, there are 4 red-, 8 pink-, and 4 white-flowered plants. As to leaf shape, there are 4 broad-, 8 medium-broad-, and 4 narrow-leaved plants. Each group of characters shows a $1:2:1$ ratio of the other character in the dihybrid. The red-flowered plants all show a ratio of 1 broad-leaved plant to 2 medium- to 1 narrow-leaved plant. Likewise, the pink-flowered

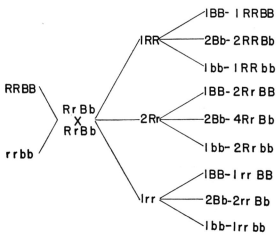

FIG. 47. A DIHYBRID WITH INCOMPLETE DOMINANCE IN BOTH PAIRS OF FACTORS
AS IN THE SNAPDRAGON.

Each biotype will condition a recognizable phenotype. The phenotypic ratio will, therefore, be numerically identical with the biotypic ratio.

and white-flowered plants all show the $1:2:1$ ratio of leaf shape. Exactly similar ratios of 1 red-flowered plant, 2 pink-flowered plants, and 1 white-flowered plant are to be found in each of the groups of leaf shapes, broad-, medium-broad-, and narrow-leaved plants. Here, as in the monohybrid, incomplete dominance increases the number of phenotypic classes over that expected where complete dominance prevails.

The study of inheritance has revealed combinations of characters in the dihybrid which show complete dominance in one pair of factors and incomplete dominance in the other. This is illustrated by cattle with the combination of the polled-horned condition (P-p, complete dominance) and the red-white-coat color (R-r, incomplete dominance) (Fig. 48). From matings of cattle, $PPRR$, the genotype for polled (hornless) and red-coat color, with cattle, $pprr$, the genotype for horned and white coat, F_1 hybrids will have the genotype $PpRr$ and be polled and roan in color. When F_1 male and female are mated, the random union of the gametes with the genes PR, Pr, pR, and *pr* will result in the recombination of genes in the F_2 zygotes to form 16 genotypes. Because of the full dominant action of the factor *P*, all heterozygotes, *Pp*, as well as the homozygotes, *PP*, will show the polled character. Because of the incomplete dominance of the factor pair *R-r* conditioning coat color, only the homozygous dominants, *RR*, will be red; all heterozygous

FIG. 48. HORNED AND HORNLESS BREEDS OF CATTLE.
Left, a Shorthorn bull representative of a breed of horned cattle. *Right*, an Angus bull typical of a hornless breed. In crosses the hornless or muley condition is dominant over the horned. (Left photograph courtesy, Cook and Gormley; right, courtesy, W. H. Tomhave, Secretary, American Aberdeen-Angus Breeders Association.)

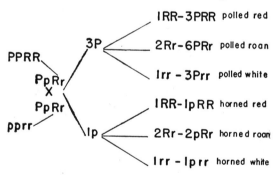

FIG. 49. SIMULTANEOUS INHERITANCE OF POLLED-HORNED CHARACTERISTICS AND RED-ROAN-WHITE TRAITS IN CATTLE.

individuals, *Rr*, will be roan, while the homozygous recessives, *rr*, will be white (p. 67). The F_2 phenotypic ratio conditioned by two pairs of factors, one of which shows complete dominance and the other incomplete dominance, is therefore $3:6:3:1:2:1$ (Fig. 49).

MENDEL'S LAW OF ASSORTMENT LIMITED IN ITS APPLICABILITY. In the preceding chapter it was shown that Mendel's First Law of Heredity, segregation, has universal application to all sexually reproducing organisms. It is necessary, however, to emphasize that the law of independent assortment has a somewhat *limited* application. Free assortment of genes is based upon the independent separation of the members of each of two or more pairs of homologous chromosomes. Thus, the principle of independent assortment may hold true for any number of pairs of characteristics provided the conditioning genes are located in *distinct pairs* of homologous chromosomes. (Fig. 42).

In contrast, if two or more pairs of characters are being considered for which the determiners are all located in *one pair* of homologous chromosomes, the principle of free assortment of genes does not hold, and the phenomenon of *linkage* is observed (p. 130). Since the number of genes in an organism is very large and the number of pairs of chromosomes is limited to relatively few, it naturally follows that all pairs of chromosomes carry a large number of genes. Thus, for any two or more of the large number of genes on any single pair of homologous chromosomes, Mendel's Second Law of Heredity, Free Assortment, does not apply, because these genes generally fail to separate and tend to be inherited together.

Gene Assortments and Recombinations in Polyhybrids

Since all organisms have innumerable heritable traits, it must be evident that the abstraction of one or two pairs of contrasting characters for study is merely for the purpose of simplifying the problems of heredity.* As the number of pairs of contrasting characters is increased in trihybrids, tetrahybrids, and polyhybrids, determination of the numbers of gene assortments in the gametes, calculation of the recombination of genes in the F_2 genotypes, and analysis of the phenotypic classes becomes more complicated.

CALCULATION OF GAMETIC AND RECOMBINATION CLASSES. Based on the constancy of the biological processes meiosis and fertilization, mathematical formulae, as Mendel showed, may be used in the calculation of the classes of F_1 gametes and of the genotypic and phenotypic classes of the F_2 generation.

The number of different gene assortments formed by any given hybrid may be calculated from the equation $(2)^n = y$. The (2) in the first term indicates the uniform

---

* To review briefly, the term *monohybrid* is applied to an organism heterozygous for one pair of allelic genes conditioning the development of a single pair of contrasting characters, such as C-c, the genes conditioning black- and white-coat color in guinea pigs. The term *dihybrid* has likewise been presented in the discussion of the inheritance of coat color and hair characters in the guinea pig. It is applied to an organism heterozygous for two pairs of allelic genes. Similarly, the term *trihybrid* is applied to an organism heterozygous for three pairs of allelic genes, each conditioning the development of any one of three pairs of contrasting characters. The terms *tetrahybrid* and *pentahybrid* are sometimes used to indicate heterozygosity in four and five pairs of allelic genes, respectively. The general term *polyhybrid* is perhaps more frequently used. The term *polyhybrid* indicates heterozygosity in many pairs or an indefinite number of allelic genes. The terms *multifactor hybrid*, *multihybrid*, and *multiple hybrid* are also used synonymously to indicate the heterozygous condition of many pairs of genes in one organism.

Table IX

THE 16 THEORETICALLY POSSIBLE GENOTYPES OF AN F₂ DIHYBRID GENERATION ARRANGED TO SHOW THE GENOTYPIC, BIOTYPIC, AND PHENOTYPIC RATIOS BASED UPON (1) INCOMPLETE DOMINANCE IN TWO PAIRS OF GENES, (2) COMPLETE DOMINANCE IN ONE PAIR OF GENES WITH INCOMPLETE DOMINANCE IN ONE PAIR, AND (3) COMPLETE DOMINANCE IN BOTH PAIRS OF GENES

	AA BB	Aa BB	AA Bb	Aa Bb	AA bb	Aa bb	aa BB	aa Bb	aa bb
The 16 Theoretically Possible Genotypes	AA BB 1	Aa BB 1	AA Bb 1	Aa Bb 1 / Aa Bb 1 / Aa Bb 1 / Aa Bb 1	AA bb 1	Aa bb 1 / aA bb 1	aa BB 1	aa Bb 1 / aa bB 1	aa bb 1
Genotypes Grouped into Biotypes	AA BB 1	Aa BB 2	AA Bb 2	Aa Bb 4	AA bb 1	Aa bb 2	aa BB 1	aa Bb 2	aa bb 1
F₂ biotypic ratio	1	2	2	4	1	2	1	2	1
Phenotypic Expression of Biotypes, based upon the action of 2 pairs of incompletely dominant genes	Homozygous dominant in both characters	Heterozygous intermediate in 1st Dominant in 2nd	Homozygous dominant in 1st Heterozygous intermediate in 2nd	Heterozygous intermediate in both characters	Dominant in 1st Recessive in 2nd	Intermediate in 1st Recessive in 2nd	Recessive in 1st Dominant in 2nd	Recessive in 1st Intermediate in 2nd	Recessive in both characters
F₂ ratio	1	2	2	4	1	2	1	2	1
Phenotypic Expression of Biotypes, based upon the action of one pair of genes, Aa showing full dominance and Bb showing incomplete dominance	Dominant for both characters	Dominant for both characters	Dominant for the 1st Intermediate for the 2nd	Dominant for the 1st Intermediate for the 2nd	Dominant for the 1st character Recessive for the 2nd	Dominant for the 1st character Recessive for the 2nd	Recessive in 1st Dominant in 2nd	Recessive in 1st Intermediate in 2nd	Recessive in both characters
F₂ ratio	3		6		3		1	2	1
Phenotypic Expression of Biotypes, based upon the complete dominance of one member of each pair of factors	Both characters dominant in all homozygous and heterozygous combinations				Dominant for the 1st character Recessive for the 2nd	Dominant for the 1st character Recessive for the 2nd	Recessive in 1st Dominant in 2nd	Recessive in 1st Dominant in 2nd	Recessive in both characters
F₂ ratio	9				3		3		1

or regular separation or segregation of the members of any single pair of contrasting alleles, as Aa, into two different gametes, A and a; the exponent, n, the number of contrasting pairs of allelic genes involved in the hybrid; and the last term of the equation, the product, y, the total number of possible gene assortments in the gametes that may be formed by any given hybrid. Thus, for a monohybrid such as Aa, the formula becomes $(2)^1 = 2$. In this case the base (2) indicated that A will be segregated from a. Since there is only one pair of alleles, the exponent is 1; and expansion of the term, $(2)^1 = 2$, shows that two kinds of gametes, A and a, will be formed by the monohybrid Aa.

When two or more pairs of genes are involved in a hybrid, the members of the pairs of contrasting alleles are simultaneously segregated, and the genes occur in all possible combinations in the gametes. In the formula for a dihybrid as $AaBb$, the base again is 2, indicating independent segregation of the two members of each pair of alleles, and the exponent becomes 2, showing the number of pairs of allelic genes. The formula then becomes $(2)^2 = 4$, indicating the possibility of four different gene assortments to the gametes from any dihybrid.

In a trihybrid, involving three pairs of allelic genes, the formula for calculating the number of gene assortments is $(2)^3 = 8$, where again (2) indicates the segregation of the members of each pair of allelic genes and the exponent, 3, the number of pairs of alleles in the trihybrid. Thus, the equation $(2)^3 = 8$ indicates the possibility that the trihybrid may produce gametes with 8 different kinds of gene assortments. When large numbers of gametes are involved, the possibilities become strong probabilities.   Under normal conditions and with sufficiently large numbers, these possibilities and probabilities become almost certainties   Formulae for calculating the numbers of possible gene assortments in the gametes of tetrahybrids and other multi- or polyhybrids are shown in Table X.

Table X

RESULTS OF SEGREGATION AND ASSORTMENT

Segregation of Genes in A Heterozygous Organism with:	Formula	The Numbers of Gene Assortments in the Gametes
(1) a single pair of allelic genes	$(2)^1 =$	2 kinds of gametes
(2) two pairs of allelic genes	$(2)^2 =$	4 kinds of gametes
(3) three pairs of allelic genes	$(2)^3 =$	8 kinds of gametes
(4) four pairs of allelic genes	$(2)^4 =$	16 kinds of gametes
(5) five pairs of allelic genes	$(2)^5 =$	32 kinds of gametes

In addition to formulae for calculating the probable number of gene assortments in the gametes of hybrids, schemes have been devised to aid in visualizing the process of segregation and the resulting gene assortments. The two types of gametes produced by a monohybrid as Aa may be simply written as:

$$A \quad \text{and} \quad a.$$

In the dihybrid $AaBb$, A is separated from a. Likewise, B and b are segregated. The formula $(2)^2 = 4$ indicates the possibility of four gene assortments with all possible chance combinations among the two allelic pairs. The A gene will have equal opportunity to be associated in the same gamete with either B or b. Likewise, random

5 9963

segregation indicates an equal number of combinations of *a* with *B* and with *b*. In the four kinds of gametes, *A* will be in two of them and *a* in the other two. This distribution may be shown as:

$$A \qquad a$$
$$A \qquad a.$$

The possible combinations of *A* with *B* and with *b* and of *a* with *B* and with *b* may be shown as follows:

$$AB \qquad aB$$
$$Ab \qquad ab.$$

The formula $(2)^3 = 8$ indicates the possibility of eight gene assortments in the gametes of a trihybrid as *AaBbCc*. In these eight kinds of gametes, *A* will occur in four and *a* in four; these may be written:

$$A \qquad a$$
$$A \qquad a$$
$$A \qquad a$$
$$A \qquad a.$$

The random and equal combinations of the gene pairs *B-b* and *C-c* with *A-a* and with each other may be shown in following assortments where half of the *A* genes are associated with *B* and half with *b*. Similarly, the *a* gene appears in a 1:1 ratio with *B* and *b*. Identical numerical proportions are found for *B-b* and *C-c*:

$$ABC \qquad aBC$$
$$ABc \qquad aBc$$
$$AbC \qquad abC$$
$$Abc \qquad abc.$$

The gene assortments in the gametes of a tetrahybrid *AaBbCcDd*, based on the formula $(2)^4 = 16$, may be visualized in a similar way:

$$ABCD \qquad aBCD$$
$$ABCd \qquad aBCd$$
$$ABcD \qquad aBcD$$
$$ABcd \qquad aBcd$$
$$AbCD \qquad abCD$$
$$AbCd \qquad abCd$$
$$AbcD \qquad abcD$$
$$Abcd \qquad abcd.$$

THE TRIHYBRID.   In addition to the character pairs colored, *CC*, vs. albino, *cc*, and rough, *RR*, vs. smooth, *rr*, that have been used to illustrate a dihybrid in guinea pigs, a third pair of hair characteristics, dominant-short hair, *SS*, vs. the recessive-variation-long hair, *ss*, may be added to illustrate inheritance in a trihybrid. A cross involving the characteristics

black, rough-coated, short-haired female, *CCRRSS*,

×

albino, smooth-coated, long-haired male, *ccrrss*

illustrates inheritance in this trihybrid (Fig. 50). Union of parental gametes *CRS* and *crs* will produce the dominant-black, rough-coated, short-haired

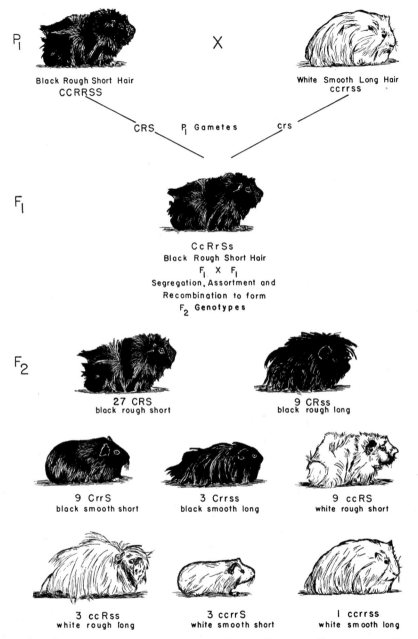

FIG. 50. SIMULTANEOUS INHERITANCE OF THREE PAIRS OF CONTRASTING CHARACTERISTICS IN GUINEA PIG. (Modified after W. E. Castle, Carnegie Publication #23, Washington, 1905.)

F_1, $CcRrSs$. The assortments of genes in the gametes of the F_1 trihybrid guinea pigs will be CRS, CRs, CrS, Crs, cRS, cRs, crS, and crs, produced in equal numbers with the ratio of $1:1:1:1:1:1:1:1$ in male and female.

Mating trihybrids *inter se* in a sibcross F_1 male $\times$ F_1 female will give opportunity for these eight types of gametes to unite at random. The genes will thus be recombined into 64 genotypes. As the monohybrid F_2 generation is $3 + 1$, the dihybrid $(3 + 1)^2$, the trihybrid is, therefore, $(3 + 1)^3$. In a sufficiently large F_2 population, eight phenotypic classes may be expected in a ratio of $27:9:9:3:9:3:3:1$ as shown in Figure 51.

THE TETRAHYBRID. An illustration of the tetrahybrid is found in the work of Little and Phillips with four pairs of unit characters in mice.

Table XI

INDEPENDENT GENES IN A TETRAHYBRID MOUSE

Genes	Characters Conditioned
A-a	In the dominant state, the wild type of gray coat called agouti;* in the homozygous-recessive state, any color excepting the gray type
B-b	In the dominant state, black color; in the homozygous recessive, any color excepting black, usually some brown type
D-d	In the dominant state, density of coloration; in the homozygous recessive, dilution of color, any color present in the coat.
P-p	In the dominant state, dark-colored eyes; in the homozygous recessive, pink-eye color though not the albino type

* The term *agouti* as applied to coat color has its origin in the name of a small South American animal which is a conspicuous example of this type of coat color. In the agouti coat, the individual hairs are marked near their tips by a band of lighter-colored pigment. In many of the rodents which have been studied, the presence of this band depends upon the conditioning action of a dominant factor designated by A. In the homozygous-recessive state, the allele a conditions the lack of the band on the hair. Animals with the genotype aa may be any color except gray.

Following a cross combining these four pairs of genes in a tetrahybrid, an F_2 generation contained 16 classes of individuals with numbers closely approximating the expected $81:27:27:9:27:9:9:3:27:9:9:3:9:3:3:1$ phenotypic ratio (Fig. 52). The large number of animals necessary in crosses involving trihybrids and tetrahybrids makes experimentation with many genes inadvisable. In actual practice the breeder follows Mendel's technique and reduces the number of pairs of factors used in experiments.

THE TESTCROSS. The backcross or testcross may be utilized in studies involving dihybrids, trihybrids, and tetrahybrids by mating F_1 individuals to the recessive strain. In these cases of di-, tri-, or tetrahybrids, the F_1 individuals would be mated with the double, triple, or quadruple recessives, that is, the stock which is homozygous recessive for the two, three, or four gene pairs, respectively.

If a sufficient population is obtained, there will be as many phenotypic

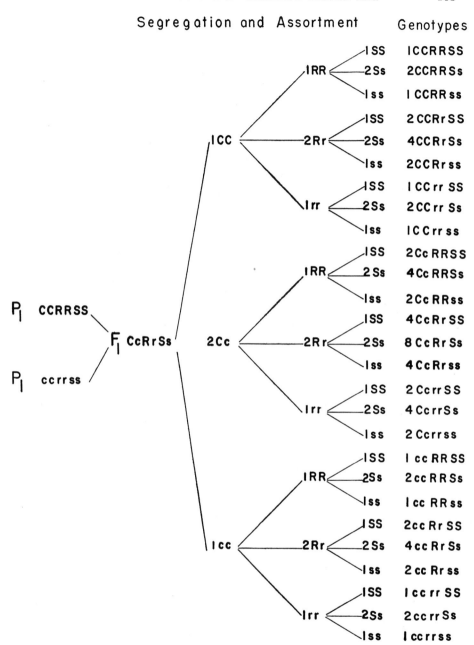

FIG. 51. THE 27 POSSIBLE BIOTYPES AND THE NUMBER OF GENOTYPES IN EACH BIOTYPE RESULTING FROM SEGREGATION OF GENES TO THE GAMETES OF A TRIHYBRID IN THE GUINEA PIG.

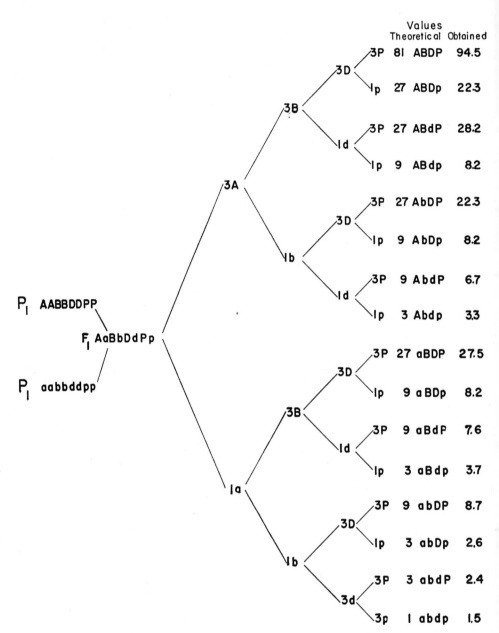

FIG. 52. EXPECTED AND OBTAINED VALUES FOR NUMBERS OF INDIVIDUALS IN THE F₂ GENERATION OF A TETRAHYBRID CROSS IN MICE.

The character pairs involved were gray *vs.* any other color, *A-a*; black *vs.* brown (usually), *B-b*; density of color *vs.* dilution of color, *D-d*; and dark-colored *vs.* pink but not albino eyes, *P-p*. The F₁ tetrahybrid mice had the gene constitution *AaBbDdPp*. Since complete dominance obtains in each pair of genes, 3*A* indicates the number of recombinations in which one or more dominant genes may be present. The small letters indicate genes in the recessive state, without the corresponding dominants. Multiplication of the terms indicates the number of times the genes may be expected in final recombinations. The first column indicates the theoretical or expected values, and the second shows the values obtained in a large F₂ generation, statistically treated for comparison. (Data of actual values from Little and Philips.)

classes in the backcross or testcross generation of polyhybrids as may be expected in the corresponding direct cross. Thus, in a dihybrid testcross generation, four phenotypic classes may be expected, in a trihybrid eight, and in a tetrahybrid sixteen. Theoretically the individuals will be equally numerous in each class, and they will occur in a ratio of $1:1:1:1:1:1$, etc.

Diagrammatic Schemes to Indicate Segregation Assortment and Recombination

Diagrammatic representation of the nuclear-division spindles showing separation of the members of one, two, or more pairs of homologous chromo-

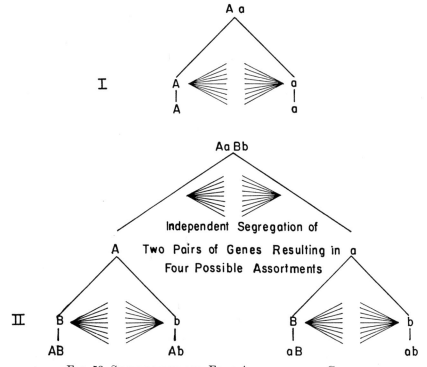

FIG. 53. SEGREGATION AND FREE ASSORTMENT OF GENES.

Scheme I, the segregation of members of a single pair of genes, A-a, in any heterozygous organism. Two types of germ cells are those containing A and those containing a, in a ratio of $1A:1a$.

Scheme II, the independent and simultaneous segregation of two pairs of genes, A-a and B-b (applicable to any organism heterozygous for two pairs of genes). Following separation of the members of the homologous chromosomes, the members of each pair of genes are segregated. Based upon the arrangements of the members of the two pairs of homologous chromosomes on the spindle at the reduction division, A has equal opportunities to be combined with B or b; likewise, a with B or b. Hence four theoretically possible assortments of genes may occur in the ratio of $1AB:1Ab:1aB:1ab$. These schemes are based upon the behavior of chromosomes at meiosis (Fig. 9 and 14).

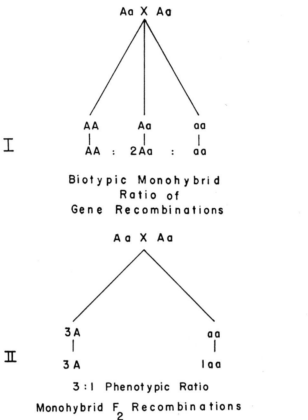

FIG. 54. GENE RECOMBINATIONS WHICH RESULT FROM MATING $F_1 \times F_1$ OR FROM SELFING AN F_1 WITH THE GENOTYPE "Aa."

These schemes are applicable to any organism heterozygous for a single pair of factors.

Scheme I represents segregation and recombination of a single pair of genes to form the monohybrid F_2 biotypic ratio of gene combinations of $1AA:2Aa:1aa$.

Scheme II represents a much abbreviated diagram of segregation and recombination of genes. Complete dominance of A over a is assumed. This is indicated by the number 3 for each A-. There will be, therefore, a monohybrid F_2 recombination ratio of 3 dominant genes ($3A$-) to 1 recombination (aa) of the homozygous recessive. This will result in the phenotypic ratio of 3 dominants to 1 recessive. Note that these schemes are based upon the behavior of the chromosomes and their associated genes at meiosis and at fertilization.

somes during meiosis has thus far been used to indicate the cellular mechanism for the segregation and assortment of genes. But with increasing numbers of alleles in polyhybrids, this method becomes cumbersome. Shorter and more direct methods have been devised to illustrate the derivation of gene

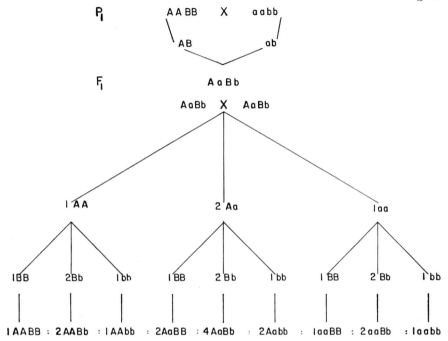

The 9 Possible Biotypes Resulting from Recombination of Two Pairs of Allelic Genes

FIG. 55. INDEPENDENT SEGREGATION, FREE ASSORTMENT, AND RECOMBINATION OF TWO PAIRS OF ALLELIC GENES WHICH RESULT FROM MATING $F_1 \times F_1$ OR SELFING THE F_1 WITH GENOTYPE "AaBb."

This scheme is applicable to any organism heterozygous for two pairs of genes. Each pair of genes shows the recombination of dominants and recessives as $A^2 + 2Aa + a^2$. If each gene pair is expanded in this way and each member is combined with all the members of the expansion of the second pair, it is possible to indicate all biotypes. Multiplication of the terms results in the 9 possible biotypes in the ratio of $1AABB : 2AABb : 1AAbb : 2AaBB : 4AaBb : 2Aabb : 1aaBB : 2aaBb : 1aabb$. The genotypes and biotypes may also be found in the squares of the checkerboard. All features of this scheme are based upon the behavior of the chromosomes during meiosis and at fertilization.

assortments involving more than two pairs of genes. The accompanying diagrams illustrate the segregation and assortment of one or more gene pairs (Fig. 53 and 54). The interpretation of these diagrams should always include the thought that the cellular mechanism involved in segregation and assortment is the nuclear spindle of the meiotic divisions, separating the members of the several pairs of homologous chromosomes (Fig. 42).

Recombination of genes to form the F_2 genotypes of monohybrids and dihybrids has been indicated by use of the checkerboard or Punnett's square. Beyond the dihybrid, however, calculation of the recombination of genes likewise becomes increasingly burdensome. In all monohybrids there is the theoretical recombination of genes in the 1:2:1 (or 1 + 2 + 1) ratio, that is,

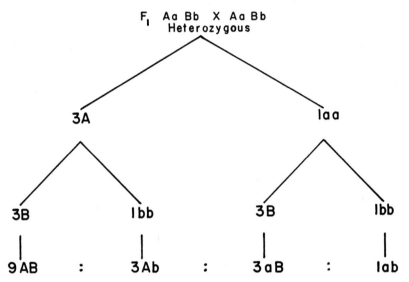

FIG. 56. INDEPENDENT SEGREGATION, FREE ASSORTMENT, AND RECOMBINATIONS OF TWO PAIRS OF ALLELIC GENES WHICH RESULT FROM MATING $F_1 \times F_1$ OR SELFING THE F_1 WITH THE GENOTYPE "AaBb."

Assumption of complete dominance in each factor pair, A-a and B-b, is indicated by the figure 3 for each A and each B. Multiplication of the terms will indicate the recombinations in the F_2. The numerical value of the F_2 phenotypic classes will be indicated in the product of the multiplications. In this case it is 9 double dominants, A-B; 3 recombinations of dominant A with recessive b, A-b; 3 recombinations of recessive a with dominant B, a-B; and one double recessive, ab. This short-cut scheme of calculating a dihybrid phenotypic ratio is based upon the behavior of the chromosomes during meiosis and at fertilization.

1 homozygous-dominant, 2 heterozygous, and 1 homozygous-recessive genotype. This 1:2:1 ratio is basic to the theoretical recombination of genes in the genotypes of all dihybrids and polyhybrids.

The number of genotypes in a dihybrid is represented by $(1 + 2 + 1)^2 = 1:2:1:2:4:2:1:2:1$; that of a trihybrid, by $(1 + 2 + 1)^3$; and a tetrahybrid, by $(1 + 2 + 1)^4$. The diagrams in Figures 55 and 56 represent schemes for illustrating the possible recombinations of genes in F_2 genotypes.

When the foregoing diagrams for showing segregation and assortment are combined with a system of numbers to indicate the phenotypic classes, based on the dominant-recessive relationship of each pair of genes in the genotypes, it provides a short method of obtaining the phenotypic ratios. With a single pair of alleles as A-a, the genotypes of the F_2 generation are $1AA : 2Aa : 1aa$. Assuming full dominance of A over a, the first two classes of the ratio $1AA$ and $2Aa$ determine phenotypic dominance, regardless of whether the genotype is AA or Aa. It is customary to indicate the dominant relationship of A in these genotypes by writing $A -$. This designation indicates that A is dominant regardless of its recombination with another A or with a. Thus

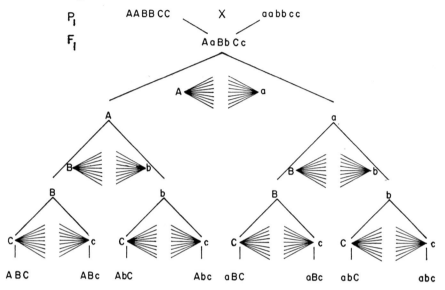

The 8 Possible Assortments of Genes Produced by a Trihybrid

Fig. 57. Independent Segregation and Free Assortment of Three Pairs of Allelic Genes, "A-a," "B-b," and "C-c."
The pairs of genes are segregated simultaneously at meiosis and actually on the same division spindle (Fig. 42). Chance arrangements of the chromosomes on the division spindles assure all possible combinations of genes in the resulting germ cells. The 8 possible assortments of genes into the germ cells may be visualized by tracing the gene designations A-a, B-b, and C-c through the diagram. The 8 assortments are indicated at the bottom.

with full dominance, the ratio of $1AA : 2Aa : 1aa$, occurring on the monohybrid checkerboard, may be written as $3A - : 1aa$ (Fig. 54), with 3 indicating the three phenotypically dominant classes of the F_2 generation and 1 the recessive class.

The same scheme may be expanded to apply to dihybrid, trihybrid, and polyhybrid ratios (Fig. 58). In Figures 51 to 56 it will be seen that figures may be multiplied through and dominant and recessive classes indicated for each assortment of genes. This scheme is actually just another way of writing the gene product of $(3 + 1)(3 + 1) = 9:3:3:1$ for a dihybrid, $(3 + 1)^3$ for a trihybrid, and $(3 + 1)^4$ for a tetrahybrid.

Translation of assortments of genes in accordance with their gene actions will show the expected phenotypic ratios. Even in complicated cases involving more unusual gene actions, which will be considered later, the phenotypic ratios may be obtained by this scheme.

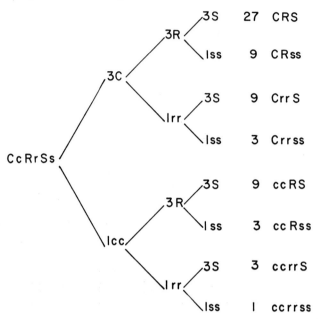

FIG. 58. F_2 RATIO IN A TRIHYBRID CROSS IN THE GUINEA PIG WHEN THERE IS FULL DOMINANCE IN EACH CHARACTER.

The principles involved are the segregation, assortment, and recombinations of the genes and the conditioning effect of each pair of genes. Segregation is indicated by the brace separating C and c. Complete dominance of C over c in the F_2 produces 3 dominants to 1 recessive as indicated in the scheme by 3C- and 1c. These principles apply to each pair of the genes R-r and S-s as well as to C-c. Multiplication of the terms as indicated yields the ratio of $27CRS : 9CRs : 9CrS : 3Crs : 9cRS : 3cRs : 3crS : 1crs$. By attention to the effect of the genes, these symbols may be translated into the characters of the F_2 generation of guinea pigs.

The Essential Feature of Mendelian Heredity

Modern Mendelian heredity based, as it is, on the chromosomes and their behavior is essentially an explanation of the *physical* system basic to the distribution and transfer of the hereditary units from one generation to another. Segregation, assortment, and recombination of genes are the steps by which the hereditary units *pass from parents to the offspring* in succeeding generations. These laws of heredity are applicable to all sexually reproducing organisms, plant and animal, including man.

Summary of Mendel's Second Law of Heredity

1. The phenomena of contrasting characters, pairs of allelic determiners, and segregation are observed in dihybrids and multiple hybrids as in monohybrids.
2. The members of pairs of genes in a dihybrid or polyhybrid are simultaneously

and independently segregated when gametes or spores are formed during maturation. The products of independent segregation of genes are grouped into all possible assortments in the gametes, and the different kinds of gametes thus produced are equally numerous. This constitutes the law or principle of assortment of genes.

3. Just as two kinds of gametes are formed by a monohybrid, there will be four possible kinds of gametes formed in a dihybrid. Table X shows the number of gametes formed in monohybrids, dihybrids, and polyhybrids.

4. Following self-fertilization of an F_1 or mating $F_1 \times F_1$ hybrids, recombinations of the genes occur in the genotypes of the F_2 generation. There is random union of the several kinds of gametes. Each of the several types of eggs has an equal chance of being fertilized by any one of the several kinds of sperms. If a sufficiently large number of individuals is involved, there is an opportunity for all possible recombinations of genes to occur in the genotypes of the F_2 generation. The recombinations may be visualized by the expressions $(a + b)^2$, $(a + b)^3$, $(a + b)^4$, etc. Checkerboards and other diagrammatic schemes may be used as aids in visualization of the recombination of genes in the F_2 genotypes.

5. The nature of the individuals of the F_2 generation depends, first, upon the segregation, assortment, and recombination of the genes involved and, second, upon the action of the genes finally recombined in the F_2 individuals. There is always some sort of dominant-recessive relationship between the members of a pair of genes. This relationship may be one of complete dominance of one member of the pair or one in which there is lack of dominance of either member (incomplete dominance).

6. Among the individuals of the F_2 dihybrid generation, there may be expected some which resemble the dominant parent, some the recessive parent, and some with new combinations of the parental characters. The F_2 individuals may be grouped into classes which will show certain numerical ratios, depending upon the dominant-recessive relationship of the genes involved.

7. The genetic constitution of the F_2 individuals will determine their breeding behavior. Some F_2 individuals which are homozygous for certain genes will breed true for the characters conditioned by these genes. Most of the F_2 individuals will be heterozygous for the genes, and they will not breed true but will show the segregation characteristic of hybrids.

8. Large populations in the F_2 generations are even more important in a study of dihybrids and polyhybrids than they are in monohybrids. The greater number of genes involved increases the number of possible recombinations in the F_2 genotypes and necessitates larger populations if the expected phenotypic ratios are to be obtained. The use of the backcross or testcross increases the chances of realizing the expected phenotypic ratios with smaller populations.

Probabilities and Goodness of Fit in Dihybrid Ratios—Application of the Chi-square Test

In the discussion on probabilities of recombinations in monohybrid ratios, an analogy with tossing two coins simultaneously was proposed. In that comparison one coin represented male gametes, heads and tails corresponding to the dominant and recessive genes of a pair of alleles. The second coin represented the female gametes, likewise carrying dominant and recessive genes (p. 77).

PROBABILITIES OF RECOMBINATIONS IN DIHYBRID RATIOS. Since the probabilities of recombination of genes in monohybrids may be shown by tossing two coins, in dihybrids they may be demonstrated in a similar manner by tossing four coins. The possible combinations of heads and tails when four coins are tossed together is shown in the expansion of $(h + t)^4$, in which h and t represent the faces of each coin and the exponent, 4, indicates the number of coins. Thus, $(h + t)^4 = 1hhhh + 4hhht + 6hhtt + 4httt + 1tttt$. Since, in the toss of any one coin, the chance of getting a head or a tail is 1/2, in each case, the probabilities of the various combinations of h and t of the above equation may be seen in the following expansion:

$$(1/2 + 1/2)^4 = (1/2)^4 + 4(1/2)^3(1/2) + 6(1/2)^2(1/2)^2 + 4(1/2)(1/2)^3 + (1/2)^4$$
$$= 1/16 + 4/16 + 6/16 + 4/16 + 1/16$$

1 chance in 16	4 chances in 16	6 chances in 16	4 chances in 16	1 chance in 16

In these equations if it is assumed that a head, h, indicates a capital letter or a dominant gene and a tail a small letter or a recessive gene, the probabilities of obtaining any given genotype may be calculated for the F_2 dihybrid generation in Mendelian heredity. What is the probability of getting a combination of four heads at any one toss of the four coins? Because with a single coin there is an equal chance of getting a head or tail in any one toss, the chance of getting heads under these circumstances may be expressed mathematically as 1/2. With four coins tossed together, the chances of getting four heads at one toss are as:

$$h^4 = (1/2 \cdot 1/2 \cdot 1/2 \cdot 1/2) = 1/16$$

By analogy in the F_2 generation of a dihybrid cross, the probability of obtaining an individual homozygous dominant for any two pairs of genes as $AABB$ or one homozygous recessive as $aabb$ would be:

$$(1/2)^2 (1/2)^2 = 1/16$$

Such individuals would be expected in the F_2 generation at the rate of 1 in 16.

In the above expansion of $(h + t)^4$, the third or middle term, $6hhtt$, shows the probability of getting two heads and two tails. By analogy, the probability of obtaining genotypes with two dominant genes recombined with two recessives is the same, i.e., 6 chances in 16. The possibilities are $1AAbb$, $4AaBb$, and $1aaBB$. With large numbers involved in an F_2 population, the possibilities become probabilities.

The probability of getting any other combination of heads and tails, as three heads and one tail, may be computed. In the second term of the above expansion of $(h + t)^4$, the combination of $hhht$ is shown to occur 4 times in 16. Similarly, there are 4 chances in 16 of getting three tails and one head, or 1 in 4. This probability is shown in the fourth or next to the last term of the expansion, $4httt$.

Again by analogy, the probability of obtaining any particular recombination of genes in the F_2 dihybrid genotypes may be determined from the same mathematical principles. For example, among F_2 genotypes of a dihybrid as shown on a checkerboard, four containing 3 dominant genes recombined with 1 recessive as $AABb$, $AABb$, $AaBB$, and $AaBB$; similarly, there are four with 1 dominant and 3 recessives.

THE CHI-SQUARE TEST FOR GOODNESS OF FIT IN THE DIHYBRID RATIO. With an F_2 population of only 556 individuals, as Mendel found in the cross involving the colors, yellow and green, and the forms, round and wrinkled, in pea seeds, the validity of a 9:3:3:1 ratio may well be questioned, especially if the observed numbers in the four classes deviate to any considerable extent from the expected values.

The numbers theoretically expected for a 9:3:3:1 ratio in a total population of 556 may be calculated by following the general method suggested for the determination of the expected numbers in a 3:1 ratio (pp. 77–79). In the case of the dihybrid, however, where there are sixteen possible genotypes, $\frac{9}{16}$, $\frac{3}{16}$, $\frac{3}{16}$, and $\frac{1}{16}$ of the total F_2 population of 556 must be calculated. From these figures and considering full dominance, the expected values for the four classes are thus 312.75 yellow round : 104.25 yellow wrinkled : 104.25 green round : 34.75 green wrinkled. These values contrast with the numbers 315:101:108:32 as observed by Mendel.

Statistical methods for applying the **chi-square test** to a dihybrid ratio have also been developed. The general principle is the same as that for determining chi-square in the monohybrid ratio (pp. 77–79), namely, squaring the deviations for each term of the ratio, dividing each square by the expected number for that term. Thus, where X is the observed number, m the expected number, and $X - m$ the deviation, for a dihybrid ratio of $9:3:3:1$, the formula for chi-square is:

$$\chi^2 = \frac{(X_1 - m)^2}{m} + \frac{(X_2 - m)^2}{m} + \frac{(X_3 - m)^2}{m} + \frac{(X_4 - m)^2}{m}$$

Substituting the expected and observed values of Mendel's experiment in this formula, the ratio becomes:

$$\chi^2 = \frac{(315 - 312.75)^2}{312.75} + \frac{(101 - 104.25)^2}{104.25} + \frac{(108 - 104.25)^2}{104.25} + \frac{(32 - 34.75)^2}{34.75}$$

$$= \frac{(2.25)^2}{312.75} + \frac{(-3.25)^2}{104.25} + \frac{(3.75)^2}{104.25} + \frac{(-2.75)^2}{34.75}$$

$$= \frac{5.0625}{312.75} + \frac{10.5625}{104.25} + \frac{14.0625}{104.25} + \frac{7.5625}{34.75}$$

$$= 0.0162 + 0.1013 + 0.1349 + 0.2176$$

$$= 0.4700$$

Thus:

$$\chi^2 = 0.4700$$

What are the implications as to the validity of Mendel's $9:3:3:1$ ratio when it shows a chi-square of 0.4700? The chi-square tables indicate that this value of chi-square is relatively low. It is far below the critical 5-per-cent point of 3.841 and thus indicates that, although the total number of variates is small, the deviations from the theoretical ratio are not significantly high. The chi-square test confirms the validity of Mendel's conclusions as to the $9:3:3:1$ ratio.

Questions and Problems

The simultaneous inheritance of two pairs of contrasting characteristics, with the consideration of the behavior of two pairs of allelic genes, is involved in dihybrids. The general directions for the solution of problems in monohybrids are also applicable to the solution of problems in dihybrids (pp. 79–83). In addition, the solution of problems in dihybrids requires consideration of the principle of the independent segregation of two pairs of allelic genes during meiosis in the F_1 generation.

It is important to keep in mind that all of the pairs of homologous chromosomes in a dihybrid will simultaneously separate during the meiotic divisions during the maturation process. Each dihybrid will theoretically produce four kinds of gametes, each with one of the four possible assortments of genes as AB, aB, Ab, or ab. These assortments occur in equal numbers in the ratio of $1:1:1:1$. Spindle diagrams to illustrate the chromosome behavior during meiosis should be shown for each dihybrid (pp. 19, 65, 88).

Mendel computed the possible recombinations of the determiners by algebra. However, a checkerboard of 16 squares with the four assortments of genes written across the top and repeated on one side may be used. The two sets of genes written into the vertical and horizontal columns will show all possible recombinations (pp. 87–93). When completed, each square of the checkerboard will represent a genotype of a member of the F_2 generation. Consideration of the dominant genes present will make it possible to calculate the F_2 phenotypic ratio.

DATA ON DOMINANCE AND RECESSIVENESS

	Dominant	*Recessive*
In rodents	full coloration, C	albino, c
	rough coat, R	smooth, r
	self color, S	spotted, s
In maize (corn)	red aleurone, R	white aleurone, r
	purple aleurone, Pr	red aleurone, pr
	starchy endosperm, Su	sugary endosperm, su
In peas	tall plants, T	dwarf plants, t
	red flowers, W	white flowers, w
	round seeds, R	wrinkled seeds, r
	yellow seeds, Y	green seeds, y
In Drosophila	gray body, B	black body, b
	gray body, E	ebony body, e
	red eyes, Pr	purple eyes, pr
	red eyes, P	pink eyes, p
	red eyes, S	sepia eyes, s
	long wings, V	vestigial wings, v
	straight wings, Bt	bent wings, bt
In cattle	polled (hornless), P	horned, p

DATA ON INCOMPLETE OR PARTIAL DOMINANCE

In shorthorn cattle, red and white are incompletely dominant.

In snapdragons, broad leaves and narrow leaves, red flowers and white flowers are incompletely dominant.

THE DIRECT CROSS
$F_1 \times F_1$
Dihybrids in Rodents

1. Assume that a black rough-coated female guinea pig, $CCRR$, is mated with a white smooth-coated male, $ccrr$. What will be the genotype and the appearance of the F_1 animals? Determine the phenotypic ratio of the F_2 generation. What are the genetic principles involved? What would be the expectation for the F_3 generation?

2. By applying the law of random assortment of genes, determine the kinds of gametes which may be expected from the genotypes shown in the F_2 generation found in problem 1.

Dihybrids in Plants
F_1 Self-pollinated

3. Assume that a corn plant, $RR\ SuSu$, which produces red starchy grains is pollinated with pollen from a plant, $rr\ susu$, which produces white sugary (sweet) grains. Determine the genotype of the F_1 plants and the kinds of grains they may be expected to produce. What kinds of grains will the F_2 plants produce?

4. Assume that a corn plant, $PrPr\ susu$, which produces purple sweet grains is pollinated with pollen from a corn plant, $prpr\ SuSu$, which produces red starchy

grains. Determine the genotype of the F_1 plant and predict the kinds of grains it will produce.

5. Assume that a tall pea plant, $TTWW$, bearing red flowers is pollinated with pollen from a dwarf plant, $ttww$, bearing white flowers. By following the general directions, determine the genotype of the F_1 generation. What will be the phenotypic ratio of the F_2 generation obtained by selfing F_1 plants? What genetic principles are involved?

6. If a pea plant, $YYRR$, producing yellow smooth round (starchy) seeds, is pollinated with pollen from a plant, $yyrr$, producing green wrinkled (sugary) peas, what will be the genotype of the F_1 plants? What sorts of seeds will the pods of the F_1 plant contain? What genetic principles are involved in obtaining these results?

Dihybrids in Drosophila

7. Assume that a wild-type female Drosophila, $BBSS$, with normal gray body and red-colored eyes is mated with a mutant-type male, $bbss$, with black-body color and sepia-colored eyes. By following the general directions, determine the F_1 genotype. After mating $F_1 \times F_1$, what classes of flies may be expected in the F_2 generation?

8. A student mated a wild-type female Drosophila, $PrPr\ EE$, with normal red-colored eyes and normal gray body to a mutant-type male fly, $prpr\ ee$, with purple-colored eyes and ebony body. The males and females of the F_1 generation were all normal wild flies with red eyes and gray body. By mating F_1 males to the F_1 females, an F_2 generation was obtained which consisted of 96 wild-type flies with red eyes and gray body, 38 flies with purple eyes and gray body, 34 flies with red eyes and ebony body, and 12 flies with purple eyes and ebony body. Explain the genetical and biological principles basic to these results.

9. When a wild-type female Drosophila, $VVSS$, with normal long wings and normal red eyes is mated to a mutant-type male fly, $vvss$, with (short) vestigial wings and (brown) sepia-eye color, the F_1 generation consists of normal flies. A student in the laboratory mated the three F_1 females of this cross to an F_1 male and counted 223 wild-type flies with normal long wings and red eyes, 70 flies with normal red eyes and vestigial wings, 73 flies with normal long wings and sepia eyes, and 24 flies with vestigial wings and sepia eyes. Explain the genetics of this cross with emphasis on the free assortment of genes.

THE DIHYBRID BACKCROSS AND TESTCROSS
$F_1 \times P_1$
General Directions

In most backcrosses or testcrosses, the F_1 dihybrid is mated or back-crossed to the P_1 or to double-recessive stock (that is, the stock which shows the two recessive characters, hence termed the double recessive). In each problem and in each instance, it is essential that the gametes of F_1 be indicated. These are obtained as usual by observing the principles of the assortment of genes. A recombination of the genes in F_1 gametes with those of the double-recessive P_1 gametes furnishes the basis for the calculation of the backcross generation. By noting the action of the genes as to dominance and recessiveness, the backcross or testcross phenotypic ratio may be calculated.

10. Assume that a black rough-coated female guinea pig, $CCRR$, is mated to a white smooth-coated guinea pig, $ccrr$. If the F_1 dihybrid animals are backcrossed to the dominant parental stock, what results may be expected in the backcross generation? If the F_2 dihybrid animals are backcrossed to the recessive-albino smooth-coated animals, what results may be expected?

THE TEST CROSS IN PLANTS

11. A Four H Club boy selected as a project some hybridization work with corn. He obtained red starchy field corn which he used in a cross with a variety of white sweet corn. The seeds from this cross were planted the next year. Several different pollination techniques were tried with the resulting F_1 plants. From one pollination an ear was produced which yielded four kinds of grains. There were 98 red starchy grains, 94 white starchy grains, 99 red sweet grains, and 96 white sugary grains. What type of pollination was practiced to obtain these results? What genetical principles were involved?

12. If the hybridization project mentioned in problem 11 should be continued, what results could be expected by selfing plants from each of the four classes in the F_2 backcross generation? What could be expected if plants from each class were again backcrossed to the double-recessive plants?

INCOMPLETE DOMINANCE IN A DIHYBRID

13. Consulting data on pp. 95–96, determine the results of crossing red polled cows, $PPRR$, and a white horned bull, $pprr$. What will be the genotype and the appearance of the F_1 generation? Assume that male and female F_1 animals resulting from this cross are mated $F_1 \times F_1$. What are the expectations for the F_2 generation?

14. With incomplete dominance in both pairs of contrasting characters, what is the expectation for F_1 and F_2 when a red-flowered snapdragon with broad leaves, $RRBB$, is pollinated with pollen from a white-flowered plant with narrow leaves, $rrbb$? What is the relationship between the biotypic ratio (ratio of genotypic classes) and the phenotypic ratio in this case? What is the effect of incomplete dominance on the number of phenotypic classes? Is there a corresponding change in the number of genotypes with incomplete dominance?

Polyhybrids

15. What do you understand by the terms *monohybrid, dihybrid, trihybrid, tetrahybrid,* and *polyhybrid*? What are multifactor hybrids, multihybrids, and multiple hybrids?

16. Using the data on pp. 91–92, demonstrate the results in F_1 and F_2 following the mating of a black rough-coated short-haired guinea pig to an albino smooth-coated long-haired guinea pig. What are the results of the segregation and assortment of genes to the gametes of the F_1 animals? What is the F_2 phenotypic ratio?

17. Demonstrate the use of some convenient diagrammatic schemes to show the results of the segregation and assortment of genes to the gametes of dihybrids and trihybrids.

18. Demonstrate the use of some convenient diagrammatic schemes which may be substituted for the algebraic calculations in showing the recombination of the segregated and assorted genes in dihybrids and trihybrids.

19. Demonstrate how diagrammatic schemes may be expanded to show assortment of genes in tetrahybrids. What modification is necessary to show the recombination of genes?

20. Using the data on p. 104, show the phenotypic ratio resulting in the progeny of tetrahybrid mice bred *inter se, i.e.,* $F_1 \times F_1$.

21. What are some of the most important features of Mendelian heredity? Explain these in some detail.

22. What are some of the biological facts which make Mendel's Laws of Heredity universally applicable to all sexually reproducing organisms?

23. Name some of the results biologically and genetically which follow from the reduction division of the meiotic processes. Explain these in some detail.
24. How many kinds of gametes are produced by a monohybrid, a dihybrid, a trihybrid, and a tetrahybrid?
25. Why are polyhybrids seldom used in genetical studies?

References

CASTLE, W. E.: *Mammalian Genetics*, Cambridge, Harvard University Press, 1940.

LITTLE, C. C., and J. C. PHILLIPS: "A Cross Involving Four Pairs of Mendelian Characters in Mice," *Am. Naturalist* **47**:760–762 (1913).

MORGAN, T. H.: *The Theory of the Gene*, 2nd ed. New Haven, Yale University Press, 1928, Chapters I, II, III, 1–44.

SHULL, A. F.: *Heredity*, 4th ed. New York, McGraw-Hill Book Company, Inc., 1948.

SNEDECOR, GEORGE W.: *Statistical Methods*, 4th ed. Ames, Iowa State College Press, 1946.

section 3

Linkage and Crossing Over

In the early days of the new science of genetics, accumulated evidence pointed to the universal application of Mendel's second principle, the free or random assortment of genes. With considerable astonishment Bateson in England found instances in which the 9:3:3:1 ratios were not obtained in the F_2 generation of dihybrids. From these early investigations, confirmed by Morgan in America, it became evident that some *further* principles of inheritance *outside the realm of pure Mendelism* were being encountered.

The additional principles of heredity have to do in part with the concept of the linkage of genes associated in the same chromosome, the limitation of a linkage group to genes carried by a single pair of homologous chromosomes, and the assumption that the genes are arranged in a linear order in the chromosome. Though they may not have the universal application accredited to Mendel's Law of Segregation, they have attained the status of principles of heredity.

chapter 5

The Discovery of Linkage and Identification of Linkage Groups

In 1905 Bateson and associates in England had learned that purple-flower color was dominant over red in sweet peas and yielded a $3:1$ ratio in the F_2. Likewise, long or ovoid pollen grains were fully dominant over round in this plant. When any two of these characters were introduced together into a cross, the parental characters tended to remain together through the following generations and were generally found associated in the same F_2 plants. Following hybridization of plants with purple flowers and long pollen, $PPLL$, and plants with red flowers and round pollen, $ppll$, the F_1 plants, $PpLl$, were self-pollinated. The F_2 generation then showed 1,528 PL plants with purple flowers and long pollen like the dominant parent and 381 pl plants resembling the recessive parent with red flowers and round pollen. In addition 106 Pl plants, combining the dominant purple-flower color with the recessive-round pollen, and 117 pL plants, with the reverse association of red flowers with long pollen, comprised new combinations of the original parental characters. This was an F_2 ratio of approximately $14:1:1:3.5$ instead of the $9:3:3:1$ normally expected. To have realized the expected Mendelian ratio in this F_2 dihybrid population of 2,122, there should have been about $1,194PL:398Pl:398pL:132pl$. The observed ratio was a significant deviation from this, with the parental types in excess and new combinations of the parental traits much reduced below expectations.

From their data, the investigators concluded that the parental combinations of genes PL and pl were about seven times as numerous as would be expected under conditions of free assortment postulated by Mendel. They calculated that the F_1 plants must have produced gametes containing the genes, P-p and L-l, in four combinations in the ratio of $7PL:1Pl:1pL:7pl$, instead of the ratio of $1:1:1:1$ expected in Mendelian assortment of genes. Recombination of the genes to form the F_2 genotypes may be shown on the checkerboard (Fig. 59). The gametes with their numerical frequencies of $7PL:1Pl:1pL:7pl$ may be placed in the customary horizontal and vertical rows above and to the left of the square. Numerical frequencies of F_2 geno-

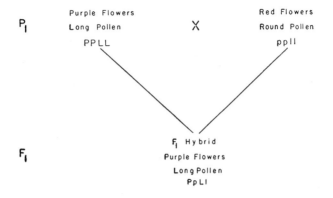

F_1 Gametes of unequal numbers
Four Kinds of Female Gametes

		7 PL	I PI	I pL	7 pl
7 PL		49 PPLL purple flowers long pollen	7 PPLl purple flowers long pollen	7 PpLL purple flowers long pollen	49 PpLl purple flowers long pollen
I Pl		7 PPLl purple flowers long pollen	1 PPll purple flowers round pollen	1 PpLl purple flowers long pollen	7 Ppll purple flowers round pollen
I pL		7 PpLL purple flowers long pollen	1 PpLl purple flowers long pollen	1 ppLL red flowers long pollen	7 ppLl red flowers long pollen
7 pl		49 PpLl purple flowers long pollen	7 Ppll purple flowers round pollen	7 ppLl red flowers long pollen	49 ppll red flowers round pollen

(Left margin: F_2 — Four Kinds of Male Gametes)

FIG. 59. RECOMBINATION OF THE COUPLED GENES "P-p" AND "L-l" FOLLOWING
SELF-POLLINATION OF F_1 IN A DIRECT CROSS IN THE SWEET PEA.

types obtained by multiplying the numbers in each case are recorded in the
appropriate squares. Summation of similar genotypes from the sixteen
squares will indicate the phenotypic ratio. In this case the theoretical ratio is
$177PL:15Pl:15pL:49pl$ plants or about 12:1:1:3.3, a close approximation
of the observed 14:1:1:3.5 ratio.

Table XII

BATESON AND PUNNETT'S RESULTS IN COMPARISON WITH MENDELIAN EXPECTATIONS

	PL, purple flowers, long pollen	Pl, purple flowers, spherical pollen	pL, red flowers, long pollen	pl, red flowers, spherical pollen
Observed number of plants	1,528	106	117	381
Approximate ratio obtained	13.7 :	1 :	1 :	3.41
Theoretically expected number of plants	1,194	398	398	132
Mendelian-ratio expectations with free assortment	9 :	3 :	3 :	1

Bateson's Explanation—Coupling and Repulsion

To account for the excess of *PL* and *pl* gametes, the investigators assumed that, in the production of gametes in the F_1 plants of this cross, there must have been an unusually close association or "coupling" of the two dominant genes, *P* and *L*, determining the development of the purple-flower color and the elongated pollen, respectively. The recessive genes, *p* and *l*, were likewise associated or coupled. The postulated association of genes *P* with *L* and *p* with *l* the investigators called *gametic coupling.*[*] They thought that in this cross there was a tendency for the dominant and recessive factors to repulse each other. Thus, the dominant factor *P* was seldom found in the same gamete with the recessive gene *l*. Similarly, *p* was seldom found in the same gamete with *L*. This hypothesis was a corollary to the idea of gametic coupling and was called *gametic repulsion*. Coupling and repulsion were actually the same tendency observed in reverse and giving similar results. In the hypothesis of coupling and repulsion, it was the particular combination of genes entering the cross from each parent, regardless of the dominant and recessive relationship of the genes involved, that remained coupled.

Chromosomal Relationship of Genes in Linkage

In the years following 1910, Morgan and his associates in America found a large number of heritable mutations in the fruit fly, *Drosophila melanogaster*. The numerous changes from the normal or wild type involved many characteristics such as eye color, body color, and wing structure. There were mutations from the normal red-eye color to white, purple, pink, a brown called sepia, and to many other colors. Involving body colors were changes from the wild-type gray to yellow, black, and ebony. Among mutations of wing structure were several shortened and subnormal types, described as vestigial, miniature, and rudimentary wings. The mutations affecting body

* As early as 1900 Correns, in Germany, working with stocks, first used the idea of coupling in inheritance when he referred to Merkmals-Koppelung, meaning character coupling. He also used the terms *conjugierte* or *gekoppelte Merkmale*.

characteristics in Drosophila were thought to result from a change in a specific gene in a chromosome.

As the studies progressed, Morgan found that certain of these characteristics in the fruit fly tended to be inherited together in a manner similar to the inheritance of coupled characters in the sweet pea observed by Bateson. To explain this behavior, Morgan proposed the hypothesis that characters inherited together in this manner were conditioned by genes located in the same chromosome.* To designate these phenomena in heredity, he proposed the term **linkage** which has replaced the older terms *coupling* and *repulsion*.

The Physical Basis of Linkage—Linkage Groups

The number of chromosomes in any organism is definitely limited, usually to a relatively few, while the number of genes is very large. Estimates have been made that 10,000 or 15,000, possibly more, genes exist in each complex organism. Evidently then, each pair of homologous chromosomes in every organism carries a very large number of pairs of genes. The association of many pairs of genes in a single pair of chromosomes provides the physical basis of linkage. The total number of gene pairs or alleles in the two members of a single pair of homologous chromosomes constitutes a **linkage group.** Any of these gene pairs in a linkage group may show linkage with any or all of the others, and such genes are said to be linked.

Evidence That Genes are Carried in the Chromosomes

The scientific proof that the chromosomes actually contain the genes and transfer them from generation to generation has had ample demonstration and is generally accepted. The fact that the sperm, with little cytoplasm, contributes as much in heredity as the larger egg was an early indication that the nucleus was of primary importance in determining the character of the offspring of two parents. Experimental embryology in which only one gamete functioned when different species were hybridized, two sperms caused to fertilize a single egg, and sperms used to activate enucleated eggs added to the accumulating evidence of the importance of the nucleus in heredity. Where these experiments were successful, the developing embryo resembled the parental type furnishing the functioning nucleus. In cases in which only one nucleus was left to function, that nucleus predominated in control of the development.

The differentiation of the homologues **X** and **Y** in the sex chromosomes was reported by McClung in 1901–2. He suggested that the unlike members of this pair of chromosomes might be influential in sex determination. A further cytological observation was that of Sutton in 1902–3 who observed the paternal and maternal derivation of the two members of each pair of homologous chromosomes. He suggested that chromosome separation during meiotic divisions *might be the mechanism for the segregation of Mendelian factors*. Within a few years both of these ideas were confirmed as facts.

Some of the clearest studies of mutant characters in Drosophila were with those later recognized as **sex-linked traits,** such as white eye, yellow body, and certain

---

* In 1906 R. H. Lock in England had suggested a possible relation of linkage to chromosomes. It remained, however, for Morgan to offer scientific proof of this relationship.

wing modifications. The mutation white eye, for example, passed from a male through his female offspring and then reappeared in his second-generation male progeny. Moreover, such sex-linked characters never passed from a male parent directly to his male progeny. These characters always zigzagged or crisscrossed from a male to a female and then back to males. When it was realized that these mutant traits were following the course of the **X** chromosome through the generations because their controlling genes were located in the **X** chromosome, they came to be regarded as sex-linked characters. The facts of crossing over indicate the chromosomes as gene carriers.

Variations in chromosome numbers in certain organisms also support the idea that genes are carried in the chromosomes. In the derangements and rearrangements following accidental and induced chromosomal breaks, relocation of genes in the reorganized chromosomes has been demonstrated both genetically and cytologically (p. 366). The giant salivary-gland chromosomes of Drosophila and other flies have proved to be useful in the identification of gene positions in disrupted chromosomes as well as in normal positions and have offered substantial indications that the genes occupy definite loci in linear order in the chromosomes.

Identification of Linkage Groups

The problem of determining which chromosome carried a specific gene and the linkage group to which a gene belonged confronted early investi-

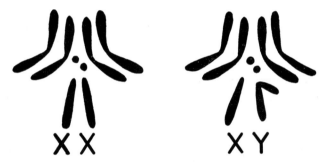

FIG. 60. THE FOUR PAIRS OF CHROMOSOMES IN DROSOPHILA.
The female, left, has two **X** chromosomes and three pairs of autosomes. The male, right, has one **X** and a **Y** chromosome and three pairs of autosomes. The sex chromosomes, **XX** or **XY**, are designated as I; the two other large pairs of the autosomes, as II and III; the small pair of autosomes, as IV. The genes located in each of these pairs of chromosomes constitute a linkage group. Thus there are four linkage groups: I, II, III, and IV. (Modified after Bridges.)

gators in genetics, and its solution led to breeding techniques which identified the *four* linkage groups of Drosophila. Because he recognized them first, Morgan called the sex chromosomes, **X** and **Y,** the first pair or chromosome pair **I.** The genes such as white eye and yellow body, carried in the **X** chromosome, were sex-linked and thus represented part of the first linkage group in Drosophila (Fig. 60).

Among the earliest mutations to be discovered in Drosophila were black body and pink eye as contrasted with the normal gray body and the normal red eye. For some time these two mutations were the only "workable" ones definitely known to be normally Mendelian in inheritance and not sex-linked. Morgan and his associates had recognized sex linkage and knew that the gene producing white eye was carried in the **X** chromosome. Since these other genes did not show sex-linked behavior, their chromosomal relationship was problematical. Did the genes for black body and pink eye belong to the same or to different linkage groups? It was known that a cross between flies having black bodies and flies having pink eyes produced an F_1 generation of normal wild-type flies. This occurred because the mutant-black-bodied flies of F_1 had normal and dominant-red eyes and the mutant-pink-eyed flies of P_1 had normal and dominant-gray bodies. The flies composing the F_1 generation were therefore heterozygous for both of the recessive traits, black body and pink eyes, which were not visible in the heterozygous F_1 generation.

Mating these heterozygous flies in a direct cross or sibcross $F_1 \times F_1$ yielded an F_2 generation of four phenotypic classes, gray body with red eyes, black body with red eyes, gray body with pink eyes, and black body with pink eyes, in a 9:3:3:1 ratio (Fig. 61). This is the expected Mendelian dihybrid ratio under conditions of free assortment, and because the gene for black body had been allocated to chromosome **II,** the gene for pink eye was then considered to be in chromosome **III.**

In the course of the investigations, flies were found with a structural variation showing very small stubby or scalelike wings, called vestigial. In order to locate the gene for this character, a series of crosses was made involving the previously determined mutations, pink eye and black body.

In the cross of vestigial-wing flies $\times$ flies having pink eyes which belong to the III-chromosome group, the F_1 generation was composed of normal wild-type male and female flies, all having normal long wings and red eyes. The F_2 generation yielded four classes of flies, normal wild type with long wings and red eyes, a new combination of long wings and pink eyes, another with vestigal wings and red eyes, and finally both recessive-vestigial wings and recessive pink eyes, in a 9:3:3:1 ratio. This ratio in the F_2 generation demonstrated free assortment of the two pairs of genes and confirmed the location of the gene for vestigial wing in some chromosome other than chromosome III where the gene for pink eye had been located. It was necessarily, then, in some other linkage group that did not contain the gene for pink eyes.

THE 2:1:1:0 DIHYBRID RATIO.   In further efforts to find the chromosome in which the gene for vestigial wing was located, a cross was made between flies having mutant-type black body with normal long wings, $bbVV$, and flies having normal gray body with mutant-type vestigial wings, $BBvv$. This cross produced an F_1 of heterozygous wild-type gray long-winged flies, $BbVv$. Mating F_1 males and F_1 females yielded an F_2 consisting of only three phenotypic classes instead of the four classes normally expected in a dihybrid. There was one F_2 class of normal wild-type flies, having gray bodies and long wings, representing recombinations of the dominant traits of both

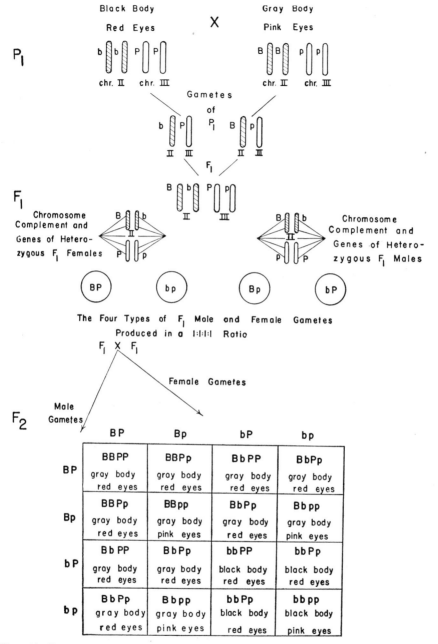

FIG. 61. INHERITANCE OF TWO MUTANT GENES WHEN THESE ARE LOCATED IN DIFFERENT PAIRS OF CHROMOSOMES.

This is the 9:3:3:1 ratio typical of all Mendelian dihybrids. It indicates the characteristic free assortment of genes located on two pairs of chromosomes.

parental types; a second class of gray flies, with vestigial wings, representing one parental type; and a third class of black flies, with long wings, like the second parental type. There were no recombinations of double-recessive-black flies with vestigial wings as would be expected in a normal Mendelian dihybrid ratio with free assortment of genes. The three classes of F_2 flies appeared in a $2:1:1:0$ ratio (Fig. 62). This is not a typical Mendelian dihybrid ratio but resembles an F_2 monohybrid ratio of $1:2:1$. The occurrence of the F_2 phenotypes in this type of cross in a $1:2:1$ ratio, like a Mendelian monohybrid, is an expression of the location of the two pairs of determining genes in the two members of one pair of homologous chromosomes. In this cross the homologous members of a pair of chromosomes, carrying genes Bv and bV, respectively, segregate normally at meiosis, and at fertilization recombinations occur in the zygotes as in a monohybrid.

Since the mutant genes b, for black body, and v, for vestigial wings, and their normal dominant alleles B and V did not show free assortment as would have been indicated by a $9:3:3:1$ ratio, it was concluded that they could not be in different linkage groups. The gene b, conditioning black body, was known to be in chromosome II. From the results of the cross, it was, therefore, concluded that the gene v, for vestigial wing, must also be carried in chromosome II with the mutant gene b.

DETERMINATION OF LINKAGE GROUPS BY USE OF TEST STOCKS.   An efficient technique for allocating new mutant genes to their proper linkage groups involves crossing of the new mutant race with a test stock which carries known recessive characters. Other test stocks have definite cytological features.

NUMBERING CHROMOSOMES AND LINKAGE GROUPS.   Since the sex chromosomes, pair I, were known early, the investigators arbitrarily designated the chromosome pair which carries the gene for black body as the second or chromosome II and the chromosome pair which carries the gene for pink eye as the third or chromosome III, in the order of their discovery (Fig. 60). In all subsequent investigations, mutant characters found to be linked with black body have been located in the second linkage group and the corresponding genes located in the II pair of chromosomes. The mutant characters showing linkage with pink-eye color have been considered as being in the third linkage group and their controlling genes in the III pair of chromosomes. Eventually, a few nonsex-linked mutant characters such as bent wing and eyeless found in Drosophila, gave evidence of free assortment with characters from both the second linkage group and the third linkage group. These characteristics were considered to be conditioned by genes located in the small chromosome **IV** and thus to belong to the fourth linkage group. Only a few pairs of alleles have so far been assigned to the fourth linkage group. The four pairs of chromosomes and their corresponding linkage groups were identified and designated **I, II, III,** and **IV** in the order of their identification.

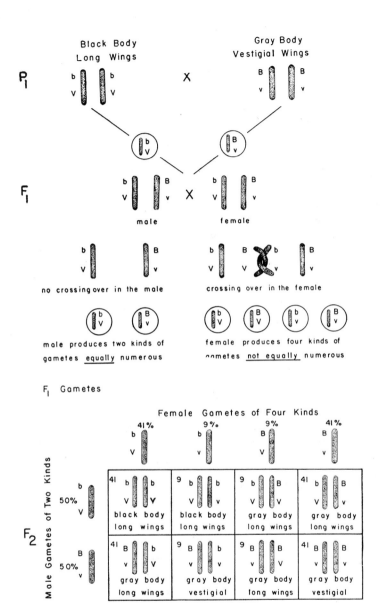

FIG. 62. DIAGRAM OF RESULTS OF CROSSING TWO MUTANTS IN DROSOPHILA.
Above, the P_1 female, at left, with normal long wings but the mutation black body; and male, at right, with normal gray body but the mutation vestigial wings. The genes are indicated in linked position on chromosome II. Gametes of P_1 are shown. Middle, F_1 male and female both heterozygous for genes but normal in appearance. Below, checkerboard shows recombination of the four kinds of female gametes and the two types of male gametes. The sorts of flies and their percentage of the total F_2 population are indicated in the squares of the checkerboard. The number of flies of each class is based upon the percentages of the four kinds of gametes produced by the F_1 female flies. The 2:1:1:0 ratio is found when two linked mutants are crossed.

129

THE TEN LINKAGE GROUPS OF MAIZE.   Corn or maize with about 400 to 500 recognized genes is genetically one of the best-known plants. While Drosophila chromosomes were numbered in the order of the identification of the linkage groups, I, II, III, and IV, the ten pairs of chromosomes of corn or maize have been numbered on the basis of their size from 1, the longest, to 10, the shortest. The maize chromosomes have other distinguishing morphological characteristics besides size which make the microscopic differentiation of each pair possible.

LINKAGE GROUPS IN VARIOUS ORGANISMS.   Besides those of Drosophila and maize, genes belonging to definite linked groups are known in several other organisms as in the Jimson weed or Datura, the cultivated tomato, peas, the domesticated fowl, certain fishes, and in many other plants and animals, including man, where the linkage relations of a few genes have been investigated. The number of linkage groups equals the number of pairs of homologous chromosomes in each organism.

Relationship of Genes to Chromosomes in Mendelian Free Assortment Compared with that Existing in Linkage

Repeatedly it has been emphasized that the physical basis of heredity is in the cell structures of organisms, particularly in the genes in the chromosomes. The Mendelian principles of segregation, assortment, and recombination of genes are thus dependent upon the behavior of the chromosomes at the critical stages of meiosis and fertilization in the life cycles of organisms. **Linkage** *is an exception to the free or random assortment of genes.* Linkage, however, is not based upon any exceptional behavior of the chromosomes. The physical behavior of the chromosomes in linkage is in no wise different from that encountered in the random assortment of genes but is precisely the same in both cases Since both free assortment and linkage of genes are dependent upon the relatively constant physical behavior of the chromosomes during meiosis, it is perhaps better to consider both free assortment and linkage as merely two aspects of the relationship of pairs of genes to the members of the pairs of homologous chromosomes (pp. 20, 125). The difference between linkage and free assortment lies in the relationship of the genes to the chromosomes. **Any two pairs of genes** *located in one pair of homologous chromosomes will be linked* in heredity. *If each of* **the two pairs of genes** *is in a different pair of homologous chromosomes, free assortment* will result.

This situation can be made clear in an example of two pairs of homologous chromosomes and their associated genes (Fig. 63). One pair of homologous chromosomes may carry the linked alleles *A-a, B-b, C-c, D-d, E-e,* and *F-f,* which constitute *a linkage group* (Fig. 63 I). The other pair of synaptic mates may carry the linked genes *G-g, H-h, I-i, J-j, K-k,* and *L-l,* which constitute a *second linkage group* (Fig. 63 II). Two pairs of genes, as the alleles *A-a,* from one linkage group and a second pair, as *G-g,* from a second

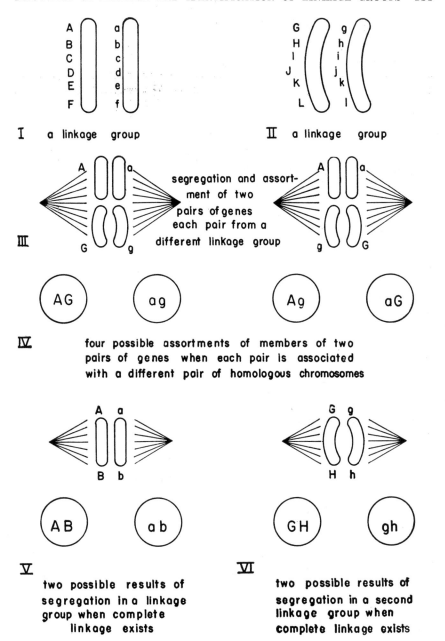

FIG. 63. DIAGRAM OF COMPARATIVE RELATIONSHIP OF GENES TO CHROMOSOMES IN FREE ASSORTMENT AND IN LINKAGE.

linkage group are thus located in *different* pairs of homologous chromosomes (Fig. 63 III). Following hybridization involving these two pairs of genes in a direct dihybrid cross, when F_1 is mated to F_1, the resulting F_2 ratio of $9:3:3:1$ or a testcross ratio of $1:1:1:1$ will indicate free assortment of the genes (Fig. 63 IV). In a similar manner any combination of genes consisting of any pair of alleles, either *A-a*, *B-b*, *C-c*, *D-d*, *E-e*, or *F-f*, from the *first* linkage group with any one of the pairs of genes, either *G-g*, *H-h*, *I-i*, *J-j*, *K-k*, or *L-l*, from the *second* linkage group in a dihybrid will also *exhibit free assortment of genes*. This relationship will hold true for the genes in any two separate linkage groups.

In a cross involving the gene pairs *A-a* and *B-b*, however, *linkage will be observed*, because these two pairs of alleles *are in the same pair of chromosomes* and thus belong to the same linkage group (Fig. 63 V). Since the gene pairs *G-g* and *H-h* are in another pair of chromosomes and thus belong to a *second* linkage group, they likewise *will be inherited together as linked genes* (Fig. 63 VI). This will be indicated by a marked numerical modification of the $9:3:3:1$ and $1:1:1:1$ ratios as Bateson and, later, Morgan found. In general, then, any combination of *genes from the same linkage group*, such as *A-a*, *B-b*, *C-c*, *D-d*, *E-e*, and *F-f*, will exhibit *linkage*. Likewise, any single gene pair of the group *G-g*, *H-h*, *I-i*, *J-j*, *K-k*, and *L-l* will exhibit a *linkage relationship* in heredity with any other pair of alleles in this linkage group. A similar relationship will prevail among the genes within any other single linkage group.

Summary of Relationship of Genes to Chromosomes in Heredity

When gene pairs under consideration are in different chromosome pairs and therefore in different linkage groups, they will show free assortment. All gene pairs of one linkage group show free assortment when involved in a cross with gene pairs of any other linkage group. If, however, the gene pairs involved in a cross are located in the same pair of chromosomes and thus in the same linkage group, these genes will show linkage in heredity.

Questions, Problems, and References at the end of the Section (p. 170.)

chapter 6

Complete and Incomplete Linkage

Use of the Testcross in Linkage Studies

In the study of the Mendelian principles of segregation and free assortment of genes, the normal Mendelian F_2 ratios have generally been obtained by means of the sibcross or direct cross through mating $F_1 \times F_1$ or by self-pollinating the F_1 in the case of self-fertilized plants. Although linkage of characters was discovered in direct crosses in which the F_1 plants of sweet peas were self-pollinated, or mated $F_1 \times F_1$, these crosses tend to obscure linkage relations (pp. 122, 158). Especially large numbers are sometimes necessary in order to determine the linkage relations if the direct cross is used. The **backcross** or **testcross** technique has been used extensively in linkage studies, because results may be obtained from smaller numbers than with the direct cross.

As mentioned under the discussion of Mendelian principles, the testcross consists of mating the F_1 progeny to a stock recessive for all of the characters under investigation. Since, in linkage studies, at least two pairs of characters are considered in one cross, the recessive stock must be homozygous recessive for both of them. A stock or an organism homozygous recessive for two pairs of characteristics is frequently referred to as "double recessive." Thus, in a Drosophila cross involving the mutant character black body linked with vestigial wings, *bbvv*, and the normal allelic characters gray body linked with long wings, *BBVV*, heterozygous F_1 males and females, with the genotype *BbVv*, would be mated to double-recessive, *bbvv*, females or males as the case may be. Stocks of individuals homozygous recessive for three or four pairs of allelic genes are called *triple* or *quadruple* recessive, respectively. When the testcross technique is used in linkage investigations, the resulting testcross progeny is generally classified on a percentage basis.

Complete and Incomplete Linkage

Early investigations by Morgan and his associates revealed that in Drosophila there were both *perfect* or **complete linkage** and *partial* or **incomplete linkage.** Inheritance of linked characters may be illustrated by

133

crosses of fruit flies involving certain mutations. An ordinary wild-type Drosophila with normal gray body, BB, and normal long-type wings, VV, crossed with a fly having the mutant-black body, bb, and the mutant type of stubby wings known as vestigial, vv, produced a heterozygous F_1 generation, $BbVv$, all of the wild type with gray bodies and long wings.

COMPLETE LINKAGE. When two Mendelian characters consistently appear together through two or more generations with no deviation from this behavior, they may be regarded as showing complete linkage. **Complete linkage** *is rare.* It is a phenomenon depending upon the nature of an organism and not upon the selection of any particular pair of characters. Complete linkage has been found in males of **Drosophila melanogaster** and in the members of a few other species of insects.

In the above cross in Drosophila, F_1 males, $BbVv$, were mated with double-recessive females, $bbvv$ (Fig. 64). This testcross progeny consisted of *only two classes,* flies with gray bodies and long wings, $BbVv$, and flies with black bodies and vestigial wings, $bbvv$. Each of the two classes was phenotypically like one of the original parental types. Further, the individuals in the two classes were *equally numerous.* Complete linkage of the characters was evident. To explain the results, it was assumed that the F_1 male fly produced *two equally numerous types of sperms,* each carrying a different combination of genes. One type must have had B and V both located in one member of chromosome pair II. The second kind carried b and v located in the other member of chromosome pair II. Union of the two types of sperms, BV and bv, with eggs, bv, from the double-recessive female produced genotypes $BbVv$ and $bbvv$. Action of the gene combinations yielded testcross progeny in the phenotypic ratio of approximately 50 gray-bodied long-winged flies : 50 black-bodied vestigial-winged flies or a ratio of 1:1. Phenotypically, the two classes were like the *two parental combinations of characters* that entered the cross; there were no new combinations of traits, and *linkage of characters was complete.*

In other cases flies with gray bodies and vestigial wings, $BBvv$, were crossed with flies having black bodies and long wings, $bbVV$. When F_1 males, $BbVv$, from this cross were subjected to the testcross by mating them to the double-recessive females, $bbvv$, again the testcross progeny consisted of *two* approximately *equal classes,* one, gray body with vestigial wings, $Bbvv$, and the other, black body with long wings, $bbVv$. Since the two characters entering the cross from *each* of the *two parental types appeared together* again in the two classes of the testcross progeny, *linkage* in these cases *was* once more *demonstrated to be complete.*

Explanation of the cause of complete linkage lies in the undisturbed alignment of the genes in the chromosomes. When complete linkage occurs, the genes must remain undisturbed in their original positions in the chromosomes throughout all the processes involved in gamete formation in the heterozygous F_1. This situation actually pertains in all male Drosophila. In the above cross the alignment of genes in the chromosomes of the F_1 male, $BbVv$, remained intact throughout the processes leading to the production of sperms. The homologous members of chromosome pair II remained intact during their passage from the P_1 generation through the male flies of F_1

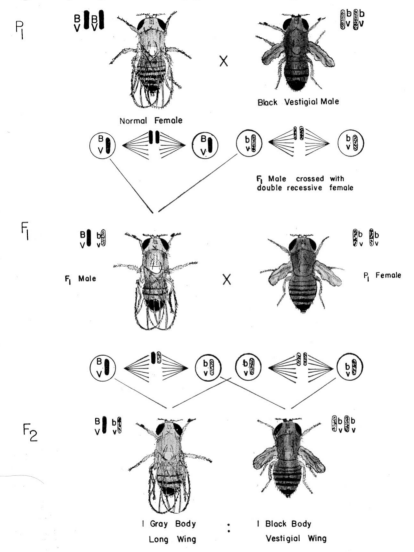

FIG. 64. DIAGRAM OF COMPLETE LINKAGE IN DROSOPHILA.

and into the testcross progeny. The genes BV and bv in the first cross and Bv and bV in the second *entered the cross together and remained undisturbed during the maturation processes* of the F_1 male Drosophila. In each case the chromosome bearing its genes in the original alignment was passed into a different sperm. Union of the two sperm types produced by the F_1 male of each test-cross with the bv eggs of the female resulted in the development of *two equal classes* of testcross progeny.

SUMMARY OF COMPLETE LINKAGE.   Complete linkage, in which two or more characteristics are inherited together, is rare. It occurs in the male Drosophila and certain other insects where there is no break in the alignment of genes in the chromosomes. Heterozygous male Drosophila produce two kinds of sperms in a 50:50 ratio, and the testcross yields two phenotypic classes in the same proportion.

INCOMPLETE LINKAGE.   Complete or perfect linkage occurs regularly in male Drosophila, but in female Drosophila and in most other animals and perhaps all plants, linkage of traits is generally incomplete. Bateson and associates, in the early study of the linked characters flower color and pollen shape, found that *coupling*, as they called it, was not quite complete in sweet peas. In crosses involving the flower colors purple and red with the pollen shapes long and round, some few of the F_2 individuals showed new combinations of the parental characteristics (pp. 122, 158).

As a part of the early studies of inheritance in Drosophila, the F_1 female flies from the cross gray long, $BBVV$, $\times$ black vestigial, $bbvv$, were also tested for linkage relations by mating them to double-recessive males, $bbvv$ (Fig. 65). The resulting testcross progeny was found to consist of *four* phenotypic classes *instead of only two* as when F_1 males were testcrossed. Two of the classes each contained rather large numbers of individuals, while the other two classes were generally smaller. In one of the large classes, the flies had gray bodies with long wings, and in the other large class the flies had black bodies with vestigial wings, *like the two parents* entering the original cross. The two smaller classes were made up of individuals showing *new combinations* of the parental characters, the flies in one of the small classes having gray bodies with vestigial wings and those in the second small class having black bodies with long wings.

Results of varying the parental combination of characters were also studied by mating flies with gray bodies and vestigial wings, $BBvv$, to those with black bodies and long wings, $bbVV$. The heterozygous F_1 females, $BbVv$, from this cross likewise yielded *four* classes of testcross progeny when mated to the homozygous-double-recessive males, $bbvv$. As before, there were two large and two small classes in the testcross progeny. One of the large classes was made up of flies having gray bodies with vestigial wings, $Bbvv$. The second large class contained flies having black bodies with long wings, $bbVv$, the identical combinations of traits typical of the parental types entering the cross. The two smaller classes were again made up of flies showing new combinations of parental characters. In one small class the combination was gray body with long wings, $BbVv$, while the other small class contained flies having black bodies with vestigial wings, $bbvv$. Experiments of Morgan and his associates yielded data from a total of 23,731 testcross-generation

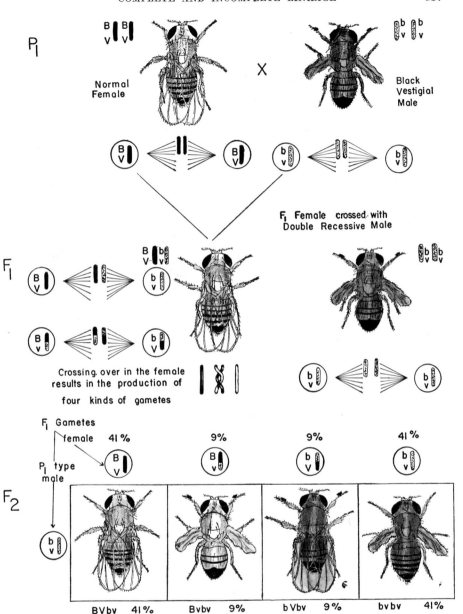

FIG. 65. DIAGRAM OF INCOMPLETE LINKAGE OF BLACK-BODY COLOR AND THE VESTIGIAL-WING CHARACTER OF DROSOPHILA.

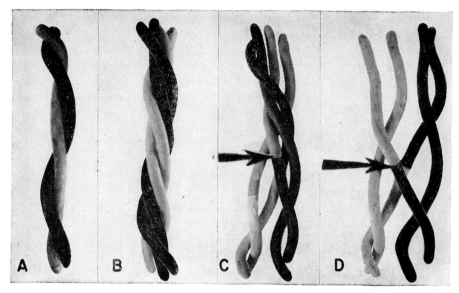

Crossing over and Chiasmata

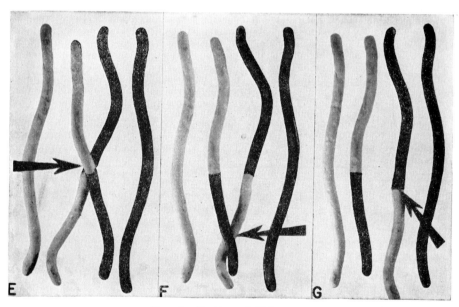

Terminalization of Chiasmata

FIG. 66. CLAY MODELS TO ILLUSTRATE CROSSING OVER.

A, a pair of homologous chromosomes at prophase of first meiotic division; the two members of the pair, one light and one dark, are shown coiled about each other. *B*, each member of the homologous pair longitudinally split which is thought to set up torsions leading to breaks in two of the four chromatids. *C*, arrow at left

(Continued on facing page.)

flies showing linkage relations of the mutant characters, black-body color and vestigial wings, with their normal dominant alleles, gray body and long wings. Of the total of 23,731 backcross or testcross progeny, 20,153 or 84.922 per cent could be divided into *two equal classes*, each showing *one or the other* of the parental combinations of characters. In addition to the two large classes representing the exact parental types, there were 3,578 flies or 15.078 per cent of the total showing *new combinations* of the parental characteristics. In each case the new combinations were also divided into *two classes* of flies approximately *equal* numerically.

Statistical analysis of the testcross progenies resulting from mating the F_1 females to double-recessive males in each of the two crosses showed the following results:

Gray body long wings, *BBVV*, × black body vestigial wings, *bbvv*

> 41% gray body long wings, *BbVv*
> 9% gray body vestigial wings, *Bbvv*
> 9% black body long wings, *bbVv*
> 41% black body vestigial wings, *bbvv*

Gray body vestigial wings, *BBvv*, × black body long wings, *bbVV*

> 41% gray body vestigial wings, *Bbvv*
> 9% graybody long wings, *BbVv*
> 9% black body vestigial wings, *bbvv*
> 41% black body long wings, *bbVV*

Causes of Incomplete Linkage—Crossing over and Crossover Gametes

As an explanation of the occurrence of new combinations of genes in the gametes of the F_1 females, from the preceding and other similar crosses, Morgan suggested the possibility of an *occasional exchange of transverse segments* of approximately equal size *from one homologue to another* in pairs of synaptic mates. This exchange of chromosome parts, it was thought, occurred sometime during the reproductive processes leading to gamete formation. In the exchange of chromosome segments, the contained genes would be carried to new positions in the reorganized chromosomes and provide the physical basis for the new gene combinations in some of the gametes (Fig. 66). Because, in the exchange, genes in the segments concerned crossed

---

FIG. 66—(*Continued*)

indicates region where an exchange of pieces has occurred between two nonsister chromatids; note light and dark parts. *D*, chromatids separating and chiasmata approaching ends of strands. *E*, further separation of chromatids. *F*, terminalization of chiasmata almost completed. *G*, separate chromatids as may be visualized following second division of meiosis. Two chromatids are intact in their original condition, but two show exchanged pieces, light and dark, following a single crossover.

from one chromosome to its homologue, the process was called **crossing over,** and the gametes with the new combinations of genes came to be called **cross- over** *gametes.*

For a period after the discovery of linkage and crossing over, the explana- tion of the causes and the theories about the physical basis underlying this behavior rested entirely upon the genetical data obtained from crosses. The assumption of the exchange of pieces of homologous chromosomes was sup- ported only by the analysis of the flies. It explained the experimental data so well, however, that crossing over soon became a working hypothesis in genetics.

Although the theories of linkage and crossing over still rest largely on genetic data from crosses, cytological techniques have clearly demonstrated that an exchange of segments between homologous chromosomes occurs regularly in the meiotic prophase of most reproductive cells. Under magnifi- cation, evidence of this crossing over is seen in the presence of crossed threads called **chiasmata.** It is believed that each chiasma is formed by an exchange of pieces between nonsister chromatids.

The Physical Basis of Crossing Over

It may be recalled that, in the early stages of meiosis, the two members of each pair of homologous chromosomes in the meiocytes come together or pair in synapsis, forming the **bivalent** chromosome, and that each member of the pair is split lengthwise into two parts or chromatids (pp. 19, 89). The two chromatids from each chromosome are called *sister* chromatids or *identical* chromatids. The two pairs of sister chromatids, that is, four chroma- tids in all, are intimately associated together during the early stages of the first meiotic division, forming the *chromosome tetrad* or, more properly, the *chromatid tetrad* (Fig. 66). This early stage has been called the *four-strand stage* because of the four threadlike chromatids.* It is believed that the exchange of pieces of chromatids, or crossing over, normally occurs soon after this split stage has been reached.

The fungus *Neurospora* has been used in studies of inheritance which have confirmed the hypothesis that crossing over occurs at the four-strand stage. *Neurospora* with its typical production of eight ascospores in each ascus was used in discovering that usually only the first two divisions leading to the production of four meiospores are reductional or meiotic, while the third, leading to the production of eight ascospores in the ascus, is generally equational or mitotic. The characteristics of the haploid mycelia developed

---

* Because certain plants (polyploids) have more than two sets of chromosomes, pairing or synapsis of more than two homologous chromosomes may occur. When these split lengthwise, more than four strands would be formed, and the term *four-strand stage* would not be strictly applicable. For this reason and because each chromosome splits longitudinally, forming two chromatids, it has been suggested that the term *double strand* is more applicable.

from individual ascospores indicate the division at which segregation must have occurred. An ingenious analysis of the linkage data obtained for several characters has been accepted as demonstrating that the crossovers occur in the four-strand stage.

SUMMARY OF INCOMPLETE LINKAGE. Because of the occasional breaking and exchange of pieces between the members of a chromosome tetrad, four kinds of gametes are formed in most organisms heterozygous for two pairs of alleles, as the heterozygous F_1 female Drosophila. The new alignments of genes in the crossover chromosomes lead to the different kinds of gametes which are *not equally numerous*, as follows:

1. Those with a chromatid from the male parent, which would be intact with the *original parental alignment of genes*
2. Those with a chromatid from the female parent, which would be intact with the *original alignment of parental genes*
3. Those with one of the broken and reorganized chromatids containing a *new alignment of genes*
4. Those with the second broken and reorganized chromatid also containing a *new alignment of genes.*

When these four types of gametes are fertilized by gametes bearing recessive genes, two of them will form *new* combinations of characters. The new combinations will express themselves in the phenotypic ratio of the testcross progeny, which may vary with the *distance separating the genes* and the amount of crossing over.

Comparison of Complete and Incomplete Linkage

The occurrence of *four classes* in the testcross *progeny* of heterozygous F_1 females contrasts with the testcross progeny of heterozygous F_1 males in any combination of linked characters. In the testcross progeny of heterozygous F_1 males, there were only *two classes of offspring*. The material cause of this difference in the testcross progeny of F_1 males and females is in the crossing over between homologous chromosomes of female Drosophila. The exchange of pieces of homologous chromosomes leads to new alignments of genes in the chromosomes and eventually to some new combinations of genes in the gametes of heterozygous F_1 females. Thus, heterozygous *female* flies *produce four kinds of gametes not equally numerous.*

During meiosis in the male Drosophila, however, crossing over does not occur, and consequently the alignment of genes in the chromosomes is not disturbed. For this reason the male Drosophila produces only *two equally numerous types of gametes* as contrasted with the four unequally numerous classes produced by the female flies. Recombination of genes at fertilization results in the production of genotypes yielding the phenotypic ratios of the testcross progeny in each case.

Coincidence and Interference

Within a large segment of a pair of chromosomes, crossovers may occur *not only singly but repeatedly.* Two single crossovers occurring in a general region constitute a **double** crossover. There may be triple, quadruple, or greater numbers of crossovers in long segments. Multiple crossing over affects the kinds and numbers of gametes produced and leads to deviations in linkage ratios expected from a dihybrid cross. Although each crossover is a single event, successive crossovers are *not absolutely independent.* The occurrence of one crossover in a region influences the possibility of another one nearby.

COINCIDENCE. When two things happen at the same time or in the same place, they coincide and the occurrence may be considered a *coincidence.* The application of this idea to biological material may be illustrated by data from one of the Mendelian dihybrids. In the guinea-pig cross involving the independent characteristics colored–albino and rough–smooth coat, the F_2 generation contained, among other phenotypes, 25 per cent albinos and 25 per cent smooth-coated animals (p. 92). The occurrence of albinos that were also smooth-coated represents the *coincidence* of these traits. The expected coincidence of these two traits may be calculated for the F_2 generation. If 25 per cent of the F_2 population is albino and 25 per cent is smooth-coated, the expected percentage of albinos that are also smooth-coated animals is 25 per cent of 25 per cent or $6\frac{1}{4}$ per cent of the total F_2 population. This is calculated $.25 \times .25 = .0625$. The checkerboard of this dihybrid shows a theoretical population of 16 (Fig. 45). Calculation of the percentage of expected smooth-coated albinos, $16 \times .0625 = 1$, indicates that one of the 16 F_2 individuals is expected to be both albino and smooth-coated. With sufficient numbers this proportion may be obtained in the F_2 generation. The term **coincidence** as used in linkage studies *refers* to the *occurrence of two or more* distinct crossovers at about the same time or successively in the same general region of a pair of chromosomes. These constitute a double crossover or multiple crossovers, and the crossovers are said to coincide. From accumulated data the expected percentage of double or multiple crossovers in a region of a chromosome may be calculated.

In chromosome II of Drosophila, the genes *B-b* for gray-black body are located at 48.5, *P-p* for red-purple eyes are at 54.4, and *V-v* for long-vestigial wing occupy loci at 67. The observed crossing over is 6 per cent between the loci of *B-b* and *P-p* and approximately 12 per cent between those of *P-p* and *V-v* (p. 150). The occurrence of a single crossover between *B-b* and *P-p* with another single one between *P-p* and *V-v* constitutes a double crossover. The expected percentage of double crossing over in the region between 48.5 and 67 in chromosome II may be roughly calculated as 6 per cent of 12 per cent, that is, $.12 \times .06 = .0072$ or about $\frac{3}{4}$ of 1 per cent. The same principle may be used in calculating the approximate percentage for any region of a chromosome where single crossover values are known. The observed amount of double crossing over is frequently considerably less than that expected. Calculations of expected percentages of double crossing over are more reliable over long distances than for short segments of chromosomes. The occurrence of one crossover at any point in a chromosome tends to reduce the probability of a second one in the immediate vicinity.

INTERFERENCE. The lessened likelihood of further crossing over close to a previous break is called **interference.** The term means *interference with the expected amount* of double crossing over. The physical basis of interference is found in the behavior of the chromosomes in meiosis. Of several theories of the mechanism of crossing over, that proposed by the British cytologist Darlington locates the forces responsible for crossing over in *torsions* and *stresses* within the chromosomes during meiosis. The hypothesis of torsions, breakage, and union of broken ends of nonsister chromatids in one crossover explains in part the interference with further crossing over nearby. *Breakage* and union *of the chromatids* incident to one crossover may tend to *relieve torsions* in that region and to *reduce* the chances of another break. Longitudinal cohesion of the chromosomes may be an additional force tending to interfere with crossing over by distributing the stresses along the length of the chromosome tetrad. As the distance from the first break in the chromosome increases, the *interference decreases*, until finally, at about 30 to 40 units distance, the influence is entirely lost and a second break may occur freely. This is especially likely in long chromosomes. Many variables are involved in the number of crossovers and chiasmata in any pair of chromosomes, but usually the number ranges from one to three or four.

chapter 7

Chromosomal Relations of Genes in Linkage

Linkage Relations of Various Mutant Characters in Drosophila

Morgan and his associates studied linkage relations of several mutant characters of Drosophila. In addition to black body and vestigial wing, the linkage relations of a third character, purple eye, also belonging to group II were considered. Conclusions as to linkage relations of these three pairs of characters were based upon observation of more than 90,000 F_2 and testcross flies. These numerous data emphasize that conclusions as to linkage relations are based upon large numbers. According to data from Bridges and Morgan, more than 50,000 testcross flies were produced from hundreds of crosses involving all combinations of the mutant characters

Table XIII

INCOMPLETE LINKAGE IN DROSOPHILA—THE GENERATION FOLLOWING TESTCROSSES

Parental Types		Testcross Progenies		
Linked Normal Dominant Characters	Linked Mutant Recessive Characters	Parental Combination of Characters	New Combinations of Characters	Total Testcross Generation
Gray body and red eye	Black body and purple eye	48,931 or 94.175%	3,026 or 5.825%	51,957
Red eye and long wings	Purple eye and vestigial wings	13,601 or 89.421%	1,609 or 10.579%	15,210
Gray body and long wings	Black body and vestigial wings	20,153 or 84.922%	3,578 or 15.078%	23,731

black body and purple eye with the normal wild-type gray flies having red eyes. Table XIII shows the generation following testcrosses with the number of flies and percentages with the original and new combinations of the parental characters.

144

To have obtained these linkage relations in the testcross generation, the heterozygous F_1 females, resulting from the cross of wild-type gray body and red eyes, *BBPP*, $\times$ black body and purple eyes, *bbpp*, must have produced four kinds of gametes in the same proportions as were found in the classes of the testcross progeny. Table XIV shows the ratios of the four kinds

Table XIV

Linkage Ratios in Drosophila—The Generation Following the Testcross

Parental Types		Testcross Progenies			
Crosses Involving Linkage Relations Between					
Normal	Mutant	1st Parental Combination	1st New Combination	2nd New Combination	2nd Parental Combination
Gray body and red eyes	Black body and purple eyes	47 %	3 %	3 %	47 %
Red eyes and long wings	Purple eyes and vestigial wings	44 %	6 %	6 %	44 %
Gray body and long wings	Black body and vestigial wings	41 %	9 %	9 %	41 %
Mendelian expectations under conditions of free assortment		25 %	25 %	25 %	25 %

of flies in the testcross progeny corresponding to the four kinds of gametes. These four classes of F_1 gametes uniting with the gametes carrying the genes *bv*, from the double-recessive type, were therefore able to produce the testcross progeny as indicated. In reciprocal crosses the same percentages of parental and new combinations occurred. As for example, the F_1 females, *BbPp*, of the cross of flies with gray body and purple eyes, *BBpp*, and flies with black body and red eyes, *bbPP*, produced four classes of gametes as follows: 47 per cent *Bp*, 47 per cent *bP*, 3 per cent *BP*, and 3 per cent *bp*. The testcross progeny showed phenotypes in the same percentages.

Bridges and Morgan also summarized data from crosses of the normal wild-type flies, which have red eyes and long wings, *PPVV*, with flies having the combination of mutant characters purple eyes and vestigial wings, *ppvv*. From these data, it appeared that the heterozygous F_1 females must have produced four types of gametes with different gene combinations. About 44 per cent must have had the parental combination *PV* and 44 per cent the other parental combination *pv*. In addition to these two large classes, there were also two small classes of gametes of about 6 per cent each with new combinations of parental genes *Pv* and *pV*. Again, F_1 females of the reciprocal cross, red eyes and vestigial wings, *PPvv*, × purple eyes and long wings, *ppVV*, would produce gametes with a different combination of genes, namely, 44 per cent *Pv*, 44 per cent *pV*, 6 per cent *PV*, and 6 per cent *pv*. The testcross phenotypic classes would appear in the same percentages.

Linkage and crossover relationships were also obtained in crosses involving gray body and long wings with black body and vestigial wings but with different percentages as indicated in Tables XIII and XIV.

Table XV

PERCENTAGES OF DIHYBRID TESTCROSSES

Dihybrid involving the linked characters black body *vs.* gray body and vestigial wings *vs.* long wings	Parental-type dominant wild-type gray body combined with long wings 41 %	Recombination of dominant-gray body with recessive-vestigial wings 9 %	Recombination of recessive-black body with dominant-long wings 9 %	Parental-type recessive-black body combined with recessive-vestigial wings 41 %
Any other combination of linked genes	The percentages may vary in the four classes			
Dihybrid involving the characters black body *vs.* gray body and pink *vs.* red eyes. These characters show free assortment	Parental-type normal dominant-gray body with red eyes 25 %	Recombination of dominant-gray body with recessive-pink eyes 25 %	Recombination of recessive-black body with dominant-red eyes 25 %	Parental-type recessive-black body combined with recessive-pink eyes 25 %
Any other dihybrid with free assortment of genes as *Aa*, *Bb*	*AB* 25 %	*Ab* 25 %	*aB* 25 %	*ab* 25 %

Linked Characters in Maize

The known heritable characters in Indian corn or maize include endosperm characters, seed colors, plant colors, a variety of growth habits, and numerous leaf characters such as modifications of extent of chlorophyll tissues. Of all the traits in maize, the seed characters are perhaps most diverse and numerous. Corn grains may be red or purple in a number of shades, while the common yellow and white varieties may be either starchy or sugary. Sweet corn may be early or late, and it, as well as popcorn, may be of many colors. Flint and dent corn are represented by many kinds. The character of the endosperm is dependent on a number of identified genes. There are the contrasting characters full *vs.* shrunken, determined by the genes *Sh-sh*, and starchy *vs.* waxy, *Wx-wx* (Fig. 67). These genes belong to the same linkage group as the genes *C-c* for the contrasting characters colored *vs.* colorless aleurone, which is a layer of the endosperm tissue. The

FIG. 67. LINKAGE IN CORN.

Above, the endosperm character shrunken is linked with purple aleurone. Most of the purple grains are shrunken. Most of the white grains show full endosperm, because colorless aleurone and full endosperm are linked. As a result of crossing over, there are a few full, purple grains and a few shrunken, white ones. *Below,* the reverse linkage relations, white grains mostly shrunken and purple mostly have full endosperm. However, there are some purple, shrunken and some full, white grains. These are the result of crossing over. (Specimens courtesy, George Carter, Clinton, Connecticut.)

genes are located not far apart in the ninth pair of chromosomes, and their linkage relations as well as those of many other endosperm characters have been investigated extensively.

As with other endosperm characters, these traits manifest themselves in the grains of the ears produced on the F_1 plants (pp. 30, 86). This feature makes them especially favorable material for study, since large numbers may be obtained with a minimum of effort. Tables XVI and XVII include summaries of linkage relations of seed characters in maize in various parental combinations and their testcross progenies.

Position of Genes in Linkage Relations

Data on the F_2 and testcross generations following crosses in Drosophila show that linkage is incomplete in females but complete in male flies. In maize, crossing over leading to incomplete linkage occurs regularly in both

Table XVI

INCOMPLETE LINKAGE IN CORN—THE GENERATION FOLLOWING THE TESTCROSS

Parental Types		Testcross Progenies		
Linked Normal Dominant Characters	*Linked Mutant Recessive Characters*	*Parental Combinations*	*New Combinations*	*Total Testcross Progenies*
Colored aleurone and full endosperm	Colorless aleurone and shrunken endosperm	72,338 or 96.706 %	2,464 or 3.294 %	74,802
Full and starchy endosperm	Shrunken and waxy endosperm	14,345 or 79.145 %	3,780 or 20.855 %	18,125
Colored aleurone and starchy endosperm	Colorless aleurone and waxy endosperm	226,044 or 73.825 %	80,145 or 26.175 %	306,189

Table XVII

LINKAGE RATIOS IN CORN—PERCENTAGES FOLLOWING TESTCROSSES

Crosses Involving Linkage Relations Between Parental Types		Testcross Progenies			
Normal	*Mutant*	*1st Parental Combination*	*1st New Combination*	*2nd New Combination*	*2nd Parental Combination*
Colored aleurone and full endosperm	Colorless aleurone and shrunken endosperm	48.35 %	1.65 %	1.65 %	48.35 %
Full starchy endosperm	Shrunken waxy endosperm	39.5 %	10.5 %	10.5 %	39.5 %
Colored aleurone and starchy endosperm	Colorless aleurone and waxy endosperm	37.0 %	13.0 %	13.0 %	37.0 %
Mendelian expectations under conditions of free assortment		25.0 %	25.0 %	25.0 %	25.0 %

microsporocytes and megasporocytes. Analysis of results indicates further that the percentage of linkage varies with different genes (Tables XVI and XVII). Similar results have been found in the linkage relationships in many characteristics of other organisms, both plant and animal.

Morgan's hypothesis of breakage in chromosomes and mutual exchange of pieces between the two members of a pair of homologous chromosomes with consequent crossing over of genes has been widely accepted as an explanation of the phenomenon of incomplete linkage. What, then, is the explanation of the varying percentages of new combinations in the testcross progeny when the linkage relations of different characters are studied? Why should there be such diverse results with different combinations of characters? The answer to these questions may be sought in the relative positions of the genes in the chromosomes. Although the exchange of pieces was assumed to take place between members of all pairs of chromosomes, it was soon recognized that only in a small percentage of times would breaks, leading to crossing over, occur in any particular region of the chromosome. Thus when certain genes are involved, breakage and exchange of pieces of chromosomes at the location of these genes could be expected only occasionally. For this reason many genes in a chromosome remain undisturbed by crossing over in parts of the chromosome at a distance from their location.

In the Morgan hypothesis it was postulated that the genes had a linear arrangement in the chromosome. Further, it was assumed that the distance separating the loci of any two pairs of alleles determined the amount of crossing over between them. Between two pairs of alleles located very near together in the chromosome, only a small intervening section would be liable to crossing over. The *amount of crossing over* observed in any case *would*, therefore, be *directly proportional to the distance* in the chromosome *separating* the two pairs of alleles involved in the cross.

Since the crossing over observed between black-body color and purple eyes was only 6 per cent, the conditioning genes were assumed to be closer together in the chromosome than those conditioning purple eyes and vestigial wings which had 12 per cent of crossing over. Similarly, the genes conditioning black body and vestigial wing with 18 per cent of crossing over were thought to be still farther apart on the chromosome than either of the other two pairs of alleles. In relating the amount of crossing over and the distances separating the different pairs of alleles in a chromosome, it is assumed that *one per cent of crossing over indicates one unit of distance* between the two pairs of alleles in the chromosome.

Calculating the Linkage Relations of Genes

Since crossing over is proportional to the distance separating the gene pairs involved, there will be greater chance for a crossover between distant loci than between loci close together. For example, if two genes as *A-a* and *B-b* are 20 units apart and two other gene pairs, *C-c* and *D-d*, are only 2 units apart, the chance of a crossover between *A-a* and *B-b* is ten times as great as between *C-c* and *D-d* (p. 151). Linkage between *C-c* and *D-d* is relatively strong, and that between *A-a* and *B-b* is relatively weak. Linkage strength in any case is indicated by the crossover percentage or crossover value; *a high crossover value indicates weak linkage* and *a low crossover value, strong linkage.* Crossover value varies inversely with linkage strength.

Calculating Loci of Genes in Chromosomes

From the linkage studies in Drosophila (Chapter 6), it was assumed that there was a fairly constant relationship between percentages of new combinations in the phenotypic testcross ratios and distance between the locations of any two pairs of alleles in the chromosomes. Each one per cent of

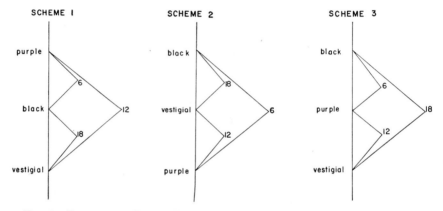

Fig. 68. Diagram of Three Possible Relationships of Genes Conditioning Black Body, Purple-eye Color, and Vestigial Wing in Chromosomes of Drosophila.

crossing over indicates one unit of distance between two pairs of alleles under consideration. The testcross data were interpreted as locating the gene for black body approximately 6 units from the gene for purple eye and the gene for purple eye 12 units from the gene for vestigial wing.

It is also possible to learn from the crossover data about the order in which the loci of linked genes occur The order might be (1) purple, black, vestigial; (2) black, vestigial, purple; or (3) black, purple, vestigial (Fig. 68). Using the above determinations for distances, how do the data fit these assumptions? Under assumption (1), the distance between black and vestigial is indicated as $11.8 - 6.2 = 5.6$. The observed percentage of crossing over is 17.8 between black and vestigial. The order, therefore, *cannot* be purple, black, vestigial. Under (2), the distance between black and purple is indicated as $17.8 + 11.8 = 29.6$. The observed percentage of crossing over between these loci is, however, only 6.2 per cent. The order, therefore, *cannot* be black, vestigial, purple. Assumption (3) *fits the observed crossover percentages much better.* In this case the distance between black and vestigial is indicated as 6.2 + 11.8 = 18 which is a close approximation of the distance of 17.8 units calculated from the observed crossover percentages. The data show that the loci for black and vestigial are about 18 units apart with the locus for purple occupying a position between them. The order, therefore, is black, purple, vestigial. Location of these genes in the chromosome may be further confirmed by determining linkage and crossover relations with other nearby loci.

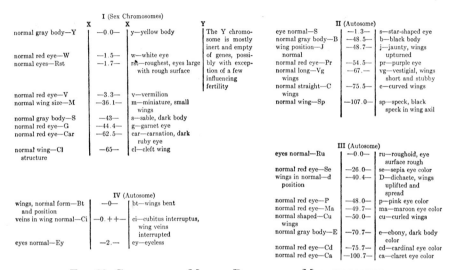

FIG. 69. CHROMOSOME MAP OF DROSOPHILA MELANOGASTER.
    The four chromosome pairs are shown, I at left above, II at right, III at right, IV at left below. Gene locations, as to relative loci in one of the four linkage groups, are indicated for a few of the best-known mutant factors. The normal allele conditioning the wild type occupies a corresponding locus. (Modified after data of Bridges and Brehme, Carnegie Publication #522, Washington, 1944.)

    The number of observed new combinations of linked characters involving two pairs of widely separated genes is generally somewhat less than the number of units of distance between them would indicate. Double crossovers, that is, two exchanges of segments in a given region instead of only one, may sometimes occur between widely separated loci of genes. In fact, if the distance is sufficiently great, more than two crossovers may occur in a given region between two pairs of alleles. Double crossovers would compensate each other and leave the genes in their original alignments. The effect of double crossing over would then tend to make the distance appear *less* than the actual amount. Many factors may intervene to complicate the calculations. Among them, besides double crossing over, are interference with crossing over and differences in the rates of crossing over that appear to be inherent in some chromosomes. Besides the disturbance of linkage and crossing over by these physical mechanisms, certain mutant genes also exert an effect upon the rates of crossing over. These genes are, of course, inherited in regular Mendelian fashion.

CHROMOSOME MAPS. By use of data on percentages of new combinations resulting from crossing over of linked genes and with improved techniques in breeding experiments, it has been possible to overcome the complications and to calculate relative positions of about 500 to 600 genes

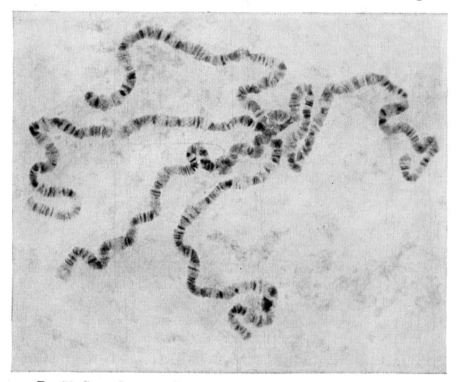

FIG. 70. GIANT SALIVARY CHROMOSOMES OF DROSOPHILA MELANOGASTER.
The structures observable along the length of the chromosomes are presumably correlated with the genic loci on linkage maps. (Courtesy, B. P. Kaufmann, Carnegie Institution of Washington.)

in the chromosomes of the Drosophila. From data on linkage relations of genes, maps of chromosomes have been constructed, indicating relative positions of a large number of alleles. The published chromosome map of the Drosophila shows the location of some of the genetically most useful genes (Fig. 69, p. 151), but the location is known for many more genes than those shown on the map. Work on the giant salivary chromosomes has identified the relative positions calculated in genetic studies and the actual positions in the giant chromosomes (Fig. 70). Similar maps locate important genes for maize, domesticated fowls, and other organisms (Fig. 71 and 72).

Relative and observed loci of genes and distances separating them have been to a large extent coordinated in the Drosophila. In many other organisms, however, through lack of accurate analysis and observation, gene positions still remain largely relative. With the unit of distance in a chromosome set as equal to one per cent of crossing over between two pairs of genes, the total relative length of a chromosome was regarded as 100 units.

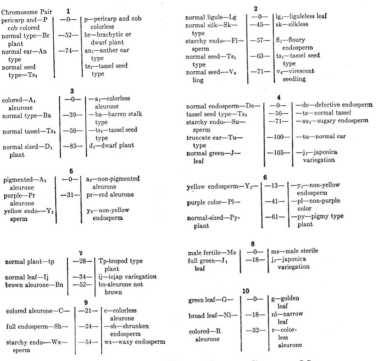

FIG. 71. CHROMOSOME MAP OF INDIAN CORN OR MAIZE.

The ten pairs of chromosomes in this plant are numbered according to their size from the longest, 1, to the shortest, 10. The locations, as to relative loci in one of the ten linkage groups, are indicated for a few of the best-known mutant genes. The normal allele of each mutant gene occupies a corresponding locus. (Modified after data of Emerson, Beadle, and Fraser, Cornell University Agricultural Experiment Station Memoir #180, Ithaca, 1935.)

In pioneer work in the determination of gene positions, some gene was arbitrarily selected and assigned to a fixed position or locus. The gene y, which conditions yellow body in Drosophila, was assigned the position at 0 (zero) on the **X** chromosome, but it is not actually at the end of the chromosome. Other genes have since been found which occupy loci beyond y. Since no one can predict when the gene at the zero end of the **X** chromosome will be discovered, y is still regarded as zero, and the loci of new genes beyond y have been assigned minus values. Likewise, genes at the other

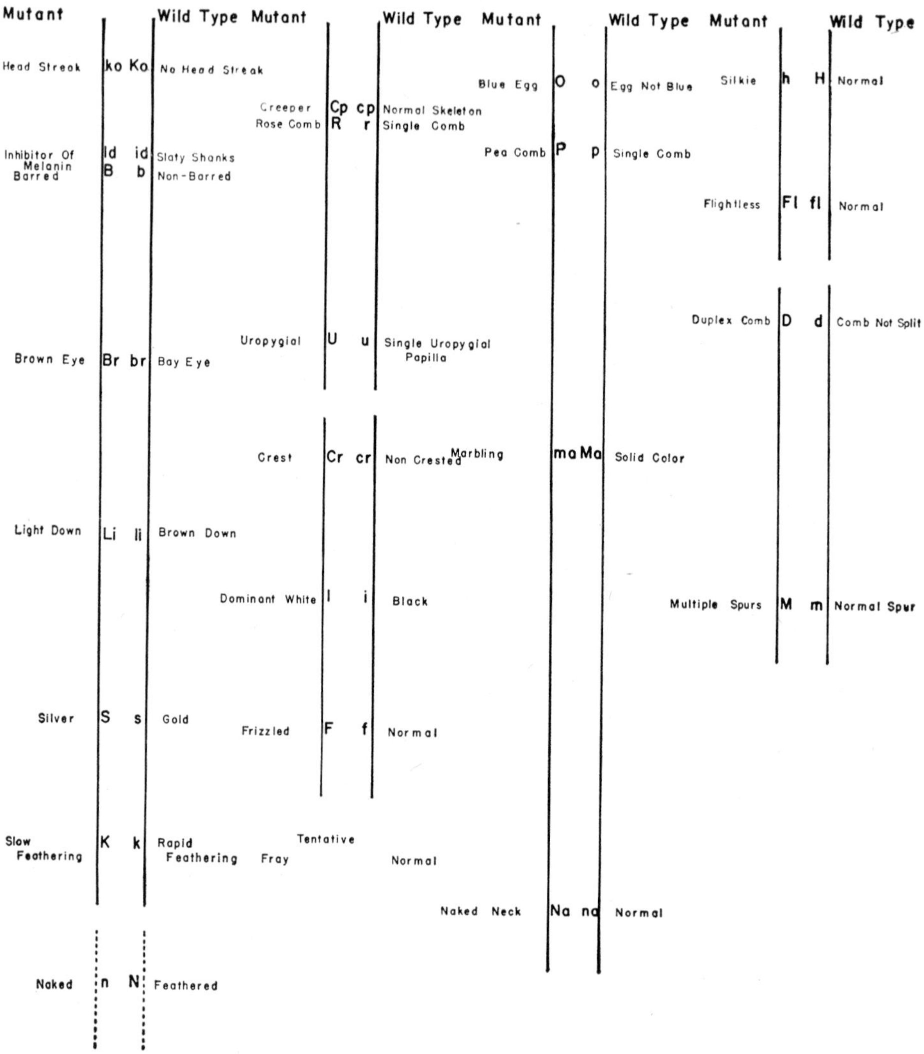

FIG. 72. LINKAGE MAP OF FOWL.

Relative positions of loci of 23 genes in 6 linkage groups, the largest number located in pair of sex chromosomes, are shown. Mutant alleles are listed on left and normal or wild type on right of each pair of chromosomes. (Modified after F. B. Hutt and W. F. Lamoreux, from *J. Heredity*.)

end of chromosome **X** have been given values of **100 +** (Fig. 69). Similar situations may be found for the large autosomes II and III in Drosophila. Chromosome maps are built from calculations of relative positions for the loci of the genes, starting at an arbitrary point. Chromosome maps for Drosophila have been refined by years of patient research and are now regarded as fairly accurate for several hundreds of genes.

CHIASMA FREQUENCY AND CROSSOVER FREQUENCY. During meiosis each chromosome member of a pair of synaptic mates is split lengthwise, forming two in a group of four chromatids (pp. 19, 138). At any one point the exchange of pieces, or crossing over, occurs between only two of the four chromatids of the chromosome tetrad. With the restriction of chiasmata to only two of the four strands, at any one point or level, it follows that at this point two of the four strands are not included in the exchange of chromatid segments. Because the alignment of genes in them remains undisturbed, these chromatids contain the original parental combinations of genes. Since the exclusion of two chromatids from the chiasma reduces the amount of crossing over by one-half, the crossover frequency or exchange frequency is only one-half the chiasma frequency. In other words, considering the whole chromosome tetrad of four strands, chiasmata indicate only 50 per cent efficiency, because half of the chromatids are untouched in each case. Specific examples may serve to illustrate these relationships. In a case considered earlier, the normal wild-type Drosophila, $BBVV$, with gray body and long wings was mated to the double-recessive mutant, $bbvv$, with black body and vestigial wings. In the testcross progeny, these chromosome II genes showed about 18 per cent of crossing over in the heterozygous F_1 female. Because each chiasma indicates only 50 per cent crossing over in each chromosome tetrad, on the average 36 of each 100 oöcytes will be required to produce 18 per cent crossover eggs. Assuming that in each of these 36 oöcytes there was one chiasma in two of the four strands of the chromosome tetrad, 18 eggs with new combinations or crossovers might be expected, $9Bv$ and $9bV$. Because crossing over is restricted to only two of the four strands of each chromosome tetrad, the original alignment of genes remained undisturbed in half of the chromatids in the 36 oöcytes in which crossing over occurred. These produced 18 eggs carrying the parental combinations $9BV$ and $9bv$.

Besides the statistical 36 oöcytes in the heterozygous F_1 female that showed effective crossing over, there would be remaining 64 of each 100. In this group of oöcytes, chiasmata might have been formed in chromosome II, but they were at a distance from the loci of the genes B-b and V-v. These genes were, therefore, undisturbed by the chiasmata. The 64 oöcytes produced eggs carrying the original gene combinations. On the average there were $32BV$ and $32bv$ eggs from the 64 oöcytes. If similar gametic products of the 36 and 64 oöcytes are added, there are $9 + 32 = 41BV$ and, likewise, $9 + 32 = 41bv$ eggs. They represent the original parental combinations of genes. In addition, there are the crossover gametes $9Bv$ and $9bV$. Original and crossover eggs combine to make the statistical total of 100 per cent, that is, $41BV + 41bv + 9Bv + 9bV = 100$.

Compared with the above, the cross of flies having gray body and red eyes, $BBPP$, mated with those showing the mutations black body and purple eyes, $bbpp$, gave about 6 per cent crossing over in the F_1 female, $BbPp$. This indicated a distance of 6 units separating the loci of B-b and P-p. In a total of 100, 88 per cent of the oöcytes will show no crossing over, and the original alignment of genes will be found in the eggs they produce. There will be 44 per cent BP and 44 per cent bp because the chiasmata are some distance from the region, six units in length, which contains the genes B-b and P-p. Crossing over will occur in 12 per cent of the oöcytes because, in these cases, the chiasmata are formed between the locus of B-b and that of P-p. Assuming that in each of the oöcytes of this 12 per cent there is just one chiasma between two of the four strands, from these oöcytes eggs will be produced with 6 per cent of new combinations or crossovers, 3 per cent of Bp, and 3 per cent of bP.

The chromatids from the two strands not included in the chiasmata will also pass into eggs. These eggs will constitute 6 per cent with the original alignment of linked genes, 3 per cent of BP, and 3 per cent of bp. The percentages are then added to the percentages of eggs produced by the 88 per cent of oöcytes having no crossovers in the black-purple region. Thus, there will be 44 per cent + 3 per cent = 47 per cent BP and likewise 44 per cent + 3 per cent = 47 per cent bp. The 3 per cent of Bp and 3 per cent of bP completes the total of 100 per cent.

Phenotypic Ratios in Linkage

In linkage studies, whenever the distance between two pairs of alleles is known, it is easy to calculate the expected phenotypic ratios. For example, in Drosophila the gene, b, conditioning black body is located at 48.5, and the gene, p, conditioning purple eye is located at 54.5, both in chromosome II. The dominant alleles, B and P, conditioning the normal wild characters, gray body and red eye, respectively, are located at corresponding loci. These two pairs of alleles are 54.5 − 48.5 = 6 units apart. The assumption that each per cent of crossing over equals one unit of distance on the chromosome is the key to the solution of such problems.

Following a cross between a normal wild-type fly, $BBPP$, having gray body and red eyes and a mutant fly, $bbpp$, having black body and purple eyes, a heterozygous F_1 generation, $BbPp$, will be obtained. Because of dominance, the F_1 flies will be normal wild type. Because of crossing over of the genes in the F_1 female, some of her progeny will show new combinations of the linked parental characters in addition to the two parental types. Very briefly then, 6 per cent of new combinations of the genes Bp and bP will be expected in the gametes of a heterozygous female fly and will occur in equal numbers, 3 per cent of each Bp and bP. Now the number of original parental combinations BP and bp may be calculated by subtracting the amount of recombinations, 6 per cent, from the total. That is, 100 per cent − 6 per cent = 94 per cent.

Since the parental combinations BP and bp occur in equal numbers, 94 per cent divided by 2 or 47 per cent each of BP and bp may be expected. Female gametes will be produced containing the four gene combinations in the following proportions: 47 per cent BP, 3 per cent Bp, 3 per cent bP, and 47 per cent bp. As is usual in dihybrids, four classes of gametes are produced, but they are not equally numerous. There are two large classes of 47 per cent and two small classes of 3 per cent. Similar calculations can be made for any two pairs of linked characters, provided the distance separating the loci of their conditioning genes is known. Phenotypic ratios correspond to these gene combinations.

THE EFFECTS OF LINKAGE IN THE DIRECT CROSS. Modifications of the Phenotypic Ratios. It will be recalled that Bateson's discovery of linkage followed from his observation of the modification of an expected 9:3:3:1 dihybrid ratio. Now it is known that linkage is an important cause of modified ratios and that the closer the linkage the greater the deviation from Mendelian expectations. Linkage introduces complications, especially in the direct cross where F_1 is selfed or mated to F_1. To clarify the nature of the modifications and complications resulting from linkage and crossing over, some phenotypic ratios of direct crosses may be considered,

From the cross of Drosophila with gray body and red eye, *BBPP*, × black body and purple eye, *bbpp*, F₁ flies, *BbPp*, of both sexes may be expected. Since linkage is complete with no crossing over in the male, F₁ flies would produce two kinds of sperms, *BP* and *bp*, in equal numbers. From knowledge of crossover percentages, the heterozygous female flies may be assumed to produce four kinds of eggs with gene combinations in the ratio of 47*BP*:3*Bp*:3*bP*:47*bp*. Union of the male and female gametes in the direct cross may be expected to produce a phenotypic ratio of 147 gray red:3 gray purple:3 black red:47 black purple (Fig. 73).

This phenotypic ratio may be calculated by multiplying the expected frequencies of each kind of female gamete by 1*BP* and 1*bp*, the frequencies of the male gametes. The products are entered in the appropriate square of a checkerboard, and addition of like phenotypes yields the theoretical ratio of 147:3:3:47 noted above. Direct-cross ratios for any two pairs of linked genes may be calculated provided their loci or their crossover percentages are known.

The Four Kinds of Female Gametes

	47 BP	3 Bp	3 bP	47 bp
I BP	47 BBPP gray body red eyes	3 BBPp gray body red eyes	3 Bb PP gray body red eyes	47 BbPp gray body red eyes
I bp	47 BbPp gray body red eyes	3 Bbpp gray body purple eyes	3 bbPp black body red eyes	47 bbpp black body purple eyes

The Two Kinds of Male Gametes

FIG. 73. RECOMBINATION OF LINKED GENES "B-b" AND "P-p" FOLLOWING MATING OF F₁ × F₁ IN A DIRECT CROSS IN DROSOPHILA.

Because there is crossing over in the formation of both male and female gametes in plants and many kinds of animals, even greater complications arise with linked genes when the direct cross is used in these organisms. As an example, the linkage relations of waxy endosperm and colored aleurone in maize may be cited. The gene pairs concerned are *C-c* conditioning colored and colorless aleurone and *W-w* conditioning starchy and waxy endosperm. Hybridization of plants with colored aleurone, starchy endosperm, *CCWW*, and with white aleurone, waxy endosperm, *ccww*, yields F₁ *CcWw* plants.

Self-pollination of the F₁ *CcWw* in a direct cross can be expected to result in a greatly modified F₂ ratio (Fig. 74). There is 26 per cent of crossing over between the loci of these genes (pp. 153, 158). Since this occurs equally in both anthers and ovules, male and female gametes are both expected in the ratio of 37*CW*:13*Cw*: 13*cW*:37*cw*. This ratio of gametes is so near to a 3:1:1:3 ratio that this numerical relation may be substituted for the actual figures in the checkerboard calculations of the present problem.

The slightly modified gametic ratios 3*CW*:1*Cw*:1*cW*:3*cw* may be written at the top and at the left side of the checkerboard (Fig. 74). The gene designations indicating the possible recombinations may then be entered as usual in the squares of the checkerboard. The gametic numbers written at the top and side may now be successively multiplied and the products written in the appropriate squares; the figures indicate the number of genotypes that may be expected for a particular gene combination. By considering dominance of the genes, the number of phenotypes conditioned by each gene combination may also be calculated. Summation of similar

F_2 Generation	The Four Kinds of Female Gametes			
	3 CW	**I C w**	**I c W**	**3 c w**
3 CW	**9 CCWW** red starchy	**3 CCWw** red starchy	**3 CcWW** red starchy	**9 CcWw** red starchy
I C w	**3 CCWw** red starchy	**I CCww** red waxy	**I CcWw** red starchy	**3 Ccww** red waxy
I c W	**3 CcWW** red starchy	**I CcWw** red starchy	**I cc WW** white starchy	**3 ccWw** white starchy
3 c w	**9 Cc Ww** red starchy	**3 Ccww** red waxy	**3 cc Ww** white starchy	**9 ccww** white waxy

(left side label: The Four Kinds of Male Gametes)

FIG. 74. RECOMBINATION OF LINKED GENES "C-c" AND "W-w" FOLLOWING SELF-POLLINATION OF F_1 IN A DIRECT CROSS IN INDIAN CORN.

phenotypes indicates a ratio of 41 red starchy:7 red waxy:7 white starchy:9 white waxy, which is a fairly close approximation of the theoretical ratio expected in this case. The checkerboard technique may be used to calculate the expected linkage modification of the phenotypic ratio for any plant or animal having crossing over in both sexes, provided the crossover percentages or loci of the genes are known. In cases in which the crossover values are unknown and a direct cross is used that yields F_2 results indicating linkage, crossover percentages may be calculated by mathematical formulae.

chapter 8

Sex Linkage

Sex determination in Drosophila depends upon the presence of the sex chromosomes, the female having two **X** chromosomes, or **XX**, and the male one **X** and a **Y**, or **XY**. Males produce sperms of two types, those bearing **X** and those bearing **Y**. Females produce eggs of one kind, all carrying an **X** chromosome. Females are developed when an **X** egg is fertilized by an **X** sperm, and males are produced when an **X** egg unites with a **Y** sperm. Thus, a male receives an **X** chromosome only from the female and never from the male parent and a **Y** chromosome only from the male parent, never from the female. This type of sex determination is also found in some fishes, in mammals, including man, and in many plants.

Sex Chromosomes and Sex Linkage

Because of their close association with the sex-determining factors, genes carried in the **X** and **Y** chromosomes are called **sex-linked genes,** and the characters they condition are called **sex-linked** characters.* Sex-linked genes are not restricted in their action to purely sexual traits. They may affect any portion of the body or any physiological function. In many organisms, as in Drosophila, the **X** chromsome is the principle carrier of sex-linked genes, and in the earlier discussions of sex linkage, the term referred largely to genes carried in the **X** chromosome. The **Y** chromosome of the Drosophila is said to be genetically empty or inert. Although in Drosophila the **Y** chromosome carries few hereditary factors, in some other organisms both **X** and **Y** chromosomes contain genes. Those in the **X** chromosomes are said to be **X-linked** and those in the **Y** are **Y-linked.**

Since the male fly is developed following the union of an egg containing

---

* In contrast with sex-linked characters, certain secondary sexual characteristics, such as plumage of male fowls, horns on animals, and the beard of man, are strongly influenced by the sex hormones. Such characters are called **sex-limited** characters (p. 426). Sex-limited characters, however, have a fundamental hereditary basis and may be conditioned by genes occurring in the autosomes or in the sex chromosomes. They are not necessarily sex-linked. The development of many distinctive sexual and secondary sexual characters may be influenced by genes carried in the autosomes.

an **X** chromosome and a sperm containing a **Y** chromosome, it never receives any **X**-linked genes from the male parent, but it receives **Y**-linked genes only from the male parent. The female, determined by the union of an egg containing an **X** chromosome and a sperm also containing an **X** chromosome, inherits **X**-linked characters equally from the male and female parents. Thus, a sex-linked gene, carried by an **X** chromosome, follows the course of that chromosome in a crisscross manner through the generations, first in one sex and in the opposite sex in the next generation. The males of the Drosophila, with but one **X** chromosome and an inert **Y,** will show the effects of any **X**-linked gene carried by that chromosome, whether it is in the dominant or in the recessive state. In the absence of dominant **X**-linked allelic genes, the effects of **X**-linked recessive genes are never obscured in the male. In the female flies, however, with two **X** chromosomes, the effects of a recessive gene may be submerged by the action of its dominant allele. A male with only *one* **X** chromosome is said to be *hemizygous* for its **X**-linked genes.

Reciprocal Crosses Involving Sex Linkage

One of the first mutations that Morgan studied in the Drosophila was the recessive sex-linked character white eye. White eyes *vs.* red eyes are determined by the gene pair **W-w,** carried in the **X** or chromosome I. The behavior of these genes is typical of all sex-linked genes carried in the **X** chromosome of Drosophila, some other insects, and of mammals. Any trait exhibiting crisscross inheritance is recognized as a sex-linked character. The situation may be illustrated by the cross of fruit flies having white eyes with those having the contrasting character, normal red eyes (Fig. 75).

The early students of Drosophila genetics made use of the striking criss-cross inheritance of sex-linked traits to determine the linkage relations of new mutations (p. 123). Sex-linked characters also show other peculiarities of behavior in the types of ratios they produce. Since a female Drosophila has two **X** chromosomes and a male only one **X,** reciprocal crosses of the direct type involving sex-linked genes yield different results in both the F_1 and F_2 generations. In some instances the monohybrid F_2 ratios are 3:1, but in other cases the F_2 ratios are 2:2 (Fig. 76 and 77). In Drosophila reciprocal crosses may be made that involve the recessive sex-linked character white eye and its contrasting allele, the normal red eye, in one case by mating a red-eyed female fly with a white-eyed male and in the second case by the reverse, that is, a white-eyed female with a male having red eyes.

Mating a homozygous red-eyed female, WW, to a white-eyed male fly, w, produces an F_1 generation consisting of males and females both having red eyes (Fig. 76). The F_1 females are heterozygous, Ww, since they inherit an **X** chromosome from each parent. The **X** from the male parent containing the recessive gene w for white eyes thus has crisscrossed from P_1 male to F_1 female. Although they carry the recessive gene for white eyes, F_1 females will have red eyes because of the dominance of W.

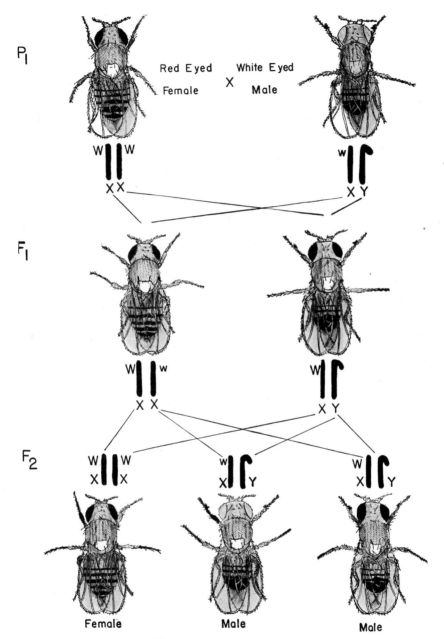

FIG. 75. DIAGRAM OF THE CRISSCROSS INHERITANCE TYPICAL IN SEX-LINKED INHERITANCE.

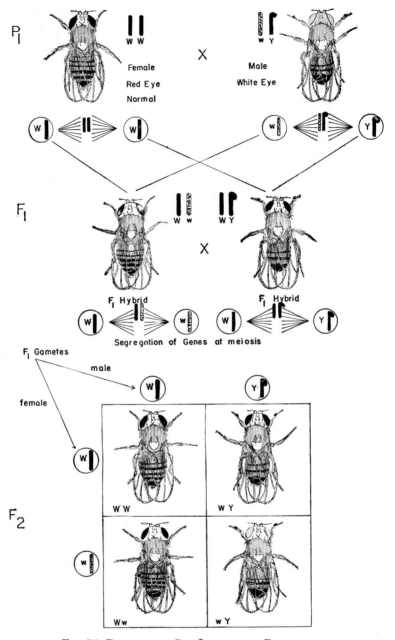

FIG. 76. DIAGRAM OF SEX LINKAGE IN DROSOPHILA.

Disregarding the sexes, there are 3 flies with red eyes to 1 with white eyes, a 3:1 ratio. Note contrast in reciprocal cross (Fig. 77).

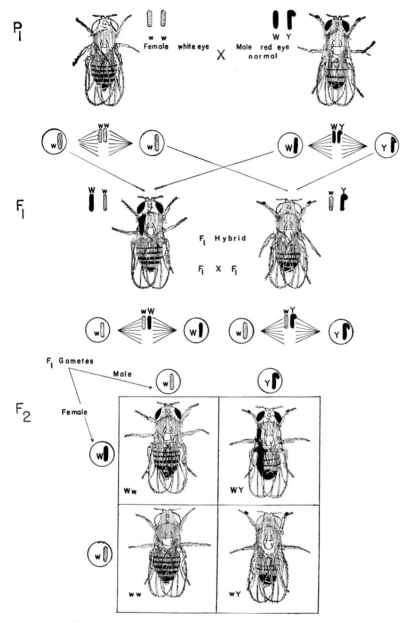

FIG. 77. DIAGRAM OF SEX LINKAGE IN DROSOPHILA.

The reciprocal cross of that shown in Fig. 76. Compare Fig. 76, noting that F_1
generations are unlike in reciprocal crosses and also that males inherit their sex-
linked characters from their female parent and never from their male parent. The
ratio is, therefore, 2:2 instead of the 3:1 ratio characteristic of the reciprocal cross.

The heterozygous F_1 female will produce two kinds of eggs. In one kind the **X** chromosome carries the W gene, and in the other kind of egg the **X** chromosome carries the w gene. The hemizygous F_1 male also produces two kinds of gametes. One kind of sperm carries the empty **Y** chromosome; the other carries the **X** chromosome which, in this case, contains the dominant gene W. Mating the male and female F_1 flies in a sibcross will yield an F_2 generation with the genotypes formed by the recombinations of the two kinds of gametes from each male and female. The union of the **Y** sperms from the F_1 male with eggs containing either W or w in the **X** chromosome will determine the production of **XY** F_2 males. However, the **X** chromosomes contain either W or w with equal frequency, and half of the F_2 male flies will have red eyes, W and half white eyes, w. The union of the **X** sperms which carry only the dominant gene W with eggs containing either W or w will result in the production of the genotypes WW and Ww. Since the F_2 genotypes contain two **X** chromosomes, they will determine development of females. Because these are either homozygous-dominant WW or heterozygous Ww, they will all have red eyes. Thus, the cross of the red-eyed female with a white-eyed male yields an F_2 generation of flies with red eyes and flies with white eyes in a $3:1$ ratio.

In the reciprocal cross the P_1 consists of a white-eyed female and a red-eyed male fly. The white-eyed female of P_1 carries the recessive gene w in each of her two **X** chromosomes. The red-eyed male of P_1 carries the dominant gene W in his single **X** chromosome. Because of the crisscross inheritance of sex-linked characteristics, mating a female with white eyes to a male having red eyes produces an F_1 generation consisting of heterozygous red-eyed females and hemizygous white-eyed males. This result differs from the preceding reciprocal mating. Mating these male and female F_1 flies in a sibcross will yield an F_2 generation with the genotypes formed by the recombinations of the two kinds of gametes produced by F_1 flies of both sexes (Fig. 77). The eggs from the F_1 female each carry one **X** chromosome. However, in one kind of female gamete, the **X** contains the dominant gene W, and in the other type, the **X** contains the recessive gene w. The two types of sperms from the F_1 male are those carrying the **Y** chromosome and those carrying the **X** with its recessive gene w.

The union of the **Y** sperms from the F_1 male and eggs containing with equal frequency either W or w in the **X** chromosome will determine the production of hemizygous F_2 males. Thus, half of these F_2 male flies will have red eyes, W, and half white eyes, w. The union of the **X** sperms which carry the recessive gene w with eggs containing either W or w in the **X** chromosome will produce F_2 females with red eyes, Ww, or white eyes, ww. Therefore the cross of a female with white eyes and a male with red eyes yields an F_2 generation of flies with red eyes and flies with white eyes in a $2:2$ ratio which differs from the reciprocal cross.

In the fruit fly a large number of sex-linked mutant characters has been recognized. *All that has been said concerning the linkage relationships of autosomal genes, definite loci for the alleles, chiasmata, recombinations, and interference with crossing over are equally applicable to sex-linked genes carried in the X chromosomes.*

Sex Linkage in Man

Mammals have the same type of sex determination as the Drosophila; that is, sex in mammals is also determined on the basis of the **XX–XY** combination of chromosomes. For this reason the inheritance of several sex-linked characters in man follows the same scheme as that described in the Drosophila. Two recessive sex-linked characters known in human beings are the defect in vision called color blindness and the physiological abnormality hemophilia (p. 492). The genes basic to these defects are carried in the X chromosome. Each of these traits shows the typical crisscross inheritance seen in the sex-linked characters in the Drosophila, such as white eyes.

Color blindness is a fairly common defect of vision in man. The character expresses itself in an inability to distinguish accurately between red and green colors. In females, with two **X** chromosomes, the recessive genes must be in the homozygous state to manifest themselves. Males have only a single **X** chromosome, and in them a single recessive gene can determine color blindness. Because of the relationship of the hereditary factor to the X chromosomes, more men than women show color blindness. (See further discussion, pp. 484–487.)

Sex Linkage in Birds

Poultry breeders and fanciers are interested in the inheritance of sex-linked characters in fowls and birds. The mechanism for sex determination in birds differs from that in Drosophila and in mammals. In birds the male has two functional sex chromosomes and the female only one. This type has been called the **W-Z** type of sex determination. However, it is better to regard the sex chromosomes of birds also as **X** and **Y**. The male birds have **XX** and the females have **XY** chromosomes. The sex-linked characters, of which there are several in birds, such as the dominant-feather characters barring and penciling, all follow the course of the **X** chromosome through the generations (Fig. 78–80). The situation as to chromosomes and sexes introduces only minor complications.

Various Types of Sex Linkage

Through the investigations of Koller and Darlington, Haldane, Snyder, and others, it has become evident that the inheritance of sex-linked genes is more complicated than was indicated by early investigations of inheritance of such sex-linked characters as white eye in the Drosophila, hemophilia, and the red and green color blindness in human beings.

Cytological investigations of the synaptic relations of the **X** and **Y** chromosomes show that in many cases these sex chromosomes are related in three distinct ways (Fig. 81). First, there is a portion of the **X** chromosome which is nonhomologous with any part of the **Y** chromosome. The non-homologous parts of the **X** and **Y** chromosomes do not pair nor undergo crossing over during meiosis. Genes such as those determining white eye and yellow body in Drosophila, hemophilia, and the red-green type of color blindness in human beings are carried in the parts of the **X** chromosome that are nonhomologous with any part of the **Y** chromosome. These genes are completely **X**-linked and because of their location determine the ordinary type of sex-linked characters. Such genes never pass directly from father to son but always from father through daughter to her sons. Second, there is a portion of the **Y** chromosome which is nonhomologous with any part of the

FIG. 78. BLACK COCK, LEFT, AND BARRED HEN, RIGHT.
The barred character in fowls is a sex-linked trait and is dominant in crosses with black fowls. Reciprocal crosses are shown in Fig. 79 and 80. (Courtesy, A. O. Schilling.)

X chromosome. Genes carried in this part of the **Y** chromosome, called **holandric** or *wholly male genes*, are completely **Y**-linked and thus are trans-mitted directly from father to son and never from father to daughter, be-cause only the sons inherit a **Y** chromosome. Normally, the daughter receives an **X** chromosome from both parents. In some species of fishes, the **Y** chromo-some carries holandric genes or **Y**-linked genes as well as **X** or ordinary sex-linked genes. Third, there are portions of both the **X** and the **Y** chromosomes which are homologous. These parts pair at synapsis and in some organisms may show chiasmata resulting from crossing over during the early meiotic processes. Genes located in the homologous parts of the sex chromosomes are not completely linked to either the **X** or the **Y** chromosome but may cross over from one to the other exactly as do those belonging to any autosomal linkage group (pp. 130, 151–154).

FIG. 79. P₁, F₁, AND F₂ GENERATIONS OF A CROSS INVOLVING SEX-LINKED CHARAC-
TERS IN FOWLS.

P₁, at A, a barred Plymouth Rock male; at B, a black Rose Comb Bantam female.
Middle, the F₁ generation at C and D, barred in both sexes. Mating the F₁ individuals
produces F₂ below at E, F, G, and H. The F₂ consists of barred and black fowls in
the ratio of 3:1. Crisscross inheritance is shown. (Courtesy, M. A. Jull and J. P.
Quinn, from J. Heredity.)

FIG. 80. P₁, F₁, AND F₂ GENERATIONS OF THE RECIPROCAL CROSS OF THAT ILLUS-
TRATED IN FIG. 79.

The P₁, at *A*, a black Rose Comb Bantam male; at *B*, a barred Plymouth Rock
female. Middle, the F₁ barred male at *C* and black female at *D*. Note the effects of
crisscross inheritance. The F₂ of this cross consists of males and females, half of each
are barred and half black. The ratio of color in the F₂ is 2 barred : 2 black. Compare
this with the reciprocal cross. (Courtesy, M. A. Jull and J. P. Quinn, from *J. Heredity*.)

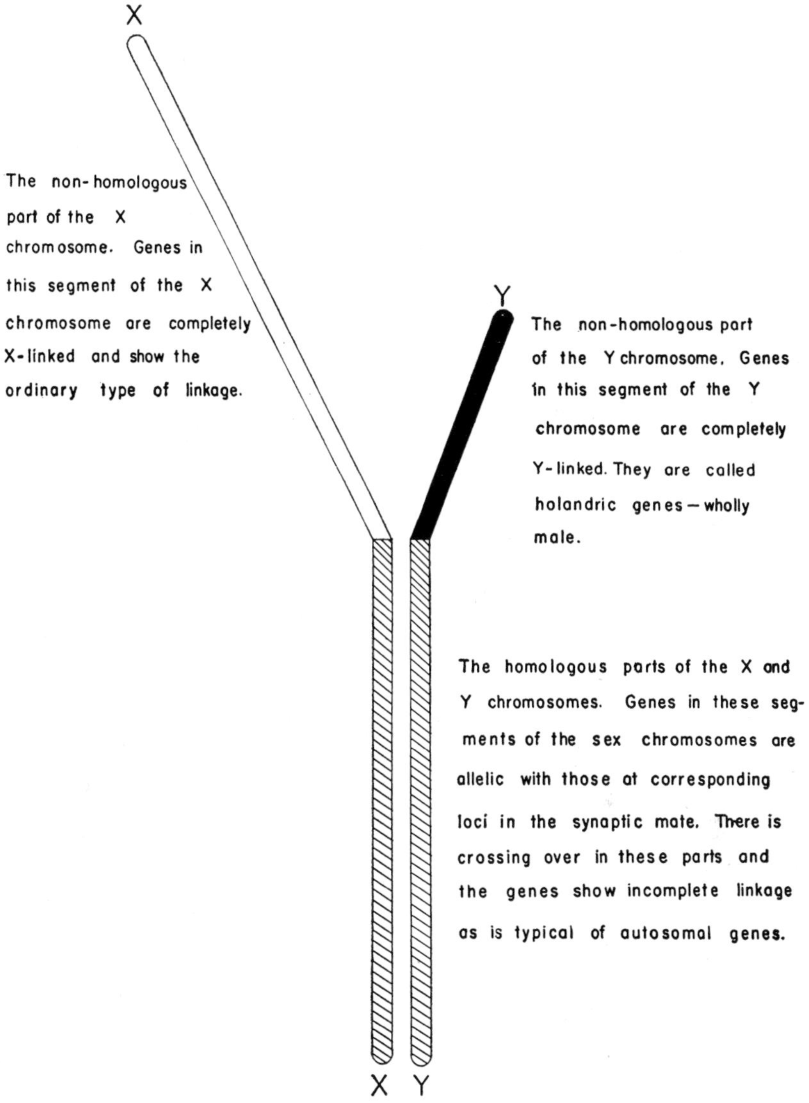

X

The non-homologous part of the X chromosome. Genes in this segment of the X chromosome are completely X-linked and show the ordinary type of linkage.

Y

The non-homologous part of the Y chromosome. Genes in this segment of the Y chromosome are completely Y-linked. They are called holandric genes — wholly male.

The homologous parts of the X and Y chromosomes. Genes in these segments of the sex chromosomes are allelic with those at corresponding loci in the synaptic mate. There is crossing over in these parts and the genes show incomplete linkage as is typical of autosomal genes.

X Y

Fig. 81. Diagram of the Possible Relationship of the Parts of the Sex Chromosomes.

In some cases parts of the **X** and **Y**, as in lower part of diagram, may be homologous. Parts of **X** and **Y** are nonhomologous. Genes located in the nonhomologous part of the **X** chromosome are completely **X**-linked, and genes located in the nonhomologous part of the **Y** chromosome are completely **Y**-linked. (Diagram based on the researches of Koller and Darlington, Snyder and Palmer, and Kaliss and Schweitzer.)

Questions and Problems

1. What happens in linkage? Who discovered the phenomenon of linkage? In what organism was linkage first discovered? What names were first applied to linkage? Who proposed the term *linkage?*

2. What is the relation of genes to chromosomes which makes linkage possible? What is the physical basis of linkage? Do the relative numbers of genes and chromosomes have any bearing on the linkage of genes?

3. What is a linkage group? How many chromosomes are basic to a linkage group? What is the relation of the number of chromosomes to the number of linkage groups? How many linkage groups are known in the Drosophila?

4. How many linkage groups are there in maize or Indian corn?

5. Make a diagram to illustrate the relationship of genes to chromosomes in which free assortment is possible.

6. Make a diagram to illustrate the relationship of genes to chromosomes under which linkage is possible.

7. What do you understand by the terms *complete linkage* and *incomplete linkage?* Which of these is the more common?

8. Compare some of the testcross or backcross percentages which occur under conditions of free assortment and under conditions of linkage in Drosophila.

9. Have linkage relations been found in organisms other than the Drosophila?

10. Compare some of the percentages resulting from the testcrosses under conditions of linkage in corn. How do these compare with testcross percentages under conditions of free assortment?

11. What differences may be observed in the progeny of parents which show complete linkage and those which show incomplete or partial linkage?

12. What is the physical basis of incomplete linkage? What phenomenon of chromosome behavior accounts for incomplete linkage?

13. What is crossing over? What are chiasmata?

14. Do chiasmata cause crossing over or are they one of the results of crossing over?

15. What is "interference" with crossing over? What physical forces within the chromosomes may be responsible for interference? What physical property of the chromatids may influence interference?

16. What are the units of distance as applied to positions of genes on chromosomes? How were they determined? Why are all chromosomes considered to be 100 units long regardless of their actual size?

17. Describe the method of handling genetic data on the linkage relations of two pairs of genes when the relative positions of those genes in the chromosome are to be determined. What specific fact must be kept in mind?

18. What is a chromosome map? How are chromosome maps made? What is the locus of a gene?

19. Why is it possible to calculate the expected phenotypic ratio in any linkage relationship if the relative positions of the two pairs of genes are known?

20. Does crossing over take place in every organism? Name an organism in which crossing over does not occur.

21. In those organisms in which crossing over is known, does it occur in all the oöcytes? Does crossing over occur in all chromosomes within those oöcytes?

22. Upon the supposition that the behavior is constant in every pair of meiotic chromosomes and chiasmata are present in most pairs of homologous chromosomes, why is crossing over between most pairs of genes restricted to relatively low percentages?

23. Describe the method which Morgan and his associates used in determining the linkage relationship of mutant forms in Drosophila.

24. How is sex determined in Drosophila and many other animals? How many kinds of chromosomes are recognized in animals and in some plants? How do they differ?
25. What is the relation of the kinds of chromosomes to the kinds of linkage? Why is sex linkage easier to recognize than autosomal linkage?
26. Describe a case of crisscross inheritance.
27. What is sex linkage? What is the difference between sex linkage and autosomal linkage?
28. What are **X**-linked genes?
29. What are **Y**-linked genes?
30. What are holandric genes?

Data on Linkage Relationships in Drosophila

The important data on linkage come from genetic experiments in which (1) the percentages of crossing over have been computed and (2) the chromosome maps indicate the relative positions of the pairs of genes; they include the facts (3) that the linkage relations of any specific group of gene pairs are changed by crossing over in only a few of the meiocytes in any single case and (4) that the male Drosophila is one of a few instances in which no crossing over takes place. Reference to the chromosome map in Figure 69, p. 151, and careful study of the topic of calculating linkage relations (pp. 130, 159) are suggested in the solution of these problems.

The following are data on the loci of a few pairs of genes in *Drosophila melanogaster*.

Chromosome I (**X**)

Alleles	locus			phenotypic characters
Y-y at	0.0	conditioning	normal gray $vs.$ mutant-yellow body	
W-w "	1.5	"	" red $vs.$ " -white eyes	
V-v "	33.0	"	" red $vs.$ " -vermilion eyes	
G-g "	44.4	"	" red $vs.$ " -garnet eyes	
Br-br "	57.0	"	mutant-bar $vs.$ normal round eyes	

Chromosome II

B-b at	48.5	"	normal gray $vs.$ mutant-black body	
Pr-pr "	54.5	"	" red $vs.$ " -purple eyes	
Vg-vg "	67.0	"	" long $vs.$ " -vestigial (short) wings	
C-c "	75.0	"	" straight $vs.$ " -curved wings	

Chromosome III

Se-se at	26.0	"	normal red $vs.$ mutant-sepia (brown) eyes	
St-st "	44.0	"	" red $vs.$ " -scarlet eyes	
P-p "	48.0	"	" red $vs.$ " -pink eyes	
E-e "	70.7	"	" gray $vs.$ " -ebony (dark) body	

31. With diagrams and thorough discussion, describe the physical basis for the free assortment of genes. By using diagrams, describe how the two allelic pairs of genes C-c and K-k must be related to the pairs of homologous chromosomes in order that free assortment of these genes occurs (Fig. 63, p. 131).
32. With diagrams and thorough discussion, describe the physical basis of linkage. By using diagrams, describe how the allelic pairs of genes C-c and D-d must be related to homologous chromosomes in order that linkage of these genes may occur. (Fig. 63, p. 131).
33. When Drosophila which show two second-group mutant characters, black body and purple eyes, are mated with homozygous wild-type flies having normal gray bodies and normal red eyes, the F_1 generation all have gray bodies and red eyes. Taking into account the linkage relations of the conditioning genes, determine

the types of gametes the F_1 flies may be expected to form. Will these gametes be equally numerous in each sex or will they occur in some other ratio? What phenotypic ratio may be expected if the F_1 females should be backcrossed to males from the double-recessive black-purple stock of flies? What phenotypic ratio may be expected if the F_1 males are backcrossed (or testcrossed) to females from the double-recessive black-purple stock of flies?   ⁻

34. Assume that a female Drosophila with the mutant character black body and with normal red eyes is mated to a male fly with normal gray body and mutant-type purple eyes. What will be the nature of the F_1 flies in respect to these characters? What types of gametes will these F_1 flies produce? Will they be equally numerous in each sex or will they occur in some other ratio? If F_1 flies, both females and males, are testcrossed by mating to the double-recessive purple-black stock, what phenotypic ratios may be expected? Why is there a difference in these ratios?

35. Assume that purple-eyed flies with black bodies are crossed to the normal homozygous wild type. If the F_1 flies from this cross are mated *inter se*, what phenotypic ratio may be expected? *Note:* It is necessary to consider crossing over and the numerical relations of the F_1 gametes in this problem.

36. In *Drosophila* when flies with mutant-black bodies are mated to flies with mutant-type purple eyes, what will be the nature of the F_1 generation flies with respect to these characters? Assume that the F_1 flies are mated *inter se*. What phenotypic ratio may be expected? What does this ratio indicate? *Note:* Crossing over and the numerical relations of the F_1 gametes must be considered in this problem (pp. 126, 151).

37. A student mated flies with black bodies and vestigial wings to the homozygous wild-type Drosophila. The wild-type F_1 generation was mated *inter se*, $F_1 \times F_1$. The F_2 generation consisted of 271 wild-type flies, 18 flies with gray body and vestigial wings, 16 flies with black body and long wings, and 78 flies with black body and vestigial wings. What does this ratio suggest as to the linkage relations of the characters black and vestigial?

38. When Drosophila which show both the second-group mutant characters black body and vestigial wing are mated with homozygous wild-type flies having normal gray body and normal long wings, the F_1 generation flies are all wild type like their dominant normal parent. What phenotypic ratio may be expected if the F_1 females are mated to double-recessive males with the mutant characters black bodies and vestigial wings?

39. Assume that normal homozygous wild-type flies are mated with flies showing the second-group mutant characters purple eyes and vestigial wings. What would be the phenotype of the F_1 of such a cross? What classes of flies would be expected as a result of backcrossing the F_1 females to males from the double-recessive purple-vestigial stock of flies?

40. When Drosophila showing the third-group mutant characters pink eyes and ebony body are crossed with homozygous wild-type flies with normal red eyes and gray bodies, the F_1 generation will be composed of flies with normal wild-type characters. What phenotypic ratio may be expected if the F_1 generation is mated to the double-recessive pink-ebony stock?

41. Assume that Drosophila with the third-group mutant characters scarlet eyes and ebony body are mated with the homozygous wild-type flies. What eye and body colors would the F_1 generation flies show? What phenotypic ratio could be expected in the F_2 generation?

42. Assume that Drosophila showing the third-group mutant characters sepia (a brown color) eyes and ebony body are mated to homozygous wild-type flies. Disregarding the complications which double crossing over might introduce,

calculate the phenotypic ratio which may be expected in the progeny following the testcross to the double-recessive sepia-ebony stock. Is double crossing over a factor in linkage cases in which the two pairs of genes are widely separated?

43. When Drosphila showing the mutant character sepia eyes and the normal wild-type gray body are mated with flies showing the normal wild-type red eyes and the mutant-ebony body, the F_1 generation is composed of wild-type flies with red eyes and gray bodies. Considering the linkage relations involved, determine the types of gametes which the F_1 females and the F_1 males will produce. In what ratios may these gametes be expected to occur in each sex? What phenotypic ratios may be expected if the F_1 females are backcrossed to males from the double-recessive ebony-sepia stock of flies? What phenotypic ratio may be expected if F_1 males are backcrossed to females from the double-recessive ebony-sepia stock of flies?

44. Consider the phenotypic ratios obtained in problems 40 and 41. Compare them with each other and with the expected backcross ratio when a dihybrid with free assortment of genes is backcrossed to the double recessive.

45. When Drosophila which show the second-linkage-group mutant character vestigial wings and the third-linkage-group character pink eyes are mated with homozygous wild-type flies having normal red eyes and normal long wings, the F_1 generation are all wild-type flies with red eyes and long wings like their normal dominant parent. What phenotypic ratio may be expected if the F_1 females are mated to double-recessive males with the mutant characters pink eyes and vestigial wings?

46. A student made a cross between a homozygous wild-type female and a male with vestigial wings and sepia-colored eyes. He found that the F_1 flies were all wild type. Following the mating of the F_1 flies *inter se*, $F_1 \times F_1$, he had an F_2 generation consisting of 326 wild-type flies, 104 flies with red eyes and vestigial wings, 106 flies with sepia eyes and long wings, and 34 flies with sepia eyes and vestigial wings. When the F_1 generation was testcrossed to the double-recessive sepia-vestigial stock, the progeny consisted of 125 wild type, 129 flies with long wings and sepia eyes, 124 flies with red eyes and vestigial wings, and 123 flies with sepia eyes and vestigial wings. What were the linkage-group relations of the characters under consideration in this experiment?

DATA ON LINKAGE RELATIONSHIPS IN MAIZE

In corn (maize) one pair of the basic complementary-color factors, C-c, conditions colored aleurone in the dominant and colorless aleurone in the homozygous-recessive state. These genes are located at 21 on chromosome IX. The genes Sh-sh condition the endosperm character full endosperm (full grains) and shrunken endosperm in the dominant and recessive states respectively. These genes are located at 24 also on chromosome IX. Considering these data, solve the following problem. (See p. 153).

47. Assume hybridization between varieties of corn as:

Corn producing grains with colored aleurone and full endosperm		Corn producing grains with white aleurone and shrunken endosperm	
C	C	c	c
Sh	Sh	sh	sh

a. What testcross ratio may be expected if the F_1 plants are backcrossed to the double-recessive plants with shrunken endosperm and colorless-aleurone layer?

   b. Considering the fact that there is crossing over in both the female and the male in corn, calculate the expected F_2 ratio following self-pollination of the F_1 plants of this cross.

   c. Why is there a difference between problems a and b above?

48. Review the following aspects of linkage. By using diagrams, explain them. (a) The physical basis of linkage. (b) Complete and incomplete linkage. (c) Exchange of sections of chromatids and genetic crossing over. (d) Sex chromosomes and autosomes. (e) Chromosome numbers and linkage groups. (f) Crossover frequency and its relation to chiasma frequency. (g) Interference with crossing over. (h) Double crossing over. (i) What is a chromosome map? (j) Why are organisms with low numbers of chromosomes preferred for genetical research?

DATA ON SEX LINKAGE

All that has been said concerning crossing over of genes, due to exchange of pieces of chromosomes between synaptic mates, applies equally well to autosomal linkage and sex linkage. There is, however, little or no exchange between most parts of the **X** and **Y** chromosomes. The same general principles concerning location of genes and crossover relationship found for autosomal genes hold true for sex-linked genes on the **X** chromosome. Sex-linked genes are perhaps more easily recognized than autosomal genes because the characters follow the sex. This is because the sex and the sex-linked characters are conditioned by factors located on the same chromosome, namely, on the **X** chromosome. (See data on sex-linked characters, pp. 151, 162). Note that the **Y** chromosome is mostly inert and carries few genes.

49. a. Assume a cross between a female Drosophila with sex-linked white eyes and a wild-type red-eyed male. Genes conditioning these characters are carried in the **X** chromosome. Determine the characters of the F_1 males and females. What ratio may be expected in the F_2 generation?

   b. For the reciprocal cross, assume mating between a female Drosophila with red eyes and a male with white eyes. Compare the characteristics of the male and female F_1 flies with those in the reciprocal cross under problem "a" above. What ratio may be expected in the F_2 generation following mating the F_1 males and females? Compare the F_2 ratios of reciprocal crosses.

50. When a female Drosophila with sex-linked yellow body is crossed with a wild-type male with the normal gray body, the F_1 females are wild-type phenotypes, but the F_1 males have yellow bodies. Compare the reciprocal cross as regards the body colors in the F_1 generation. Compare the F_2 generation in reciprocal crosses in which the F_1 flies of each cross are mated *inter se*.

51. The bar-eye character in Drosophila is conditioned by a dominant sex-linked mutation *Br*. Compare the F_1 and F_2 generations of the reciprocal crosses involving this dominant-mutant character and the normal wild-type round-eye *brbr* which is recessive.

52. Color blindness in man is inherited as a recessive sex-linked character (pp. 162, 484), comparable to that of white eye in the Drosophila. It has been observed that color blindness is much more common in men than in women. Why is this true?

53. Explain why it is impossible for a man to inherit color blindness from his father but possible for him to inherit the defect from his grandfather if that individual was color-blind.

54. The following is an actual situation. Mr. Jones who has normal vision marries Miss Smith who also has normal vision. After taking a course in genetics, Mr. Jones is concerned about the possibility of color blindness in his young son, Robert. It happens that Mr. Smith, Robert's grandfather is completely color-

blind. What are the chances that Robert may inherit the defect? If other children are born in the Jones family, what are the expectations as to their vision? What are the expectations that the Jones children in their turn may transmit color blindness to future generations?

55. When a female with the sex-linked mutant characters yellow body and white eyes is mated with the wild type with normal gray body and red eyes, the F_1 generation flies are of two kinds. Explain. Assume that the heterozygous F_1 females are mated to the double-recessive yellow-bodied white-eyed stock. What testcross ratio may be expected in this case? Considering all the facts about crossing over in the male and female Drosophila, calculate the expected F_2 results if F_1 flies are mated *inter se*, $F_1 \times F_1$.

56. Work out the F_1, F_2, and backcross ratios in the reciprocal of the cross in problem 50.

57. Demonstrate the inheritance of the two sex-linked characters in the Drosophila, yellow-body and vermilion-eye color, in reciprocal crosses. Compare the F_1 generations, the direct cross F_2, and the testcross ratios following mating to the double-recessive stock in these reciprocal crosses.

DATA ON SEX LINKAGE IN FOWLS

Among birds and fowls the males have two **X** chromosomes and the females but one **X** and a **Y**. Thus, the females are the heterogametic sex which is the reverse of the condition characteristic of Drosophila and most mammals. In fowls the well-known color variation *barred* is a dominant sex-linked character. *Barred* is a color pattern consisting of alternating colored and white areas on the feathers (Fig. 78). The barred Plymouth Rock is a breed of fowls in which this trait is well developed.

58. When a male Plymouth Rock homozygous for the barred character is mated to a female from one of the nonbarred colored breeds, the F_1 generation consists entirely of barred fowls because of dominance. What are the expectations for the F_2 generation when the F_1 fowls are mated *inter se?*

59. Assume a cross, reciprocal to that designated in problem 58, in which a barred female is mated to a colored male homozygous for the nonbarred character. What will be the color characteristics of the F_1 generation? Compare these with the F_1 generation of the reciprocal cross in problem 58. What are the expectations for the F_2 generation produced by mating the F_1 fowls *inter se?* In general, how do the ratios from these crosses compare with the reciprocal crosses involving sex-linked characters in the Drosophila? What differences are found in reciprocal crosses involving sex-linked characters in Drosophila and in fowls?

60. What is the difference between a sex-linked character and a sex-limited character? Upon what does each depend? How is each inherited?

References

BATESON, WM.: *Mendel's Principles of Heredity*, Cambridge, England, Cambridge University Press, 1909.

BELLING, J.: "Chromomeres of Liliaceous Plants," *Univ. of Cal. Publ. in Botany* **16**:153–170 (1931).

DARLINGTON, C. D.: *The Evolution of Genetic Systems*, Cambridge, England, Cambridge University Press, 1939.

————: *Recent Advances in Cytology*, Philadelphia, P. Blakiston's Son & Co., Inc., 1937.

MATHER, K.: "Crossing Over," *Biol. Rev. Cambridge Phil. Soc.* **13**:252–292 (1938).

MORGAN, T. H.: *The Physical Basis of Heredity*, Philadelphia, J. B. Lippincott Company, 1919.

———, A. H. Sturtevant, H. J. Muller, and C. B. Bridges: *The Mechanism of Mendelian Heredity*, New York, Henry Holt & Company, Inc., 1922.

SHARP, L. W.: *Introduction to Cytology*, 3rd ed. New York, McGraw-Hill Book Company, Inc., 1934.

STURTEVANT, A. H., and G. W. BEADLE: *An Introduction to Genetics*, Philadelphia, W. B. Saunders Company, 1939.

WADDINGTON, C. H.: *An Introduction to Modern Genetics*, New York, The Macmillan Company, 1939.

Actions and Interactions of Genes in Development of Heritable Characters

Besides the normally expected dominance and recessiveness that typify each pair of alleles, genes have other relationships. Among these is a relationship of genes and environment. Organisms with certain genotypes may react in a definite way in a given environment, while others may respond in an entirely different manner or may be unaffected in such environments. Plants, especially, are subject to external influences. Although not affected as much or as directly as plants by minor changes, animals do respond to external environmental influences and also to their own physiological condition, which in turn may be under genetic control.

Mendel thought the hereditary unit was the determiner of a single visible character. It is now realized that a hereditary unit or *gene acts* to produce *one primary effect* or characteristic *but that it may have several other minor effects.* Conversely, *a single characteristic may be influenced in its development by a single gene* exerting a primary effect which, however, acts within a genetic environment or association of many other genes. The development of a heritable character actually *may be dependent on all of the genes in the organism*, but it may be said that the development of *a trait is conditioned, not definitely determined, by the action or influence of a single gene or a small group of genes.* Since it is impossible to study the entire genotype, consideration is generally restricted to one or to a few genes with the most prominent influence in the development of a trait. In this discussion attention is first given to the action and effects of single genes in special external and internal environments. Then later, the interaction of several genes is considered. In numerous instances the interactions of two or more pairs of definitely nonallelic genes are known. A group of genes of this nature is called a **gene or factor complex.**

177

chapter 9

Action of Genes in Development

The genetic-environmental relationship of genes includes not only the factors of the external environment but also the internal or physiological environment. Certain hormones may alter physiological or cellular environments for the products of gene activity within the animal body. Many physiological functions as well as structural features are certainly under gene control. Some genes, influencing the development of vital structures or physiological processes which may cause the death of the organism, are called lethal genes. Further, there is the action of multiple alleles which result from a series of mutations at one locus in a chromosome. They affect the same character or trait but in each case to a different degree.

Examples of Genetic-environmental Relationships

Environmental conditions often influence the expression and even limit the action of the genotype. Although the genotype cannot act in the absence of suitable environmental factors, the influence of *the environment*, however favorable it may be, *cannot exceed the potentialities of the genotype*. Genes can act only within the limitations imposed by their environment. Conversely, the environment can effect organic changes only within the potentialities of the genotype. Even though genes act to condition the development of hereditary traits and the environment acts to modify them, neither genes nor environment acting alone determine the presence or the absence of characters. Rather, *the trait is the result of an interaction between the hereditary units and the environmental factors.* An excellent example of this relationship is found in maize or Indian corn. One of the color mutations of this plant is known as *sun red*. Among other expressions of the sun-red gene is the development of red pericarp covering the grains. Plants with the sun-red genotype develop red pericarp on grains exposed to sunlight, while covered grains with the same genotype develop colorless pericarp. *Only plants with certain hereditary factors in their genotype behave in this way.* In some plants with other genotypes, red pericarp will be developed in covered ears from which sunlight is excluded, while under the influence of still other genotypes,

179

red pericarp is never developed regardless of the exposure to light. Thus the response of these plants to the environmental conditions of sunlight is definitely dependent upon specific genes in their genotypes.

Certain genotypes conditioning development of chlorophyll, as well as anthocyanin pigments, are also influenced by the external environment. Collins found a strain of barley developing chlorophyll at ordinary growing temperatures but at lower temperatures producing albinic plants due to lack of chlorophyll. This was the expression of a recessive gene at colder temperatures such as prevail in a cold chamber or cold frame in the winter. Only specific strains of barley behave in this way; most kinds of barley continue to produce chlorophyll at temperatures above freezing.

Although apparently not so susceptible to external conditions as plants, animals with certain genotypes also show the influence of environment. In the fruit fly, *Drosophila*, some strains because of their genetic constitution tend to develop an extra pair of legs. This feature is called reduplicated legs. Hoge found an environmental effect on the production of reduplicated legs in Drosophila which had developed from pupae kept at low temperatures. The low temperature was found to be more effective in the production of the abnormality when the developing flies were cooled at early stages.

The influence of cold in modifying the expression of the recessive genotype for albinism and its alleles to be more like the dominant-colored form and of the brown to be like the dominant black in races of rabbits was reported in 1936 by Danneel. Schultz also indicated the possibilities of influencing the production of pigment in white hair of the albino by lowering the temperature of the hair roots.

Penetrance and Expressivity

Experiments such as those discussed above involving interactions between environment and genotypes as well as other phenomena of expressions of genes have led to the conceptions of **penetrance** and **expressivity.** *Penetrance is a statistical concept;* it expresses in percentages the relationship between number of observed phenotypes and number of phenotypes expected from a knowledge of genotypes involved. Schmalhausen has defined penetrance as the "percentage of manifestation" of a mutation. To be recognized in the phenotype, mutations are ordinarily assumed to be expressions of alleles which must be homozygous when they are recessive. The concept of penetrance is usually associated with the phenotypic expressions of dominant genes in heterozygotes and of recessives in homozygotes.

Penetrance is complete when every individual carrying a dominant gene shows the trait it conditions or when every individual homozygous for a recessive gene shows the trait; penetrance is reduced when some individuals fail to have the trait. So far as is known, complete penetrance is shown by genes conditioning the various blood groups in mammals (pp. 494–498). The character abnormal abdomen in Drosophila exemplifies partial or reduced penetrance. About 15 per cent of a population of Drosophila homozygous for the gene determining it shows the character. This then is 15 per cent penetrance.

As explanations for variations in penetrance, varying interactions between genes or between genes and environment have been suggested. Possibly genes showing low penetrance have weak or unstable effects that are easily upset by accompanying modifying genes, while the action of genes with high penetrance is so strong that it is rarely blocked. As indicated elsewhere (pp. 207–224), some modifying genes may strengthen and others reduce or even inhibit the actions of other genes.

Not only may the percentage of individuals that show a trait vary, but there may be variations in the degree of its expression. This phenomenon has been called **expressivity.** One well-known example of variation in expressivity is the character of tremor in fowls. The tremor may be greater in some animals than in others and thus show greater expressivity. A dominant mutant found in a strain of mice protractedly treated with the carcinogen methylcholanthrene shows in its progeny an example of high penetrance with *varied expressivity.* The mutation involves a tail abnormality called pintail, the gene designated as *Pt.* Pintail descendants show variability in tail length and shape. The heterozygotes vary from mice with nearly normal tails to animals with tails lacking twenty or more caudal vertebrae. *Genes may therefore vary in both or either penetrance and expressivity.* Under some circumstances elaborate statistical analyses are needed to distinguish between the expressivity of a genotype and its penetrance. These variations may frequently be involved where unexpected phenotypic ratios occur.

Expression of Genes Influenced by Internal Secretions

In the higher animals glands situated in different parts of the body secrete chemical substances known as **hormones.** The hormones are circulated by the blood or the lymph and have profound effects on growth and development. Disturbed functioning of one or more of these glands results in physiological and structural abnormalities of varying degree. The effects of the secretions of the thyroid and pituitary glands, particularly, are now fairly well recognized. Likewise the sex hormones, secreted by the sex glands, the ovaries and testes, produce general body changes in addition to the commonly recognized sexual characteristics. Among heritable traits influenced by sex hormones are horns in males and their absence in females of some species of animals, distinctive plumage of the sexes in birds and fowls, and the presence of beard in men and the lack of it in women.

INHERITANCE AND DEVELOPMENT OF HORNS IN SHEEP. Some breeds of sheep, as the Dorset (Fig. 82), have well-developed horns in both sexes, but the horns of females are somewhat smaller than those of males. Other breeds, as the Shropshire, Southdown (Fig. 83), Cotswold, and Suffolk, are completely hornless in both sexes. In the Merino

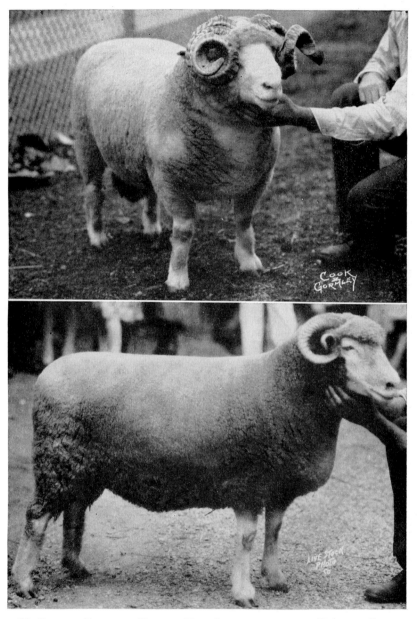

FIG. 82. DORSET RAM AND DORSET EWE ILLUSTRATING THE HORNED CONDITION
IN BOTH SEXES.
(Courtesy, J. R. Henderson, The Continental Dorset Club.)

FIG. 83. SOUTHDOWN RAM AND SOUTHDOWN EWE, HORNLESS IN BOTH SEXES. (Courtesy, W. L. Henning, Secretary, Southdown Breeders Association.)

breed (Fig. 84) males have horns, and females are hornless or have only short knobs in place of horns. The development of horn types has been interpreted as dependent upon a series of three primary horn genes acting under the influences of sex hormones.* The genes involved may be designated: (1) H' is a normally dominant gene of great potency in horn development; $H'H'$ produces well-developed horns in both sexes, as in the Dorset breed, but those of males developed under the stimulating influence of the male sex hormone are larger than those of females. (2) H is a second allele of lesser potency in horn production; HH animals have small horns and these, as in the Merino breed, develop only in males where the genotype acts under the horn-promoting influence of the male sex hormone. (3) The recessive gene of the series is $h;$ with hh genotype both sexes are hornless as in Suffolks, Southdowns, etc. Crosses between the different types of horned animals indicate genetic dominance of H' over H and h, with h recessive to both the other genes. Since F_1 individuals and F_2 ratios differ in the two sexes, it has been assumed that male and female sex hormones in sheep influence the development of horns in the heterozygous animals.

In crosses between the horned Dorset, $H'H'$, and the hornless breed as Suffolk, hh, the F_1 $H'h$ males have horns because of the action of H' under the influence of the male sex hormone in the promotion of horn development. The $H'h$ females, lacking the stimulating hormone, are hornless in the heterozygous state (Fig. 85).

Table XVIII

EFFECT OF INTERNAL SECRETIONS ON PHENOTYPIC EXPRESSION IN SHEEP

F_2 Genotype	Effect of Internal Secretions	Phenotypic Expression In Sheep
$1H'H':2H'h:1hh$	Physiological condition affected by male sex hormones	3 horned, 1 hornless in males
$1H'H':2H'h:1hh$	Physiological condition affected by lack of male sex hormones	1 horned, 3 hornless in females

THE INHERITANCE OF COLOR IN AYRSHIRE CATTLE. A similar case of sex-hormone stimulation is reported in the inheritance of the colors of Ayrshire cattle (Fig. 86). In this breed there are two coat colors, a dark brown called mahogany and a contrasting red with characteristic white markings in each case. The genes M-m condition the development of

---

* In 1940 Castle reviewed the inheritance of horns in sheep. He suggested a simple explanation based upon the action of a series of three allelic genes, H', H, and h, with effects of sex hormones. In this volume designation of the genes has been changed to follow the order customarily used in discussions of multiple allelic genes (pp. 195–199) and differs from that of the original authors.

FIG. 84. CHAMPION DELAINE MERINO RAM AND EWE.
The horned character in the male and the hornless in the female are shown. (Courtesy, Gowdy Williamson, The American and Delaine Merino Record Association.)

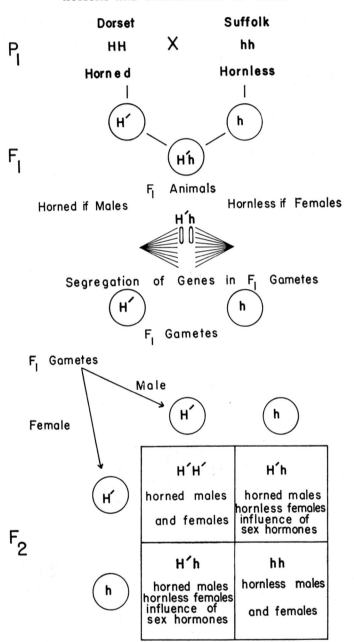

FIG. 85. DIAGRAM OF EFFECTS OF HORMONES IN PRODUCTION OF MENDELIAN
RATIOS.

The F_2 ratio in males is 3 horned : 1 hornless, while in females the ratio is 1 horned :
3 hornless.

FIG. 86. AYRSHIRE CATTLE.
Above, bull showing dark mahogany or brown in colored areas; below, cow showing lighter red in the colored areas. Production of mahogany is stimulated by the male sex hormone. (Courtesy, Cook and Gormley.)

these colors. The genotype MM determines mahogany color in either sex, while mm determines the contrasting red coat in either sex. The mahogany color is promoted by the male sex hormone. Thus, all heterozygous males, Mm, are mahogany color and all heterozygous females, also Mm, are red.

Table XIX

EFFECT OF INTERNAL SECRETIONS ON PHENOTYPIC EXPRESSION IN CATTLE

F_2 Genotype	Effect of Internal Secretions	Phenotypic Expression
$1MM:2Mm:1mm$	Physiological condition affected by male sex hormone	3 mahogany, 1 red in males
$1MM:2Mm:1mm$	Physiological condition affected by lack of male sex hormone	1 mahogany, 3 red in females

OTHER EFFECTS OF HORMONES. Hormones other than sex hormones are also factors in the development of heritable characteristics. In a study with rabbits, Iljin found that the quantity of the hormone of the thyroid gland in the blood changed the quality of the hair in density, length, and color. An optimum amount of thyroid hormone would produce the best quality of fur. Reducing the amount of hormone, as in thyroidectomy, that is, the removal of the thyroid gland, caused a darkening of the hair. Increasing the amount of the hormone caused the hair to become lighter. There were also some temperature effects. Feeding thyroid to rabbits kept at temperatures from 18° to 21° caused dark hair to come in white, while at slightly higher temperatures, depigmentation was less.

Lethal Genes

The very life of any organism is dependent upon the products of hereditary factors which influence basic vital functions. Of necessity, if the species is to survive, such hereditary factors must remain stable from generation to generation. Any changes in the fundamental hereditary basis which seriously interfere with the vital functions of an organism will quickly result in its elimination. Genes which act in such a manner as to cause the death of the individual are termed **lethal,** that is, death-dealing factors. Often their presence may be suspected in populations in which phenotypic ratios vary from the normal. Although death of the organism is generally the most conspicuous and the most important expression of lethal factors, frequently it is not their only effect. Many diverse characteristics of body in animals are influenced by genes in heterozygotes which have a lethal effect in the homozygous state.

Lethal genes usually express themselves early in the life of the embryo, but some of them function at practically any stage of the life cycle of organisms from gametes to maturity. Lethal genes are known which have their effect apparently entirely in the haploid structures. Thus, some lethal genes eliminate a portion of the gametes if they occur in the gametic complement of genes. Many plants carry lethal genes which cause pollen grains or pollen tubes to become functionless and result in male sterility. Their presence has been demonstrated in numerous cases of abnormal phenotypic ratios as in the evening primrose, *Oenothera*. In maize, Beadle reported 15 genes which condition degeneration of the microsporocytes or of the pollen grains. Heilborn, from a study of pollen sterility in certain apple varieties, concluded that the abortion of pollen grains in many of these diploid apples depends on lethal gene combinations. Buchholz and Blakeslee reported a gene which conditions the bursting of a high percentage of pollen tubes within the styles of some varietal Datura hybrids and proposed this explanation for the deficiency of recessive phenotypes.

Other lethal genes indicate their presence by unfavorable developments in the diploid structures, generally early in the embryonic stages. Instances are known, however, in which death due to the action of lethal genes does not ensue until later stages. Some of the known lethal genes show their effects only in the homozygous state, but Mangelsdorf's investigations of some of them in corn indicate a weakening effect even in the heterozygous state. Though full dominance of the lethal genes tends to result in the complete destruction of any stock carrying them, dominant lethal genes have been discovered in organisms which have been carefully analyzed.

LETHAL GENES IN PLANTS. Genes conditioning the development of chlorophyll or its lack in plants include excellent examples of lethal genes. Since production of carbohydrates depends upon the presence of chlorophyll, genes which condition the lack of chlorophyll may have lethal effects. Some strains of the cultivated snapdragon, *Antirrhinum majus*, produce a yellowish-green type of plant called *golden* as well as fully green plants (Fig. 87). If the genes G-g condition the contrasting characters normal green and non-

Table XX

LETHAL GENES IN SNAPDRAGONS

		Golden × Golden		
	Heterozyous Gg		Gg Heterozygous	
Genotype :	GG :	Gg	: Gg :	gg
Phenotype : 1 green :		2 golden	: 1 yellow dies	

green (or yellow), the heterozygous golden plants will have the genetic constitution Gg. Following hybridization of two heterozygous golden plants, $Gg \times Gg$, or selfing of a golden plant, Gg, the resulting genotypic ratio is expected to be 1:2:1. However, since the members of one class of homozygous plants, the yellow seedlings, gg, die because of lack of chlorophyll, the final living phenotypic ratio is two golden plants, *Gg*, to one green, *GG*, a 2:1 phenotypic ratio resulting from the lethal effect of the genotype *gg*. Lethal genes of this type exist only in the heterozygous state and are transmitted only by heterozygous plants as the golden, *Gg*, type of snapdragon.

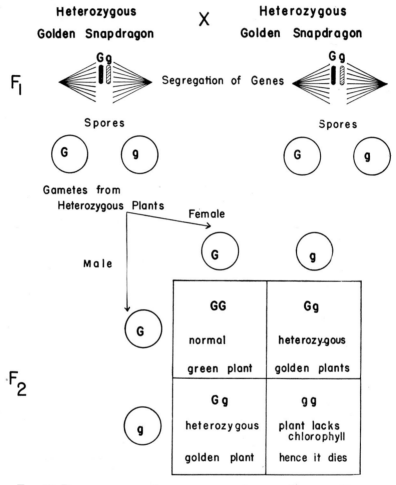

FIG. 87. DIAGRAM OF THE INHERITANCE OF LETHAL GENES IN PLANTS.

Chlorophyll deficiencies are very common in plants. In corn, especially, a large number of genes is known to influence chlorophyll development, and some of them are lethal (Fig. 88). Inherited chlorophyll deficiencies have been reported in sorghum and in rice in which two types of deficient plants, yellow and white, were found. Some mutations of genes affecting the development of chlorophyll do not completely inhibit its production and are not necessarily lethal. Mutations may reduce the amount of chlorophyll in the cells or may affect its distribution in the tissues. Plants showing various

FIG. 88. ALBINO AND GREEN SEEDLINGS OF ZEA MAYS IN GREENHOUSE AT BUCKNELL
UNIVERSITY.
(Courtesy, C. E. Knopf.)

degrees of yellowing or variegation may develop enough chlorophyll for
survival.

LETHAL GENES IN ANIMALS. Numerous cases of lethal genes
have been reported in animals. Besides those found in the fruit fly, *Drosophila*, lethals have been reported in cattle, fowls, and other animals, including man.

LETHALITY IN YELLOW MICE. One of the earliest observations of lethal
genes in animals was reported by Cuénot in yellow mice and later confirmed
by Castle and Little. Yellow mice never bred true for color and always
produced smaller litters than other mice. Offspring were found to occur in
the unexpected ratio of 2 yellow:1 black, with no true-breeding yellow
types. Investigation of the embryonic development of yellow and normal
mice revealed that a certain proportion of zygotes of yellow mice failed to
survive the time of implantation in the uterus.

It is assumed that the genes Y-y are involved in the development of
yellow and black mice.* The Y gene has two effects. One conditions the
development of yellow coat in mice. The second is a lethal effect in homozygous YY embryos. The heterozygous state, Yy, produces living yellow mice.

* Actually these genes are members of the agouti multiple allelic series and are
properly designated as $A^y - a$ (p. 199).

Mice with yy, are black. In 1942 Robertson reported on his investigations of histological and physiological effects of the Y gene. According to this study, the specific effect of the gene is to stop enzyme activity in homozygous YY embryos at about the fifth day of their development. As a result, these embryos die and disintegrate. The proportion of zygotes lost was approximately that expected in the missing homozygotic class. No such loss was found in normal mice used as checks.

Table XXI

LETHAL GENES IN MICE

F_2 Genotype	YY	Yy Yy	yy
Color relationship	unknown	2 yellow	1 black
Lethal effect	1 dies	3 survive	

LETHALITY IN DEXTER CATTLE. An instance of lethal factors in cattle is found in the Dexter breed of the British Islands. The Dexter is a breed of small-sized cattle which originated by mutation from the Kerry, a breed of normal size. When Dexter is mated to Dexter, the offspring consist of one malformed embryo which is called "bulldog" on account of its facial deformities and is always born dead, two typical Dexters, and one normal-sized individual of the Kerry breed. This behavior is explained on the assumption that the Dexters are heterozygous, Dd, for a pair of factors which have a lethal effect in the homozygous condition, dd (Fig. 89). The normal-sized Kerry can be interpreted as being the homozygous dominant, DD.

LETHALITY IN CREEPER FOWLS. The creeper type of fowls, so called because of the creeping type of locomotion necessitated by the characteristically short legs and wings, never breeds true. The result of mating creeper × creeper is the production of two classes of fowls, in the ratio of two creepers to one normal. As in the yellow mice, there is a deficiency in the number of individuals in the creeper class with a percentage of the eggs always failing to hatch.

Landauer, when he investigated the embryonic development in eggs produced by mating creeper × creeper fowls, found that about one-fourth of the eggs showed embryos with definitely arrested development. Apparently in most of these eggs, the embryos ceased developing about 72 hours after incubation had started. In rare instances very poorly developed embryos were found alive until nearly hatching time. In these, the extremities showed arrested development compared with normal embryos. The genetics of the creeper fowl may be interpreted on the basis of the action of a single pair of factors, Cp-cp (Table XXII).

Table XXII

LETHAL GENES IN CREEPER FOWLS

	Creeper × Creeper		
	Heterozygous *Cpcp*		*Cpcp* Heterozygous
Genotype	*CpCp*	*Cpcp* *Cpcp*	*cpcp*
Phenotype	1 dies	2 creeper	1 normal

Evidently the genes concerned in the development of Dexter cattle and creeper fowls condition skeletal characteristics. In one homozygous class the skeleton is so imperfectly developed that the individuals die, while in

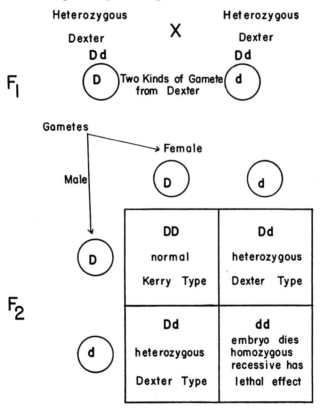

FIG. 89. DIAGRAM OF INHERITANCE OF A PAIR OF LETHAL GENES IN THE KERRY-DEXTER BREED OF CATTLE.

the other homozygous class the skeleton is normal. Since the genes are incompletely dominant, the members of the heterozygous class appear with partially developed, defective skeletons and are thus intermediate between the extremely defective, nonviable homozygous and the normal homozygous classes.

Table XXIII

HEREDITARY LETHAL AND SUBLETHAL CHARACTERS

Organism	Evidence of Defect	Author	Year
Cattle	Hairless and amputated	Mohr & Wriedt	1928
Drosophila	⎧Lethal ⎨Cell lethal ⎩Decreased fertility in females	Demerec & Hoover	1936
Horse	Intestinal malformation	Yamane	1927
Maize	Defective seeds	Jones	1920
Cattle	Short spine	Mohr & Wriedt	1930
Mouse	Dominant spotting	Keeler	1931
Dog	Paralysis	Stockard	1930
Fowl	Embryonic abnormalities	Upp	1934
Barley	Lethal	Wiebe	1934
Rice	Chlorophyll deficiency	Codd	1935
Cotton	Chlorophyll deficiency	Bizzell	1925
Matthiola	Gametic lethal	Kuhn	1935
Maize	Dormancy and premature germination	Mangelsdorf	1930
⎧Dark ⎨Cornish ⎩Fowl	Shortening of long bones	Landauer	1935

LETHALITY IN VARIOUS ORGANISMS.   Lethal factors continue
to be found in a variety of organisms where they are often carried in the
heterozygous state as recessives. Any breeding program which uses inbreeding, or mating of closely related organisms, tends to increase the homozygosity of the hereditary units. In some cases the heterozygous recessive lethal
genes may be segregated as homozygous recessives and may manifest their
lethality. A number of lethal genes has been found in domestic animals and
cultivated plants.

Table XXIV

NUMBER OF LETHAL FACTORS KNOWN IN COMMON FARM ANIMALS

Hutt, 1934	Lerner, 1944
Cattle 11	Cattle 25
Horses 2	Horses 7
Swine 4	Swine 9
Sheep 6	Sheep 7
Fowls 5	Fowls 19
Ducks 1	Ducks 1
	Turkeys 2

LETHAL GENES IN HUMAN BEINGS.   There is growing evidence
that mutant genes with lethal effects occur in human beings. Numerous

unusual cases of fatal abnormalities in man are attributed to so-called sublethal genes. Such genes permit life to continue for a period but cause developments which sooner or later terminate fatally. Among these are a recessive nervous ailment expressing itself in night blindness; the development of leatherlike skin, *Ichthyosis congenita*, which is attended by the formation of cancerous growths usually fatal by the twelfth year; an infantile hereditary form of spinal progressive muscle atrophy; homozygous *spina bifida;* and possibly homozygous hemophilia. Certain types of dwarfism in man apparently are comparable to the conditions found in Dexter cattle and creeper fowls.

Multiple Alleles

In rodents, cats, other animals, and in some plants, there are groups of genetically related color variations. Rabbits show the full-colored types

A   Normal Wild   B   Chinchilla

C   Himalayan   D   Albino

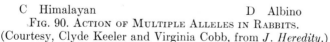
.FIG. 90. ACTION OF MULTIPLE ALLELES IN RABBITS.
(Courtesy, Clyde Keeler and Virginia Cobb, from *J. Heredity.*)

black, brown, the well-known gray or *agouti,* and the pink-eyed albino, which entirely lacks pigments usually present in eyes and fur of the colored animals. The complete albino type is found in a breed known as the Polish. Besides the full-colored types and the albino mutation, there are some intermediate color variations in this series. One kind of rabbit called chinchilla is a light or silver gray (Fig. 90) as distinguished from the ordinary dark-gray rabbit. Among chinchilla types the variations are of three heritable types, dark, intermediate, and light. Another variation in colored forms is the Himalayan, which approaches the albino in being white with pink eyes but has some colored points.

Crossing among these animals indicates that any color is dominant to the albino and that there is a regular sequence of dominance and recessiveness in which the more deeply colored types are dominant to those of lighter or less color, as follows.

DOMINANT TYPES	RECESSIVE TYPES	F_1 GENERATION	F_2 RATIO
Any full-colored type, black, brown, or gray	× chinchilla, silver gray	all full-colored	3 full-colored: 1 chinchilla
chinchilla, silver gray	× Himalayan, white with black points	all chinchilla	3 chinchilla: 1 Himalayan
Himalayan, white with black points	× albino, entirely white with pink eyes	all Himalayan	3 Himalayan: 1 albino
albino	× albino	all albino	all albino

The above crosses, all yielding an F_2 ratio of 3:1, indicate that the difference between any two types is determined by a single pair of allelic genes. Since crosses between any two of the types yield the 3:1 ratio, there is indication of an allelic relationship between all of the various pairs of genes differentiating the color types.

ALLELES OF THE BASIC-COLOR GENE.   It may be recalled that in rabbits and other rodents color and albinism are determined by the pair of allelic genes C-c. Colored rabbits of all types carry the genes CC, or Cc, in their genotypes, and the albino variation carries cc. Full coloration in normal or wild-type animals is determined by the dominant gene C. The albino type arose as a mutation, that is, a modification or change in the gene C to form a new gene, c. The mutant gene, c, and the normal gene, C, then are alleles. *There may be further mutations at any given locus in a chromosome.* A gene may *mutate a second* time, forming three genes that are allelic, or it may *mutate several* or many times, thus forming a series known as multiple alleles. The term **multiple allelism** designates the concept of multiple alleles. Dawson and Whitehouse in England propose the term **panallele** to cover all gene mutations at a given locus in a chromosome. Genes determining this whole color series in the rabbits, the three shades of chinchilla, the Himalayan, and the albino thus arose as mutations of the basic-color gene C and are all allelic one to another.

Only one gene can exist at any one locus of a chromosome; its allele is carried at the identical locus in the other member of the pair of homologous chromosomes. For this reason any diploid organism may carry any two genes, but no more than two, of a multiple allelic series. The genes of a multiple allelic series are similar in two distinct ways, (1) they are all allelic one with another because they arose at the same locus by mutation and (2) they all influence the development of the same characteristic but in slightly different ways and generally to a different degree.

Although they affect the same trait, the various genes of an allelic series are characterized by different manifestations or degree of influence in the development of the trait. As Sturtevant says, they are carrying on the same function but with varying degrees of efficiency. Or on the analogy of a lock and key, they are keys to the same lock but the different keys of the same series do not fit equally well.

In the development of colors, genes act in some way to control the various steps in a chemical reaction (Chapter 21). Perhaps each gene forms an enzyme that promotes or influences a particular step, possibly an oxidation reaction, in a complicated chemical process. Production of color in the hair of animals is the result of several distinct steps in a chemical process. Each of the various genes C, c^{ch}, c^H, c influences some or all of the reaction steps to produce one of the color types of the series. Apparently the dominant gene C, at the head of the multiple allelic series, can form the necessary enzyme to carry on the essential reaction step or steps in the chemical process leading to full coloration. The action of the c^{ch} gene determines the production of some color in the fur. The chinchilla rabbit has white-tipped hairs in the fur and eyes which are red (not pink as in the albino). The white-tipped fur gives chinchillas a silver-gray color in contrast with the dark gray of the wild rabbit which has black-tipped hairs in the fur. Three distinct types of chinchilla rabbit have been found, dark, intermediate, and pale. The genes controlling the three types are c^{ch1}, c^{ch2}, and c^{ch3}, respectively. The chinchilla genes 1–3 may be thought of as being less efficient in pigment formation than the dominant C gene. The Himalayan rabbit, with white fur and pink eyes, approaches the complete albino but differs from it chiefly in having colored hair on the extremities, the feet, ears, and generally the nose and tail. These colored points distinguish the Himalayan from a true albino. The Himalayan gene c^H acts with less efficiency than the chinchilla gene c^{ch} but with greater efficiency in pigment production than the albino gene c, that determines absence of color. The basic-color genes in rabbits occur in a multiple allelic series of six forms:

C—determining full color
c^{ch1}—determining dark chinchilla
c^{ch2}—determining intermediate chinchilla
c^{ch3}—determining pale chinchilla
c^H—determining Himalayan
c—determining complete albinism.

SEGREGATION AND RECOMBINATION OF MULTIPLE ALLELES. Since a normal gamete carries one member of a multiple allelic series, the union of two gametes brings only two genes of an allelic series together in the diploid zygote. These two members may be any possible combination of the genes of the series. The other members of the allelic series may be found in various combinations, one or two kinds in other individuals.

In earlier discussions of Mendelian principles, it was shown that an F_2 generation was composed of homozygous-dominant, heterozygous, and homozygous-recessive individuals (pp. 48–66). Following a cross between a full-colored black rabbit, CC, and the Polish complete albino, cc, the F_1 is Cc and the F_2 $1CC:2Cc:1cc$. The principles of segregation and recombination underlying the production of this ratio would be applicable to crosses between any other two types of that series. A cross between the Himalayan white rabbit, $c^H c^H$, and the complete albino, cc, will produce an F_1 with the genotype $c^H c$. The F_2 will consist of $1c^H c^H : 2c^H c : 1cc$. Similarly, a cross between chinchilla rabbit, $c^{ch}c^{ch}$, and the Himalayan white, $c^H c^H$, will produce an F_1 with the genotype $c^{ch}c^H$. The F_2 following this cross will consist of $1c^{ch}c^{ch} : 2c^{ch}c^H : 1c^H c^H$. Crosses involving the allelic types of any other allelic series behave genetically in a similar manner. The appearance of the F_1 and F_2 individuals will depend upon the degree of dominance, complete or partial, of the genes involved in each case.

COLOR-GENE ALLELES IN THE CAT. Mutation of the basic-color gene to form a multiple allelic series has occurred in the cat, where some of the color variations are similar to those in rabbits. In cats full coloration, as

FIG. 91. DOMESTIC CATS SHOWING EFFECTS OF MULTIPLE ALLELES.
(Courtesy, Clyde Keeler and Virginia Cobb; modified after Edwin Gray, from *J. Heredity*.)

in the Persian black and other black breeds, is determined by the dominant basic-color gene C. There is a type known as silver or smoke, $c^{ch}c^{ch}$, which corresponds closely to chinchilla of rabbits. Besides these there is an albinistic type known as the Siamese breed, $c^{H}c^{H}$. This near albino has a white coat with some slight pigmentation in the hair over the body. It has darkly pigmented feet, tail tip, ears, and face. The eyes show only a little red (not pink). The Siamese cat corresponds to the Himalayan white in rabbits (Fig. 91). The multiple allelic series of the color genes in cats consists of four alleles of the basic-color gene, each determining a variation. In the order of decreasing pigmentation, these color variations are:

full coloration, C —expressed in the tabby and black
silver or smoke, c^{ch}—expressed in a rather uniform reduction in color
Burmese, c^{B} —expressed in further reduction in color
Siamese, c^{H} —expressed in a type approaching the albino, white coat.

A possible variation between Burmese and Siamese has been described by L. Volk.

DESIGNATION OF THE MEMBERS OF A MULTIPLE ALLELIC SERIES. With the discovery of multiple alleles in diverse organisms, investigators have used several different ways of designating the members of the series. As shown in the series in rabbits and cats, the gene designation often indicates the characteristic determined. With C indicating color and c lack of color, genes intermediate in the series are designated c^{ch}, indicating chinchilla, and c^{H}, Himalayan. In other examples of multiple allelism, the designation of the genes of the series is by figures following the gene initial as a-1, a-2, a-3, etc., or by letters as m-a, m-b, m-c, etc., in the order of their discovery in each case.

MULTIPLE ALLELISM IN OTHER ORGANISMS. Besides the examples mentioned in rabbits and cats, multiple allelism has been found in numerous other mammals, in insects, and in plants. The basic principles are the same in all cases and need not be further discussed. Among the numerous series known, the following may be cited.

The agouti alleles in mice:

A^{y}, the lethal yellow gene
A, the agouti gene determining gray
A^{w}, the white-belly agouti or gray
A^{t}, the black and tan
a, the nonagouti or nongray.

Multiple allelism in domestic animals:
black, black and tan in dogs; dun, palomino, and bay in horses are probably alleles; blood groups in cattle are determined by multiple alleles with possibly as many as 80 different alleles in the series determining blood-cell characteristics; blood types of human beings are well-known examples of multiple allelisms (see section on human heredity).

The multiple allelic series in the Drosophila:
At 1.5 on the **X** chromosome, the locus of the gene determining white eye in the fruit fly, there is an extensive series of multiple alleles:

W, conditioning wild-type red-eye color
w^a, apricot
w^c, coral
w^e, eosin and many others to
w, determining white eye.

Multiple allelism in plants:
Of the numerous instances of multiple allelic series in plants, pericarp colors in Indian corn or maize have been carefully studied by Anderson. The genes of the allelic series influence pericarp color of the grains and cob color of the ear. Some of the designations are:

p^{rr}, determining red cob and red pericarp
p^{wr}, determining red cob and colorless pericarp
p^{ww}, determining white cob and white pericarp with several
      others included.

Questions and Problems

1. What are hereditary factors? What are environmental factors? Why are both types of factors essential in the development of the characteristics of living organisms?
2. What environmental factors appear to influence the production of color in plants? Is it possible to disregard heredity completely in accounting for the development of color in plants?
3. Indicate the influence of changes in temperature in the production of color in the coats of animals.
4. What are hormones in animals?
5. What experimental evidence is there to indicate the influence of the thyroid hormone on the fur of animals?
6. What do you understand by the term *lethal gene?* How do lethal genes originate?
7. At what stage in the life cycle do lethal genes generally manifest themselves? Are they known at any other stages? Which ones?
8. What is a common effect of lethal genes in plants? Why do genes conditioning the lack of chlorophyll have a lethal effect in plants? At what stage in the life cycle of the plant does death result from chlorophyll deficiency?
9. At what stages in the life cycle of individuals do the lethal genes manifest themselves in Dexter cattle, yellow mice, and creeper fowls?
10. Are lethal genes regarded as of frequent occurrence in domestic animals and in man? Are they numerous in experimental organisms? Cite some instances.
11. Assuming a simple explanation based upon a single pair of genes, H'-h, demonstrate the F_1 and F_2 results following crosses between the horned and the hornless breeds of sheep. By the use of diagrams and discussion, show the relation of the sex hormones to the production of horns and hornlessness in sheep.
12. By the use of diagrams and discussion, indicate the relation of the sex hormones to the production of red and mahogany brown in the colored areas of Ayrshire cattle following crosses between mahogany and red.
13. Diagram and explain the results which may be expected when two heterozygous golden snapdragons are hybridized. What ratio may be expected in the immediate progeny? Explain the result based upon the action of the factors. Note that the parents in this case are heterozygous.

14. By diagrams and discussion, explain the results of mating two yellow mice. Emphasize the action of the genes. Note that in this case the parents are heterozygous.
15. By diagrams and discussion, explain the results of mating male and female Dexter cattle. Emphasize the action of the genes.
16. By diagrams and discussion, explain the results of mating male and female creeper fowls. Emphasize the action of the factors.

DATA ON MULTIPLE ALLELES

Certain colors in rabbits are conditioned by an allelic series of the basic-color genes. These are:

C, the dominant gene conditioning full coloration as black
c^{ch1}, dark chinchilla
c^{ch2}, intermediate chinchilla
c^{ch3}, pale chinchilla
c^{H}, Himalayan albino
c, complete albino, known as the Polish breed.

17. Describe phenotypic types and ratios expected in the F_1 and F_2 generation of the following direct crosses between homozygous rabbits:

black × albino	Himalayan × albino
dark chinchilla × Himalayan	dark chinchilla × albino
black × Himalayan	dark chinchilla × pale chinchilla.

18. Describe the results expected in the immediate progeny of the following crosses:

$Cc \times cc$	$c^{ch1}c^{H} \times c^{ch1}c^{H}$
$Cc^{ch1} \times cc$	$c^{ch1}c^{H} \times cc$
$Cc^{ch1} \times Cc^{H}$	$c^{ch1}c \times c^{H}c.$

19. Where are some of the most extensive series of multiple alleles found?
20. How many genes of a multiple allelic series may a normal haploid gamete carry?
21. How many genes of a multiple allelic series may a normal diploid organism carry if it is homozygous? If heterozygous?
22. Describe some of the phenotypic effects of multiple allelic genes in the various organisms in which they are known.
23. What is the dominant-recessive relationship in a multiple allelic series?

References

ARKELL, T. R.: *Some Data on the Inheritance of Horns in Sheep.* (New Hampshire Agricultural Experiment Station #160) Concord, 1912.

BAUR, E., E. FISCHER, and F. LENZ: *Human Heredity,* New York, Macmillan Company, 1931.

CASTLE, W. E., and C. C. LITTLE: "On a Modified Mendelian Ratio Among Yellow Mice," *Science* **32**:868–870 (1910).

KEMPTON, J. H.: "A Dominant Lethal Chlorophyll Mutation in Maize," *J. Agr. Research* **XXIX**:307–309 (1924).

LANDAUER, W., and L. C. DUNN: "Studies on the Creeper Fowl," *Genetics* **23**:397–413 (1930).

SCHMALHAUSEN, I. I.: *Factors of Evolution,* Philadelphia, The Blakiston Company, 1949.

SINNOTT, EDMUND W., L. C. DUNN, and TH. DOBZHANSKY: *Principles of Genetics,* 4th ed. New York McGraw-Hill Book Company, Inc., 1950, Chapters IV, V.

chapter 10

Interaction of Genes in Development—Complementary and Supplementary Actions

As a background for this discussion, Mendelian heredity may be briefly reviewed under two headings:

I. THE PHYSICAL BASIS OF HEREDITY. Mendel formulated the fundamental idea of independent hereditary units existing in pairs. Without actual knowledge of the chromosomes and their behavior during meiosis and fertilization, he offered an explanation of heredity based upon a hypothesis of the segregation, assortment, and recombination of independent determiners. His explanation essentially anticipated knowledge of the actual chromosome behavior at critical points in the life cycle of organisms. The fundamental features of Mendelian principles of heredity are: (*1*) *relatively constant hereditary units or genes, occurring in pairs,* (*2*) *independent segregation of the members of each pair of genes,* and (*3*) *recombination of the hereditary units at fertilization.* These principles remain permanent foundation stones of all modern theories of heredity. The physical basis is continuously operative and must be taken into account in all such studies.

II. THE ACTION AND INTERACTION OF THE GENES. *A dominant-recessive relationship exists between the members of each pair of allelic genes.* Dominance may be complete in some instances and only partial or incomplete in others. The dominant and recessive relationship is fundamental and essentially constant with each pair of genes, regardless of the possible interactions of the genes of one pair with the members of other pairs of alleles. Mendel knew only the simpler aspects of gene action. It has, therefore, been necessary to expand the original conception of the determining action of genes in order to interpret new data properly. Investigations since Mendel's time have indicated that *genes have diverse actions* and that *there may be interaction between members of several different pairs of alleles.*

Inheritance of Flower Color in the Sweet Pea—Genes with Complementary Action

Bateson, the British geneticist, was the first to report a case of a dihybrid ratio which did not conform to Mendelian expectations. He had in his cultures two true-breeding white-flowered varieties of sweet peas which differed in the shape of the pollen grains, one producing spherical and the other ovoid pollen grains. In hybridizing these two white-flowered varieties of sweet peas, incident to a study of the inheritance of shape in pollen grains, Bateson found to his astonishment that the F_1 hybrid plant produced colored flowers. The F_2 generation consisted of two phenotypic classes, colored- and white-flowered, in the ratio of 9:7, which was a modification of the expected dihybrid F_2 ratio of 9:3:3:1 (Fig. 92). Bateson assumed different genotypes in the two white-flowered plants, one with the dominant genes *CC*, the other with the dominant alleles of a second pair, *RR*, and each variety with the alternate homozygous recessive. The full genotypes for the parent varieties were *CCrr* and *ccRR*, respectively, and for the F_1 hybrid between them, *CcRr*. It was further assumed that the genes *C* and *R* *interact* and that *the presence of both is essential for the production of color* in the flowers. This type of interaction is called *complementary action*, that is, the action of each gene complements or completes the action of the other. *C* and *R* may be regarded as basic-color genes with complementary action. Complementary action, however, is not restricted to basic-color genes but may occur in any type of gene.

Inheritance of Aleurone Color in Corn Grains

East and Hayes, working on inheritance of characteristics of Indian corn, reported a similar type of inheritance of color in the aleurone layer of the seeds. In hybridizations between two varieties of white-grained maize or between plants with red aleurone and some varieties of white corn, the F_2 ratio was 9 colored:7 white grains, rather than the 9:3:3:1 ratio expected in dihybrids. The aleurone colors in maize, like the flower colors in sweet peas, were assumed to be dependent upon the interaction of two pairs of basic genes, *C-c* and *R-r*, with the *two dominant alleles having complementary action*. When the dominant genes *C* and *R* are together in a genotype, color in the aleurone layer of the grains is produced. When the homozygous recessive of either pair is present in the genotype, as *cc* or *rr*, *no color* is developed in the aleurone tissue.

Crossing a variety of corn, *CCRR*, with colored grains and a variety, *ccrr*, with white grains resulted in the development of F_1 plants, *CcRr*. Segregation and assortment of the two pairs of genes *C-c* and *R-r* resulted in the production of four types of megaspores and microspores and eventually gametes *CR*, *cR*, *Cr*, and *cr*. Following self-pollination, the genes were recombined at fertilization according to Mendelian expectations, but because of the *complementary action* of the genes *C* and *R*, the F_1 plant yielded colored and white grains in the ratio of 9 colored to 7 white.* Crossing other varieties

---

* It should be emphasized that the aleurone layer in the corn grain is a seed tissue. As such it shows segregation in the seeds produced by the F_1 plant (pp. 42, 86). Such seeds are F_2.

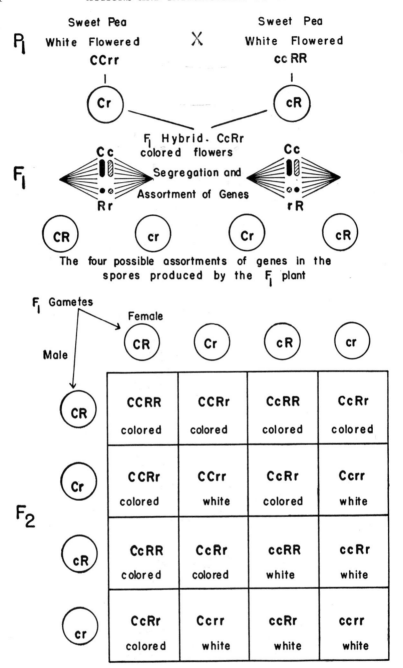

FIG. 92. DIAGRAM OF INTERACTION OF BASIC COMPLEMENTARY FACTORS
CONDITIONING COLOR IN FLOWERS OF THE SWEET PEA.

of corn which both produced *white* grains, such as $CCrr \times ccRR$, gave comparable results. The F_1 plants having the genotype $CcRr$ also yielded grains in the ratio of 9 colored to 7 white.

Later, Emerson, who was investigating the gene complex underlying the production of aleurone colors in corn, found that at least three pairs of basic factors with complementary action are concerned in production of

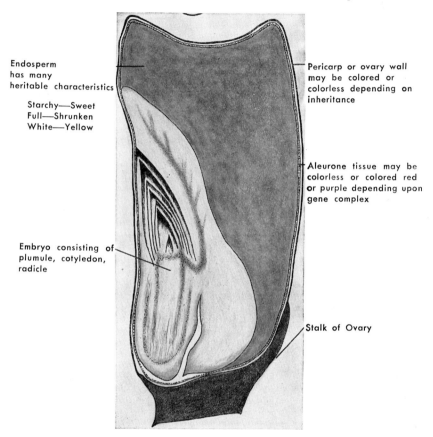

Endosperm has many heritable characteristics

Starchy—Sweet
Full—Shrunken
White—Yellow

Pericarp or ovary wall may be colored or colorless depending on inheritance

Aleurone tissue may be colorless or colored red or purple depending upon gene complex

Embryo consisting of plumule, cotyledon, radicle

Stalk of Ovary

FIG. 93. DIAGRAM OF A SECTION THROUGH A CORN GRAIN.
(Modified after L. F. Randolph.)

colored aleurone in grains of corn (Fig. 93 and 94). These three genes are the C-c and R-r gene pairs, which had been previously discovered, and a third pair of genes, A-a. Further investigation has revealed the presence of additional alleles which also act as complementary genes in the complex. The dominant members of the three gene pairs must all be present in the genotype in order that any color may be developed in the aleurone layer of the grain. Colored aleurone is thus produced by the complementary interaction of the dominant members of three pairs of basic genes. An F_1 trihybrid plant, *AaCcRr*, will undergo segregation and assortment, eventually leading to the production of eight types of both male and female gametes. These types are *ACR*, *ACr*, *AcR*, *Acr*, *aCR*, *aCr*, *acR*, and *acr*. Following self-pollination of the F_1 plants, recombination will occur at fertilization,

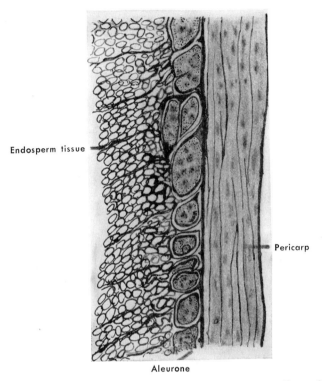

Endosperm tissue

Pericarp

Aleurone

FIG. 94. A SECTION THROUGH OUTER PORTION OF A CORN GRAIN.

Shown are the position of tissues, pericarp, endosperm, and aleurone, a single layer of cells forming outer layer of endosperm tissue. In colored corn grains, the yellow carotenoid pigments are located in the endosperm cells and the purple and red pigments in the aleurone layer. Red pigments found in the pericarp constitute the pericarp colors. (Modified after L. F. Randolph, from *J. Agr. Research.*)

and interaction of the three pairs of basic complementary genes will result in the production of colored and white grains in the modified F_2 trihybrid ratio of 27 colored:37 white (Fig. 95).

Summary of Complementary Genes

Certain plant colors characteristic of flowers and other structures are conditioned not by a single pair of determiners but by two or more pairs of basic genes. The nature of these genes is such that neither one acting alone can produce color. Representatives of both pairs, usually the dominant members, must be present in a genotype in order that their interaction may condition the production of color. Genes of this nature are said to have complementary action, that is, each completes the action of the other. The *interaction of two pairs of genes with complementary action* results in the modification of the expected dihybrid ratio of 9:3:3:1 to a 9:7 ratio in the

FIG. 95. SEGREGATION OF COLORED AND COLORLESS ALEURONE IN CORN.
   Top, segregation due to the action of one pair of genes, as *A-a.* This ear shows colored grains and white grains in approximately a 3:1 ratio. *Center,* segregation due to interaction of two pairs of complementary genes, as *AaCc.* Because of the complementary interaction, the ratio is approximately 9 colored to 7 white grains. *Bottom,* segregation of three pairs of complementary genes, as *AaCcRr.* This interaction results in the production of colored and white grains in the ratio of 27 colored to 37 white. (Specimens courtesy, George Carter, Clinton, Connecticut.)

F_2 generation. *Three pairs of genes with complementary action* yield a 27:37 F_2 phenotypic ratio (Fig. 96).

Interaction of Genes—Supplementary Actions

   Among the great variety of characteristics exhibited by cultivated plants and animals, colors are readily observed. Sweet peas may produce red, blue, or purple flowers in a range of coloration from dark or intense to dilute. The red or purple of the aleurone tissue of maize may likewise show varying degrees of intensity. Variations of color in plants result from the interaction of additional genes with the basic-color genes.

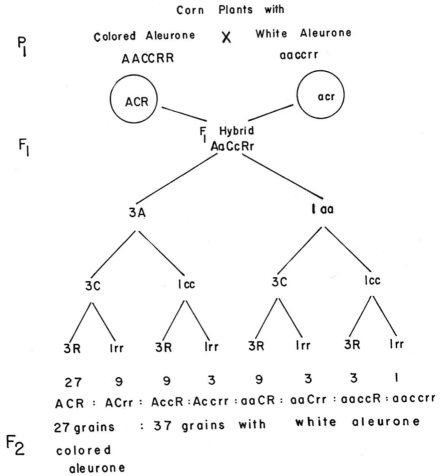

FIG. 96. DIAGRAM OF INDEPENDENT SEGREGATION, ASSORTMENT, AND RECOMBINATION OF THE BASIC-COLOR GENES "A-a," "C-c," AND "R-r" DETERMINING ALEURONE COLOR IN CORN.

Assumption of complete dominance in each factor pair is indicated by the figure 3 before each *A*, *C*, and *R*. Multiplication of the terms indicates recombinations in the products. All genotypes lacking one of the dominant genes condition plants with white grains. The 27 genotypes with *A*, *C*, and *R* in the dominant state are expressed in colored grains.

The common domestic animals are likewise characterized by a variety of colors. As in plants, these colors are the result of interactions between basic-color genes and additional genes in the genotype. Of animals that have been studied, perhaps the laboratory mouse shows the greatest range of coloration. In mice, as in all mammals, color or albinism is determined by a single pair of basic-color genes, *C-c*. Color in the coat is determined by the dominant member *C*. Specific colors, such as gray or agouti, black, and brown, *results from the interaction of additional genes with the basic-color genes C-c.* Uniform distribution of color *vs.* white spotting is determined by a second pair of genes, *S-s.* The presence of the genes *SS* or *Ss* in a genotype allows uniform or self-coloration, while with homozygous recessive, *ss*, white spots develop in the coat. Other genes modify the size and the extent of the spotting as well as the position and distribution of white spots on the body.

INHERITANCE OF SPOTTING IN RODENTS—EPISTASIS

Mating a solid-colored black mouse, *CCSS*, with an albino, *ccss*, results in the production of an F_1 hybrid. The heterozygous F_1 *CcSs* mice are uniformly black or self-colored animals, since the dominant basic-color gene, *C*, determines color and the dominant gene, *S*, allows the color to be distributed uniformly over the body. Mating F_1 mice involves the segregation, assortment, and recombination of the two pairs of genes *C-c* and *S-s*. The 16 possible genotypes of the F_2 generation are shown on the checkerboard (Fig. 97). Four of these genotypes contain the recessive genes, *cc*, with various recombinations of the distribution or spotting genes, *S-s*. All mice with *cc* will be albino, and the *S-s* genes can have no visible effect; since the coat is uniformly white and there is no color to distribute, no spotting can appear. The 4 albino individuals are thus grouped into one phenotypic class regardless of the spotting genes in their genotypes.

Twelve of the expected F_2 genotypes will contain the dominant basic-color gene, either as *CC* or *C-*, with various recombinations of *S-s*. All mice with the *C* gene, either homozygous or heterozygous, will be colored, and the distribution genes *S-s* will be effective in each case, *S* allowing uniform distribution of color and *ss* determining spotting. Because *S-s* are recombined in a $1:2:1$ ratio and *S* is completely dominant, 9 of the 12 animals will be *SS* or *S-* and therefore self- or uniformly colored. Three of the 12 animals will be the recessives, *ss*, and will be spotted. The F_2 generation will show three phenotypic classes, uniform or self-colored, colored with white spots, and white or albino mice in the ratio of $9:3:4$. Genes that act as *S-s* are said to have a *supplementary action*, that is, they have a *modifying influence* on the action of other genes, in this case the primary or basic ones, *CC*, that determine color. *An interaction between the two distinct pairs of alleles is*, therefore, *involved.* For example, genotypes containing the color gene *C* provide the basis for coat color. Interaction between the recessive-spotting genes *ss* and *C* results in the production of spotted animals. The genes *ss* appear to interfere with or influence to some extent the full normal action of *C*. Again, in genotypes containing *cc*, no color is produced, and the supplementary genes *S-s* have no effect on the resulting albino animals. The recessives, *cc*, of the basic-color genes thus *interfere with the action of* the *S-s* genes that are nonallelic with *C-c*. Genes that act in this way, interfering with or influencing the action of other nonallelic genes, may be called

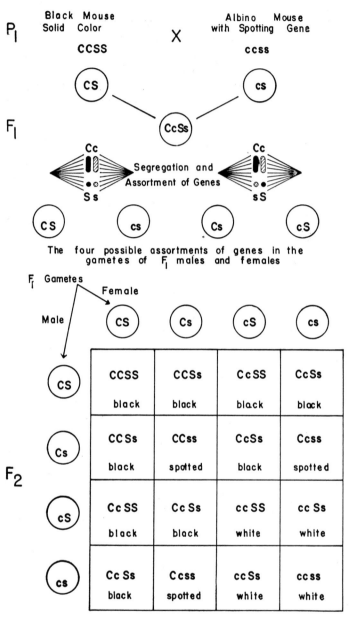

FIG. 97. DIAGRAM OF THE INTERACTION OF THE BASIC-COLOR GENES "C-c" AND A PAIR OF SUPPLEMENTARY GENES, "S-s," CONDITIONING COLOR AND SPOTTING IN THE MOUSE.

epistatic genes, and the condition resulting from the action of an epistatic gene is called **epistasis.** These terms come from the Greek words *epi, meaning upon* or over, and *stasis, standing.* Epistatic means literally standing upon or standing over. Thus, an epistatic gene stands upon or over another gene, interfering with its normal action. The adjective is pronounced ep′i-stat′ik and the noun, e-pis′ta-sis, although ep-i-stā′sis is preferred by many. In this type of interaction, the genes that are interfered with, have their actions modified, masked, or suppressed are called **hypostatic** genes; they are genes *that are under* or are stood upon.

Supplementary Genes in the Larger Domestic Animals

The production of distinctive color patterns characteristic of the various breeds of domestic animals, while not so well understood as coloration in rodents, is thought to result similarly from the interactions of a single pair of basic-color genes and numerous pairs of additional genes with supplementary actions (Fig. 98–100). These supplementary actions affect the intensity and distribution of color in larger domestic animals much as in rodents.

Through years of crossbreeding, inbreeding, and selection by making them homozygous, man has fixed some of the color and pattern variations in breeds of domesticated animals. The results are seen in some breeds of dogs, swine, and cattle in which, as in the Dalmatian or coach dog, belted Hampshire swine, and white-faced Hereford cattle, the color patterns are conspicuous.

Supplementary Genes in Maize

It may be recalled that the development of color in the aleurone layer in corn seeds is dependent upon the complementary interaction of the basic genes *A-a, C-c,* and *R-r.* Coloration varies from light and dark red to light and dark purple. Besides the basic-color genes, additional pairs of genes are involved in the production of aleurone colors. Among them are the purplered genes *Pr-pr, Pr* determining purple and *pr* red.

THE 9:3:4 RATIO IN CORN. *Action of the Purple-red Genes.* In corn a pair of supplementary genes, *Pr-pr,* in the presence of the *basic-color* genes *ARC* acts to produce purple or red grains. A corn plant with the genotype *AACCRRprpr* will produce colored grains because of the complementary interaction of the factors *ACR* which condition the production of pigments. The presence of the genes *prpr* in the homozygous recessive determines that the color will be nonpurple and, in the presence of *ACR,* therefore *red.* The genotype *AACCRRPrPr* will condition the development of purple aleurone because of the interaction of the dominant gene *Pr* with *ARC.* A corn plant having the genotype *AACCrrPrPr* will produce white grains because of the homozygous-recessive state of one of the pairs of basic complementary genes, *rr.* Crossing two types of corn plants as *AACCRRprpr*

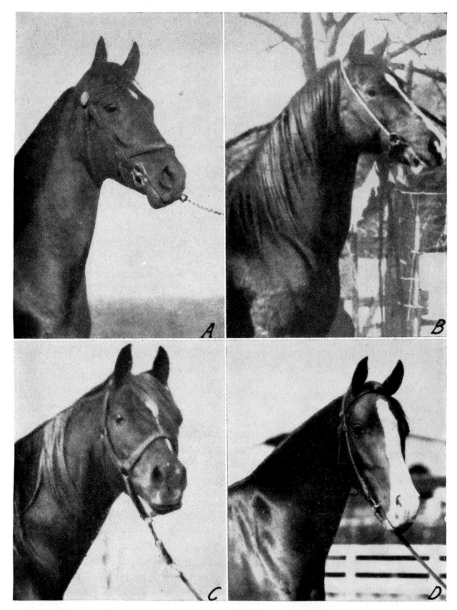

FIG. 98. CHARACTERISTIC FACIAL MARKINGS IN ARABIAN HORSES.
A, star; B, star, strip, snip, and chin spot; C, star and strip; D, star, strip, snip, and chin spot. These markings are forms of spotting determined by spotting genes and their modifying factors interacting in a gene complex basic to coat coloration in horses. (Courtesy, C. T. Blunn, from Blunn and Howell, from J. Heredity.)

$\times AACCrrPrPr$ will produce F_1 plants $AACCRrPrpr$. Since the basic complementary genes AA and CC occur in the genotypes of both parents, both A and C will be present in the homozygous state in all their progeny. Their segregation, assortment, and recombination need not be further con-

FIG. 99. SPOTTED PONY.

Markings result from a supplementary spotting gene interacting in the gene complex conditioning coat coloration in horses. This type of spotting is regarded as recessive to self-coloration. A dominant type of spotting has also been reported in horses. (Courtesy, Cook and Gormley.)

sidered in the calculation of the F_2 dihybrid ratio. Hybridization will, however, involve *one pair* of basic complementary-color genes, R-r, and the *additional pair* of supplementary genes, Pr-pr. Since the Pr-pr genes act in addition to the basic genes, they may be said to supplement the action of A, C, and R in the production of colors. The supplementary action of Pr-pr determines what the color will be, purple or red.

FIG. 100. A REGISTERED DUTCH BELTED COW AND HER HEIFERS.

A, University's Harvest Queen 309. *B* and *C*, heifers 393 and 427, both daughters of University's Harvest Queen by a pure-bred Jersey bull, who carried a recessive factor for white spotting. Both heifers were red with a white belt. The white-belt pattern is probably dominant over the Jersey factor for solid-colored body or at least exhibits itself fully in the presence of the recessive factor for white spotting. (Courtesy, R. B. Becker, from *J. Heredity*.)

Because in the F_2 the members of any single pair of genes recombine in a $1:2:1$ ratio, the basic-color genes R-r will be recombined in the ratio of $4RR:8Rr:4rr$ in the F_2 of the dihybrid (Fig. 101 and 102). With complementary interaction of the A-a, C-c, and R-r genes, the genotypic class containing the recessive $4rr$ will produce colorless aleurone. Although present in these genotypes, the supplementary-color factors Pr-pr are without visible effects, since they cannot *produce* color but only *modify* it when present. Thus there will be 4 white grains in the expected F_2 total of 16.

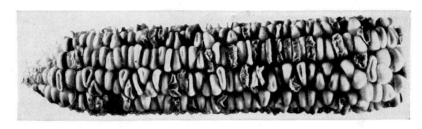

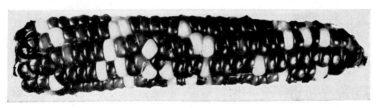

Fig. 101. Interaction of Factors in a Dihybrid Leading to the Production of Two Indistinguishable Classes in Corn.
Top, interaction of two gene pairs, *Su*-*su* and *Sh*-*sh*, conditioning starchy-sweet and full-shrunken, respectively. The recessive, *susu*, determines the production of sugary grains. The genes *Sh*-*sh* also affecting the endosperm produce no visible effect on any of the sugary grains, because all are wrinkled. Thus the full and shrunken characters are not visible in a sweet grain. The ratio is 9 starchy full:3 starchy shrunken:4 sugary. The latter contain both full and shrunken, but these are not distinguishable. *Bottom*, the ratio of 9 purple:3 red:4 white is due to the interaction of genes. (Specimens courtesy, George Carter, Clinton, Connecticut.)

The genotypic classes containing $4RR$ and $8Rr$ in combination with A and C present in all genotypes provide the basic complementary genes essential for the development of color in the aleurone tissue of 12 grains. The supplementary factors Pr-pr will be distributed in a $3:1$ ratio in these 12 genotypes with the dominant Pr gene in 9 and $prpr$ in 3 of them. With the interaction of Pr resulting in purple aleurone color, $\frac{9}{16}$ of the total F_2 population will be purple grains and $\frac{3}{16}$ will be red. The F_1 plant will produce purple, red, and white grains in the ratio of $9:3:4$ (Fig. 102). This is a modification of the expected $9:3:3:1$ dihybrid ratio which is characteristic of all crosses involving a single pair of basic genes and a pair of supplementary genes.

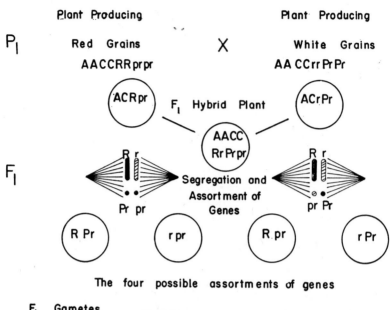

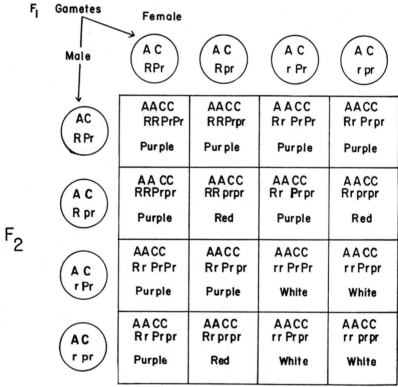

FIG. 102. DIAGRAM OF INTERACTION OF SUPPLEMENTARY GENES, "Pr-pr," WITH THE BASIC-COLOR GENES, "A-a," "C-c," AND "R-r."

ACTION OF THE DILUTION OR INTENSITY GENE. In the coloration of aleurone in corn, the *dilution* genes *D-d* also act as supplementary genes, *modifying the intensity* of color, the dominant gene, *D*, conditioning the dilution of red or purple to pale red or pale purple and *dd*, no dilution. When the gene is in the homozygous-recessive state, *dd*, the interaction results in the production of intense coloration, dark red or dark purple. Hybridization between corn plants with the genotypes *AACCRRddprpr* and *AACCrrDDprpr*, producing dark-red grains and white grains, respectively, will yield an F_1 dihybrid plant, *AACCRrDdprpr*, heterozygous for one pair of the basic complementary genes, *R-r*, and the supplementary-dilution factors, *D-d*. Upon self-pollination the genes *R-r* and *D-d* in the F_1 dihybrid undergo segregation, assortment, and recombination. An F_2 population of dilute-red, dark-red, and white grains will be produced in the ratio of 9:3:4.

Inheritance of Two Pairs of Supplementary Genes

Simultaneous interaction of two pairs of supplementary genes in a gene complex may result in modification of the character under consideration. Supplementary genes not only interact to modify the product of the basic genes, but in many instances they *interact together*. In organisms which are homozygous for the dominant-basic genes for any given character, two pairs of supplementary genes involved in a cross tend to yield the typical 9:3:3:1 dihybrid ratio in the F_2 generation.

A CROSS IN CORN INVOLVING TWO PAIRS OF SUPPLEMEN-TARY GENES. *The 9:3:3:1 Ratio.* If a corn plant *(AACCRR)PrPrDD* producing pale- or dilute-purple grains is crossed with another as *(AACCRR)-prprdd* producing dark-red grains, the F_1 hybrid plant *(AACCRR)PrprDd* is heterozygous for two pairs of supplementary genes (Fig. 103). These are *Pr-pr*, which determine purple or nonpurple aleurone, and *D-d*, the *dilution* or *intensity* genes that influence the production of pale- or dark-aleurone colors.

Selfing the F_1 plants results in the production of the expected sixteen genotypes in the F_2 generation. These genotypes may be divided into four groups each of which conditions a recognizable phenotypic class. Since all F_2 plants contain the basic complementary genes *AACCRR*, they will all have colored aleurone. Nine genotypes are expected to contain the dominant supplementary genes *Pr* and *D*. *Pr* will interact with *A*, *C*, and *R* to produce purple aleurone, and *D will determine the dilution of the purple*. The phenotypic expression of this group will be *nine* light-purple-aleurone grains. The second class of three genotypes contains the genes *Pr* and *d* which interact in the production of *three* intense-purple-aleurone grains. The third class of three genotypes contains the homozygous recessive genes *prpr* and the dominant gene *D* which result in the production of *three* dilute-red-aleurone grains. The fourth class contains only *one* genotype, the homozygous recessive of both supplementary genes, *prprdd*. This genotype conditions dark-

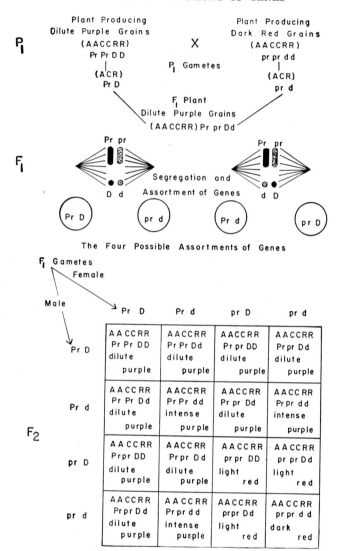

FIG. 103. DIAGRAM OF INTERACTION OF SUPPLEMENTARY GENES, "Pr-pr" AND "D-d," DETERMINING THE CHARACTERS PURPLE-RED AND DILUTE-INTENSE.

Presence of the dominant basic color genes *AACCRR* is assumed throughout. The 16 possible genotypes are expressed in the F_2 phenotypes, dilute purple, intense purple, light red, and dark red, in the ratio of 9:3:3:1.

red-aleurone grain. The ratio in this case is therefore the expected unmodified ratio of 9:3:3:1.

TWO PAIRS OF SUPPLEMENTARY GENES IN FOWLS. *The 9:3:3:1 Ratio in Comb Characters.* The development of the common comb types of fowls was found to be based genetically upon the interactions of at least five pairs of genes. The comb characters most commonly recognized in fowls are the rose comb, the walnut comb, the pea comb, and the single comb (Fig. 104–107). Of this group of combs, the single and the most simple is inherited as a recessive to all the other common comb types. However, there is a European breed, the Breda, which is almost combless. The Breda type of comb is apparently recessive even to the single-comb type (Fig. 108). In the genetic interpretation offered by Bateson, it was suggested that *fundamental to all comb formation* is a pair of *basic genes* designated as *C-c* which determines whether any comb is formed. Accordingly the combless

FIG. 104. COMB CHARACTERS IN FOWLS.
Rose comb of the White Wyandotte male at left and pea comb of the Light Brahma pullet at right. (Courtesy, A. O. Schilling.)

Breda breed of fowls has the genotype *cc*. Since the genotype *CC determines the development of some kind of comb structure*, in contrast with the *combless cc*, it follows that all other recognized breeds of fowls which have well-developed combs are homozygous dominant *CC*.

Besides the basic gene, several pairs of supplementary genes interact in the gene complex underlying the development of comb types. Among these are the genes *R-r* which in the dominant state modify the comb to the rose type and *P-p* which change it to the pea type. Crosses between fowls with the rose comb, *CCRRpp*, and the pea comb, *CCrrPP*, produce an F_1 *CCRrPp*. Because of the *interaction between R and P* genes in combination with *CC*, the *heterozygous* fowl develops a *walnut* type of comb (Fig. 109).

FIG. 105. COMB CHARACTERS IN FOWLS.
Rose comb of Black Hamburg male at left and pea comb of Cornish at right.
(Courtesy, A. O. Schilling.)

FIG. 106. WALNUT TYPE OF COMB.
Malay hen to left and Malay cock to right, a breed typically carrying this type
of comb, sometimes also called the strawberry comb. (Courtesy, A. O. Schilling.)

Heterozygous F_1 walnut fowls bred together produce an F_2 of four distinct comb classes, walnut, rose, pea, and single, in a $9:3:3:1$ ratio. As a result of the recombination of genes, the supplementary genes R-r and P-p both occur in the dominant state in combination with CC in nine of the expected sixteen F_2 genotypes. Under the influence of the genes RP interacting in combination with the *basic* gene C, development of the walnut comb occurs in nine cases. Three other genotypes, containing the dominant allele R but the recessive pp, characterize the rose-comb fowls. Of the remaining genotypes, three contain the dominant gene P but the recessive rr and develop pea-comb fowls. Genotypes which contain the supplementary genes in the recessive state, $rrpp$, in combination with CC condition the

FIG. 107. COMB CHARACTERS IN FOWLS.
Left, single comb of a White Leghorn male. *Right,* a combless Breda cock. (Leghorn courtesy, A. O. Schilling; Breda courtesy, M. J. Sirks, Wageningen, Holland.)

development of the single-comb type. Only one such genotype is expected among sixteen in the F_2 generation. Thus, following a cross involving the two pairs of supplementary genes R-r and P-p, four classes of fowls, walnut-, rose-, pea- and single-comb types, are produced in the F_2 generation. A similar phenotypic ratio could be obtained in crossing a walnut-type fowl which has the genotype $CCRRPP$, homozygous and dominant for both pairs of supplementary genes, with a single-comb type which has the genotype $CCrrpp$.

In considering these crosses, it is important to realize that the *supplementary genes R-r and P-p do not determine the development of combs or comblessness.* The comb structures are determined by the genes C-c, the *action of which is basic in comb development.* Genes P-p and R-r *have only supplementary interactions* that *tend to modify* the comb structure into specific types as walnut, rose, pea, and single. Other supplementary genes exert further modifications in comb structure.

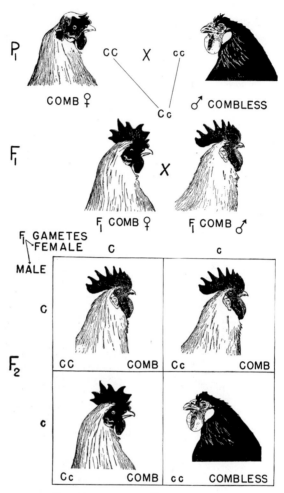

FIG. 108. DIAGRAM OF INHERITANCE OF GENES DETERMINING COMB DEVELOPMENT IN FOWLS.

In the F_2 the phenotypes are comb, and combless in the ratio of $3:1$. (Based on data from Bateson.)

Summary of Supplementary Genes

Many of the heritable characteristics of animals and plants are dependent for their development not upon a single pair of determiners but upon the combined effects of two or more pairs of hereditary units interacting in a group called a *gene complex*. Genes with supplementary action, commonly called *supplementary* genes, are also variously designated as modifying genes, intensity, dilution, pattern, and distribution genes. A gene with supplementary action does not itself *determine the development of a character;* it merely *modifies* a character otherwise determined by basic genes.

A supplementary gene apparently interacts with the basic genes and/or with other supplementary genes of the genetic complex in a manner to continue, to sup-

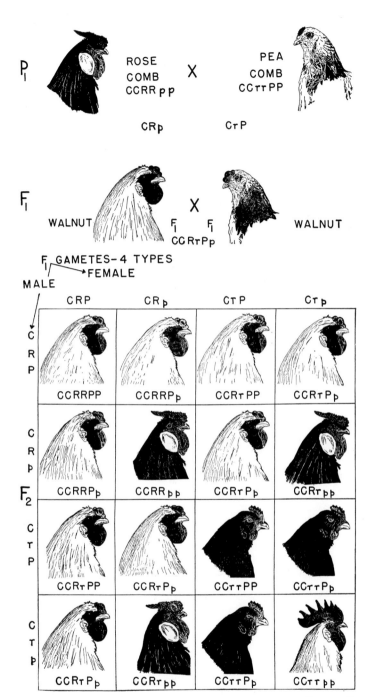

FIG. 109. DIAGRAM OF SEGREGATION AND RECOMBINATION OF GENES CONDITION-
ING COMB PRODUCTION IN FOWLS.

F_1 hybrids have the walnut comb resulting from the interaction of the genes
$RrPp$. Genes of 4 types of F_1 gametes recombine in 16 possible genotypes, expressed
in the production of the F_2 fowls with walnut, rose, pea, and single combs in the
ratio of 9:3:3:1.

plement, to restrict, or to change the action already started by the basic members of the gene complex. This action is similar whether the basic factors are a single pair of determining factors, such as the basic-color genes C-c in rodents, or two or more pairs of basic complementary factors, such as A-a, C-c, and R-r which determine color in the aleurone tissue of the corn grain. In some types of coloration, a given supplementary gene may act to *intensify* the color, making it brighter or darker. In other cases a supplementary gene may *dilute* the color, making it lighter or less intense. In these cases, then, the supplementary genes are called intensity or dilution genes. Very commonly the distribution of color both in plants and in the coats of animals producing *distinctive-color patterns* is due to the action of supplementary distribution genes.

In gene interactions, often there is interference in the actions of nonallelic genes. For example, in rodents the genes for spotting, ss, restrict the action of C in the production of coat color. Again, the recessive genes cc, allelic to C, interfere with the normal action of the color-distribution genes S-s which are nonallelic to C-c. This type of interaction is called *epistasis*. *A gene that interferes with the normal action of another gene, not its allele, is an epistatic gene.* When *a pair of basic genes* and *a pair of genes with supplementary action* are involved in a cross, the resulting F_2 dihybrid ratio is 9:3:4. Two pairs of genes each with supplementary action involved in a cross yield an F_2 ratio of 9:3:3:1.

Questions and Problems

DATA ON THE INTERACTION OF GENES

In Sweet Peas. White and colored flowers in the sweet pea are conditioned by two pairs of basic genes, C-c and R-r, which have a complementary interaction when in the dominant state. Dominant C and dominant R together in a genotype condition colored corolla. Either alone in the dominant state or both c and r present in the recessive state condition white flowers.

In Corn or Maize. The colors in the aleurone layer of corn grains are conditioned by three pairs of basic genes, A-a, C-c, and R-r, which have a complementary interaction in the dominant state. The dominant member of each pair of alleles, A, C, and R, must be present in the genotype of a corn plant to condition the development of colored aleurone in the grains. Plants with genotypes containing genes in the homozygous recessive state for any of the three pairs of genes condition white aleurone. Because colored-aleurone tissue is a part of the seed and develops as a result of fertilization, segregation of aleurone colors actually occurs in the grains developed on the ear produced by the F_1 plant.

1. When Bateson crossed two varieties of white-flowered sweet peas, he obtained an F_1 generation with colored flowers. How did he explain this result?
2. Self-pollination of the F_1 plants mentioned in the Problem above led to the production of an F_2 generation consisting of two kinds of plants, those bearing colored flowers and those bearing white flowers. These plants were in the ratio of 9 red- to 7 white-flowered plants. How were these results explained? Do Mendelian principles apply in this case? What, then, was the cause of the modification of the ratio?
3. What are complementary factors? How do they interact? Are complementary factors segregated, assorted, and recombined according to Mendelian principles?
4. Would hybridization between a red-flowered variety, $CCRR$, and a white flowered variety, $ccrr$, of sweet peas yield different results from the crossing of two white varieties? Explain the principle involved.

5. A variety of corn producing colored aleurone, $AACCRR$, differs from a variety of "white" corn, $AACCrr$, by only one of the three pairs of basic complementary genes, R-r. What results may be expected in the F_1 and F_2 generations if these two varieties are hybridized? Emphasize the action and interaction of the factors.

6. Another variety of corn, $AACCRR$, producing colored aleurone differs from a variety of white corn, $AAccrr$, in two of the three pairs of basic complementary genes, C-c and R-r. Following hybridization of these two varieties, what results may be expected? Emphasize the interaction of the factors leading to the production of segregating grains on the ear produced by the F_1 plant.

7. Other varities of corn, $AACCRR$, with colored-aleurone tissue differ from certain varieties of white corn, $aaccrr$, in all three of the basic complementary genes, A-a, C-c, and R-r. Following hybridization of such colored and white varieties, what ratio of colored to white grains may be expected on the F_1 plant? Emphasize the interaction of the genes.

8. Two varieties of white corn, $aaCCRR$ and $AAccRR$, are hybridized. What kinds of grains will the F_1 plants produce? Explain the ratios and the interaction of factors responsible for them. This may be regarded as a dihybrid (omit RR which are common to all the genotypes). Do Mendelian principles apply in this case?

9. Assume hybridization between the white varieties of corn, $aaCCRR$ and $AACCrr$. This may be regarded as a dihybrid (omit CC which are common to all the genotypes). What results may be expected from this cross?

10. Assume hybridization between the white varieties, $AACCrr$ and $AAccRR$. This may be regarded as a dihybrid (omit AA which are common to all the genotypes). What results may be expected from this cross?

11. White aleurone will be developed by corn plants having the genotypes $aaCCRR$, $AAccRR$, and $AACCrr$. Assume hybridization between each of these varieties and the other two as in the problems above. From these crosses, determine the number and kinds of genotypes which will condition the production of white aleurone in the grains. The checkerboard diagrams may be helpful in obtaining all of the genotypes.

12. Summarize the action of complementary genes in the factor complex as seen in the problems in sweet peas and in corn.

DATA ON THE INTERACTION OF GENES IN RODENTS

Coloration in all animals depends upon the interaction of the genes in a factor complex. Interaction of the genes in the factor complex conditioning color variations of rodents is the best known in mammals. The factor complex in rodents contains the genes C-c, A-a, and S-s. C-c is a single pair of basic-color genes. The dominant gene C is essential to the development of any coat color whatever. The homozygous-recessive state cc conditions the albino. Most variations in the coat colors of rodents depend upon the interaction of supplementary modifying factors with the dominant basic-color gene C (209; Fig. 97, 210). The wild gray color or agouti is conditioned by the interaction of the dominant gene A which acts as a pattern factor modifying the distribution of color on individual hairs. Under the influence of A-, a light-colored band is developed just below the tip of each hair. The homozygous recessive state aa conditions nonagouti. A pair of alleles, B-b, interacting in the complex, conditions black in the dominant and brown in the homozygous recessive state. The distribution of color in rodents is conditioned by spotting factors, one of which is the pair of alleles S-s. Interacting in the factor complex, S conditions the distribution of color evenly over the body of the animal. That is, S in the dominant state conditions the solid color or self color. The homozygous recessive, *ss*, conditions the development of white areas distributed over the body. Still other modifying factors influence the amount and extent of the spotting.

DATA ON THE INTERACTION OF FACTORS IN CORN

In the corn plant aleurone color is dependent upon the interaction of three pairs of complementary genes, *A-a*, *C-c*, and *R-r*. The three dominant genes, *A*, *C*, and *R*, when present in the genotype condition the development of color. Because of the complementary interaction of these genes, the presence in the genotype of any one of the three in the homozygous recessive state conditions the development of colorless aleurone. The specific color or the intensity of the coloration depends upon the interaction of supplementary modifying genes. The supplementary genes, *Pr-pr*, interacting in the factor complex condition the development of purple and red aleurone. The dominant gene, *Pr*, conditions the development of purple aleurone, while the homozygous recessive state, *prpr*, conditions red. A pair of intensity or dilution factors, *D-d*, conditions the dilution or the intensity of aleurone coloration in corn. The dominant gene, *D*, conditions dilute coloration of all the color types, while the homozygous recessive state, *dd*, conditions intense coloration.

DATA ON THE INTERACTION OF GENES IN THE SWEET PEA

In the sweet pea the color of the flower is dependent upon a factor complex consisting of two pairs of complementary basic-color genes, *C-c* and *R-r*. The supplementary modifying genes, *B-b*, condition blue and red. In the dominant and recessive states, respectively, *B* conditions blue and *bb* conditions red. In addition a pair of supplementary modifying or intensity genes *I-i* conditions intense color in the dominant state, *I*, and dilute coloration in the homozygous recessive, *ii*.

13. When mutant black mice, *CCaa*, are mated with mutant albino mice, as *ccAA*, the F₁ generation is the wild-type agouti or gray. Explain the genetics of this reversion to the wild, ancestral type of coloration.

14. Should the F₁ generation from *CCaa* × *ccAA* in the problem above be mated *inter se*, that is, F₁ × F₁, what genotypes may be expected in the F₂ generation? Considering the interaction of factors, determine the phenotypic classes of the F₂ generation. What is the F₂ phenotypic ratio?

15. When a self-colored (solid) black mouse, *CCSS*, is mated to albino types as *ccss*, members of the F₁ generation are all self black. If the F₁ generation is mated *inter se*, F₁ × F₁, what genotypes may be expected in the F₂ generation? Considering the interaction of the factors, determine the F₂ phenotypic classes and the F₂ phenotypic ratio.

16. A brown mouse has the genotype *CCbb*, but some albinos may carry the factor for black in their genotypes, as *ccBB*. Considering the interaction of factors, explain what may be expected in the F₁ and F₂ generations following mating these brown and albino mice.

17. Corn plants of genotype *AACCRRPrPr* produce purple grains, and those with genotype *AACCrrprpr* produce white grains. What results may be expected if these types of plants are hybridized? This may be regarded as a dihybrid, omitting genes *AACC* which are common to all genotypes. Explain on the basis of factor interaction.

18. Assume hybridization between corn plants of genotypes *AACCRRprpr* and *AACCrrPrPr* which produce red grains and white grains, respectively. (Omit *AACC* in calculations.) Consider the factor complex and the factor interactions in determining the F₂ phenotypic ratio.

19. Corn plants with the genotypes $AACCrrPrPr$ and $AAccRRprpr$ each produce grains with colorless aleurone (white). When these types of corn are hybridized, a trihybrid F_1 plant is produced (omit AA). Considering the interaction of the genes in the factor complex, determine the colors of grains which self-pollinated F_1 plants may be expected to produce. What is the ratio? How do you account for the large number of white grains in this generation?

20. Hybridization between corn plants with the genotypes $AACCRRPrPrdd$ and $AACCrrPrPrDD$, conditioning intensely purple grains and white grains, respectively, will produce a dihybrid F_1 plant (omit genes common to all genotypes). Considering the interaction of the genes in the factor complex, determine the ratio of the grains of various colors produced by self-pollinated F_1 plants.

21. Corn plants with the genotype $AACCrrPrPrDD$ produce white grains. Those with genotype $AACCRRprprdd$ produce dark-red grains. Assume hybridization between these two types of corn plants. The F_1 plant will be a trihybrid. Considering the interaction of genes in the factor complex, determine the phenotypic ratio of grain colors produced by the F_1 plant.

22. Sweet-pea plants of the genotype $CCrrBB$ produce white flowers, and plants with the genotype $CCRRbb$ produce red flowers. Following hybridization between these two kinds of plants, what will be the color of the flowers on the F_1 dihybrid plant (omit CC)? If F_1 plants are allowed to self-pollinate, what genotypes will be found in the F_2 generation? As regards flower colors, what ratios may be expected in the F_2 generation?

23. Assume hybridization between sweet-pea plants with genotypes $CCrrBB$ and $ccRRbb$, both producing white flowers. What flower colors may be expected in the F_1 and F_2 generations? Explain the interaction of the factors in these plants.

24. In the sweet pea, plants with the genotype $CCRRBBII$ will produce blue flowers; those with the genotype $CCrrBBii$ will produce white flowers. Hybridization between these types of plants will produce an F_1 dihybrid (omit $CCBB$). Following selfing of the F_1, what will be expected in the phenotypic ratio? Explain the interaction of the factors in the factor complex.

25. The factors $CCRRBBII$ condition intensely blue and $CCRRbbii$, pale-red flowers in the sweet pea. Assuming hybridization, describe phenotypic expressions which may be expected in the F_1 and F_2 generations. Explain the factor interactions involved.

26. Assume hybridization between corn plants with the genotypes $AACCRRPrPrDD$ and $AACCRRprprpdd$, producing pale- or dilute-purple grains and dark-red grains, respectively. Describe the phenotypic expressions in the F_1 dihybrid and the F_2 generation. ($AACCRR$, common to all genotypes, may be omitted in the calculations.)

27. Who made some of the early investigations on the comb characters in fowls? What is the evidence for assuming the existence of a pair of genes C-c which are basic to comb development? How many other pairs of genes are known to be present in the factor complex conditioning comb characters in fowls?

28. By reference to pp. 218, 222, describe the interaction of the supplementary genes, R-r and P-p, when pea comb, $CCPPrr$, and rose comb, $CCppRR$, are crossed. Describe the F_1 and F_2 generations.

29. a. How many pairs of genes are regarded as basic factors in the factor complex conditioning coat coloration in rodents?

   b. How many genes may be considered as basic in the factor complex conditioning coloration of flowers in the sweet pea? What is the nature of these basic genes?

c. How many genes may be considered as basic in the factor complex conditioning coloration in the aleurone tissue of corn grains? What is the nature of these basic genes?

30. What F_2 ratios may be expected if the basic genes alone are involved in a hybrid in each of the three cases a, b, and c in the problem above?

31. What terms have been used to designate modifying factors? What is the nature of the interaction of modifying factors? What is the nature of some of the characteristics of plants and animals which are conditioned by supplementary or modifying factors?

chapter II

Interaction of Genes in Development—Inhibitory Genes—Epistasis

Domestic fowls like other animals under domestication exhibit a diversity of coloration. Among the various colors and patterns are black, red, buff, barred, and white. The domestic fowl carries basic-color genes designated C-c which condition the development of colored and white feathers. In studies of the inheritance of white in fowls, genetically different white

FIG. 110. A RECESSIVE WHITE WYANDOTTE HEN AT LEFT AND A DOMINANT WHITE LEGHORN COCK AT THE RIGHT.
(Courtesy, A. O. Schilling.)

types have been found (Fig. 110 and 111). Colored breeds are homozygous dominant for the basic genes CC. White Wyandottes and White Rocks behave as recessive whites in matings with colored breeds because they are homozygous recessive for the basic-color genes cc. Crosses between recessive whites, cc, and colored breeds, CC, yield colored F_1 and colored and white in a 3:1 ratio in the F_2. The dominant white breed, White Leghorn, has the dominant color genes *CC*, but the development of color is prevented by action of an **inhibitory** gene, *I*, which cancels the effects of the dominant color gene *C*. Mating the dominant White Leghorn with a colored breed yields an F_1 generation of white fowls, with possibly some colored feathers, and an F_2 of white and colored birds in the ratio of 3:1. The genotype of the dominant white is *IICC*, the recessive white is *iicc*, and the colored breeds are *iiCC*.

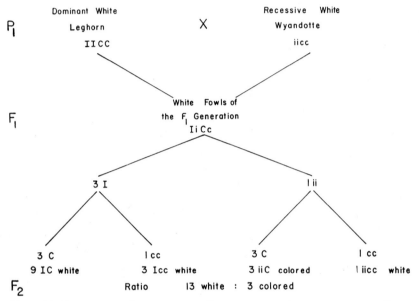

FIG. 111. DIAGRAM OF INDEPENDENT SEGREGATION, ASSORTMENT, AND RECOMBINATION OF THE BASIC COLOR GENES, "C-c," AND THE INHIBITORY GENES "I-i," IN FOWLS.

All genotypes except *iiC* condition white fowls.

DIHYBRIDS INVOLVING THE BEHAVIOR OF AN INHIBITORY GENE AND A BASIC COLOR GENE.

The 13:3 Modified F_2 Phenotypic Ratio in Fowls. By mating the dominant White Leghorn, *IICC*, and the recessive White Wyandotte, *iicc*, a white-feathered F_1 dihybrid with the genotype *IiCc* is obtained. As a result of segregation, assortment, and recombination, these two pairs of genes are recombined in the 16 expected F_2 genotypes (Fig. 111).

The chief interest in this cross lies in the phenotypic expression in the F_2 generation which is dependent upon the *interactions of the inhibitory gene and the basic color genes*. When both *I* and *C* are present, as they are in 9 of the expected 16 F_2 genotypes, the normal action of the basic color gene *C* in the production of color is inhibited by the interaction of the dominant inhibitory factor *I*. This interaction results in the suppression of color in the feathers. Thus, 9 dominant white fowls are produced. The recessive state of the basic color gene *cc* also conditions lack of color in the feathers. Four additional genotypes of the 16 contain the recessive genes *cc*, and thus there are 4 recessive whites in the F_2.

Statistically all types of white fowls, 9 + 4, constitute an F_2 phenotypic class of 13 possible individuals. The 3 remaining possible genotypes contain the basic color genes in either the homozygous dominant state, *CC*, or the heterozygous state, *Cc*. The alleles of the inhibitory genes are present in these genotypes in the homozygous recessive state, *ii*. They have no effect on coloration, and thus a phenotypic class of 3 individuals with colored feathers is produced. Because of the interaction of these factors, a dihybrid cross involving a pair of inhibitory factors and a pair of basic color genes results in the production of an F_2 generation of white and colored individuals in the phenotypic ratio of 13 white to 3 colored.

Inheritance of Aleurone Coloration in Maize

The gene complex underlying the development of color in the aleurone layer of corn grains consists of a large group of genes with various actions and interactions. In addition to the three pairs of basic genes, *A-a*, *C-c*, and *R-r*, with complementory actions conditioning color, there are the genes *Pr-pr* and *D-d* with supplementary actions and interactions determining specific color types. More important than these, in the present consideration, is a pair of genes, *I-i*, in which the dominant allele, *I*, *acts to prevent or inhibit the production of any color* in the aleurone tissue. This inhibitory action occurs regardless of the presence of the complementary genes *AACCRR*. Their effects are completely cancelled by the action of I. The homozygous recessive *ii*, however, interacts in the gene complex to allow the development of aleurone color. The actions of the inhibitory genes in the two organisms Indian corn and domestic fowls are essentially parallel.

Because of the interaction of the basic complementary and inhibitory genes, there are several varieties of corn with colored or white grains. Among these, the genotype *AACCRRii* conditions colored aleurone; *AACCrrii*, *AAccRRii*, *aaCCRRii*, and other combinations of the complementary genes condition colorless aleurone; and the inhibitory action of the gene *I* in the genotype *AACCRRII* also determines colorless aleurone. Because of their behavior in monohybrid crosses, white varieties with genotypes like *AACCrrii* are called *recessive* whites, and those like *AACCRRII*, *dominant* whites (Fig. 112). In crosses with colored varieties, the recessive whites yield 3 colored to 1 white in the F_2 generation, but the dominant whites give 3 whites to 1 colored. The dominant- and recessive-white varieties of corn, while perhaps genetically more complex, are in principle quite similar to the dominant- and recessive-white breeds of fowls.

A PAIR OF INHIBITORY FACTORS AND ONE OF THE THREE PAIRS OF BASIC COMPLEMENTARY GENES INVOLVED IN A CROSS. *The 13:3 Ratio in Corn.* In hybridization between a dominant

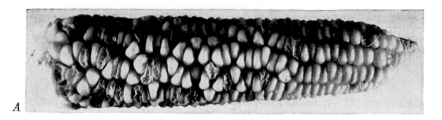

FIG. 112. ENDOSPERM AND COLOR CHARACTERS IN CORN.

A, segregation of dominant-starchy and recessive-sugary grains on an ear of corn in an approximate ratio of 3 starchy:1 sugary grain. Two ears of corn, *B* and *C*, showing segregation of characters in a dihybrid. The characters are dominant-white and recessive-colored grains and dominant-starchy and recessive-sugary endosperm. While the aleurone-color genes are dominant, the epistatic factor *I-i* acts as an inhibitor of all aleurone color. Thus in the presence of *I* the prevention of colored aleurone causes white grain to appear as a dominant character. There are approximately 9 white starchy:3 white sugary:3 purple starchy:1 purple sugary grain. *D*, segregation in a tetrahybrid corn plant. The grains on the ear show an approximate ratio of 81 purple:27 red:148 white. On the photograph the purple grains are the darkest ones, the red are intermediate, and the white grains are the lightest ones. The genotype *AaCcRrPrpr* of the plant producing this ear contained the basic complementary color genes *AaCcRr* and the supplementary factor pair *Pr-pr*. (Specimens courtesy, George Carter, Clinton, Connecticut.)

white-grained variety of corn with the genotype *AACCRRII* and a recessive white-grained variety with the genotype *AACCrrii*, the inhibitory alleles *I-i* and one of the three pairs of basic complementary color genes *R-r* are involved in the resulting dihybrid F_1 plant *AACCRrIi*. Upon self-pollination of the F_1 plant, segregation, assortment, and recombination of the basic complementary genes, *R-r*, and the inhibitory genes, *I-i* occur, producing the expected 16 F_2 genotypes. Factor interaction in each of these conditions the production of white and colored grains in a phenotypic ratio of 13:3 (Fig. 113 and 114). Thus, following a cross involving *a pair of inhibitory genes* and *one* of the three *complementary color genes basic* to aleurone coloration in corn, two phenotypic classes are produced in the F_2 generation in the ratio of 13:3.

FIG. 113. EAR OF CORN SHOWING RESULTS OF INTERACTION OF AN INHIBITING FACTOR WITH THE BASIC COLOR GENE.
The genotype of the dihybrid is *IiRr*. Interaction of these two pairs of genes results in approximately 13 nonpurple:3 purple grains. The genes *Su-su* are present and have conditioned starchy and sugary grains on this ear. (Specimens courtesy, George Carter, Clinton, Connecticut.)

DIHYBRIDS INVOLVING THE BEHAVIOR OF AN INHIBITORY FACTOR AND A SUPPLEMENTARY GENE.   *The 12:3:1 Modified F_2 Phenotypic Ratio in Corn.*   In hybridization between a variety of white-grained corn with the genotype *AACCRRIIPrPr* and a variety of red-grained corn with the genotype *AACCRRiiprpr*, the pair of inhibitory alleles *I-i* and a pair of supplementary genes *Pr-pr* are involved in the cross (Fig. 115). The resulting dihybrid F_1 plant *AACCRRIiPrpr* is therefore heterozygous for the inhibitory genes *I-i* and the supplementary genes *Pr-pr*. The basic complementary color factors *AACCRR* will be present in all genotypes of the P_1, F_1, and F_2 generations. Though the presence of these genes in the genotype normally conditions the production of colored aleurone tissue, their phenotypic expression will be modified by the interaction of the supplementary factors *Pr-pr* and the inhibiting action of the inhibitory factors *I-i* which, according to Mendelian principles, will be distributed to the several genotypes.

Following self-pollination of the F_1 plant, the genes *I-i* and *Pr-pr* are segregated, assorted, and recombined to form the 16 genotypes expected in the F_2 generation. Each of these pairs of alleles will be recombined to give a ratio of 3 dominants to 1 homozygous recessive. Thus, the dominant inhibitory factor I will occur in 12 of the 16 possible genotypes and will condition the production of colorless aleurone, regardless of the presence of the dominant basic complementary factors $AACCRR$. These 12 genotypes will therefore produce white grains.

In the 4 remaining genotypes, the inhibitory genes $I\text{-}i$ are in the homozygous recessive state ii. Since a full complement of the basic complementary color genes $AACCRR$ is present and there is no inhibitory action, 4 grains with colored aleurone tissue will be developed. The specific coloration will be

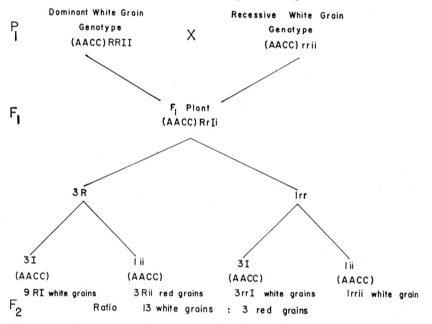

FIG. 114. DIAGRAM OF INTERACTION OF BASIC COMPLEMENTARY-COLOR AND INHIBITORY GENES IN A CROSS BETWEEN CORN PLANTS WITH DOMINANT-WHITE, "(AACC)RRII," AND RECESSIVE-WHITE GRAINS, "(AACC)rrii."

Wherever a dominant R is accompanied by recessive ii, grains will be colored (red). Otherwise, the grains will be white.

determined by the interaction of the supplementary genes $Pr\text{-}pr$ distributed to these genotypes. According to Mendelian principles, Pr and pr will be expected in these genotypes in the ratio of 3 dominant Pr to 1 homozygous recessive $prpr$. Following this distribution, 3 genotypes will determine the production of purple aleurone, 1 $iiPrPr$ and 2 $iiPrpr$. The fourth of these genotypes containing both pairs of genes in the homozygous recessive state, $iiprpr$, will condition the production of red aleurone tissue. Following a cross between varieties of corn involving the pair of inhibitory genes $I\text{-}i$ and the supplementary genes $Pr\text{-}pr$, the F_2 generation will be expected to consist of 3 phenotypic classes of grains in the ratio of 12 white, 3 purple and 1 red.

Because the results are sharp and definite, inhibitory genes furnish good examples of *epistatic* action. This is shown especially well in organisms containing the inhibitory gene *I* and the basic color gene *C* or other color genes. In preventing the normal effect of *C* in the production of color, *I* exerts an epistatic influence over *C*, completely eliminating its action, as shown in the 13:3 phenotypic ratios. In the cases discussed above, the epistatic action of *I*, inhibiting the production of color by the basic color genes, influences the action of certain supplementary genes, as shown in the 12:3:1 phenotypic ratios.

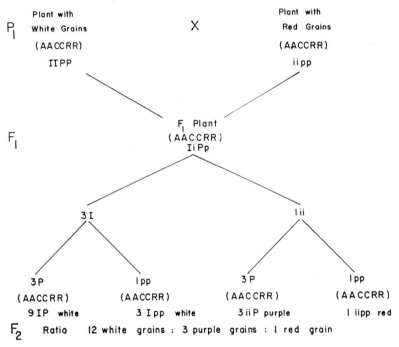

FIG. 115. DIAGRAM OF INDEPENDENT SEGREGATION, ASSORTMENT, AND RECOMBINATION OF THE BASIC COMPLEMENTARY COLOR GENES, "ACR," AND THE INHIBITORY GENES, "Pr-pr" AND "I-i," IN THE PRODUCTION OF COLOR OF GRAINS IN CORN.

Inhibitory Genes in Other Organisms

Inhibitory action of genes has been observed in several instances such as in the production of color in the fruits of the squash plant, in onion bulbs, in potato tubers, and in the coats of swine.

INHERITANCE OF COLORS IN SQUASH FRUITS. Fruits of the summer squash are white, yellow, and various shades of green as the expression of chlorophyll and carotenoid pigments located in the plastids. Production of any color at all is dependent upon some fundamental genetic basis such as a basic color gene or a group of basic genes present as homozygous dominant in all plants. Besides the basic-

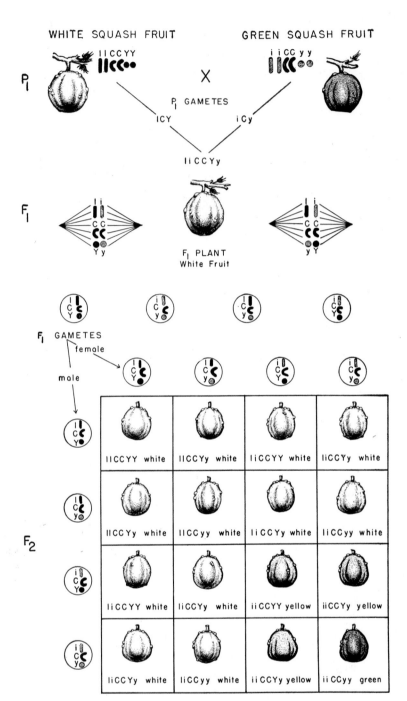

FIG. 116. DIAGRAM OF INTERACTION OF AN INHIBITORY FACTOR WITH A SUPPLE-
MENTARY FACTOR IN THE SQUASH PLANT.

The F₂ generation consists of plants producing white, yellow, and green fruits, respectively, in the phenotypic ratio of 12:3:1. (Based on plants grown from seeds furnished by E. W. Sinnott.)

color genes, that may be designated CC, a pair of genes with supplementary action Y-y and an inhibitory gene I with its recessive, i, may be assumed. Hybridization between a white-fruited squash, $CCYYII$, and a green-fruited squash, $CCyyii$, involves the inhibitory gene I and its recessive allele and the pair of supplementary genes Y-y with the basic genes CC present in each genotype of the P_1, F_1, and F_2 generations. Upon self-pollination of the F_1 plant, $CCIiYy$, these genes segregate, assort, and recombine to produce the modified F_2 phenotypic ratio of 12 white- : 3 yellow- : 1 green-fruited squash plants (Fig. 116).

Production of colors in this ratio may be considered as dependent upon the actions and interactions of the three pairs of alleles C-c, Y-y, and I-i. The genes CC may be regarded as basic to both chlorophyll and carotenoid pigments. Since squash fruits are generally chlorophyll green in their young stages and assume their final colors as they approach maturity, the genes Y-y must exert a supplementary action in chlorophyll development with Y acting to restrict the development of green pigments but allowing the yellow to remain and with the recessive supplementary gene y allowing the development of green colors in the fruits. The dominant inhibitory gene, I, exerts an epistatic action on the other genes, C-C and Y-y; its presence completely cancels their action, inhibiting the production of all color and thus conditioning the production of white fruits. The recessive allele of the inhibitory gene in the homozygous state, ii, allows unrestricted production of color in the fruits.

INHERITANCE OF COAT COLORS IN SWINE. Hetzer reported data on crosses between the nonalbinotic white Danish Landrace and the black English breed Large black. Involved in the cross are the basic color genes CC; a series of multiple allelic extension or spotting genes, E, E^P, and e, that for simplicity may be designated S-s; an inhibitory gene, I; and its recessive allele, i. The extension genes have a supplementary influence on the distribution of color, and the inhibitory gene I is epistatic to C and all extension or spotting genes. The above cross yielded white-coated F_1 animals and an F_2 generation consisting of 397 white:84 black:40 white-spotted pigs, a fairly close approximation to a 12:3:1 ratio.

A GENE COMPLEX IN THE ONION. Clark, Jones, and Little report the presence of a gene complex basic to the development of red, yellow, and white bulbs in the cultivated onion. In this complex the basic gene C determines color and the supplementary genes R-r determine the specific color of bulb in all C-type onions with R acting in the production of red color and rr determining that the color will be yellow. Besides these, members of a pair of incompletely dominant genes, I-i, act to inhibit and to restrict full coloration. Plants with II have white bulbs; the heterozygous Ii plants have an intermediate or light shade of color, either red or yellow.

A GENE COMPLEX IN THE POTATO. Studies of the inheritance of colors in the potato indicate the presence of a gene complex similar to that in corn. Flower color, skin color of tuber, and a light type of russeting in the Katahdin potato depend upon complementary genes. Other studies show the action of supplementary genes in the production of blue color in tubers, while supplementary genes with duplicate action are influential in changing tissue color in the tuber from red to blue.

Summary of Actions of Inhibitory Genes

Inhibitory or inhibiting genes, as the name indicates, are genes which by their interaction in the gene complex tend to restrict or prevent the development of a character. An **inhibitory gene,** *by interacting with a single gene or with several genes, prevents the usual action of this gene or complex of genes* and thus cancels, or suppresses, the results normally expected. Some of the best-known instances of inhibiting factors are found in gene interactions conditioning the production of color in plants and animals. While the action of inhibitory factors has been studied in several cases, this type of gene appears to be of relatively rare occurrence. To account for their scarcity, it has been suggested that the inhibiting action might, in some cases, interfere with the development of essential organs or processes. In these cases their effect might occasionally be lethal, and the death of organisms having such genes would tend to eliminate that race or species. Perhaps true inhibitory genes are observed only in cases in which the inhibiting action affects a character of indifferent survival value.

Involved in crosses, inhibitory genes condition modification of the expected dihybrid ratio as follows: A *dominant inhibitory gene* and its recessive allele *involved* with *a pair of basic genes* in a dihybrid cross yield an F_2 phenotypic ratio of 13:3; a *dominant inhibitory gene* and its recessive allele *involved* with *a pair of supplementary genes* in a dihybrid cross yield an F_2 phenotypic ratio of 12:3:1.

Behavior of the Genes in a Gene Complex

In chemical studies of coloration in plants and animals, a definite relation has been found of oxidizing enzymes to production of colors. For example, it is known that the enzyme *tyrosinase,* found in the tissues of plants and animals, acts to promote or hasten the oxidation of the amino acid tyrosine and related substances. This oxidation results in the production of the black pigment melanin as an end product. As oxidation proceeds, intermediate steps exhibit a series of colors varying from pink and red to violet and finally to black. The amino acid *tyrosine* or related substances may be regarded as the basic *chromogen* or color former. Oxidation of the chromogen through the influence of enzymes such as tyrosinase finally results in the production of the pigments. Basic genes may be assumed fundamental in the production of the basic color formers or chromogens. Other genes may be fundamental in the production of oxidizing enzymes. Genes conditioning development of these reacting chemical substances may thus appear to interact in a complementary manner. Or, more specifically, if one of the complementary genes, as C, conditions the development of the basic chromogen, as for example tyrosine, a second complementary factor, as R, then may condition the production of the oxidizing enzyme, for example tyrosinase, which will promote the oxidation of the basic chromogen. Further interactions of supplementary genes may influence the rate or extent of the oxidation process and may thus extend or restrict the development of color. An inhibitory gene may interact in such a manner as to prevent the oxidation, perhaps by interfering with the normal action or development of the oxidizing enzymes.

The Gene Complex

The units of the gene complex have been classified according to their actions and relationships to other genes in the genotype. The genes of a genetic complex may be grouped into two categories, *basic genes* and *modifying genes.* The basic genes determine the development of the character; they are in a sense fundamental to the production of the trait under consideration. Modifying factors by themselves do not determine the development of any character. They interact with the basic genes to modify or change the expression of a character. The types of genes recognized by their actions and interactions in the several gene complexes may be classified as follows.

THE GENE COMPLEX, the whole group of interacting factors.

1. BASIC GENES

These genes are fundamental in the determination or conditioning of any manifestation of the character. Basic genes may be:

    a. A single pair of genes which act as determiners, such as for example the basic color genes C-c, concerned in the production of coat color in rodents

    b. Two or more pairs of factors with complementary action, such as C-c and R-r, conditioning flower colors in the sweet pea and aleurone color of corn grains.

2. MODIFYING GENES

These genes do not condition the development of a character. They merely interact to modify or change a character. Two types of modifying genes may be recognized:

    a. *Supplementary genes* interact with the basic genes to change the action. They merely supplement the action of the basic genes. Most modifying genes are supplementary to the basic genes in their action

    b. *Inhibitory genes*, by their action and interaction with the basic genes, inhibit or prevent the production of the character usually conditioned by the basic genes.

PHENOTYPIC RATIOS CONDITIONED BY THE INTERACTION OF GENES IN THE GENE COMPLEX.

Two pairs of genes with complementary action.	9:7.
Three pairs of genes with complementary action,	27:37.
One pair of basic genes and one pair of genes with supplementary action,	9:3:4.
Two pairs of supplementary genes interacting in the presence of the fundamental basic gene,	9:3:3:1.
One pair of basic genes and one pair of genes with inhibitory action,	13:3.
One pair of genes with inhibitory action and one pair of genes with supplementary action,	12:3:1.

Epistasis and the Actions of Epistatic Genes

Although the terms *complementary*, *supplementary*, and *inhibitory genes* have been presented, many authors explain gene interactions without them. In their explanations most cases of gene interactions are interpreted entirely on the basis of epistasis and the actions of epistatic genes.

DOMINANCE AND EPISTASIS. Confusion has sometimes occurred in the use of the terms **dominance** and **epistasis**. These terms applied to different phenomena may be contrasted. The members of each pair of allelic genes generally have a dominant and recessive relationship. Dominance between alleles may be complete, as in the relationship between the members of the gene pair *C-c* which condition coloration or albinism in rodents. Dominance may also be incomplete, as in the relationship between the alleles *R-r* conditioning red-, roan-, and white-coat colors in Shorthorn cattle. **Dominance and recessiveness** *are relationships between the members of a pair of alleles or of the members of a series of multiple alleles.* In contrast with dominance and recessiveness, **epistasis and hypostasis** *are relationships between genes belonging to different allelic pairs functioning in a gene complex.* In cases of epistasis, it is consistent with the facts to refer to the influential gene in the complex as the **epistatic gene** and to the masked or suppressed genes as the **hypostatic genes.** Genes with this sort of action may be dominant to their allelic mates, but they are not dominant to the whole gene complex or to other nonallelic genes. While an epistatic gene may have a dominant-recessive relationship with its allele, its relationship to the genes of other allelic pairs is one resulting in epistasis and hypostasis, not dominance and recessiveness. Some authors refer to dominant epistasis and recessive epistasis when the genes involved show either dominant or recessive actions. Perhaps to avoid confusion, it would be preferable to say epistasis resulting from the action of a dominant gene or epistasis resulting from the action of a recessive gene, respectively.

EXAMPLES OF EPISTASIS RESULTING FROM GENES SHOWING DOMINANCE AND RECESSIVENESS. Cases of inheritance involving the interaction of genes are replete with examples of *epistasis resulting from either dominant or recessive genes* and in some instances from both types acting at once. The modified F_2 $9:3:4$ dihybrid phenotypic ratio may be explained on the basis of the action of a gene in the homozygous recessive state. In rodents, for example, a pair of supplementary genes, *S-s*, interacts with a pair of basic color genes, *C-c*, when the two are involved in a cross (Fig. 97). Normally, in combination with dominant *C* determining coloration, the presence of dominant *S-* results in a self-colored coat and that of *ss* in the development of white spots on the animal. However, the basic color gene in the recessive state *cc*, occurring in $\frac{4}{16}$ of the progeny, results in albinism, thus having an *epistatic* influence over the color distribution genes *S-s*, and neither of these can then express itself.

A DOMINANT GENE WITH EPISTATIC ACTION. *The 12:3:1 Phenotypic Ratio.* An explanation of the modified F_2 dihybrid *12:3:1* ratio may be made on the basis of the dominant inhibitory gene *I* which has an epistatic effect in either the homozygous or heterozygous state, *II* or *Ii*, preventing the development of color in the aleurone tissues of corn. In crosses involving the gene pair *I-i* and a pair of supplementary genes such as *Pr-pr*, determining purple or red aleurone, the dominant *I* is epistatic to both of the genes *Pr* and *pr*. In crosses of this type, 12 of the 16 F_2 genotypes will contain the dominant inhibitory gene *I*. Each of these genotypes shows epistasis in suppression of the action of the supplementary genes *Pr* and *pr* by the epistatic action of dominant *I*. As a result, colorless aleurone is developed in grains with these genotypes. Four of the theoretically possible 16 F_2 genotypes contain the recessive allele *ii* in the homozygous state. These in the presence of the basic color genes determine colored aleurone in the ratio of 3 purple to 1 red. The complete F_2 phenotypic ratio is 12 colorless:3 purple:1 red grain (Fig. 115). Similar conditions of epistasis are found in the development of colors in squash fruits (Fig. 116).

DOMINANT AND RECESSIVE GENES BOTH SHOWING EPISTATIC ACTION. *The 13:3 Phenotypic Ratio.* In fowls when the inhibitory gene *I* and its recessive allele i are involved in a dihybrid with the basic color gene pair C-c, the F_2 genotypes produce a phenotypic ratio of 13 white to 3 colored fowls (Fig. 111). Of the 16 F_2 genotypes in such dihybrids, the recombination of genes results in the production of 12 with the dominant members of the gene pairs I-i and C-c. In these 12 genotypes a condition of epistasis exists, because the action of the dominant gene, I, suppresses the development of color normally expected from genotypes containing the basic color gene, C. These genotypes, therefore, effect the production of phenotypically white F_2 fowls. A condition which may be regarded as epistasis is found in one other genotype, namely, $iicc$. In this instance the lack of color is the result of the epistatic action of the recessive basic color genes, cc, as noted above in the 9:3:4 ratio.

TWO RECESSIVE GENES RESULT IN THE 9:7 RATIO. The 9:7 ratio of colored to white both in the flower color of sweet peas and the aleurone color of corn is commonly explained on the genetic basis of the interaction of pairs of genes with complementary action (Fig. 92). In the F_2 generation 6 of the 16 possible genotypes contain either cc or rr, and in the seventh both are present as $ccrr$. Since in these cases either cc or rr conditions the lack of color, both may be regarded as epistatic. Because they parallel each other in their actions, they may also be regarded as recessive epistatic genes with duplicate effects.

Questions and Problems

Data on the Interaction of Inhibitory Genes in the Factor Complex

In fowls coloration appears to be conditioned by a factor complex consisting of a single pair of basic color genes, C-c, and numerous supplementary modifying factors which interact within the complex to condition the color variations. A pair of factors, I-i, acts as total inhibitor of color when in the dominant state. Thus two types of white fowls are known: one type is white because of the presence of the basic genes C-c in the recessive state as cc; the other type is white because of the presence of the dominant-inhibitory gene I.

In the corn plant (maize) there is a pair of inhibitory genes, I-i, which in the dominant state interact in the factor complex to inhibit the development of coloration in the aleurone tissue. This inhibitory action completely cancels the interaction of the complementary basic genes which normally condition the production of colored aleurone tissue. Thus there are two types of white corn: one type develops colorless aleurone tissue because one or more of the basic color genes are present in the recessive state (p. 231); the other type is white because of the inhibiting action of the dominant inhibitory gene I which may be present in the genotype.

In squash plants the fruits occur in a variety of colors, white, yellow, and several shades of green. In this plant no recessive-white fruits are known. Recessive whites usually indicate the presence of a basic color gene. The interaction of the supplementary and inhibitory factors, however, is such that it is reasonable to assume the presence of some sort of basic color gene as C-c in the genotype of squash plants. A pair of supplementary genes, Y-y, conditions the production of yellow- and green-fruit colors in the dominant and recessive states, respectively. A pair of inhibitory genes, I-i, interacts in the factor complex in such a manner that, in the presence of the dominant gene I in a genotype, the development of all color is totally inhibited. Thus fruits of plants containing I are white regardless of the presence of other genes in the complex. However, when I-i is represented in the homozygous recessive state as ii, colored fruits may be produced in accordance with the interaction of the basic and supplementary genes. The various shades and patterns in green fruits are conditioned by additional supplementary, intensity, and pattern factors.

1. If the White Leghorn breed *CCII* is crossed with a colored breed, *CCii*, the F_1 generation is white; but if a White Wyandotte, *ccii*, is crossed with a colored breed, *CCii*, the F_1 generation is colored. Considering the interaction of factors, explain these different results. Assuming that the F_1 generations of each of these crosses are mated *inter se*, that is, $F_1 \times F_1$ in each case, determine what phenotypic ratio may be expected in the F_2 of each of these crosses.

2. By considering the interaction of the genes, determine the F_2 phenotypic ratio following a cross between the White Leghorn breed of fowls, *IICC*, and the White Wyandotte breed, *iicc*. Explain the factor interaction involved in the modification of the F_2 ratio.

3. If a variety of corn, *CCII*, producing grains with white aleurone tissue is crossed with the variety *CCii*, the F_2 segregation will show three white grains to one colored. However, if a variety of white corn, *ccii*, is crossed with the variety *CCii* with colored aleurone, the F_2 segregation is three grains with colored aleurone to one white grain. Considering the interaction of factors, explain the difference in these results.

4. In hybridization between a dominant white-grained variety of corn with the genotype *AACCRRII* and a recessive white variety, *AACCrrii*, the pair of *inhibitory* factors *I-i* and one pair of the *basic* color genes *R-r* are involved in the resulting F_1 dihybrid, *AACCRrIi*. (Omit the genes *AACCPr-pr* and *D-d* from consideration in the calculations.) By considering the factor interactions in the factor complex, calculate the phenotypic ratio of white to colored grains which may be expected to develop following self-pollination of the F_1 plants.

5. Hybridization between a variety of purple corn, *AACCRRPrPrii*, and a white variety, *AACCrrPrPrII*, involves one pair of *basic color* genes *R-r* and the pair of *inhibitory* genes *I-i* in the genotype of the F_1 dihybrid (omit all other genes). Considering the interaction of factors, calculate the ratio of white to colored grains following self-pollination of the F_1 plants.

6. Hybridization between a variety of white-grained corn, *AACCRRprprII*, and a variety of purple corn, *AACCRRPrPrii*, involves a pair of supplementary genes, *Pr-pr*, and the pair of inhibitory genes, *I-i*, in the F_1 dihybrid. (Omit all other genes.) Considering the interaction of the factors, calculate the phenotypic ratio following self-pollination of the F_1 plant.

7. Considering the interaction of the genes, determine the colors of fruits produced by the F_1 and F_2 plants in the following monohybrid crosses among squash plants:
   a. white, *CCYYII* $\times$ yellow, *CCYYii*
   b. white, *CCyyII* $\times$ green, *CCyyii*
   c. yellow, *CCYYii* $\times$ green, *CCyyii*.

8. Hybridization between a variety of squash with the genotype *CCYYII* producing white fruits and a green-fruited variety with the genotype *CCyyii* involves the pair of supplementary color genes *Y-y* and the pair of inhibitory factors *I-i* in the F_1 dihybrid. What will be the color of fruits produced by the F_1 plant? Considering the factor interaction, determine what fruit colors may be expected in the F_2 generation. What is the ratio of plants producing these various colors?

9. In maize the following genotypes are known. Write out the phenotypic expression of each.

AACCRRPrPrddii	*AACCrrPrPrddii*
AACCRRPrPrDDii	*AAccRRPrPrddii*
AACCRRprprddii	*aaCCRRPrPrddii*
AACCRRprprDDii	*AaCcRrPrPrddii*
AACCRRPrPrDDII	*AACCRRprprddII*

10. What kind of factor interaction is indicated when the $9:3:3:1$ F_2 ratio is modified to $9:7$? to $9:3:4$? to $13:3$? to $12:3:1$?
11. What kind of factor interaction is indicated by a $27:37$ ratio?
12. What do you understand by the term *factor complex*? What kinds of genes make up the factor complex? By the use of definite examples, explain the action and interactions of the different types of factors.
13. Distinguish between dominance and epistasis. How many pairs of alleles may be involved in each case? By use of definite examples, explain the interaction of epistatic factors which leads to the condition of epistasis. (See pp. 231, 240.)

References

BATESON, WM.: *Mendel's Principles of Heredity*, Cambridge, England, Cambridge University Press, 1909.

CASTLE, W. E.: *Genetics and Eugenics*, 4th ed. Cambridge, Harvard University Press, 1930, Chapters XVII, XVIII, XIX, XX, 156–199.

COULTER, M. C.: *Outline of Genetics*, Chicago, University of Chicago Press, 1923.

EMERSON, R. A.: *A Fifth Pair of Factors, A-a, for Aleurone Color in Maize, and its Relation to the C-c and R-r Pairs.* (Cornell University Agricultural Experiment Station Memoir #16) Ithaca, 1918.

————: *The Genetic Relations of Plant Colors in Maize.* (Cornell University Agricultural Experiment Station Memoir #39) Ithaca, 1921.

FASTEN, N.: *Principles of Genetics and Eugenics*, Boston, Ginn & Company, 1935.

SINNOTT, EDMUND W., L. C. DUNN, and Th. Dobzhansky: *Principles of Genetics*, 4th ed. New York, McGraw-Hill Book Company, Inc., 1950, Chapter V.

SNYDER, L. H.: *The Principles of Heredity*, 4th ed. Boston, D. C. Heath & Company, 1951, Chapter V.

Influence of Multiple Genes in Development

Hertiable characteristics of plants and animals, including those of man, may be designated as **qualitative** and **quantitative.** Examples of qualitative characters are colors in plants, sugary or starchy grains in corn, rough or smooth coats of rodents, and variations in eye color in man. In these traits there is a difference in the quality of the character. While there are great variations in **qualitative characters,** *such traits are* generally *sharply differentiated* with few gradations between them. Thus *they form a discontinuous series.* The progeny of hybrids between organisms differing in qualitative characters may usually be grouped into a few sharply contrasting phenotypic classes which in the F_2 generation occur in numerical ratios of $3:1$, $1:2:1$, $9:3:3:1$, or their modifications. The immediate genetic basis of qualitative characters generally consists of a single pair of genes or at most a few pairs of alleles in a gene complex (Chapters 3, 4, 10, and 11).

Examples of **quantitative characters** are heights of corn plants, lengths of ears in the several breeds and species of rabbits, and heights and weights of men in a given population. In general, quantitative characters are *measurable* and *form a continuous series* with a great range of variation and many gradations between the extremes. The progeny of hybrids between organisms representing extremes of a measurable character generally can not be grouped into definite classes, and F_2 progeny of such hybrids usually *can not be classified into definite ratios.*

Early in the study of genetics, it became apparent that many measurable or quantitative characters were produced not by a single determiner but as the result of the action and interaction of two or more pairs of genes, which had identical or at least similar effects. In fact, the development of many quantitative characters results from the action and interaction of a relatively large number of hereditary units. Furthermore the effects of many of these genes, but not all of them, were found to be additive or cumulative in the development of the traits. The terms *duplicate genes, cumulative genes, multiple genes,* and *polygenes* have been used to designate the groups of hereditary units basic to many quantitative characters.

Historically, the hypothesis of multiple factors or multiple genes as an interpretation of the inheritance of certain complex characteristics was developed and proposed independently by Nilsson-Ehle in Sweden and by East in America (pp. 247, 251). It is interesting to note that the hypothesis of multiple genes, so useful in the interpretation of the inheritance of quantitative characters, was actually developed as the result of studies in the inheritance of qualitative differences. The fundamental principle is that a relatively large number of genes is concerned in the production of a single trait or characteristic. The multiple gene hypothesis is particularly applicable to the inheritance of most quantitative characters but to only a few qualitative traits. The early work of Nilsson-Ehle and of East happened to be done on qualitative characteristics.

chapter 12

Duplicate Genes

In a study of the little plant shepherd's-purse belonging to the genus *Bursa* or *Capsella*, Shull found that plants of an American species, *Bursa bursa-pastoris*, produced flat, triangular capsules and those of a European species, *Bursa Heggeri*, produced spindle-shaped capsules (Fig. 117). Hybridization between these two types of plants produced F_1 plants bearing the triangular capsule, which indicated full dominance over the spindle-shaped type. Selfing the F_1 plant, however, produced an F_2 generation which consisted mostly of plants having triangular-shaped capsules and a very few plants bearing the spindle-shaped capsules. The F_2 ratio was determined to be 15 plants producing triangular-shaped to 1 with spindle-shaped capsules.

To account for this hereditary behavior, it was assumed that there were two pairs of genes, with the dominant member in each pair determining the production of triangular capsules. Since these two pairs of genes have identical or duplicate effects, they may be designated T_1-t_1 and T_2-t_2. Upon the assumption of full dominance and identical effects of these genes, plants which contain one or more of them in the dominant condition, such as $T_1T_1T_2T_2$, $T_1T_1T_2t_2$, $T_1T_1t_2t_2$, or $T_1t_1t_2t_2$, will produce triangular-shaped capsules. Following segregation assortment, and recombination of the genes in the dihybrid, 15 of the 16 theoretically possible F_2 plants contain at least one T and bear triangular capsules. Only plants with the genotype $t_1t_1t_2t_2$, occurring 1 in 16, produce the spindle-shaped capsule (Fig. 118). Since in this case all of the T genes have the same effect and one dominant gene, T, apparently has as much effect as TT, TTT, or even $TTTT$, these types of genes are called *noncumulative* duplicate genes.

Duplicate Cumulative Genes

Nilsson-Ehle of Sweden, investigating the inheritance of red- and white-aleurone tissues in wheat grains, hybridized varieties showing the contrasting traits. He found that the F_1 grains were colored but of a value of red lighter than that of the dark-red-grained parent. In the explanation of this type of factor action, two pairs of genes, R_1-r_1 and R_2-r_2, were assumed to be basic to the production of white and colored grains in wheat. The red-grained wheat was thought to have the genotype $R_1R_1R_2R_2$; and the white-grained wheat, the genotype $r_1r_1r_2r_2$. Following hybridization between these contrasting-color types, the F_1 hybrid would have the genotype $R_1r_1R_2r_2$. In the F_2 hybrid generation there were various hues or values of red grains,

FIG. 117. SHEPHERD'S-PURSE, BURSA BURSA-PASTORIS (OR CAPSELLA).
Left, entire plant; right, top, to show triangular capsules characteristic of the American species.

depending upon the number of incompletely dominant R genes in the geno-types. These genotypes and grain colors ranged from $1RRRR$, dark red; $4RRRr$, fairly dark red; $6RRrr$, light red; $4Rrrr$, very light red; to $1rrrr$, white (Fig. 119). When *all shades or values of red grains were grouped to-gether as red*, the ratio was 15 grains of some hue of red to 1 *white grain*. This is the typical 15:1 dihybrid ratio expected when two pairs of genes with duplicate action are involved in a cross. As in Indian corn the aleurone

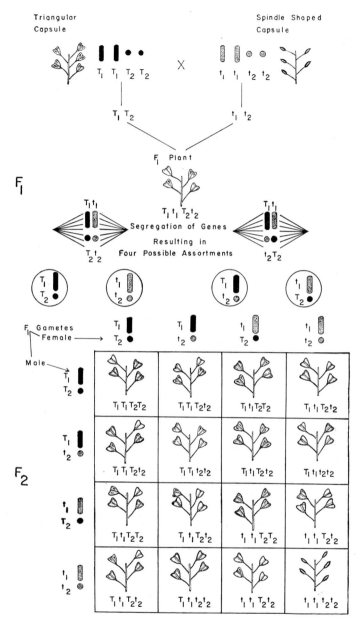

FIG. 118. DIAGRAM OF THE INHERITANCE OF CHARACTERISTICS BASED UPON COM-
PLETELY DOMINANT NONCUMULATIVE DUPLICATE GENES.

These genotypes condition the production of an F_2 of plants with triangular capsules and plants with spindle-shaped capsules in the ratio of 15:1. (Triangular types from native material; spindle types from plants grown from seeds furnished by George H. Shull.)

color in wheat is a seed character, and the F_2 phenotypes are evident in the grains containing the F_2 embryos. The grains produced on the F_1 plants show segregation into the classes of color values of the F_2 generation.

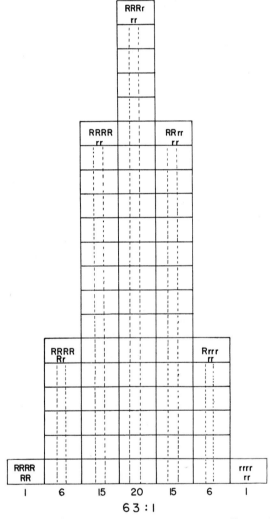

FIG. 119. DIAGRAM INDICATING ACCUMULATION OF THE COLOR GENES, "R_1-r_1," "R_2-r_2," AND "R_3-r_3," IN GENOTYPES OF THE F_2 GENERATION FOLLOWING CROSSES OF VARIETIES OF WHEAT WITH RED AND WITH WHITE GRAINS.

In further studies Nilsson-Ehle obtained additional varieties of colored wheat, especially an old one with very dark-red grains from the north of Sweden. When he used these plants in his crosses, he finally concluded that at least three pairs of genes with similar or duplicate action were concerned in the inheritance and development of grain colors in wheat. His experiments indicated that in addition to R_1-r_1 and R_2-r_2, there was a third pair, R_3-r_3. The term *triplicate genes* has sometimes been used to designate such a group of hereditary units. When all three gene pairs are involved in a trihybrid as $R_1r_1R_2r_2R_3r_3$, the F_2 phenotypic ratio is 63 grains showing various values of red to 1 white grain. The values of red in the colored grains result from the cumulative or additive effects of the incompletely dominant R genes in the genotypes. If two pairs are heterozygous, the third pair being in the homozygous recessive as $R_1r_1R_2r_2r_3r_3$, the F_2 ratio is 15:1. If only one pair is heterozygous, the other two pairs being the homozygous recessive as $R_1r_1r_2r_2r_3r_3$, the ratio is 3:1. In all cases, 63:1, 15:1, or 3:1, the red phenotypes show various hues of red grains, depending upon the number of duplicate color genes, R, which are recombined in the genotypes. This situation differs from that of the capsule form in the shepherd's-purse because of the *incomplete dominance* of the R-r genes.

YELLOW ENDOSPERM OF MAIZE. Of numerous endosperm characters in corn or maize, that of yellow color in the common varieties of field corn is well known. The grains are typically of several hues or values of yellow color which are sometimes difficult to classify. In early interpretations of the inheritance of this character, East suggested the presence of two pairs of genes that appeared to be duplicate and cumulative in their effects. This work and that of Nilsson-Ehle in wheat are of historical interest. East completed and published his early reports on this type of multiple factor without knowledge of the results obtained by Nilsson-Ehle on the same topic. They were thus pioneers in the development of the multiple factor or multiple gene hypothesis. Later investigations have pointed to a third pair of factors involved in the production of yellow endosperm. Mangelsdorf and Fraps have concluded that there are 3 genes for the yellow color. The genes may be designated as Y_1-y_1, Y_2-y_2, and Y_3-y_3; then the genotype $y_1y_1y_2y_2y_3y_3$ conditions white endosperm, and the 6 possible genotypic combinations of Y with the recessive gene y condition the various hues of yellow endosperm. In the F_2 generation, as in the case of kernel color in wheat, the genetic recombinations result in 64 theoretically possible genotypes. Of these, 63 would condition some value of yellow, and the 1 with the 6 recessive genes y would condition the white endosperm.

Additional Examples of Duplicate Gene Actions

HEIGHT IN SWEET PEAS. The inheritance of height and form in some varieties of sweet peas was studied by Bateson and Punnett in England as early as 1908. Sweet peas may be tall or dwarf. The dwarf types occur in two forms, one a dwarf-bush type and another dwarf-prostrate plant called "cupid," both recessive to the tall form. Hybridization between the standard tall plants and either one of the dwarf types produced a tall F_1 plant. Selfed F_1 plants yielded an F_2 generation consisting of 3 tall to 1 dwarf plant. Thus the difference between each of the dwarf forms and the standard tall form could be explained by the action of a single pair of genes. Hybridization of the dwarf-bush and the dwarf-cupid types produced an F_1 plant which was tall. Following selfing of this F_1, the F_2 generation consisted of 9 tall plants, 3 prostrate-cupid plants, 3 bush-dwarf plants, and 1 cupid-bush dwarf, which was a small erect plant of cupid type. The bush dwarf was assumed to have the genotype *bbCC* and the cupid the genotype *BBcc*. Hybridization between the two dwarf types involved the genes from both genotypes, *bbCC* and *BBcc*, in a dihybrid combination. Thus the tall F_1 plant has the genotype *BbCc*. The combined effects of the dominant genes *B* and *C* from both pairs of alleles resulted in the standard tallness. Segregation, assortment, and recombination of these two pairs of genes, following selfing the F_1 plant, resulted in the production of the genotypes indicated in Table XXV.

Table XXV

F₂ RESULTING FROM SELF-POLLINATING AN F₁ PLANT IN SWEET PEAS

Genotypes	4*BbCc* 2*BbCC* 2*BBCc* 1*BBCC*	2*Bbcc* 1*BBcc*	2*bbCc* 1*bbCC*	1*bbcc*
Phenotypes	9 standard tall plants	3 cupid dwarfs	3 bush dwarfs	1 cupid-bush dwarf

HEIGHT IN BROOMCORN. In broomcorn, an agricultural crop of considerable economic importance in certain sections of the United States, varieties differ in size. There are the standard type, attaining a height of about 103 inches; a dwarf variety known as western dwarf, about 62 inches; and a smaller dwarf variety, the whisk-dwarf type, only about 41 inches in height. Sieglinger found that when the standard type was crossed with either the western dwarf or the whisk dwarf, there was produced an F_1 of standard size in each case, and the F_2 consisted of 3 tall standard types to 1 dwarf type. However, when the two dwarf types were hybridized, the F_1 was standard size. The $F_1 \times F_1$ produced an F_2 generation in the ratio of 9 standard size (103 inches):3 western dwarf (62 inches):3 whisk dwarf (41 inches):1 double dwarf (25 inches or less in height).

Two gene pairs, *A-a* and *D-d*, were postulated by Sieglinger, the genotype of the western dwarf as *AAdd* and the genotype of the whisk dwarf *aaDD*. Hybridization between the two dwarfs brought a dominant height gene from each dwarf plant into the genotype of the F_1 hybrid plants. When F_1 plants of genotypes *AaDd* were interpollinated, the expected 16 F_2 genotypes were produced as shown in Table XXVI.

Table XXVI

F₂ RESULTING FROM POLLINATING THE TWO F₁ HYBRIDS IN BROOMCORN

Genotypes	4*AaDd* 2*AaDD* 2*AADd* 1*AADD*	2*Aadd* 1*AAdd*	2*aaDd* 1*aaDD*	1*aadd*
Phenotypes conditioned	9 standard (103 inches)	3 western dwarf (62 inches)	3 whisk dwarf (41 inches)	1 double dwarf (25 inches)

COAT COLORS IN DUROC-JERSEY SWINE. An interesting type of inheritance yielding an unusual F_2 ratio has been found in swine. Breeds of swine may be distinguished by typical coat colors. A red coat is characteristic in the Duroc-

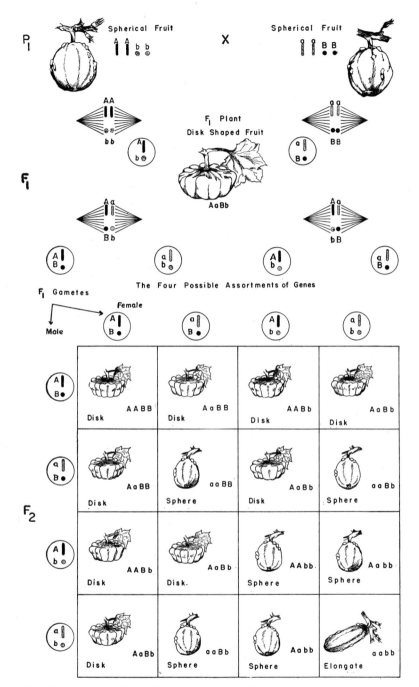

FIG. 120. DIAGRAM OF GENE INTERACTIONS IN PRODUCTION OF SHAPE IN SQUASH FRUIT.

Squash plants of different genotypes, *AAbb* and *aaBB*, both produce spherical fruits. Because of the interaction of *A* and *B* in the F_1 genotype, *AaBb*, disk-shaped fruits were produced in this generation. The F_2 showed three classes of plants yielding disk, spherical, and elongate fruits in the ratio of 9 disk:6 spherical:1 elongate. (Based on data from E. W. Sinnott.)

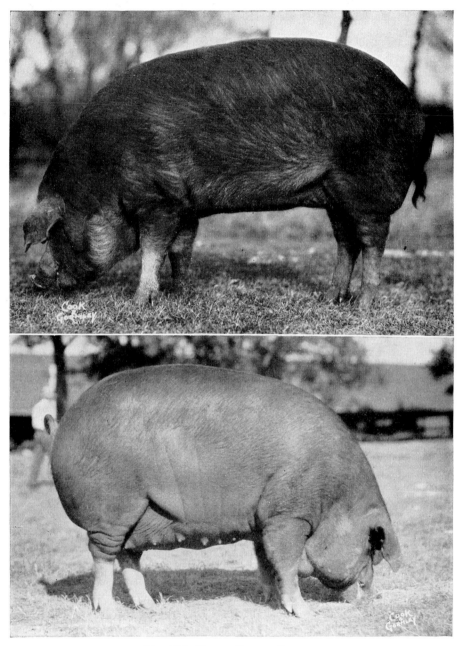

FIG. 121. DUROC-JERSEY SWINE.
Above, the dark-red type; *below,* the lighter sandy type. (Courtesy, Cook and Gormley.)

Jersey breed, but in certain strains off-type sandy individuals are found (Fig. 121). An investigation was undertaken by Wentworth to determine the inheritance of the red- and sandy-coat colors in the Duroc. The sandy strains of Duroc-Jersey always breed true but produce red F_1 progeny when mated to red strains. The F_2 of such matings show 3 red animals:1 sandy, establishing dominance for red. However, when two different strains of sandy Duroc-Jersey swine are crossed, a red-coated F_1 progeny is obtained, but mating $F_1 \times F_1$ produces an F_2 generation of red-coated, sandy-coated, and white-coated individuals in the ratio of 9 red:6 sandy:1 white. Wentworth assumed that the two strains of sandy Durocs had different genotypes, one $SStt$ and the other $ssTT$. In a cross between them, the dominant genes of both genotypes recombined in the F_1 as $SsTt$ resulted in the normal red coat of the typical Duroc. Following the mating of $F_1 \times F_1$, the members of the two pairs of genes S-s and T-t were recombined into the 16 F_2 genotypes. There were $9ST$, red coat; $3Stt$, sandy; $3ssT$, also sandy; and $1sstt$ white coat.

Questions and Problems

Data on Duplicate Genes

In the shepherd's-purse the triangular form of capsule is conditioned by the action of two pairs of noncumulative duplicate genes, T_1-t_1 and T_2-t_2. There is complete dominance of these genes.

In wheat the color of the grains is conditioned by three pairs of factors or triplicate genes, R_1-r_1, R_2-r_2, and R_3-r_3. These genes show a cumulative effect. White grains are conditioned by the triple recessive $r_1r_1r_2r_2r_3r_3$. The yellow endosperm of corn grains is likewise conditioned by three pairs of factors or triplicate cumulative genes, Y_1-y_1, Y_2-y_2, and Y_3-y_3. The triple recessive genotype $y_1y_1y_2y_2y_3y_3$ conditions a pure-breeding plant with white endosperm. The dominant Y genes condition yellow endosperm. They are cumulative in their action.

1. Hybridization between a shepherd's-purse plant with triangular capsules, $T_1T_1T_2T_2$, and one with spindle-shaped capsules, $t_1t_1t_2t_2$, results in the production of an F_1 plant which has triangular capsules. Considering the action of these genes, determine the F_2 phenotypic ratio.

2. Hybridization between a strain of wheat, $R_1R_1r_2r_2r_3r_3$, producing light-red grains and a strain, $r_1r_1r_2r_2r_3r_3$, producing white grains yields an F_1 monohybrid. What will be the segregation of red and white grains in the F_2?

3. Hybridization between a strain of wheat, $R_1R_1R_2R_2r_3r_3$, producing red grains and a strain of wheat, $r_1r_1r_2r_2r_3r_3$, producing white grains yields an F_1 dihybrid generation. Following self-pollination of the F_1 plants, what will be the segregation of F_2 phenotypes?

4. Hybridization between strains of wheat, $R_1R_1R_2R_2R_3R_3$, producing red grains and $r_1r_1r_2r_2r_3r_3$ producing white grains yields an F_1 trihybrid generation. Following self-pollination of the F_1 plants, what F_2 phenotypes may be expected?

5. Assume hybridization between two strains of wheat producing very light-red grains, $R_1R_1r_2r_2r_3r_3 \times r_1r_1r_2r_2R_3R_3$. Explain the factor action which conditions the F_2 ratio.

6. Yellow and white grains of corn occur in a 3:1 ratio in monohybrid crosses involving a single pair of the duplicate genes as Y_1-y_1. What F_2 ratio may be expected if two pairs of these genes as Y_1-y_1 and Y_2-y_2 are involved in a dihybrid cross? Explain the action of these genes.

7. What F_2 ratio may be expected following hybridization of a variety of yellow corn, $Y_1Y_1Y_2Y_2Y_3Y_3$, and a variety of white corn, $y_1y_1y_2y_2y_3y_3$? Explain the action of the genes.

DATA ON THE ACTION OF CERTAIN OTHER TYPES OF GENES WITH DUPLICATE ACTION

The red coat of Duroc-Jersey swine has been found to depend upon the cumulative effect or the interaction of two pairs of genes, S-s and T-t. The sandy or light-red coat in this breed appears to be conditioned by the action of the dominant gene of one of these pairs of genes acting alone. Thus sandy coat may be conditioned by SS or Ss and likewise conditioned by TT or Tt. The double recessive of these genes, $sstt$, conditions the white coat.

Similar duplicate gene action has been found in the development of height in the sweet pea and in broomcorn. In the sweet pea the dwarf-bush type is conditioned by the dominant effect of B in the pair of genes B-b. The more prostrate dwarf or cupid type is conditioned by the dominant action of C in another pair of alleles, C-c. The tall or standard sweet pea is conditioned by the combined effect of the dominant genes of both pairs of alleles, B and C. The double recessive, $bbcc$, conditions an extreme dwarf-cupid-bush type.

In a quite similar manner the height of two types of dwarf broomcorn, western dwarf, $AAdd$, and the whisk dwarf, $aaDD$, is dependent upon the action of the dominant genes of a single pair of alleles. The combination of the dominant alleles of these pairs in a genotype as $AADD$ or $AaDd$ conditions the development of the tall or standard broomcorn.

8. Following mating of two strains of sandy Durocs, $SStt$ and $ssTT$, the F_1 generation develops the full red coat. Following the reported action of these genetic factors, calculate the expected F_2 ratio. Explain the factor action.
9. What F_2 ratio may be expected following crossing a typical dark-red Duroc-Jersey and a white strain? Explain the action of the factors involved.
10. Bateson crossed the bush and cupid types of sweet pea. Explain the modified F_2 ratio which he obtained.
11. Sieglinger crossed the western-dwarf and the whisk-dwarf types of broomcorn and found that the F_1 plants were restored to full standard height. Upon self-pollination, the F_1 yielded an F_2 generation, consisting of tall, dwarf, and extreme dwarf types. Consult p. 252 for heights of plants and explain the modified ratio.

References

BABCOCK, E. B., and R. E. CLAUSEN: *Genetics in Relation to Agriculture*, New York, McGraw-Hill Book Company, Inc., 1927, Chapter XIX.

BATESON, WM.: *Mendel's Principles of Heredity*, Cambridge, England, Cambridge University Press, 1909.

EAST, E. M., and H. K. HAYES: *Inheritance in Maize*. (Connecticut Agricultural Experiment Station Bulletin #167) New Haven.

JULL, MORLEY A.: *Poultry Breeding*, New York, John Wiley & Sons, Inc., 1932.

SHULL, A. F.: *Heredity*, 3rd ed. New York, McGraw-Hill Book Company, Inc., 1938.

SHULL, G. H.: "Duplicate Genes for Capsule Form in *Bursa bursapastoris*," *Zeit. f. ind. Abst. u. Vererb.* #12 (1914).

SIEGLINGER, J. B.: "Inheritance of Height in Broom Corn," *J. Agr. Research* **44**:13–20 (1932).

chapter 13

Quantitative Characters and the Multiple Gene Hypothesis—Inheritance of Differences in Size

East followed his early work on duplicate genes with a series of investigations on the inheritance of such quantitative characters as corolla length in flowers, the height of plants in a field of maize, and the size of grains and the length of ears in maize. As a result of his studies, he contributed to knowledge of the inheritance of measurable characters and to the establishment and extension of the theory of multiple factors as a working hypothesis. Besides East's work, among early investigations of inheritance of quantitative characters in America were the studies of Emerson on squash fruits, beans, and Indian corn, of Emerson and East on size inheritance of maize, and of Castle on measurable traits of rodents. At about the same time Punnett in England published his results on the inheritance of weight in fowls. A. Lang of Switzerland also added a suggestion of multiple factors or genes to explain size inheritance in rabbits.

INHERITANCE OF COROLLA LENGTH IN TOBACCO FLOWERS. East studied species and varieties of the genus *Nicotiana* or tobacco which differed in corolla lengths (Fig. 122).* He hybridized two species of *Nicotiana* that differed in flower size with mean corolla lengths of 25.0 mm. and 78.8 mm., respectively. The flowers of the large parental type, *Nicotiana alata* var. *grandiflora*, were about three times as large as those of the small parental type, *N. forgetiana*, and the F_1 plants resulting from their cross had intermediate-sized flowers with a mean corolla length of 44.3 mm. The F_2 generation ($F_1 \times F_1$), however, was extremely variable with a range from the small-flowered to the large-flowered parental types. The F_2 plants could not be arranged into sharp discontinuous classes but formed a continuous series of sizes from large to small.

* Kölreuter about 1760 investigated inheritance of flower size in *Nicotiana*. He observed the intermediate F_1 generation and the wide range of variations characteristic of the F_2 plants but was unable to arrive at definite conclusions as to the method of inheritance of flower size. Later East repeated Kölreuter's work as a part of his studies of multiple genes.

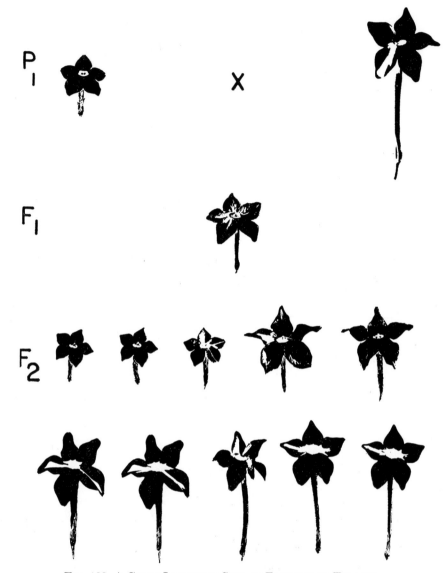

FIG. 122. A CROSS INVOLVING SIZE OF FLOWERS IN TOBACCO.

P₁, flowers of *Nicotiana forgetiana* and *Nicotiana alata grandiflora*. Flower of the F₁ hybrid. Various sizes of flowers from F₂ plants. (Modified after East, from *Botan. Gaz.* **LV,** 1913.)

In this and in other cases in tobacco where East was unable to distinguish phenotypic classes, data from a cross including P_1, F_1, F_2, and F_3 generations were analyzed statistically. He then assumed that four or five pairs of incompletely dominant genes conditioned corolla length, each one exerting only a little influence on size development.

QUANTITATIVE INHERITANCE IN MAIZE. Emerson and East reported their early investigations on the inheritance of quantitative characters in Indian corn or maize. Crosses were made between Tom Thumb popcorn with average ear length of 6.6 cm. and Black Mexican sweet corn, average ear length of 16.8 cm. The F_1 hybrid between them had ears of intermediate length, averaging about 12.1 cm., but the F_2 generation was variable with ear length ranging from 7 to 21 cm. The extremes of the F_2 ranges were accounted for on the basis of recombinations of the genes controlling ear lengths. When selected F_2 plants were used as parents of the F_3 generations, it was possible to obtain F_3 families with restricted ranges in ear length. All F_3 families tended to be less variable than F_2 families.

Besides the investigation of the inheritance of ear length in maize, Emerson and East reported their studies of the inheritance of the number of rows of grains per ear, the diameter of ears, weight of seeds, breadth of seeds, number of nodes per stalk, internode length, number of stalks per plant, combined total length of stalks, and heights of plants. The investigations all indicated dependence of these measurable characteristics upon a series of hereditary units which were cumulative in their effects.

In order to clarify their conception of the action of multiple genes, Emerson and East presented a *hypothetical* example of two plants, one assumed to be 12 inches and the other 28 inches tall. An unknown group of genes, as XYZ, was postulated to be common to both and responsible for the development of the first 12 inches in height in each of the plants. The additional 16 inches of the 28-inch plant were then determined by a single pair of incompletely dominant genes A-a, making it AA and, for the 12-inch one, aa. A cross between these two plants would produce an intermediate F_1, Aa, about 20 inches in height. Three phenotypic classes would be expected to occur in the F_2 generation, AA = 28 inches: Aa = 20 inches: aa = 12 inches. Upon this assumption each A gene would have a height-determining value of 8 inches.

Or the assumption may be made that the 16-inch increment of the 28-inch plants is the result of the action of two pairs of allelic genes, A-a and B-b, each pair incompletely dominant and each A or B gene having equal height-determining value of 4 inches. In this case the F_1, $AaBb$, generation is also 20 inches tall. Although there are nine possible genotypic recombinations, some of them are duplications of height effects. The F_2 generation would be expected to have five classes 28, 24, 20, 16, and 12 inches tall in the ratio of 1:4:6:4:1 with each of the parental types expected once in sixteen (Fig. 123).

A principle in the conception of multiple genes is that usually with added pairs of alleles in the development of a trait the effect of each gene is less. With three pairs of alleles as A-a, B-b, and C-c involved in the development of a height increment of 16 inches, the number of F_2 phenotypic classes would be increased to seven, and each A, B, and C factor would exert a height effect of $2\frac{2}{3}$ inches. When four allelic pairs, as A-a, B-b, C-c, and D-d, are assumed to be involved, nine F_2 phenotypic classes may be expected with the influence of each, A, B, C, and D, reduced to only 2 inches. This relationship continues with increasing numbers of allelic pairs.

To gain an appreciation of situations involving multiple genes, it is helpful to recall the relationship between the number of pairs of genes involved in a polyhybrid cross and the number of genotypic recombinations in the F_2 generation. With a single pair of genes, there are 3 genotypic recombinations in the ratio of $1:2:1$; with two pairs of genes, there are 9 possible recombinations in the ratio of $1:2:1:2:4:2:1:2:1$. Thus, as the number of pairs of genes increases in polyhybrid crosses, the number of gene recombinations progresses geometrically as 3, 9, 27, 81, 243, etc. With five pairs of genes postulated, as for one of the tobacco crosses, according to Mendelian

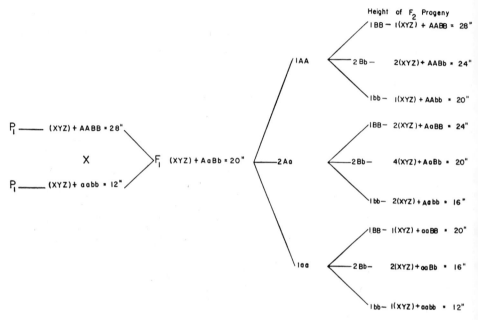

FIG. 123. DIAGRAM OF CUMULATIVE EFFECTS OF TWO PAIRS OF INCOMPLETELY DOMINANT SIZE GENES, "A-a" AND "B-b."

Genes A and B each have a value of 4 inches in determination of height in the hypothetical plants involved in the cross. The F_1 plant is intermediate between the parental types. The F_2 generation shows 9 genotypic classes conditioning 5 groups differing phenotypically in size. The sizes of the F_2 plants range from 12 to 28 inches in height and reduplicate both parental types. (Modified after Emerson and East.)

principles there would be 1,024 genotypes in the F_2 generation. Among these, 243 distinct biotypes or genotypic combinations capable of phenotypic expressions could be expected. Recombination of parental genotypes would be rare even in fairly large F_2 populations. In a cross involving five pairs of genes, the expectation would be 1 genotype of each parent in 1,024 F_2 recombinations. A much larger F_2 population than this might be needed actually to regain the parental types.

With incomplete dominance between each of several allelic pairs of genes, each one having only minor effect, there would be a tendency markedly to increase the number of phenotypic classes over the number expected with full dominance (pp. 66, 94). When the genotypes are numerous and there is incomplete dominance between most of the allelic pairs, a very large number of only slightly differentiated phenotypic classes might be expected. With added environmentally induced variations, the continuous series of size forms can then be accounted for. In multiple gene crosses there are too many phenotypic groups to classify in the ordinary Mendelian fashion, and it is customary to analyze the filial generations statistically (pp. 250, 293).

FIG. 124. COMPARATIVE SIZE OF FOWLS.

Left, a black Rose Comb Bantam cock weighing about 26 ounces; *right*, a Jersey Black Giant cock weighing 13 pounds. Large differences in size appear to be inherited in geometric proportion, as 2, 4, 8, etc. (Courtesy, A. O. Schilling.)

INHERITANCE OF SIZE IN FOWLS.   Since size of domesticated animals is of economic importance, studies of the inheritance of size have received considerable attention. Many studies have been conducted with laboratory rodents such as mice and rabbits and with domestic fowls. Fowls are good experimental material because of their rapid reproduction, cheap maintenance, and economic worth. Among breeds of domesticated fowls, there are conspicuous differences in size. The Jersey Black Giant which weighs about 13 pounds is approximately eight times the weight of the Rose Comb Bantam, only 26 ounces (Fig. 124). Other breeds also differ in size but in most cases to a lesser degree. Besides its practical value, study of body weight in fowls has yielded important information concerning the role of multiple genes in the development of measurable characters. In England Punnett, who was one of the earliest investigators in this field, crossed small Silver Sebright Bantams with large Golden Hamburgs (Fig. 125). The average weights of the Sebright Bantams were 750 grams for the

FIG. 125. COMPARATIVE SIZE OF FOWLS.
Left, Silver Spangled Hamburg cock weighing about 1,350 grams. *Right*, Silver Sebright Bantam cock weighing about 750 grams. The larger breed is thus about twice the size of the smaller. Small differences in size appear to be inherited in arithmetic proportion or in a purely additive fashion, as 2, 4, 6, 8, etc. (Courtesy, A. O. Schilling.)

male and 600 grams for the female. In the Hamburg breed the males weighed on the average 1,350 grams and the females 1,100, about twice the weight of the smaller breed. Average weights of the F_1 males and females, which were between 1,200 and 1,000 grams, were intermediate between the parental types but nearer the larger Hamburg size. The F_2 population showed a much wider range of weights than the F_1 but a similar average. There were F_2 individuals even smaller than the bantam parent and others that were larger than the Hamburg. In succeeding generations it was possible to establish strains which were genetically pure for these smaller and larger sizes as well as for some intermediate classes.

The genetical interpretation of production of body weight included the assumption of four pairs of genes, A-a, B-b, C-c, and D-d, with the dominant alleles, $ABCD$, influencing the development of large size and the recessive genes, $abcd$, small size. The Sebright-Bantam breed then was considered to be homozygous recessive for three of the four pairs of size genes and homozygous dominant for one pair, $aabbccDD$. The large Hamburg breed was considered to be homozygous dominant for three of the four pairs of size genes and homozygous recessive for one, $AABBCCdd$. The F_1 generation thus would have the genotype $AaBbCcDd$. If the size genes were incompletely dominant, this genotype would be expected to condition the development of a type of fowl intermediate in size between the two parents. The F_1 actually was of intermediate size but nearer the weight of the larger parent than that of the smaller. In the F_2 generation, produced by mating $F_1 \times F_1$, the four allelic pairs, A-a, B-b, C-c, and D-d, would recombine in all possible ways, with a few fowls containing the quadruple dominants, $AABBCCDD$ and $AABBCCDd$, and a few the quadruple recessive, $aabbccdd$. These individuals would be expected to be larger and smaller, respectively, than the parental types, since they have the influence of all the dominant genes in one case and of all the recessive genes in the other. Neither of the two parents had the genotype characteristic of the F_2 extremes.

Later Investigations in Size Inheritance and Some New Concepts

During the past several years, investigations have been conducted with material in which the larger parental character was from 10 to more than 100 times as large as the smaller; these studies involving more extreme-size differences have revealed aspects of size inheritance not found in the work with more moderate-size differences.

INHERITANCE OF EXTREME-SIZE DIFFERENCES. MacArthur and Butler and later MacArthur contributed to the study of multiple genes. They reviewed and criticized past conclusions of size inheritance and offered further interpretations.

In earlier studies with only small-size differences, crosses yielded F_1 generations intermediate between the parental types, approximately the arithmetic mean of the parental types (pp. 257, 261). The older results were generally interpreted on the basis of (1) *several genes*, which (2) were *incompletely dominant*, thus producing intermediates or "blends." It was also assumed (3) that these genes had approximately *equal influence* and (4) had an *additive or cumulative effect* in the development of a trait. Cumulative actions of the numerous genes recombined in the genotypes gave rise to the highly variable F_2 generation, with its extremes approaching the sizes of the large and small parents.

Later researches have been conducted on the inheritance of much greater size differences, as for example the size of fruits in four varieties of tomato that had been self-pollinated for 12 to 20 generations and were considered to be highly homozygous for size genes. The Red Currant produced fruits

0.8 grams in weight. Yellow Cherry had 3.6-gram fruits, while two other strains, No. 902 and Tangerine, produced fruits weighing 54.9 and 106.8 grams, respectively. The fruits of the largest-fruited variety, Tangerine, were therefore more than 100 times the size of those of the smallest-fruited

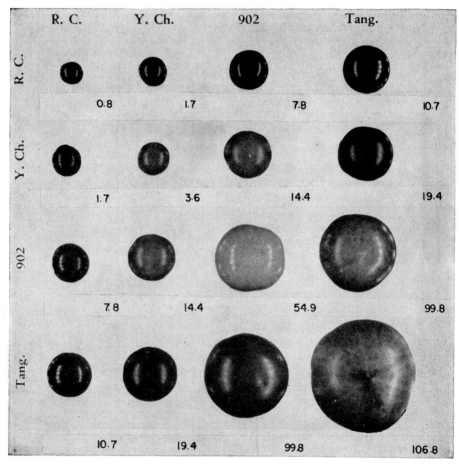

FIG. 126. SIZES OF FRUITS PRODUCED BY F₁ TOMATO PLANTS RESULTING FROM CROSSES.

In checkerboard the four genotypes in each vertical column differ from those of the other columns by a single set of chromosomes. The increases are twofold from column one to two; fivefold from column two to three; from column one to three, the increase is 9.1 times; from one to four, it is 11.3 times; and from three to four, it is 1.2 times. (Modified after MacArthur, from *J. Heredity.*)

variety, the Red Currant. Reciprocal crosses were repeatedly made between these varieties, and data were taken on all the possible hybrids (Fig. 126).

The fruits of the F₁ hybrid plants were not intermediate in size but were close to the geometric means of the parental varieties. An example of this is the cross Red Currant (weight 0.8) $\times$ Yellow Cherry (weight 3.6). The F_1 plants produced fruits averaging the square root of $0.8 \times 3.6 = 1.7$ grams which is the geometric mean of the two parents. This is in contrast with the arithmetic mean of $0.8 + 3.6 = \frac{4.4}{2} = 2.2$ grams which would have been expected for an intermediate F_1. Table XXVII shows that similar geometric means were found in five of the six possible hybrid combinations.

Table XXVII

WEIGHTS OF F_1 TOMATO FRUITS IN GRAMS

F_1 Hybrids	Observed	Geom. Mean	Arith. Mean
R. C. $\times$ Y. Ch.	1.7	1.70	2.2
R. C. $\times$ 902	7.8	6.63	27.85
R. C. $\times$ Tang.	10.7	9.24	53.8
Y. Ch. $\times$ 902	14.4	14.06	29.25
Y. Ch. $\times$ Tang.	19.4	19.61	55.2
902 $\times$ Tang.	99.8	76.57	80.85

Only the F_1 hybrid between the two largest-fruited varieties, No. 902 (weight 54.9) and Tangerine (weight 106.8), with relatively small differences in size, departs from the geometric mean. MacArthur points out one of the observations in earlier work on size inheritance, namely, that parental types differing only slightly in size tended to yield intermediate hybrids of considerable variability. His explanation is that in the cases of small differences, fruit size is conditioned by the interaction of minor genes and accessory or modifying factors, not by major or basic factors or genes.

MacArthur shows that the substitution of the genome or gametic set of chromosomes, with the associated size genes, of one variety for that of another type in the crosses increases the size of the F_1 fruits by a definite multiple (Fig. 126). For example, if the Yellow Cherry variety is substituted for the extremely small Red Currant variety, the fruit sizes of F_1 in all crosses is about doubled. Substitution of variety 902 for the Red Currant type results in a ninefold increase in the F_1 fruit sizes in all crosses. The size genes in all of the varieties used in the experiment were shown to have a similar geometric effect on the sizes of F_1 fruits (Table XXVII). MacArthur emphasizes that size in living organisms depends upon cell numbers and cell size. Cell numbers are increased geometrically by cell division from 1 to 2, 4, 8, 16, etc. Probably the increase in cell size is also geometric. Possibly the actions of the size genes determine the development of additional or more active growth substances which stimulate or control the rate of cell divisions and the amount of cell expansion. Because of these relationships, MacArthur favors an interpretation of the cumulative effects of size genes on a geometric basis rather than on a purely additive or arithmetic basis. The idea of the multiple effect of size genes has been further confirmed through investigation of size inheritance in mice.

THE ACTION AND INTERACTION OF MULTIPLE GENES. Castle has made extensive studies on the inheritance of quantitative characters of rodents, such as size inheritance in rats, mice, and rabbits. His active work has extended through a long period, from the early time of investigation of quantitative characters to the present. He has contributed to the thought of the entire period.

Castle considers doubtful the existence of specific size genes of the sort usually assumed in explanations of quantitative inheritance. Possibly there may be *genes* that *act to influence growth* of an organism as a whole. The size of a plant or an animal may be the incidental consequence or the resultant of the diverse actions of many pairs of genes. Goldschmidt in his *Physiological Genetics* pictures the development of the individual as *due to reaction velocities* in time and postulates further that the reactions involved are catalyzed by genes or their products. Since size is dependent upon cell divisions and cell expansions, these reaction velocities may be significant in determining the number of cell divisions and the rate and degree of cell expansions. Possibly the multiple gene complex underlying the inheritance and development of measurable characteristics consists of a large number of genes with many different actions and interactions. There may be basic genes determining the development of certain traits, supplementary genes acting as modifiers of characteristics, and some may be duplicate genes, cumulative in their action. Probably some genes act as accelerators of growth, as Castle suggests, while others may act as epistatic factors and as inhibitors of growth.

CUMULATIVE ACTION OF MULTIPLE GENES. Powers, in a series of articles, has emphasized that multiple genes influencing size differences and also physiological differences leading to early and late development of plants show evidences of factor interactions. He considers that the presence and nature of these interactions or the entire absence of factor interactions determines whether the genes show cumulative effects in a geometric or arithmetic (purely additive) manner. Accordingly, if there is no interaction among the genes principally concerned in the development of the character, their effects are cumulative in the phenotype, as additive effects in an arithmetic progression. The increase in size or quantity of the character is arithmetically cumulative, that is, by addition as 2, 4, 6, 8, etc. An example of this action is found by Mangelsdorf and Fraps in yellow endosperm of corn where the vitamin-A units per grain increased approximately 2.25 for each additional Y gene present in the genotype. This type of action also appears to be associated with the inheritance of small differences in size. In other cases if several pairs of genes interact as in a gene complex, their effects are also cumulative but in geometric proportions. That is, usually the increase in size or quantity of a character is geometrically cumulative by some multiple as 2, 4, 8, 16, etc., when the differences are large.

THE NUMBER OF GENES CONCERNED IN QUANTITATIVE INHERITANCE. Experiments in inheritance of quantitative characters indicate that the development of such characters is based upon the effects of a large number of genes. Rasmusson has said, "Quantitative characters are genetically determined by a number of cooperating genes. . . . It is considered more probable that 100–200 genes are usually involved in the segregation of quantitative characters than 2–20. . . . The effect of each factor in the genotype is dependent upon all the other factors present, the visible effect of a certain factor being smaller the greater the number of factors acting in the same direction."

Questions have arisen concerning the dependence of quantitative characters on many genes and qualitative differences on few. In answer it has been suggested that many of the measurable characteristics are of more fundamental importance to the organism than superficial qualitative traits. The size of an animal may be of greater survival value than the color of its coat. Early maturity in a plant, a physiological characteristic, may enable it to produce viable seed in a given locality, regardless of the color of its flowers. There are many instances in which quantitative characters may be contrasted with the more superficial qualitative traits. The fundamental quantitative characters possibly should be expected to have a more extensive genetic basis and involve a greater number of genes than the superficial differences of a qualitative nature.

HOW GENES MAY FUNCTION IN DEVELOPMENT. Though size inheritance in plants and animals has been the subject of numerous investigations, much remains to be learned about it. Recent studies have been directed at the influence of genes on development. Size depends to some extent at least on number of primordia or growth areas and on rates of growth. For some time it has been known that hormones influence growth in animals. Substances with similar effects in plants have been recognized and designated as "growth substances." Doubtless all anatomical and physiological components of growth and size relationships have a genetic basis, which probably is of the multiple gene sort. The production of hormones and growth substances may be dependent upon a similar genetic basis. In fact, certain investigations indicate that size and form in plants may be influenced through the action of genes which tend to increase or in other cases to decrease the amounts of growth substances.

Inheritance of Physiological Characteristics

Action of multiple genes has been suggested as the genetical basis for certain physiological phenomena, such as earliness and lateness in the flowering and fruiting period in plants, milk production in cattle, and egg production in fowls. Probably multiple gene bases underlie many other kinds of physiological characteristics, such as resistance to disease, high-yielding ability of plants, speed and endurance in race horses, and many psychic traits of man.

EARLINESS IN CEREALS. Thompson explained the difference between early and late varieties of wheat as dependent upon the action of multiple genes, and Aamodt explained the difference between varieties of spring wheat and winter wheat by the action of a series of multiple genes.

FIG. 127. OAT PLANTS ILLUSTRATING VARIOUS DEGREES OF EARLINESS.
The seeds to produce these plants were all planted the same day in early spring. The plants to be photographed were collected the same day in the summer. (Specimens courtesy, C. F. Noll.)

Noll, in an investigation of the genetic basis of earliness and lateness in flowering and maturity in oats, made crosses between early and late varieties (Fig. 127). The resulting F_1 generation was intermediate between the early and late parents. In the F_2 and subsequent generations, plants were obtained which were earlier than the early parental variety and some that were later than the late parent. One plant was so late that it failed to flower in one growing season. Noll concluded that earliness and lateness in the varieties of oats which he had studied were conditioned by the action of a series of multiple genes, possibly four pairs that together had a cumulative effect, with each gene having an influence of about two and a half days in earliness.

Hoshina and later Ramiah explained earliness and lateness in rice as genetically dependent upon multiple genes. Ramiah found that the several varieties differ genotypically by several pairs of genes. One variety has some pairs in the dominant and another has them in the recessive state. When varieties as $AAbbCCdd$ and $aaBBccDD$ are hybridized, the F_1 genotype will, therefore, be $AaBbCcDd$, and in the F_2 some of the genotypes may contain the factors $AABBCCDD$ or $aabbccdd$. Action of the recombined factors may result in the production of plants which exceed the range of earliness and lateness of the parents. In studies of earliness and lateness of flowering in plants, consideration must be given to the physiological influence of the environmental factors. Of special importance is the influence of the length of day on flowering in plants.

EGG PRODUCTION IN FOWLS. Egg production in fowls is a complex characteristic based on several more or less independent traits as, for example, early or late sexual maturity, rate of laying, broodiness, persistency in laying, and winter pause. Distinct genes have been suggested for the determination of each of these characteristics, the sum total of which make up capacity for egg production.

In all theories that have been advanced to account for the inheritance of egg production, at least several pairs of genes have been suggested. In the Goodale-Hays theory of egg production in which eight pairs of genes have been assumed, an F_2 population of 65,536 would be required for the probable appearance of each parental genotype. Quite likely even a greater number of pairs of genes is actually involved in the inheritance of egg production.

MILK PRODUCTION IN CATTLE. Milk production in cattle and other mammals is another physiological character based on a multiple gene complex. The number of genes in this complex has been variously estimated at from 4 to 5 pairs up to 20 pairs as a minimum.

Studies of the Guernsey and Holstein breeds indicate that 10 pairs of genes are necessary to account for differences of milk production in the two breeds. A study of butterfat production in Jersey and Red Danish cattle indicates that no less than 7 pairs of genes are necessary to account for the differences of this character in the two breeds. These and other studies suggest the possibility of a multiple factor complex of a large number of genes as determining variations in milk production in cattle.

Quantitative Characters and Multiple Genes in Man

C. B. Davenport in an investigation of inheritance of body build found that the children of slender parents did not tend toward the average weight for the race so readily as the offspring of heavily built parents. He concluded that slender persons are more likely to be homozygous for size genes than heavier ones. The heavier persons therefore carry genes conditioning slenderness. Their children, often homozygous for the slender genes, regress from the type of their parents and tend toward the average weight of the race. Davenport also concluded that the genes for heaviness of build were at least partially dominant over those conditioning slender body form. He says, "The hypothesis is indicated that genetically build is controlled by multiple factors, at least three with fleshiness tending slightly to dominate over slenderness."

In harmony with present knowledge indicating control of bodily structure by hormones from various glands in the body, Davenport suggests that the genes condition size by their influence on the functioning of thyroid, pituitary, and perhaps other glands. According to this point of view, it is likely that the number of size genes in human beings is far larger than indicated above. The glands themselves may be influenced by many factors, some of them genetic and some environmental. The development of the glandular structures would most certainly be conditioned by a complex genetic basis. Their functioning may also be influenced by the general physiological constitution of the individual and by general and special nutritional factors.

Hunt has suggested that mental ability in man is inherited on a multiple factor basis. He assumes the probability of five pairs of genes in the genotype influencing the development of mentality. Dominance of a gene is thought to influence a higher degree of mentality than the recessive member of the gene pair (pp. 508).

Questions and Problems

1. What are quantitative characters? In what respect do they differ from most qualitative characters?
2. What type of factors usually form the genetic basis of quantitative characters? Do Mendelian principles apply to these factors?
3. What is the multiple factor hypothesis? Who did the early work upon which this hypothesis is founded?
4. What were the relative sizes of the flowers of tobacco which East studied? How many factors did East think were present in the genotypes conditioning flower size in tobacco? How many biotypes would occur in the F_2 generation if five pairs of size factors were segregating? If the influence of the genes is cumulative, what effect will this number of genotypes have on the F_2 generation?
5. Describe the early work on measurable characters in tobacco. What is the size of the F_1 when the parental types differ in the size of a measurable character? What is the nature of the F_2 generation? Why are large numbers in the F_2 generation essential for complete results?
6. What were the relative sizes of the Hamburgs and Sebright bantams which Punnett used in his experiments on size inheritance in fowls?
7. What was the average size of the F_1 generation in Punnett's Golden Hamburg × Sebright bantam cross? What sizes were found in the F_2 generation of this cross?

8. How many pairs of size factors did Punnett postulate in these fowls? How many biotypes would be expected in the F_2 generation following the recombination of four pairs of size factors? If the influence of these genes were cumulative or additive, what effect could be expected in the sizes of the F_2 population? Were these effects actually observed in the F_2 generation?

9. Which did Punnett regard as dominant, the genes conditioning large or those conditioning small size?

10. In what respects does the work of later workers differ from that of Punnett and other earlier workers in size inheritance?

11. Which are regarded as dominant, genes for large or small size?

12. Are Mendelian principles generally applicable to the behavior of multiple genes? May there be any relation between the number of pairs of genes and the number of different biotypes which occur in the F_2 generation? Do these facts in any way lessen the probability that size factors follow Mendelian principles?

13. How many genes did Rasmusson consider as present in the determination of quantitative or measurable characters?

14. What are some of the more recent conclusions as to the cumulative effects of size factors? Cite some of the data to emphasize the differences in the cumulative effects when large-size differences are studied in comparison with the relatively small-size differences used in the earlier studies?

15. Compare the differences between the cumulative effects of size genes in the arithmetic and the geometric manner.

16. As regards the effective action of specific genes in a genotype, should all of the pairs of genes be thought of as influencing the development of size to the same degree? Or should some of them have greater effect than others?

17. What is the possible relationship of cell numbers to the geometric increase in size of organs and organisms? Do growth substances possibly have any influence on the development of size?

18. To what processes does Castle attribute variations in body size of organisms?

19. What are some of the physiological phenomena which have been interpreted on the hypothesis of multiple factors?

20. Explain the hereditary basis of earliness and lateness in wheat, in oats, and in rice. In general, how many pairs of factors appear to be important in the development of earliness and lateness in plants?

21. In man, which factors are dominant, those conditioning slenderness or those conditioning the heavier builds? Why may the children of heavy parents be slender persons?

22. How many pairs of genes may be involved in the factor complex conditioning size in human beings? Is the number thought to be large or small? Who has done most work on the subject of size inheritance in man?

23. How many pairs of factors does Hunt suggest as a possible basis for the inheritance of mental ability in man?

24. Discuss Table LIII on p. 508 with the relationship of genes to the several grades of mental ability. Is it possible that a scheme such as this may account for the varying degrees of mental ability in human beings?

25. What may be said about so-called blending inheritance in which apparently Mendelian principles do not apply? What is inherited? Is it the phenotypes or the genes which are inherited?

26. Why are large F_2 populations necessary in the study of quantitative inheritance? Do the number of factors necessitate large numbers of genotypes? Why?

27. Under what conditions may multiple factors have cumulative action in the arithmetic manner, and under what conditions may their action be geometrically cumulative?

References

BABCOCK, E. B., and R. E. CLAUSEN: *Genetics in Relation to Agriculture*, New York, McGraw-Hill Book Company, Inc., 1927, Chapter XIX.

CASTLE, W. E.: *Genetics and Eugenics*, Cambridge, Harvard University Press, 1930.

———: *Mammalian Genetics*, Cambridge, Harvard University Press, 1940.

———: "Size Inheritance," *Am. Naturalist* **75**:488–498 (1941).

EAST, E. M., and H. K. HAYES: *Inheritance in Maize*. (Connecticut Agricultural Experiment Station Bulletin #167) New Haven.

JULL, MORLEY A.: *Poultry Breeding*, New York, John Wiley & Sons, Inc., 1932.

LANG, A.: "Fortgesetzte Vererbungstudien," *Zeit. f. ind. Abst. u. Vererb.* **V**:97–136 (1911).

MACARTHUR, J. W.: "Size Inheritance in Tomato Fruits," *J. Heredity* **32**:291–295 (1941).

NILSSON-EHLE, H.: "Kreuzungsuntersuchungen an Hafer und Weizen," *Lund Univ. Arsk. N.F.* **5**:1-122 (1909).

———:"Über Entstehung scharf abweichender Merkmale aus Kreuzung gleichartiger Formen beim Weizen," *Ber. deut. botan. Ges.* **29**:65–69 (1911).

PUNNETT, R. C.: *Heredity in Poultry*, London, Macmillan & Co., Ltd., 1923.

chapter 14

Selection and Breeding Techniques in Relation to Quantitative Characters

Darwin's Theory of Natural Selection stimulated investigations in many phases of biology. Some of these were undertaken to test the effects of selection under experimental control and even to test the validity of Darwin's theory and the extent of its applicability. Many experiments have been undertaken with the hope of improving breeds of domesticated animals and varieties of cultivated plants. Since such experiments mostly deal with quantitative characters, their consideration follows naturally the discussion of multiple genes.

Galton's Law of Regression

As long ago as 1889, Galton in England published results of studies on inheritance of height in man. From data on more than 200 parents and 900 of their adult offspring, Galton concluded that parents of greater than average height tended to produce children who were taller than the average. Parents of average height tended to produce children of average height, while parents of less than average height tended to produce children who were shorter than the average height. But more important was the observation that the progeny of parents in both extreme classes tall and short tended to approach average height. Galton called this an example of the **Law of Regression,** because progeny of extreme variants, as very tall and very short parents, tended to *regress toward the average* or mean of the race.

Galton's Law of Regression is applicable only to large groups of the population. That is, collectively the children of tall or of short parents, considered as classes, tended to show this regression. Single individuals or the progeny of a single family, because of the particular genotype, might deviate from this law. Height in man is conditioned by a multiple gene complex, and in general individuals are highly heterozygous for these genes. Galton was therefore studying an unselected and extremely heterozygous sample of a general population.

273

There is a probability that occasionally many of the genes for tallness will be recombined in a single genotype. Likewise there is the same probability that a large number of genes for short stature will be recombined in a genotype. These probabilities make Galton's Law of Regression inapplicable to single individuals. Further, it appears that in human beings genes for short stature are dominant and may cover up the recessive genes for tallness. Tall persons could, therefore, be homozygous for the genes for tallness and have all tall children, or because of chance recombination of genes for tallness carried by short parents, some of their children may be taller than their parents.

Johannsen's Pure-line Theory and Selection

About 1900 Johannsen, a Danish botanist, undertook to test the validity of Galton's Law of Regression in controlled experiments with *homozygous* material. He studied the effects of selection on weight and size of seeds in the Princess variety of the common bean, *Phaseolus vulgaris*. Since beans are naturally self-pollinated, a high degree of homozygosity could be assumed. Johannsen's publications in 1903 and in later years gave results of these experiments and presented his Pure-line Theory.

The beans in the original stock were of various sizes. From the harvest of 1900, Johannsen arbitrarily selected progenies of 19 distinct bean plants and weighed the seeds. Each of the progenies so chosen he called a **line**. Although the seeds from each line varied in size, their weights showed means ranging from 35.1 cg. for the smallest to 64.2 cg. of the largest with the other 17 progenies falling between the extremes. *Positive results were demonstrated from selection in an unselected population* that had been made homozygous through natural self-pollination. They were achieved by isolation of the homozygous strains or lines already existing in the general unselected population.

Johannsen attempted to change the size and weight of the seeds in each line by annual selection of large and small seeds from each line to produce the next generation. The experiment was continued for several years without effecting any permanent changes in the size of the beans. The generations produced from a single line, whether from the large or the small seeds, produced beans of varying size but always of the approximate average weight which had first characterized the line. That is, the average weight of beans grown from a large seed was no greater than that of beans grown from a small seed selected from the same line. The progenies of the large seeds as well as those of the small seeds reverted to the average or mean weight characteristic of the genetically pure line from which selection was made.

The variations in size and weight of the seeds which occurred in each line were purely somatic, the effect of environmental conditions surrounding the plant and the seeds in the pods. Moisture, temperature, and soil conditions, the special conditions surrounding individual seeds and the number of seeds in a pod, all influenced the size of the seeds, but none of these fluctuating variations was inherited.

PHENOTYPE AND GENOTYPE. In this connection Johannsen first used the words **phenotype** and **genotype,** terms now in universal use in genetical literature. He considered the phenotype to be made up of measurable characters which could be seen, of fluctuations largely under environmental control. The progeny of a plant did not inherit these somatic variations but did inherit from the *underlying germ plasm or genotype common to the entire line.* The progeny of bean plants grown from both large and small seeds, selected from a line, tended on the average to be alike and as a group to regress to the mean weight for that line. The selected seeds, although differing somatically in size, were alike genotypically.

THE PURE LINE. Johannsen defined a pure line as consisting of individuals descended from a single self-fertilized individual. His work showed that selection for size in a pure line was totally without effect, since in the following generation the progeny of selected individuals merely reverted to the average of the line. Johannsen concluded, however, that the Galton Law of Regression was applicable within pure lines as a regression toward the type or mean of the line.

THE ORIGIN OF PURE LINES. If self-pollinated beans tend to become homozygous pure lines and if positive results cannot be obtained by selection in a pure line, what is the explanation of variations in the original population which were potentially ancestral to Johannsen's 19 lines? Is there no hope of change in a pure line? The answer to these questions lies in the phenomenon of mutation, the type of change occurring at rare intervals in the germ plasm (p. 386). Some time in the past history of the Princess variety of bean, a number of size mutations had occurred. In selecting the 19 pure lines, positive results had been immediate, because Johannsen isolated from the general population plants that were homozygous for size mutations and established his pure lines.

Selection in Cross-fertilized Organisms

Selection in a population of cross-fertilized organisms presents quite another problem. As a result of natural cross-fertilization, such organisms are heterozygous for many variations. Therefore, all of the inherent difficulties of selection are present, phenotypically dominant characteristics obscuring the presence of recessive genes in the genotypes, a large number of alleles, and in many cases interactions of genes in the complexes. Compared with the quick and permanent results obtained in self-fertilized plants, positive results of selection in cross-fertilized organisms are realized *slowly* only after many generations. Noteworthy results of such selection are hastened by controlling fertilization, either through self-pollination in self-fertile plants or close inbreeding in self-sterile plants and in animals. This technique is commonly used in corn-breeding programs (pp. 277–282).

SELECTION BASED ON PROGENY PERFORMANCE. Although selection of somatic variations has been repeatedly demonstrated to be without effect upon future generations, another type of selection has proved effective. Selection of individuals as parents based upon "progeny performance" or the "progeny test" is a technique for selecting germ plasm and disregarding somatic variations. As long ago as 1840–50, Louis de Vilmorin working toward the improvement of farm crops in France developed the progeny test or "genealogical selection," as he called it, for use in wheat, oats, and sugar-beet breeding. He considered a plant valuable when it produced superior progeny.

An interesting and instructive experiment on the size of mice has been based on the progeny test. Goodale used the progeny of 16 individual mice, 5 males and 11 females, all of which were ordinary commercial stock of laboratory mice. The original 5 males averaged 26.0 grams in weight, and the 11 females averaged 21.3 grams. During the course of the investigation, about 4,000 mice were studied each year. The average weights recorded were based upon 500 or more animals in each case.

The plan of the experiment was to select as parents for further breeding the individuals in each generation which produced the heaviest progeny. Regardless of their own weights, individuals which had demonstrated ability to produce heavy progeny were selected to become parents of the next experimental generation. With this technique the genes for increased weight rather than somatic variations were selected. By 1952 the weight of the selected stock had been increased (Table XXVIII). Progress in this experiment has been hampered by increasing sterility and reduced size of litters, but the leader has stated that an average of 50 grams may be maintained by proper management.

Table XXVIII

INCREASES IN WEIGHTS OF MICE

Date	Weights of the Heaviest Individuals	
	Males	Females
1930	34.2 grams	28.6 grams
1938	48.1 "	41.0 "
1941	54.3 "	49.7 "
1952	60.0 "	

Selection based upon the progeny test has assumed great importance in animal breeding. All breeders have recognized the value of an animal which is able to produce good progeny. The progeny-performance technique is useful in breeding cattle for high milk production, where the value of a sire with high-producing daughters is widely recognized. Too often such a bull has been discarded before his value, as evidenced in high-producing daughters, has been recognized. The same method of selection is important in breeding poultry for high egg production. It is also used in breeding horses for speed. The ram called the "gold nugget" because of his ability repeatedly to sire grand champions for the show ring may be cited as another example of breeding based on progeny performance.

SELECTION AND INBREEDING IN CROSS-POLLINATED PLANTS. In 1905 and through succeeding years, Shull published results of inbreeding maize or Indian corn. He showed that open-pollinated plants in an ordinary corn field are heterozygous for a large number of pairs of genes. In fact, an ordinary corn field is a mass of hybrid plants, the result of promiscuous crossing following wind-pollination among unselected plants. Shull started investigations with corn in order to learn about variation, inheritance of size, and selection in inbred lines derived by self-pollinating naturally open- or cross-fertilized plants. In the course of the experiments, corn plants were self-pollinated and the resulting inbreds grown. It was soon evident that inbreeding of maize resulted in greatly decreased size and vigor in the progeny. The decrease, greatest in the first inbred generation, continued at reduced rates through succeeding generations of self-pollination. As the investigation proceeded, it was discovered that full size and vigor were promptly restored following hybridization between inbred plants. In fact, the F_1 plants were larger, more vigorous, and more productive than ordinary open-pollinated varieties.

Hybrid Corn

Shull's experiments led, eventually, to the development of hybrid corn now extensively used in commercial corn production (Fig. 128). In 1911 Shull predicted the possibilities of increasing yield of commercial corn by this technique. Although he has received recognition as the *originator of hybrid corn*, Shull did not perfect breeding techniques for commercial production. This was done by other workers, among them, East, Hayes, Jenkins, Jones, Lindstrom, Singleton, Sprague, Richey, Henry Wallace, and many others.

The development of hybrid corn is perhaps the greatest single contribution of the science of genetics to the economic welfare of the temperate and subtropical zones where maize is grown. It has been estimated that the value of the corn crop of the United States alone may be $3,000,000,000 annually. If even 25 per cent of this results from the use of hybrid seed corn, the increase is three-quarters of a billion dollars. Stadler estimated that during the four growing seasons, 1942–45, covering the war period, the use of hybrid seed corn increased the yield of grain by 1,800,000,000 bushels with a value of more than $2,000,000,000. With the high prices of the postwar period, the estimated money value of the corn crop is even greater than in 1945. Mangelsdorf calculated that the increased yield attributable to hybrid corn in 1946 was 924,210,000 bushels. In 1952, 70,366,000 acres or 84.4 per cent of all corn acreage in the United States was planted with hybrid corn seed. The profitable use of hybrid corn is being extended to other corn-growing regions in Europe, Mexico, and Central and South America. The economic value of hybridization of inbred lines may be further supple-

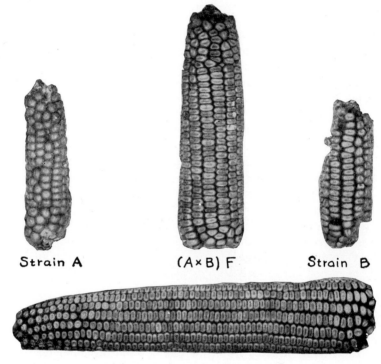

FIG. 128. FIRST HYBRID CORN FROM INBRED LINES PRODUCED BY DR. GEORGE H. SHULL.
(Courtesy, Dr. Shull, from *J. Heredity*.)

mented by its extension to cultivated plants other than corn and to domestic animals both large and small.

As Shull found, one of the most noticeable *effects of inbreeding is the rapid loss of vigor, size, and fertility.* The first generation after self-pollination, called the S_1 generation, is reduced in size and vigor by about 50 per cent. Successive self-pollinations result in further reductions in size and vigor but to a lesser degree. The S_2 loses about 25 per cent, the S_3 about 12.5 per cent, and the S_4 about 6.25 per cent. After four or five generations of self-pollination, the inbred lines become fairly stable, although homozygosity increases with continued inbreeding. Following continuous selfing, some of the inbred lines become so dwarfed and so nearly sterile that they are maintained with difficulty and may even be lost entirely. Some strains may become pollen sterile, others may produce a fair amount of pollen but fail to set seed, both difficulties in the production of commercial hybrid

FIG. 129. PLANTS ILLUSTRATING INCREASED VIGOR, HETEROSIS, IN THE F₁ (CENTER) RESULTING FROM THE CROSS BETWEEN TWO INBRED LINES.
(Courtesy, D. F. Jones, Connecticut Agricultural Experiment Station.)

corn. At the Connecticut Experiment Station, New Haven, Connecticut, some of the inbred lines of corn have been in existence since 1905–07, that is for nearly 50 years. Among them some lines have been inbred for 30 or more generations. Recent investigations indicate that long-continued inbreeding may not be necessary to the production of good inbred strains for hybridizing in corn improvement.

THE PRODUCTION OF HYBRID CORN. The hybrid corn in demand by farmers for seed is obtained by crossing two (or more) inbred strains or lines selected for their desirable characteristics. Crossing two inbred lines results in an extremely heterozygous but very uniform F_1 generation which has greatly restored vigor and yielding ability attributed to dominance of favorable-growth genes (Fig. 129–131).

Not all combinations of inbred strains produce equally high-yielding F_1 plants. To obtain a really successful hybrid corn, the corn breeder must test

FIG. 130. MATURE CORN PLANTS ILLUSTRATING INCREASED HYBRID VIGOR OR HETEROSIS OF F_1 PLANTS IN CENTER WHICH WERE DEVELOPED FROM THE CROSS OF TWO INBRED LINES AT THE SIDES.

(Courtesy, D. F. Jones, Connecticut Agricultural Experiment Station.)

several of the inbred strains in hybrid combination with many other inbred lines. Of the several inbred strains some will produce F_1 plants which are good; some will produce F_1 plants of little value. Selection of a good combination of inbred lines or good combiners is based on results of actual tests. The real test of good combiners is performance in the field of the F_1 hybrid progeny of a cross. Characteristics to be considered in this performance are vigor, disease and insect resistance, and, above all, superior-yielding ability. Many superior F_1 hybrids have become well known in commercial seed-corn production.

| Inbred × Inbred | F_1 | F_2 | F_3 | F_4 | F_5 | F_6 | F_7 | F_8 |

FIG. 131. INCREASED VIGOR IN F_1 CORN PLANT RESULTING FROM CROSS OF TWO INBRED LINES AND DECREASED VIGOR IN SUCCEEDING GENERATIONS.
Yield of grain corresponded to the vigor of the plants. (Courtesy D. F. Jones, Connecticut Agricultural Experiment Station.)

KINDS OF CROSSES. Inbred lines have been used in several different ways in commercial corn production. Top crosses, single crosses, three-way crosses, double crosses, and multiple crosses are all in general use. A top cross is a cross between an inbred line and an ordinary cross-pollinated variety. F_1 plants from seeds of the top cross are more vigorous and productive than inbreds and frequently more productive than the original cross-pollinated variety. Top crosses have recently come into use in testing the combining ability of new inbred lines of corn (pp. 277–280). The single cross, a cross between two inbred lines as line A × line B, is the typical hybrid-corn cross used originally by the early investigators (p. 277).

The double cross is a further development in which two good F_1 hybrid types are obtained by crossing inbred lines as line A × line B and line C × line D. Then the next year the two F_1 hybrids (A × B) and (C × D) are hybridized to produce the double cross, including four inbred strains in one double-hybrid generation as F_1(A × B) × F_1(C × D). Double-cross hybrids are frequently very vigorous and yield exceptionally good crops because of the much greater genetic diversity found in four than in any two inbred lines. In field practice much of the hybrid corn used is of the double-cross type.

In the multiple cross still more genetic diversity and greater heterozygosity are brought into a single hybrid plant. While four inbred lines can be brought together in a single double-cross F_1 hybrid, six or eight different inbred lines may be combined in a multiple cross. After two double crosses have been made as F_1(A × B) × F_1(C × D) and F_1(G × H) × F_1(M × N), these may be hybridized, making a multiple cross combining all eight inbred lines A, B, C, D, G, H, M, and N into one hybrid combination.

Regardless of the technique used in its production, hybrid corn is at its best, that is, most vigorous and most productive, in the F_1 generation. Succeeding generations, obtained from the open-pollination of F_1, F_2, etc., become less vigorous and less productive (Fig. 131). The loss of high-yielding qualities in the F_2, F_3, and succeeding generations is thought to be intimately related to the reduction of heterozygosity. Open-pollination of hybrid plants results in a small amount of self-pollination with attendant homozygosity and gradual loss of hybrid vigor. It has been estimated that the F_2 generation of hybrid corn is, on the average, about 15 per cent less productive than the F_1. Succeeding generations are progressively less productive each year but to a gradually lessened degree. After five to eight generations of open-pollination, there is little further loss of size, vigor, and yield, and the plants become stabilized at about the yield level of the ordinary commercial varieties from which they originated. This reduced productivity explains the necessity for constant renewal of hybrid corn from its source, preferably every year.

Effects of Self-pollinating and Crossing Inbred Lines in Plants Other Than Corn

Within recent years effects of crossing inbred lines in plants other than corn have been studied. Among other cereals crosses of barley have been successful. In one set of experiments, the average F_1 yield of seven barley crosses showed an increase of more than 20 per cent over the average of both parents.

Jones and Singleton published results of inbreeding and crossing inbred strains of strawberries (Fig. 132). These are propagated by vegetative or asexual methods. Following inbreeding strawberries, there was the characteristic segregation of plant and fruit characters with reduction in size of plant and fruit and lessened yield. Crossing the inbred strains fully restored both size and vigor. Combinations of three and four inbred strains gave desirable hybrids which have been introduced into the commercial field.

Inbreeding of cotton has resulted in higher yields, greater stability of varieties, and improvement in uniformity of length and percentage of lint. In 1941 the Bureau of Plant Industry reported pedigree selection in progress at four stations among 2,000 selfed lines representing more than 200 parental stocks. One inbred line exceeded the best commercial variety by 19.5 per cent in yield of lint per acre. In addition it had a longer staple, which resulted in a total increase of 42 per cent per acre over the best commercial variety.

Unrau and White in Canada reported results of crossing inbred lines of sunflowers. As in corn, continued inbreeding of sunflowers tended to reduce size and vigor of plants and yields of seed. The greatest decrease in yield, 35 per cent, followed after the first year of inbreeding. After four years of inbreeding, the reduction in yield of seed was 60 per cent. Reciprocal single crosses of inbred lines outyielded the average of the inbred lines by 247 per cent. F_1 plants of inbred crosses outyielded a good standard variety by from 47 to 60 per cent.

FIG. 132. LEFT AND RIGHT, INBRED STRAINS OF STRAWBERRIES; CENTER, HYBRID BETWEEN THEM SHOWING HETEROSIS.

(Courtesy, D. F. Jones and Ralph Singleton, Connecticut Agricultural Experiment Station.)

Jones and Davis report results in onions comparable to those obtained in hybrid corn. Crossing an inbred line of Stockton Yellow averaging 242 grams per bulb with an inbred line of Italian Red averaging 202 grams per bulb yielded F_1 generations averaging 641 and 775 grams per bulb (Fig. 133).

Larson and Currance reported the results of crossing varieties of tomatoes. While the yields were variable, the average yield increase of the F_1 over the parental average was 39 per cent. The F_2 increase over the parental average was 23 per cent with a high positive correlation of 0.739 between the average F_1 yield and that of its F_2.

With reports of this nature from diverse plant materials, experiments have started to investigate the behavior of numerous farm, forage, fruit, and garden crops following inbreeding and crossing. Besides hybrid field corn and sweet corn, seedsmen are listing hybrid tomatoes, cucumbers, and other vegetables in their catalogues. This is a close follow-up of current investigations in the extension of the hybridization technique made popular in commercial corn breeding.

The production of F_1 hybrid seed in commercially profitable quantities always poses a problem for growers. For corn a detasseling technique has been devised. With vegetables in commercial production, removing stamens to avoid self-pollination involves a vast amount of skilled hand labor. Techniques involving the use of self-sterile and male-sterile lines are being introduced in the production of hybrid plants in vegetable crops to reduce the time and labor otherwise involved.

Inbreeding and Crossbreeding Animals

In Shoffner's reciprocal crossing between White Leghorn, New Hampshire, and White Plymouth Rock breeds of poultry, the crossbreds exceeded the purebreds in vigor, egg production, and lessened mortality. The superiority of the crossbreds depended upon the quality and, as in hybrid corn, upon the genetic diversity of the purebred strains used in their production. Certain disadvantages of crossbreds, however, were pointed out.

FIG. 133. A CROSS INVOLVING BULB SIZE IN ONIONS.
A, an inbred line of Stockton Yellow. B, an inbred line of Italian Red. C, the F_1 hybrid $A \times B$. (Courtesy, Jones and Davis, U. S. Dep. Agr. Technical Bulletin #874, Washington, 1944.)

Winters, et al., found that crossbred swine showed an increase in vigor over pure inbreds. Crossbreds had greater survival, greater rate of gain in weight, a greater economy of grain in feeding, and a better score for body conformation than the inbreds. Crossbreds resulting from crosses between distinct breeds were better than those from crosses between lines of the same breed. This fact indicates the importance of genetic diversity of the parents used in crossing. Superior parental stock tended to produce superior crossbreds.

Recent experiments reported by Baker and Quisenberry show that crossbred beef cattle as Shorthorn × Hereford are superior to the purebreds. The crossbreds were heavier at birth, made faster gains in weight, and were heavier at all ages up to and including 30 months.

Heterosis

The remarkable increase in size and vigor of hybrids over their parents has been known since the time of the early plant hybridizers. Increased hybrid vigor was also noted by Darwin who observed its occurrence in the offspring of unrelated parents and realized that it resulted not merely from crossing but from the union of unlike germ plasms.

The phenomenon of increased size in hybrids has been called hybrid vigor and, later, heterosis, from the Greek words *heteros* meaning different and *-osis*, condition. **Heterosis,** therefore, means literally *a different condition*, that is, different from the parents. When the term was first introduced, it was as a substitute for the expression "stimulus to growth due to heterozygosity." The terms *heterosis*, referring to the developmental stimulus of the union of different germ plasms, and *hybrid vigor* have been used synonymously. Hybridity, however, may express itself in either smaller or increased size. Powers considers that heterosis exists when the phenotypic expression of a character in the F_1 generation is either greater or less than the magnitude of such expression in either parent. According to this view, heterosis and hybrid vigor are not equivalent terms Hybrid vigor refers to increased vigor and increased size, while heterosis may be of *two types*, **positive** or *plus*, that is, beneficial heterosis and **negative** or *minus*, that is, nonbeneficial heterosis.

GENERAL AND SPECIFIC EFFECTS OF HETEROSIS. In a study of heterosis, East considered effects on the various parts of plants, roots, stems, leaves, hairs, flowers, fruit, and seeds. His conclusion was that **hybrid vigor** is something which *concerns the organism*, plant or animal, *as a whole*. There is a general increase in vigor and rate of growth, branching is more profuse, the root system is increased, and leaves are larger. There is greater profusion of flowers and fruit although no notable increase in size of flowers or of fruit. East believed that cell divisions more than cell size were influenced by heterosis. Kiesselbach and Weihing found that the F_1 hybrid plants of inbred lines of corn showed material increases over the parents in size of the parts above ground, in depth to which the roots penetrated the soil, in the combined length of all main roots per plant, and in the diameter of the main roots. The F_2 plants were intermediate in these respects, thus showing a regression toward the normal or average size.

East and Hayes and, later, East, who studied hybrids in nearly 40 different genera, emphasized that the amount of hybrid vigor expressed in an F_1 plant is roughly proportional to the genetic diversity in two parents, provided normal development of the hybrid is possible. East pointed out that interspecific crosses, that is, hybridization between two distinct but compatible species, show greater hybrid vigor than intraspecific crosses, in which two varieties of a single species are hybridized. The importance of genetic differences has been recognized in commercial corn-breeding programs. In general, better F_1 hybrids are produced by crossing inbred lines of diverse origins than from crosses between closely related inbred lines.

The effects of single genes and of combinations of small numbers of genes on heterosis have been studied. East observed that certain genes exert greater effects on heterosis than others and also that a given gene can have greater effects in some combinations than in others. Particular combinations of small numbers of genes may also have special effects on heterosis. Kemp and Rothgeb have studied the effects of heterozygosity in a single pair of genes or in a few pairs. In 1943 they reported that corn kernels heterozygous for starchy-sweet endosperm are slightly larger and heavier than when homozygous for either character. Likewise, kernels heterozygous for yellow-white-endosperm color are slightly larger than those homozygous for either yellow or white endosperm. Double-heterozygous kernels, as starchy-sweet and yellow-white, are heavier than heterozygotes for a single one of these factor pairs.

In 1944 Jones published data confirming his earlier observation that heterozygosity in a single pair of genes produces hybrid vigor (pp. 287, 288). Later evidence for heterosis accompanying single-gene differences was found when certain plants showing slight variations presumably based on gene mutations were backcrossed to the inbred parental lines. Hybrids between the variation and the parental strain gave evidence of increased growth efficiency in earlier flowering and earlier maturity than their parents. F_1 plants were reported to be greener and more thrifty in appearance and to give better yield.

In commercial meat production, crossbreeding is quite commonly practiced. Crossbred cattle as well as swine are used, and crossbred lambs have proved especially popular. Experimental work with swine is being conducted in the Midwest states where the value of heterosis is being confirmed in increased weights from smaller amounts of feed per animal and more rapid growth of crossbred animals. Poultry breeders have developed inbred lines of fowls and are marketing young hybrid chicks which they assert will show high egg production.

THE GENETIC EXPLANATION OF HETEROSIS. Investigators have sought the cause of the important phenomenon of heterosis. The earliest explanation of hybrid vigor was offered by Keeble and Pellew in 1911. They had crossed two half-dwarf varieties of the garden pea, *Pisum sativum*, and found that the F_1 was materially taller than the parental types. One of these varieties, the Autocrat, was 3–4 feet in height, had strong thick stems, large leaves, short internodes about 3 inches in length, and a slow-growth rate. The other variety, Bountiful, was 3.5–4 feet in height, had thin stems, smaller leaves, long internodes about 5–7 inches in length, and a rapid rate of growth. The F_1 plants were 7–8 feet high and had thick stems with long internodes. The author's explanation of the large and vigorous hybrid plants rested on the interaction and additive effects of the genes determining thick stems and those determining long internodes from the two parents recombined in the F_1. This gene action is similar to that mentioned for height in sweet peas and in broomcorn (pp. 251, 252). More recent investigators have thought that the explanation of Keeble and Pellew is inadequate to account for all cases of hybrid vigor.

Ashby, who favored the physiological explanation of heterosis, suggested that hybrid vigor is related to increased size of F_1 embryos. But Hatcher in 1941, working on heterosis in the tomato, failed to confirm the association of hybrid vigor with an initial advantage in size of the embryo. The hybrid embryo showed heterosis, but its effect was soon lost in the expression of the developing characters of the fruit of the maternal plant. Hatcher rather favored an explanation of heterosis based on some specific effect of hybridity. Other investigators have contended that heterosis could be explained on a genetic basis. According to the genetic interpretation, increased size and vigor of hybrids are owing to the combination of favorable size and growth genes when two races are crossed. In some cases hybrid vigor may be the result of the cumulative or additive effect of these favorable genes.

In 1917 D. F. Jones published a genetic explanation of heterosis which has had generally favorable consideration among geneticists. Jones combined the earlier ideas of Shull and of East and Hayes on the stimulus of heterozygosity with the facts of linkage (pp. 119-143). As a background for his hypothesis, he emphasizes that the characteristics of size, vigor, yield, and other growth features are conditioned by a very large number of hereditary factors. Some of these genes are favorable to growth, and some of them are unfavorable. The author assumes that in general the normal or favorable characters are dominant or partially dominant over the abnormal or unfavorable ones. Organisms, as the various inbred lines of corn, differ genotypically. Specific gene pairs may be present in the dominant state in one line but in the homozygous-recessive state in a second inbred line.

These homozygous organisms may be thought of as complementary forms, for in hybridization one form may bring into the cross what the second lacks in the way of dominant genes. Thus a hybrid may have more dominant and favorable hereditary units than either of its parents, and for this reason it may have greater vigor, attain greater size, and yield more than either of the parents. Because of the favorable combination of the genetic factors involved, the hybrid may even exceed the mean of the parents in these respects.

As a simplified explanation, let it be assumed that two homozygous parents, as two inbred lines of corn, are crossed to produce an F_1 hybrid. By disregarding most of the chromosomes and concentrating on a single hypothetical pair of chromosomes, each containing six pairs of alleles, it may be possible to visualize the essential features of Jones's theoretical explanation of heterosis (Fig. 134). Let each of the dominant factors, as A, B, C, etc., have a value of 1 in growth development and assume that Inbred Line I is homozygous dominant for three favorable-growth factors, as *AA*, *CC*, and *EE*, while it is homozygous recessive for the unfavorable factors *bb*, *dd*, and *ff*. Likewise, Inbred Line **II** may be assumed to be homozygous for the favorable dominant factors *BB*, *DD*, and *FF* and homozygous for the

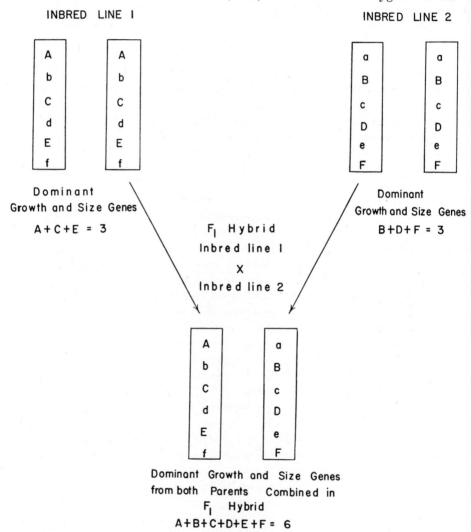

FIG. 134. DIAGRAM OF HETEROSIS IN THE F₁ HYBRID BETWEEN TWO INBRED LINES.

unfavorable recessive genes *aa*, *cc*, and *ee*. All of these genes are carried in the corresponding pair of chromosomes as pair No. 1 in each of the inbred lines. *These inbred lines may be considered complementary*, in that each line carries the favorable dominant genes lacking in the other one. Because of the assigned value of 1 for each of the dominant favorable-growth genes *A*,

C, and E carried by Inbred Line **I** and for B, C, and F carried in Inbred Line **II**, each inbred line may be regarded as having a value of 3 in growth and development. When Inbred Lines **I** and **II** are crossed, each parent contributes one member of every chromosome pair to the hybrid (pp. 50, 51). The chromosome of pair No. 1 from Inbred Line **I** carries the favorable dominant factors A, C, and E, and the unfavorable recessive genes b, d, and f. The corresponding chromosome from Inbred Line **II** carries the favorable dominant genes B, D, and F with the unfavorable recessive alleles a, c, and e. The favorable-growth and -size factors B, D, and F, lacking in the Inbred Line **I,** are supplied to the hybrid by Inbred Line **II**. The hybrid with a combination of the favorable-growth and -size genes from both parental types thus has a value of 6, because it has 6 dominant genes, A, B, C, D, E, and F. Since the genes are regarded as fully dominant or at least strongly dominant, they tend to overcome the unfavorable-growth effects of the recessive alleles a, b, c, d, e, and f also present in the hybrid combination. Similar behavior may be extended to all pairs of chromosomes and numerous pairs of size and growth genes in corn or any other species of organism.

In this explanation of heterosis, it is important to consider that inbreeding tends to increase the homozygosity of the inbred lines for all types of genes. In some cases organisms are rendered homozygous dominant for factors favorable to growth, size, and yield. Simultaneously, the same inbred line may become homozygous for some unfavorable genes. In other inbred lines the same growth factors may become homozygous but in different combinations than those found in the first inbred line. The genes occurring as homozygous dominants in the first line may be found in the homozygous-recessive state in the second inbred line, while still others may become homozygous dominant. Thus, with a large number of growth genes involved, no inbred line can have all the genes in the favorable dominant state. Some are in the unfavorable recessive state.

The fundamental feature of Jones's explanation is the assumption of a fortunate combination of favorable-growth genes associated or linked together in the members of the homologous chromosomes brought into the genotype of the F_1 hybrid. Hybridization of two inbred lines brings together a larger number of favorable-growth genes than can be found in any one line. Because of the different distributions of numerous favorable genes in the several inbred lines, no single hybrid between any two inbred lines could possibly combine all the favorable genes in the species. For this reason hybridization of $F_1 \times F_1$ has been successful in double and multiple crosses.

Jones also considered the second and successive hybrid generations and demonstrated theoretically that only the F_1 could possibly have the maximum number of favorable dominant genes. Because of recombination of chromosomes in the genotypes of F_2 and succeeding generations, there is a reduction in heterozygosity and an increase in homozygosity. Thus the number of instances with favorable dominant genes decreases, and the number with unfavorable genes in the homozygous state increases in F_2, F_3, etc. There is a reduction in the value of the genes for size and growth as self-fertilization and homozygosity progress.

Heterosis is an unfixable condition that cannot be perpetuated indefinitely from generation to generation. This fact is recognized in commercial corn growing when hybrid corn loses its initial advantage of uniformity, vigor, and high-yielding qualities in the F_2, F_3, and succeeding generations (pp. 281, 282).

In addition to the theories and explanations of heterosis mentioned above, other explanations have been offered. The problem is still unsolved.

SUMMARY AND CONCLUSION OF HETEROSIS.   Heterosis is a complex phenomenon which is difficult to explain completely. No single explanation is adequate for all cases, and none of them has been proved. In most cases involving size inheritance, a great many factors, genetic and physiological, are involved in heterosis. Each pair of alleles contributes its effect to the development of the organism. Besides the contribution of each pair of alleles, the units of the gene complex interact as complementary, supplementary, and perhaps even inhibitory factors. In the interaction the epistatic effects, too, influence the final development of the characteristics of hybrid organisms. Possibly all of the suggested causes and some as yet unknown factors are involved in the expression of heterosis in F_1 hybrids.

The relationship between heterosis and the recently active field of developmental genetics can be profitably added to the study of size inheritance and should be a fruitful field for further investigation (pp. 399–410).

Questions and Problems

1. What is Galton's Law of Regression? Upon what data is it based? To what kind of characters can Galton's Law of Regression be applied? Does a knowledge of Mendelian principles shed any light on the cause of a regression?
2. What is Johannsen's Pure-line Theory? Upon what data is it based? How did Johannsen obtain a pure line? Genetically, what is a pure line?
3. What is the effect of selection within a pure line? Discuss the reasons for your opinion.
4. What is meant by progeny test or selection based on progeny performance? What are the criteria of a good sire in a herd or a flock?
5. What were the results of Goodale's experiments with mice in selection for increased weight based on the progeny test?
6. Does the principle of selection based on the progeny test have any practical applications in animal breeding?
7. What is hybrid corn? How does the hybrid corn of commerce differ genetically from ordinary corn which is also hybrid?
8. Explain the breeding methods by which corn hybrids are produced.
9. Why is it necessary to practice selection in the inbred strains of corn? Why are inbred lines not all equally valuable in hybrid-corn work?
10. What breeding technique is used in making the double cross in corn?
11. Why is it necessary for the farmer annually to obtain hybrid-corn seed from its original source? What happens to hybrid corn in the F_2, F_3, and succeeding generations?

12. What are the data on tests of the yielding ability of F_1 corn hybrids as compared with standard open-pollinated varieties?
13. Have methods of self-pollination and crossing inbred lines been developed for agricultural crop plants other than corn?
14. Cite some of the results of the self-pollination and crossing technique in various plants.
15. What is heterosis? Does hybridity always express itself in increased size?
16. Cite some examples of heterosis or hybrid vigor.
17. In general, what theories have been offered in explanation of the phenomenon of heterosis?

References

BABCOCK, E. B., and R. E. CLAUSEN: *Genetics in Relation to Agriculture*, New York, McGraw-Hill Book Company, Inc., 1927, Chapter XXI.

BRIGGS, F. N.: "The Use of the Backcross in Plant Breeding," *Proc. 7th Int. Genet. Cong.*, Edinburgh, 1939 (1941), 81–82.

DUNN, L. C.: *Genetics in the 20th Century*, New York, The Macmillan Company, 1951.

GOWEN, J. W.: *Heterosis*, Ames, Iowa State College Press, 1952.

HAYES, H. K., and F. R. IMMER: *Methods of Plant Breeding*, New York, McGraw-Hill Book Company, Inc., 1942, Chapters XIV, XV.

JOHANNSEN, W.: *Elemente der exacten Erblichkeitslehre*, Jena, Gustav Fischer, 1926.

————: *Über Erblichkeit in Populationen und in reinen Linien*, Jena, Gustav Fischer, 1903.

JONES, D. F.: *Genetics in Plant and Animal Improvement*, New York, John Wiley & Sons, Inc., 1925.

———— and W. Singleton: *The Improvement of Naturally Cross-pollinated Plants by Selection in Self-Fertilized Lines*. (Connecticut Agricultural Experiment Station Bulletin #435) New Haven, 1940.

MURPHY, R. P.: "Convergent Improvement with Four Inbred Lines of Corn," *J. Am. Soc. Agron.* **34**:138–150 (1942).

RICHEY, F. D.: "The Convergent Improvement of Selfed Lines of Corn," *Am. Naturalist* **61**:430–449 (1927).

————: "Isolating better Foundation Inbreds for use in Corn Hybrids," *Genetics* **30**:455–471 (1945).

————, and G. F. SPRAGUE: *Experiments on Hybrid Vigor and Convergent Improvement in Corn*. (U. S. Dep. Agr. Technical Bulletin #267) Washington, 1931.

SHULL, G. H.: "The Composition of a Field of Maize," *Report of Am. Breeders Assn.* **IV**:296–301 (1908).

————: "The Genotypes of Maize," *Am. Naturalist* **45**:234–252 (1911).

————: "Hybridization Methods in Corn Breeding," *Am. Breeders Mag.* **1**:98–107 (1910).

————: "A Pure-line Method in Corn Breeding," *Report of Am. Breeders Assn.* **V**:51–59 (1909).

SINGLETON, W. R.: "Hybrid Vigor and Its Utilization in Sweet Corn Breeding," *Am. Naturalist* **LXXV**:48–60 (1941).

SMITH, HAROLD H.: "Recent Studies on Inheritance of Quantitative Characters in Plants," *Botan. Rev.* **10**:349–382 (1944).

WHALEY, W. GORDON: "Heterosis," *Botan. Rev.* **10**:461–498 (1944).

section 6

Biometry—the Statistics of Genetics

Genetical data usually lend themselves to mathematical treatment. In fact, Mendelian heredity is based on mathematical methods and was known as mathematical biology in Mendel's time. Quantitative characteristics especially need to be studied mathematically. The application of mathematics to the study of heritable traits has been called **biometry,** literally *the measurement of life phenomena.* More recently the term **statistics** has been used, but actually it is the *statistics of genetical data.* The direction of attention to the frequency of occurrence of certain genes in wild or unselected populations has given rise to *population genetics.* This study has been based on the application of the Hardy-Weinberg *Law of Equilibrium,* proposed in 1908. By the use of this law, it is possible to arrive at estimates of the frequency of certain genes in *wild* populations. It is useful also in similar estimation in *unselected* human populations.

chapter 15

Statistical Consideration of Quantitative Characters in Living Organisms

Data on measurable characteristics are frequently studied by statistical techniques, because *quantitative characters* usually *form a continuous series* which cannot be readily grouped into visible classes or ratios. The use of statistical methods makes it possible to learn about the variability of a population, the comparative variability of two or more populations, and something about the inheritance of quantitative characteristics.

When biological material is being studied by statistical methods, it is *the group, not the individual*, which is being considered. As Davenport has said, statistical analysis considers what may be expected "in the long run" or on the average in a number of cases. More recently Walker pointed out that while mathematical laws, as $c = 2\pi r$, hold universally and inescapably, statistical laws deal with trends. Thus, a statistical fact or law may be true in general for the group at large but not true for every individual in the group.

Biological Data Based on Measurements of a Sample

When a number of individuals are measured as to height, weight, or any other quantitative characteristic, this number though perhaps relatively large represents, after all, *only a small sample of the entire population* with the character. Sampling would not be necessary if it were possible to collect data on a whole population. If one wanted to know the average height of the boys entering American colleges in any given year, this problem could be solved in one of two ways. *First*, actual measurements of every entering freshman might be collected from all colleges in the United States, and the average height computed from these data. With accurate measurements and correct mathematical procedure, no error in the calculated average would be expected. But this method has the obvious objection of requiring time and an immense amount of work. To meet such objections, a *second* method, the statistical analysis of samples, has been devised. A *sample* consisting of 100, 500, or 1,000 boys entering American colleges might be measured, and the average height of all the boys *estimated* from the sample. An average computed from data on a sample may contain inaccuracies, the extent of which may very well depend in part upon the nature of the sample. *Samples should be taken at random* in order to be representative of the population, and they should be sufficiently large to include a fair distribution of the variable elements. In any event an average of this kind is recognized as a *statistical estimate*, which it is hoped represents approximately the true average height in the whole population of freshmen entering American colleges. It is with the second method that statistical analysis has to do. *Samples* of populations *are used in statistical work* in order that the whole population need not be considered.

Graphic Representation of Biological Data

Since East was unable to recognize classes and ratios in the F_2 generation of the cross between *Nicotiana forgetiana* and *N. alata grandiflora*, he undertook statistical studies of data from this cross (pp. 257, 258).* The material used in East's studies will be taken as an example of statistical treatment.

THE DATA. East measured the corolla lengths of flowers from 170 plants of the parent species, *N. forgetiana*, 167 plants of the other parent species, *N. alata grandiflora*, 111 plants of the F_1 hybrids, and 828 plants of the F_2 generation, recording one measurement from each plant. The corolla lengths ranged from 17.5–32.5 mm. in *N. forgetiana;* 62.5–92.5 mm. in *N. alata grandiflora;* 32.5–52.5 mm. in the F_1 hybrids; and 22.5–87.5 mm. in the F_2 generation plants. Statistical treatments of these measurements were used to compare the parental types and the F_1 and F_2 generations.

MEASUREMENTS OF A SAMPLE. Although measurements were taken from all F_2 plants of this cross, *they actually represent data from a sample*. The available F_2 plants were only a small sample of all the possible recombinations. There might have been 1,000, 10,000, 100,000, or 1,000,000 F_2 plants if a sufficient number of seeds of this cross had been planted and if it had been practicable to grow these large numbers of plants. As it was, the sample of 828 measurements yielded *statistical estimates* that were applied to the *entire* F_2 population. These facts should be kept in mind in any discussion of statistical analysis.

CLASSES AND THE FREQUENCY TABLE. Some kinds of measurements naturally tend to be arranged into groups or classes, for example, the number of rows of grains on the ears of corn or maize. The number of rows varies from 8 to as many as 24 on each ear. Since in corn the rows of grains generally occur in pairs, they tend to group themselves into classes, as those with 8, 10, 12, — — — to 22 and 24, with intervals of 2 rows. Most measurements of biological material show no such natural grouping. In studies of large numbers, the measurements are taken indiscriminately just as they happen

---

* East, E. M.: "Inheritance of Flower Size in Crosses between Species of Nicotiana," *Bot. Gaz.* **LV**:177–188 (1913).

to occur. Examination of such data will frequently show a relatively few extremely large and extremely small types with larger numbers of forms intermediate in size between the extremes. As the first step in statistical analysis, measurements of this kind, as, for example, those of flower sizes on 828 F_2 tobacco plants, are often arbitrarily placed into groups or classes. This grouping of measurements is a *simple classification of data* which indicates the nature and variability of the population from which the sample was taken.

The principal reason for grouping measurements into classes is to reduce the data to workable proportions and to make them easier to analyze if machine calculation is unavailable. Several methods have been devised for grouping measurements into a relatively small number of classes. In all of them, each class contains measurements of the same or approximately the same size. The choice of limits and class intervals is arbitrary but depends somewhat on the nature of the material and the size of the sample. If half units are selected as the limits of each class, for example, 8.5, 11.5, 14.5, etc., the mid-point of the first class is 10 and of the next classes 13, 16, etc. Then the mid-points of the classes are whole numbers which appear in the calculations incident to statistical analysis.

East selected a range of 5 mm. for each class. All measurements of corollas from F_2 plants falling between 22.5 and 27.5 mm. were grouped into one class. This class then had a **class center** or **class value,** generally written V, of 25 mm. The number 5, representing the number of variates or measurements in this class, is called the **class frequency,** generally written f. The next class included all measurements between 27.5 and 32.5 mm. with a class value of 30. The limits 22.5 to 27.5 and 27.5 to 32.5 are called the **class limits** or **class interval.** In grouping into classes, those measurements exactly at the class interval, as at 27.5 or 32.5, are all placed either in the class below or in the class above the interval. The data for all 828 plants were grouped into 13 classes with class values at intervals of 5 mm. ranging from 25 to 85 mm. The class interval is determined at such a value that the number of classes will be neither too great nor too small. Data from the two

Table XXIX

FREQUENCY DISTRIBUTIONS FOR LENGTHS OF COROLLA IN A CROSS BETWEEN
Nicotiana forgetiana AND *Nicotiana alata grandiflora*

Designation	Class Centers in Millimeters														
	20	25	30	35	40	45	50	55	60	65	70	75	80	85	90
N. forgetiana, 314	9	133	28	..	..	..	..	..	..	..	..	..	..	..	..
N. alata gr., 321	..	..	..	..	..	..	..	..	..	1	19	50	56	32	9
F_1(314 × 321)	..	..	..	3	30	58	20	..	..	..	..	..	..	..	..
F_2(314 × 321)1–6	..	5	27	79	136	125	132	102	105	64	30	15	6	2	..

parental types, the F_1 generation and the F_2 plants, were grouped into a table called a **frequency table** or a **table of frequency distribution.** The **class centers** or **class values** were written as even numbers from 20 to 90 mm., each at the top of a column in the table. The frequencies of the variates were then written in the proper column. The source of the measurement, parental type, F_1, or F_2, was indicated at the left of the table (Table XXIX).

The Histogram and Frequency Polygon

In order to have visual comparisons, data from the frequency table may be represented on coordinate or cross-section paper in the form of a **histogram** or **polygon.** Each class and actually each variate of the sample occupy a rectangular area in the histogram. This method of representing data has been called the "method of rectangles." The area chosen to represent each variate is quite arbitrarily selected, but the size of the area should be such that it is possible to work all the data into the histogram.

CONSTRUCTION OF THE HISTOGRAM. When the size of the area representing a single variate has been determined, this area is multiplied by the number of variates in the lowest or smallest class. In the data on the F_2 generation of the cross being considered here, the smallest group had five plants with flowers having a class value of 25. Thus the area representing the lowest class is five times the size of that representing a single variate. A rectangle corresponding to this area is then constructed on the base line. Next a similar rectangle corresponding to the area representing the second class is constructed on the base line immediately to the right of the first rectangle. Rectangles corresponding to the area representing each class are constructed until the last measurement has been used.

INTERPRETING THE HISTOGRAM. The result of assembling these rectangles is a histogram showing the proportional size distribution of the population studied. The area of the histogram represents the exact number of variates in the sample.

Figure 135 shows histograms representing measurements of the variations in corolla length of both parental species and the F_1 and the F_2 generations. These histograms show that the variability of the generations differs. Of all the types *N. forgetiana* shows least variability. The figure representing this parental type is very compact, with little spread in the range of corolla length. *N. alata grandiflora* shows slightly more diversity. The F_1 generation also has a compact histogram indicating uniformity in corolla length. In this feature the F_1 is intermediate between the two parental species.

The histogram of the F_2 generation shows the great variability of that generation. Inspection of the base line of the polygon shows the range of the size variations from class 25 mm. to class 85 mm. Comparisons with the histograms of the parental types show that the F_2 flowers do not exceed the range of size of the P_1 species. The differences in variability of the P_1, F_1,

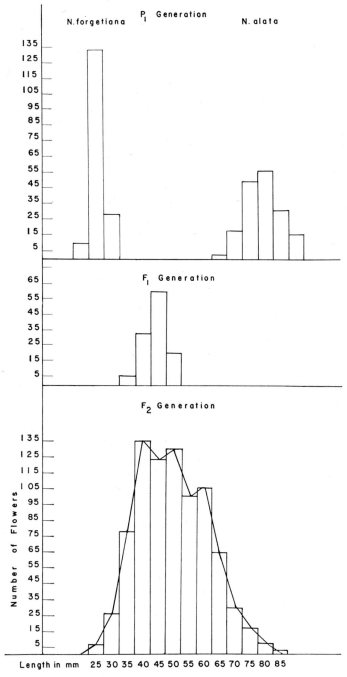

FIG. 135. FREQUENCY DISTRIBUTION OF COROLLA LENGTHS IN NICOTIANA FORGETIANA AND NICOTIANA ALATA GRANDIFLORA AND THE F_1 AND F_2 GENERATIONS OF N. FORGETIANA × N. ALATA GRANDIFLORA.

and F_2 generations are the result of the action of the group of multiple genes conditioning corolla length.

In hybridization the combination of size genes from both parents results in an F_1 heterozygous for several pairs of size genes. Some of these condition long and some short corollas, and consequently the plants of the F_1 generation tend to be intermediate between the two parents. If the parents are highly homozygous, the F_1 plants are much alike genetically and show only slight variability. If, however, the parental forms are heterozygous to a considerable degree, there will be genotypic diversity among the F_1 plants, and the F_1 generation will be variable. The slight variability of the F_1 hybrids of *N. alata grandiflora* $\times$ *N. forgetiana* indicates that the parental species were highly homozygous for corolla size genes.

Mating $F_1 \times F_1$ resulted in the recombination of the several pairs of multiple genes involved in the cross and in production of very diverse F_2 genotypes. These diverse genotypes functioned in the development of extreme variability in the F_2 generation, as shown in the histogram.

The extent of the base of the histogram or other forms of a graph, polygon, or curve is an indication of the range of diversity of the structures measured, while the height of the graph shows the number of measurements taken. Thus a tall narrow graph indicates a considerable number of variates with only slight diversity in the measured character. A broad flat graph, on the other hand, indicates considerable diversity in the measured character.

THE FREQUENCY GRAPH. The frequency graph, frequency curve, or variability curve is perhaps more generally used in published papers than the frequency histogram. This curve is smoother than the histogram and is made by connecting the center points at the top of the rectangles representing the areas of the classes and then bringing each side down until it approaches but does not quite reach the base line at the class limits.

THE NORMAL CURVE IN STATISTICAL ANALYSIS. The normal curve, the result of a mathematical abstraction, is a symmetrical graph. Because measurements of a large series of totally unrelated events, as tossing coins for heads and tails, arranged in the order of their frequency are dispersed or distributed in a form that approaches the normal curve, this graph is often called the *curve of probability* or the *curve of error*. Historically, the normal curve was discovered by the mathematician De Moivre who, in trying to aid gamblers, discovered that the random variation in the numbers of heads and tails corresponded to the form of this graph.

The normal curve may be accurately plotted with area determinations for all of its parts by a mathematical formula. When computed in this way, the symmetrical sides form the typical bell-shaped graph (Fig. 136). Since the range of variates is infinite, the sides of the curve approach but do not reach the base line, indicating their theoretical extension to infinity. In a perfect normal curve a perpendicular line erected at a point on the base, representing the mean and reaching the highest point in the graph, is the median or middle value and separates equal areas, right and left.

The type of data which most nearly fits into a normal curve is that derived from an extensive series of events, each one of which is determined purely by chance. If, for example, four or five coins are simultaneously tossed a thousand or more times, the graphs formed by grouping the data on the numbers of heads, tails, and heads together with tails may approximate the form of the symmetrical bell-shaped curve. The larger the number of the distinct events, the more nearly may the graph be expected to approach the form of the normal curve.

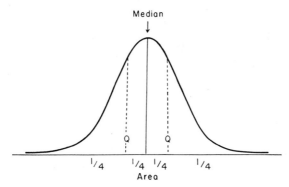

FIG. 136. A NORMAL CURVE.

Graphs made from biological data *may approach* the normal curve. For example, when the heights of the 10,000 corn plants usually grown on an acre of land are grouped in a frequency polygon, this graph may closely approximate the form of a normal curve. Such fluctuating variations of height are determined by a large number of independent causes or factors, genetic, physiological, and environmental. In this case, also, the area under the curve represents all of the measurements recorded.

PARTS OF THE CURVE.   The parts of a polygon or curve generally considered are:

1. *The range,* the distribution of the variates represented by the base of the polygon or curve
2. *The median,* the middle value of all the variates of the sample. Thus one half of the variates has a value less than the median and one half a value greater than the median. The median can be calculated mathematically and on a frequency graph; it is that point on the base line or base scale upon which a perpendicular line may be erected dividing the area of the polygon into two approximately equal halves. In this case the individual variates represented in the area to the left are smaller than those represented in the area to the right of the median. In the normal curve the median and the mean correspond. In curves

derived from measurements, the mean and the median may only
approximate each other

3. *The quartile*, the distance along the base from the median to a point
   at which a perpendicular line will divide one half of the polygon into
   two equal parts or quarters of the whole polygon area

4. *The mode*, the class represented by the tallest rectangle in the histogram or ordinate in the polygon. It is the class with the greatest
   number of variates. Actually it is the most "fashionable" class.

The points on the base line of a polygon at which the median line, quartile
lines, or other fractional subdivisions of the polygon may be erected can be
computed. Some data are of a nature to be grouped into characteristic
modifications of the basic or normal monomodal curve. Among these
modifications may be mentioned the bimodal, multimodal, and skew curves.

Biometrical Constants or Statistics

Besides methods of graphic representation, mathematical constants as
the *average* or *mean*, the *standard deviation*, the *probable error*, the *standard
error*, the *coefficient of variability*, and others are used. These constants *or,
more properly*, **statistics** are obtained by calculations from the data. Most
of these constants are derived from attributes of the normal curve. The
mathematical formulae for most of them are directly related to certain
areas under the graph of the normal curve.

STATISTICS ARE ESTIMATES.   Actually each of these constants or
statistics, the mean, the standard deviation, the probable error, the standard
error, the coefficient of variation, and the coefficient of correlation, is merely
a *mathematical estimate of the true values* or **parameters** of the population from
which a sample has been analyzed. Each such *estimate* is called a **statistic** in contrast with the parameter or true value. *Collectively these estimates are* **statistics.**

THE MEAN.   There are several kinds of means. The *arithmetic average*
or mean and the *geometric mean* are important in biological statistics. In
general when the term *mean* is used, it is the arithmetic average or arithmetic
mean. The other "means" are generally specifically designated as such
when used in publications.

Calculation of the arithmetic mean, M, involves the addition or summation of all measurements and its division by the total number of measurements, n. The Greek letter large *sigma*, Σ, is used to indicate the summation.* For example, if there are five boys in a class and if their weights are
116, 120, 126, 128, and 130 pounds, their total weight or the summation of
their individual weights, Σ, is 620.

---

* Other symbols may be encountered in statistical literature. Fisher and others use S
as the symbol for summation and s for that of the standard deviation. Fisher also uses
$S(x)$ for the sum of n variables and $\bar{x}$ for their mean; that is, $\bar{x} = \dfrac{S(x)}{n}$.

$$M = \frac{\text{Summation of total variates}}{\text{Total number of variates}} = \frac{\Sigma}{n} \text{ or, in this case,}$$

$$M = \frac{116 + 120 + 126 + 128 + 130}{5} = \frac{620}{5} = 124 \text{ pounds}$$

When machine calculation was unavailable, a more workable method was needed when there were 828 measurements, as in the F_2 generation of tobacco plants which East studied. To expedite the calculation, reference is made to Table XXX, where the grouping of measurements permits multipli-

Table XXX

DATA FOR THE CALCULATION OF THE ARITHMETIC-MEAN LENGTH OF COROLLA IN THE F_2 GENERATION *Nicotiana forgetiana* $\times$ *Nicotiana alata grandiflora*

Class Range in Mm.	Mid-class Value in Mm	Frequencies	Frequencies $\times$ Class Values
	V	f	V · f
22.5–27.5	25	5	125
27.5–32.5	30	27	810
32.5–37.5	35	79	2,765
37.5–42.5	40	136	5,440
42.5–47.5	45	125	5,625
47.5–52.5	50	132	6,600
52.5–57.5	55	102	5,610
57.5–62.5	60	105	6,300
62.5–67.5	65	64	4,160
67.5–72.5	70	30	2,100
72.5–77.5	75	15	1,125
77.5–82.5	80	6	480
82.5–87.5	85	2	170
		$n = 828$	$\Sigma(V \cdot f) = 41{,}310$

cation of class values and frequencies to reach their sum without individual treatments. Now, when machine calculation has supplanted this laborious process, the raw experimental data are used directly without sacrifice of accuracy in the grouping.

The sum or Σ, reached either directly by machine calculation or indirectly from grouping in a table, can then be divided by the number of variates to give the mean, as $M = \dfrac{41{,}310}{828} = 49.89$ mm.,* the mean length of the corollas of the flowers of the F_2 generation of the cross.

THE GEOMETRIC MEAN. The geometric mean is frequently used in biometrical work, especially during recent years in statistical analysis of quantitative characters. For example, McArthur has shown that the F_1 hybrid,

---

* Because of differences in handling the second and third place decimals, the calculations in this discussion vary slightly from those published by East.

between two tomato plants differing markedly in size of fruit, more nearly approaches the geometric mean than the arithmetic mean in respect to fruit size. This fact indicates that the actions of the major genes, controlling size in the tomato fruits, have a multiple rather than merely an additive effect (pp. 263–266).

The geometric mean of two quantities is the square root of their products, as, for example, the geometric mean of 3 and 12. Geometric mean = $\sqrt{3 \cdot 12}$ = $\sqrt{36}$ = 6, as compared with the arithmetic mean of 3 and 12 which is $\dfrac{3 + 12}{2}$ = $\dfrac{15}{2}$ = 7.5. Thus the geometric mean is slightly smaller than the arithmetic mean, unless the two quantities are equal. If a number of variates, V, are involved, the geometric mean may be calculated by the formula:

$$\text{Geometric mean} = \sqrt[n]{v_1 \cdot v_2 \cdot v_3 \cdot v_n}$$

In this calculation the nth root of the products of the series of variates is indicated.

DEVIATION FROM THE MEAN. Since the average or mean is between the lowest and highest values, most of the individual variates and class values, when grouping is used, will vary or deviate from the mean.

The standard deviation. Statistics may be calculated which are estimates of the variation of a population sample. One of these is the standard deviation, usually indicated by the small Greek letter *sigma*, σ. From a table arranged as Table XXXI, without individual multiplication, the essentials may again be calculated if a machine is not available.

The formula for calculation of the standard deviation is

$$\sigma = \sqrt{\frac{\Sigma(f \cdot d^2)}{n}} = \sqrt{\frac{105{,}090}{828}} = 11.27 \text{ mm.}$$

Thus the standard deviation, σ, for corolla lengths of the flowers of plants of the F_2 generation of *N. forgetiana* $\times$ *N. alata grandiflora* is 11.27 mm. from the mean corolla length 49.9 mm.

With the increased use of machine calculation, other formulae are employed to accommodate the use of all individual variates in data without resort to grouping. One of these is $\sigma^2 = \dfrac{\Sigma f(X - x)^2}{n - 1}$ with

$n - 1$ = the degrees of freedom*
x = the individual variates
$\bar{x}$ = the arithmetic mean
$x - \bar{x}$ = the deviation of individual variates from the mean
f = frequency.

---

* $n - 1$ is substituted for n = number of variates, particularly with small samples, to make the standard deviation more representative of the population than it would be by using n. When a sample is large as in the case of 828 corolla measurements, there is little difference between $n = 828$ and $n - 1 = 827$.

Table XXXI

DATA FOR THE CALCULATION OF THE MEAN AVERAGE DEVIATION AND STANDARD DEVIATION OF COROLLA LENGTH IN THE F_2 GENERATION OF A CROSS BETWEEN *Nicotiana forgetiana* AND *Nicotiana alata grandiflora*

Class Range in Mm.	Mid-class Values in Mm. V	Frequencies f	Frequencies × Class Values $V \cdot f$	Deviations from Mean in Mm. d	Deviations × Frequencies $f \cdot d$	Deviations Squared d^2	Deviations Squared × Frequencies $f \cdot d^2$
22.5–27.5	25	5	125	−24.9	124.5	620.01	3,100.05
27.5–32.5	30	27	810	−19.9	537.3	396.01	10,692.27
32.5–37.5	35	79	2,765	−14.9	1,177.1	222.01	17,538.79
37.5–42.5	40	136	5,440	−9.9	1,346.4	98.01	13,329.36
42.5–47.5	45	125	5,625	−4.9	612.5	24.01	3,001.25
47.5–52.5	50	132	6,600	0.1	13.2	.01	1.32
52.5–57.5	55	102	5,610	5.1	520.2	26.01	2,653.02
57.5–62.5	60	105	6,300	10.1	1,060.5	102.01	10,711.05
62.5–67.5	65	64	4,160	15.1	966.4	228.01	14,592.64
67.5–72.5	70	30	2,100	20.1	603.0	404.01	12,120.30
72.5–77.5	75	15	1,125	25.1	376.5	630.01	9,450.15
77.5–82.5	80	6	480	30.1	180.6	906.01	5,436.06
82.5–87.5	85	2	170	35.1	70.2	1,232.01	2,464.02
		$n = 828$	$\Sigma(V \cdot f) = 41{,}310$		$\Sigma(f \cdot d) = 7{,}588.4$		$\Sigma(f \cdot d^2) = 105{,}090.28$

For convenience in machine calculation, the formula above is converted algebraically into

$$\sigma^2 = \frac{\Sigma f x^2 - (\Sigma f \cdot x)\,\bar{x}}{n-1} \quad \text{or} \quad \sigma^2 = \frac{\sum f \cdot x^2 - \dfrac{(\Sigma f \cdot x)^2}{n}}{n-1}$$

$$\sigma = \sqrt{\frac{\sum f \cdot x^2 - \dfrac{(\Sigma f \cdot x)^2}{n}}{n-1}}$$

Substituting values obtained from data on corolla lengths in the tobacco cross for the mathematical symbols in the formula, the equation becomes

$$\sigma^2 = \frac{2{,}166{,}100 - \dfrac{(41{,}310)^2}{828}}{828 - 1} = \frac{105{,}090}{827} = 127.0738$$

$$\sigma = \sqrt{127.0738} = 11.27 \text{ mm.}$$

In some publications these formulae appear with other symbols.

Meaning of the standard deviation. The standard deviation is a measure of the variability of a population. It shows the range of the variates and indicates the departure of the individual variates from the mean of the population. If the values of the plus and minus standard deviations are plotted on the base line of the curve and perpendiculars are erected at these points, the area of the polygon between the two perpendicular lines will contain two-thirds of all the variates. Applied to the F_2 generation of the tobacco cross, a standard deviation of 11.27 mm. indicates that measurements of corolla lengths falling between $49.9 - 11.27 = 38.63$ mm. and $49.9 + 11.27 = 61.17$ mm. may be expected to constitute two-thirds of the total of 828 measurements. How nearly does this estimate approach the facts?

How many of the 828 variates fall within the limits of a plus and minus standard deviation of 11.27 mm. where the mean corolla length is 49.9 mm? With measurements recorded in even numbers, East's table of measurements shows that 567 or slightly more than two-thirds of the total number of 828 corollas were between 38 and 62 mm. in length. The difference between 567 and the true two-thirds value, 552, may probably be accounted for by East's disregard of fractional measurements.

The standard deviation is an indication of the nature of the population for any measurable character. It shows whether the variates are all grouped near the mean of the population or if any considerable number of them are spread at a distance from the mean. The standard deviation is an indication of the dispersal of the variates from the mean of the population. In a comparison of two populations, if the measurements are in the same terms and the means roughly comparable, the one with the highest standard deviation is regarded as the more variable of the two. A large standard deviation indicates a spread in the range of variates. Also, it is a means of comparing the degrees of variability of two populations for the same type of character measured by the same standard, as millimeters, pounds, or bushels. How this is applied may be seen from a comparison of the standard deviations of all the generations of the cross *N. forgetiana* × *N. alata grandiflora* (Table XXXI). If the differences in the means of two populations are great, the use of the coefficient of variation, C. V., furnishes a method of comparison (p. 308).

East calculated the constants or statistics for the P_1 species and for the F_1 and F_2 generations of this cross. Reference to Table XXXII shows that the standard deviation for *N. forgetiana* was 2.27; for *N. alata grandiflora*, 5.38; for the F_1 of a cross between these two species, 3.67; and for the F_2 it was 11.26. If the standard deviation is relatively large, this is an indication of considerable variability. From a comparison of the standard deviations above, *N. forgetiana*, $\sigma = 2.27$ mm., is considerably less variable than *N*.

Table XXXII

STATISTICAL CONSTANTS BASED ON DATA FROM A CROSS *Nicotiana forgetiana* × *Nicotiana alata grandiflora*

Designation	Mean	Standard Deviation	Coefficient of Variation
N. forgetiana, 314	25.6 ± 0.12	2.27 ± 0.08	8.86 ± 0.33
N. alata gr., 321	78.8 ± 0.28	5.38 ± 0.20	6.82 ± 0.25
$F_1(314 \times 321)$	44.3 ± 0.23	3.67 ± 0.17	8.28 ± 0.38
$F_2(314 \times 321)1–6$	49.9 ± 0.26	11.26 ± 0.19	22.57 ± 0.39

alata grandiflora, $\sigma = 5.38$ mm. Is there any other evidence to confirm this supposition? Reference to the histograms and frequency polygons for these two species confirms these indications visually (Fig. 135). The data from *N. forgetiana* made a very tall, narrow histogram with a narrow base indicating a small range in corolla size. The histogram for *N. alata grandiflora* required a much broader base.

Similarly the greater variability of F_2 over F_1 indicated by a comparison of their standard deviations (11.26 and 3.67) is confirmed by their histograms. The histogram for F_2 required a much broader base for its construction than that for F_1, indicating greater range of corolla length in the F_2 than in the F_1 generation.

THE COEFFICIENT OF VARIATION. Another measure of variability is a statistical constant, the coefficient of variation or coefficient of variability, abbreviated C. V. (or V). This constant is based on the standard deviation from the mean and is expressed in percentage. It is calculated by multiplying the standard deviation, σ, by 100 and dividing the product by the mean, the formula being C. V. $= \dfrac{100\sigma}{M}$. Thus in the F_2 population N.

$forgetiana \times N. alata\ grandiflora$, C. V. $= \dfrac{100 \times 11.27}{49.89} = 22.59$ per cent.

The coefficient of variation is a measure of variation or a measure of the relative dispersion of the variates in any set of data and may be used to

Table XXXIII

FREQUENCY DISTRIBUTION FOR WIDTH OF COROLLA IN THE F_2 GENERATION OF A CROSS BETWEEN *Nicotiana forgetiana* AND *Nicotiana alata grandiflora*

Class Centers in Millimeters

25	30	35	40	45	50	55	60	65	70	75
4	16	50	122	164	205	167	67	28	4	1

compare the variability of characteristics measured in different units, as, for example, height in inches or weight in pounds. By using their coefficients of variation, it is possible to compare the relative variabilities of two different characteristics, as, for example, the variability in the height of corn plants in a field and in the amount of grain produced by these plants. Or the variation in the length of ears of corn may be compared with the variation in yield of grain per plant. Likewise variation in the height of college students measured in inches may be compared with the variation in their weights measured in pounds.

STATISTICAL CONSTANTS OF ERROR. Statistical treatments usually cannot be applied to an entire population, and the number of individuals measured in any case is only a small sample of the total population. There is always a possibility that the sample chosen is not representative of the population, that is, it may not be a random sample. If the material to be studied is variable, a small number of measurements, even though it be a fairly random sample, may not include representatives of the complete range of variates; some extremes may have been left out. To correct for difficulties of this nature, a further statistical constant frequently calculated from the data is the standard error.

THE STANDARD ERROR. Although the probable error has been extensively used in statistical analysis, many investigators have discarded it in experimental work in favor of the more useful standard error of the mean, written $S.E._M$ or s or sometimes X. The formula for the calculation of the standard error of the mean is $S.E._M = \dfrac{\sigma}{\sqrt{n}}$

For the data on corolla lengths of the F_2 generation of *N. forgetiana* × *N. alata grandiflora*, the formula becomes

$$S.E._M = \frac{\sigma}{\sqrt{n}} = \frac{11.27}{\sqrt{828}} = \frac{11.27}{28.775} = 0.3916$$

The meaning and use of the standard error of the mean. In some treatments of statistics, there appears to be a tendency to confuse the standard deviation, $\sigma = \sqrt{\frac{\Sigma(f \cdot d^2)}{n}}$, with the standard error of the mean, $S.E._M = \frac{\sigma}{\sqrt{n}}$. Some authors emphasize that these two statistics have distinctly different meanings and that they should be contrasted. The standard deviation of the mean, σ, is an estimated *measure of variability of individuals* that represents the departure of the individual members of a group from the mean of the population. In contrast the *standard error of the mean is an estimated measure of the variability or deviation from the true value of the average of a group of means* which might be calculated.

Almost any set of measurements, even when relatively large, may be regarded as data taken from a sample of a population. The mean, calculated from such data, is thus the mean of a sample. Another set of measurements taken as a sample from the same population might be different from the first set and yield a slightly different value for the statistical mean. A large number of means obtained from many separate samples of a population would be a series of means of different values, large, small, and intermediate, which could be grouped into a distribution curve or frequency polygon. According to the above conception, the standard error is a measure of the variability or deviation from the value of the true mean for the population, in this hypothetical group of means. Some authors have regarded it as an estimate of the standard deviation of the group of means derived from numerous samples.

Sometimes if it is important to learn if two samples have been taken from the same or from different populations, the standard error is employed. Statisticians generally approach such problems by what is called the "null hypothesis" under which it is assumed that there are no significant differences in the two samples. The data from the samples are treated statistically to disprove, if possible, the assumption of similarity. If two samples prove by analysis to be significantly different, they may be considered as representatives of different populations. The absence of significant differences in two samples, however, does not prove that they were taken from the same population. For example, two distinctly different varieties of wheat might by chance have exactly the same yield of grain. Statistical analysis of the yields in this case would give no reason to suppose that these varieties of wheat were different but on the other hand would not prove that they were the same. The significance of the difference between the means is determined by reference to statistical tables.*

The use of the term *error* in these constants is an unhappy choice of terminology, since in the minds of some people the word carries the idea of erroneous mathematical calculations. The use of these terms, however, involves no such implications. The constants are statistical aids in the interpretation of biological data. The standard error may be considered a measure of the accuracy of estimated constants derived from a single random sample as compared with the true value of these constants for the whole population. In other words it is a measure of the reliability of an estimated constant derived from a random sample establishing plus and minus limits within which the true value of the constant probably lies.

FURTHER STATISTICS OF VARIATION.   Further consideration of quantitative characteristics may involve studies of correlation, linear regression, variance, and covariance. Detailed discussion of the calculation of these statistics is too complex to be included here. The reader is referred to current texts on experimental and statistical procedure for explanations.

Questions and Problems

Perhaps the best method of study in biometry is to collect measurements of a random sample of living material and then to treat those data statistically as outlined in the discussion of statistical analysis.

The Data

Suitable material for measuring may be found almost anywhere, as, for example, the height of plants in a corn field, the length or weight of the ears in a corn field, the weight of grain on each plant, or the weight of grain on each ear of corn. Other material may be found in the size or weight of apples on an apple tree, the size or weight of potatoes in a field, or of ungraded samples of these commodities in a store. Many organisms may be used as material for a statistical problem. If other material is not readily available, the measurements of the height and weight of the men students or of the women students in a school yield excellent biometrical data.

Measurements should be made of about 200 individual items. Care should be taken that the measurements are made on a fairly chosen, random sample. No system of selection should be practiced in taking the measurements. The individuals to be measured should be chosen purely at random. If correlation studies are to be made, care should be exercised that some possible correlation may exist in the material chosen.

Several students may select different kinds of material for measurement and statistical analysis. In this way certain comparisons may be made.

1. After selecting suitable class intervals, arrange the data from about 200 measurements in a frequency table.
2. Construct a histogram representing the data from the measurements of a sample. Note the range of the variates and the mode of the graph. Calculate the median point on the graph.

---

* Statistical tables may be found in the standard treatments of statistical analysis by such authors as Davenport, Fisher, Love, Paterson, Pearson, Snedecor, Goulden, and others.

3. From the data of the measurements, calculate the mean, the standard deviation, the coefficient of variation, and the standard error of the sample measured.
4. Obtain measurements of two characteristics of the same kind of organism such as the yield of grain and the height of corn plants or the height and weight of men. Arrange the data from these measurements in the form of a scatter diagram or correlation table. (Consult texts on statistical procedure.)
5. From the data in the correlation table made for the problem above, calculate the coefficient of correlation for the samples studied.
6. After calculating the mean and the standard deviation of the mean of a sample based on about 200 measurements, select a much smaller sample of the same material and calculate the mean and standard deviation based on about 15 or 20 measurements. Note the differences in the two constants based on the large and small samples.
7. Compare the coefficient of variability for all of the different kinds of material subjected to statistical analysis. According to this constant, are there differences in the variability of the different characters studied?
8. The range of a histogram or polygon, the standard deviation of the mean, and the coefficient of variation are all indicative of the amount of variation in the sample statistically analyzed. Compare the ranges, standard deviations of the mean, and the coefficients of variation of two or more samples. What conclusions may be drawn as to the variability of the population from which the samples were taken?

References

DAVENPORT, C. B.: *Statistical Methods*, 3rd ed. New York, John Wiley & Sons, Inc., 1914.

————, and MERLE P. EKAS: *Statistical Methods in Biology, Medicine and Psychology*, 4th ed. New York, John Wiley & Sons, Inc., 1936.

FISHER, R. A.: *Statistical Methods for Research Workers*, 9th ed. New York, G. E. Stechert & Company, 1944.

LOVE, H. H.: *Application of Statistical Methods To Agricultural Research*, Shanghai, China, Commercial Press, Ltd., 1936.

————: *Experimental Methods in Agricultural Research*, Rio Piedras, Puerto Rico, The Agricultural Experiment Station, The University of Puerto Rico, 1943.

PATERSON, D. D.: *Statistical Techniques in Agricultural Research*, New York, McGraw-Hill Book Company, Inc., 1939.

SNEDECOR, GEORGE W.: *Statistical Methods*, 4th ed. Ames, Iowa State College Press, 1946.

WALKER, HELEN M.: *Elementary Statistical Methods*, New York, Henry Holt & Company, Inc., 1943.

chapter 16

Population Genetics*

The genetic composition of a population is obviously the summation of its component parts. The laws of Mendelian inheritance which are operative for individual crosses or matings are equally applicable to whole populations. **Population genetics** *is the study of the genetic composition of whole populations.* It is a particularly important tool in the study of human genetics.

Human genetic investigations may be classified under two major categories. With respect to individual marriages, there is always an interest in predicting what the children will be like. Prospective parents are understandably concerned about whether the children they might have will be normal or defective. The dramatic undertones of this question are accentuated when the pedigree of either or both parents includes cases of abnormalities. The possibilities for individual cases may be given with reasonable assurance if sufficient information on the two parents and their relatives is available. Of broader interest will be predictions concerning the future genotypic and phenotypic make-up of the population. The economic and social aspects of hereditary defects have given impetus to **eugenic studies** *and suggested programs.* What effect will various positive or negative eugenic measures have on improving or impairing the racial qualities of future generations?

The problem may be studied theoretically if the following are known:

1. The genetic nature of the characters under consideration
2. Gene frequencies in the present population
3. The type of matings taking place
4. The extent and nature of factors affecting the gene frequencies.

The Hardy-Weinberg Law

In 1908 Wilhelm Weinberg, a Stuttgart physician, and G. H. Hardy, an English mathematician, independently discovered and published the

* By H. R. Fortmann, Associate Professor of Agronomy, The Pennsylvania State University.

facts concerning one of the basic relations in the genetics of populations. This relationship may be expressed in the statement: In the absence of disturbing influences, when two alleles, A and a, occur in the frequencies p and q $(p + q = 1)$ in a very large random-mating population, the three types AA, Aa, and aa *will remain in equilibrium* from generation to generation with the frequencies p^2, $2pq$, and q^2. *This relationship is known as the* **Hardy-Weinberg Law.**

Implied and included in the statement above are the following restrictions and assumptions:

1. No new variations (with consequent change in gene frequency) by mutation or migration
2. No selection pressure, *i.e.*, no differences in survival, mating, and reproduction potential of the various genotypes
3. Mating completely at random (panmixia). This restriction is most frequently violated in human populations. Tall people tend to marry other tall people, and short people tend to marry other short people, etc. Marriages between people within geographic and economic communities occur more frequently than the converse
4. The population shall be very large so as to minimize the effect of random fluctuations. A large population may change by chance alone, but this may be ignored for practical purposes.

The effects of some deviations from the above restrictions will be discussed later. For the immediate discussion the conditions are assumed to be as specified.

THE GENERALIZED SITUATION. The first or initial generation is designated as N_0 and successive generations by or as N_1, N_2, — — — — N_n or an indefinite number of generations. In the present or initial generation (N_0), the genes A and a occur with frequencies p and q, respectively, and $1 - p = q$.

In the succeeding generation (N_1), the frequency of types AA, Aa, and aa may be determined by the checkerboard method:

		σ gametes	
		pA	qa
φ gametes	pA	$p^2\ AA$	$pq\ Aa$
	qa	$pq\ Aa$	$q^2\ aa$

which, summarized, gives $p^2AA : 2pqAa : q^2aa$. It is apparent that the frequencies of the three types might have been arrived at by $(pA + qa)^2 = p^2AA + 2pqAa + q^2aa$. That is, the zygotic array is the square of the gametic array. The frequencies of genes A and a in generation N_1 may be derived as follows from the zygotic array:

$$A = p^2 + \tfrac{1}{2} \cdot 2pq = p^2 + pq = p(p + q)$$

since $p + q = 1$, the frequency of $A = p$

$$a = \tfrac{1}{2} \cdot 2pq + q^2 = q^2 + pq = q(p + q) = q$$

Hence the frequencies of genes A and a in generation N_1 have remained unchanged from those occurring in N_0. It is therefore clear that the zygotic and gametic frequencies in N_2, N_3, $- - - - N_n$ will remain constant. The population is in equilibrium for the character in question.

For a population in equilibrium, it will be observed that

$$\frac{2pq}{2} = \sqrt{p^2 \times q^2} = pq$$

That is, the frequency of the heterozygotes is twice the square root of the product of the two homozygote frequencies.

Numerical example.   In N_0, frequency of A, $p = $ .95
frequency of a, $q = $ .05
$$p + q = 1$$

In N_1, we get: $p^2AA : 2pqAa : q^2aa$
or: $.9025AA : .0950Aa : .0025aa$.

It will be noted that $.0950 = 2\sqrt{.9025 \times .0025}$, hence the population is in equilibrium with respect to genes A and a.

The gametic frequency from N_1 will be:

A	a
$p^2 = .9025$	$q^2 = .0025$
$pq = .0475$	$pq = .0475$
$p(p + q) = p = .9500$	$q(p + q) = q = .0500$

Attention is called to the simplification of the identity $p(p + q)$ to p which is justified since $p + q = 1$. Since the frequencies of A and a in N_1 are identical with those in N_0, it is apparent that the zygotic array in N_2 will be the same as in N_1.

A second approach to the problem of determining the zygotic array in N_2 is illustrated below:

$$N_1 = p^2AA : 2pqAa : q^2aa$$
$$N_2 = \text{The progeny of the three types above mated}$$
$$\text{at random as shown below}$$

MATING TYPE ♀ ♂	FREQUENCY OF EACH MATING TYPE	GENOTYPE AND FREQUENCY OF OFFSPRING FROM EACH MATING TYPE		
		AA	Aa	aa
$AA \times AA$	$p^2 \times p^2 = p^4$	p^4	..	..
$AA \times Aa$ $Aa \times AA$	$2(p^2 \times 2pq) = 4p^3q$	$2p^3q$	$2p^3q$	..
$Aa \times Aa$	$2pq \times 2pq = 4p^2q^2$	p^2q^2	$2p^2q^2$	p^2q^2
$AA \times aa$ $aa \times AA$	$2(p^2 \times q^2) = 2p^2q^2$	..	$2p^2q^2$	..
$Aa \times aa$ $aa \times Aa$	$2(q^2 \times 2pq) = 4pq^3$	..	$2pq^3$	$2pq^3$
$aa \times aa$	$q^2 \times q^2 = q^4$	..	..	q^4

Summarizing these frequencies gives:

$$\text{Frequency of } AA = p^4 + 2p^3q + p^2q^2 = p^2(p^2 + 2pq + q^2) = p^2[(p + q)^2]$$
$$= p^2$$
$$\text{Frequency of } Aa = 2p^3q + 2p^2q^2 + 2p^2q^2 + 2pq^3 = 2pq(p^2 + 2pq + q^2)$$
$$= 2pq[(p + q)^2] = 2pq$$
$$\text{Frequency of } aa = p^2q^2 + 2pq^3 + q^4 = q^2(p^2 + 2pq + q^2) = q^2[(p + q)^2]$$
$$= q^2$$

This somewhat longer procedure leads to the same conclusions, namely, that the zygotic and gametic frequencies in N_1 and N_2 are identical.

The *relation between gene frequencies and zygotic frequencies*, indicated by the Hardy-Weinberg Law, is useful in investigations of the genetic characteristics of populations. The genetic nature of the characters in question must be known, and the frequency of one of the homozygous types of a specified character must be determined. Then if panmixia (mating at random) and genetic equilibrium may be assumed, the frequency of the other (alternate) homozygotes and the heterozygotes can be determined.

If, for example, for the frequency of the recessive homozygote of a character determined by two alleles, A and a, has been determined, this is essentially q^2. The value of $q = \sqrt{q^2}$ and $p = 1 - q$. With p and q computed, the calculation of the frequencies of AA, p^2, and Aa, $2pq$, is routine.

As an example, it is reported that the frequency of albino deer in the Wisconsin deer population of 850,000 is about 20 or 1 in 42,500 (Fig. 137).

The following assumptions will need to be made:

1. WW and Ww = normal-colored deer
    ww = albino
2. Panmixia
3. Population in equilibrium.

Let p = frequency of W in population
q = frequency of w in population

$$q = \sqrt{q^2} = \sqrt{1/42,500} = \sqrt{.0000235294117}$$
$$= .004850713 \text{ or approximately } \tfrac{1}{206}$$
$$p = 1 - q = .995149287$$

FIG. 137. THREE ALBINO DEER.
In a herd of 19 in northern Wisconsin, they illustrate a significant departure from panmixia. If the estimated 20 albino deer in the 850,000 Wisconsin white-tailed deer population were randomly distributed, the odds against finding such a group would be about 79 billion to 1. (Courtesy, Staber Reese, Wisconsin Conservation Department.)

The zygotic frequency would be determined as follows:

$$WW \quad + \quad Ww \quad + \quad ww$$
$$p^2(850,000) \quad 2pq(850,000) \quad q^2(850,000)$$

And in the Wisconsin deer population:

$$
\begin{aligned}
841,774 &= 99.032235\% = WW = \text{homozygous normal-colored} \\
8,206 &= .965421\% = Ww = \text{heterozygous normal-colored} \\
20 &= .002353\% = ww = \text{homozygous albinos} \\
\hline
850,000 \quad & 100\% \qquad \text{TOTALS}
\end{aligned}
$$

Relative frequency of W allele = $1,691,754$; p = .995149
Relative frequency of w allele = $8,246$; q = .004851

It is interesting to note that the relation between heterozygotes, Aa, and recessive homozygotes, aa, will be:

$$\frac{Aa}{aa} = \frac{2pq}{q^2} = \frac{2(1-q)}{q}$$

Therefore, as the number of individuals having the recessive character aa becomes smaller, the heterozygotes, Aa, become proportionately more common. The expression approaches ∞ as q approaches *zero*. In the example of the Wisconsin deer population, the heterozygotes are some 400 times more frequent than the recessive homozygotes ($8,206 \div 20$). Of the 8,246 w genes present in the population, only 40 are present in the homozygotes. Elimination of the 20 recessive-albino homozygotes from the breeding population would have virtually no effect on the zygotic array in the subsequent generation. Since the frequency of type $ww \times ww$ matings is q^4, it can be shown that only 1 deer in 1,806,250,000 would be an albino from two albino parents. To express this in more comprehensible terms, if half of the 850,000 Wisconsin deer population is female and if each deer produces 1 fawn annually, the simple probability is that only once in about 4,000 years would an albino fawn result from the mating of two albino parents.

Similar examples may be selected from human populations. **Alcaptonuria** (pp. 405, 406), a recessive condition manifested by the presence of alcapton in the urine, occurs in about 1 in 1,000,000 persons. Application of the Hardy-Weinberg formula reveals that about 1 in 500 persons is a heterozygous carrier of the factor. The possible effectiveness of some suggested measures designed to eliminate or limit the incidence of undesirable genetic traits in a population is shown (Table XXXIV), in light of the facts presented above, to be extremely limited.

MULTIPLE ALLELES. The discussion thus far has been limited to a single pair of alleles. Under random mating the zygotic frequency when alleles are multiple is the same as when there are only two, namely, the

Table XXXIV

THE ZYGOTIC AND GAMETIC FREQUENCIES FOR A CHARACTER WITH
COMPLETE NEGATIVE SELECTION AGAINST THE RECESSIVE HOMOZYGOTE

Generation	Zygotic Ratio			Gametic Ratio	
	AA	Aa	aa	A	a
				(p)	(q)
N_0	.250	.500	.250	.667	.333
N_1	.4444	.4444	.1111	.750	.250
N_2	.5625	.3750	.0625	.800	.200
N_3	.6400	.3200	.0400	.833	.167
N_4	.6939	.2782	.0279	.857	.143
N_5	.7344	.2452	.0204	.875	.125
N_6	.7656	.2188	.0156	.889	.111
N_7	.7903	.1974	.0123	.900	.100
N_8	.8100	.1800	.0100	.909	.091
N_9	.8263	.1654	.0083	.917	.083
N_{10}	.8409	.1522	.0069	.923	.077
N_{20}	.9111	.0868	.0021	.957	.043
N_{30}	.9386	.0604	.0010	.970	.030
N_{40}	.9530	.0464	.0006	.977	.023
N_{50}	.9620	.0376	.0004	.981	.019
N_{100}	.9805	.0194	.0001	.990	.010
$N_{1,000}$	.9980	.001999	.000001	.999	.001
$N_{10,000}$	.9998	.00019998	.00000001	.9999	.0001
N_n	p_{n-1}^2	$2p_{n-1}q_{n-1}$	q_{n-1}^2	$\dfrac{p + nq}{1 + nq}$	$\dfrac{q}{1 + nq}$

zygotic array is the square of the gemetic array. For three alleles, A, A^1,
and a with frequencies p, r, and q, respectively, and with $p + r + q = 1$,
the following zygotic array from $(pA + rA^1 + qa)^2$ would be:

$$p^2AA + r^2A^1A^1 + q^2aa + 2prAA^1 + 2pqAa + 2rqA^1a.$$

In order to have established the fact that multiple alleles exist, it must
have been possible to identify more than two phenotypes. The four human
blood groups A, B, AB, and O have been shown to be dependent on three
alleles A, B, and O (Wiener, 1943). (The existence of subgroups of A will be
ignored in this discussion.) The frequencies of alleles A, B, and O may be
designated as p, r, and q, respectively. The blood-group composition of a
population may be illustrated as on page 319.

The relative allele frequencies may be computed from the information
available on the frequencies of the four blood groups. It is assumed in this
example that $p + r + q = 1$.

Blood Group	Genotype	Genotype Frequency	Blood-group Frequency
A	AA AO	p^2 $2pq$	$p^2 + 2pq$
B	BB BO	r^2 $2rq$	$r^2 + 2rq$
AB	AB	$2pr$	$2pr$
O	OO	q^2	q^2

From the frequency of the O group (fO), q may be determined directly:

$$q = \sqrt{fO} = \sqrt{q^2}$$

By combining the frequencies of blood groups A and O, it will be possible to compute p, since

$$fA + fO = p^2 + 2pq + q^2 = (p + q)^2$$
$$p + q = \sqrt{p^2 + 2pq + q^2} = \sqrt{fA + fO}$$

And finally, $p = \sqrt{p^2 + 2pq + q^2} - q$

With p and q determined, the simple subtraction $1 - (p + q) = r$. Since $p + r + q = 1$, it is also possible to compute p and r as follows:

$$p = 1 - \sqrt{fB + fO} = 1 - \sqrt{r^2 + 2rq + q^2},$$

and

$$r = 1 - \sqrt{fA + fO} = 1 - \sqrt{p^2 + 2pq + q^2}$$

The frequencies of alleles A, B, and O vary for different populations. For purposes of illustration and simplicity of calculation, a hypothetical population with the following allele frequencies may be assumed:

$$pA = .2$$
$$rB = .3$$
$$qO = .5$$

Substituting these values into the alegebraic identities for the blood-group frequencies would give the numerical frequencies shown below.

Blood Group	Algebraic Frequency	Numerical Frequency
A	$p^2 + 2pq$	.24
B	$r^2 + 2rq$	.39
AB	$2pr$	.12
O	q^2	.25
Total	$(p + r + q)^2$	1.00

These data may now be used to illustrate application of the formulae for calculation of p, r, and q.

Thus:

$$q = \sqrt{fO} = \sqrt{.25} = .5,$$
$$p = \sqrt{fA + fO} - q = \sqrt{.24 + .25} - .5 = .2$$

and
$$r = 1 - (p + q) = 1 - (.2 + .5) = .3$$

Or alternatively,

$$p = 1 - \sqrt{fB + fO} = 1 - \sqrt{.39 + .25} = .2$$

and
$$r = 1 - \sqrt{fA + fO} = 1 - \sqrt{.24 + .25} = .3$$

Thus the calculations have given the values for p, r, and q originally specified. In passing, it is of interest to note that blood groups are rarely a consideration in marriage. The restriction of random mating or panmixia may, therefore, be adequately satisfied. Hence blood groups are an excellent example for application of the principles of the Hardy-Weinberg Law.

Deviations from Panmixia

It is beyond the scope of this chapter to delve exhaustively into the effect of deviations from the assumptions inherent to the Hardy-Weinberg Law. Dahlberg (1948) has given a concise presentation of the situation with respect to the genetics of human populations. He lists five possible deviations.

MUTATIONS. Mutations are generally credited as the factor that has given rise to much of the variation now present in populations. From the long-range view the effect of mutations cannot be minimized. However, for those few characters in which the mutation rate has been estimated, it is apparent that mutations are too rare to have an appreciable effect on near generations.

SELECTION. Selection may be partial or complete, negative or positive. For example, amaurotic idiots never reach maturity and never have children. This would be an example of complete, negative selection. Similarly, other types of defectives might occasionally reach maturity and have children but have fewer than the norm for the population. This would be partial, negative selection. The below-average birth rate of the supposedly upper intellectual strata of our own population has given cause for concern in some circles. It is essentially a type of self-imposed negative selection. Whenever one segment of the population is subjected to negative selection, then, in effect, the other segment is subject to positive selection.

If a dominant gene determines a character against which complete, negative selection occurs, immediate elimination of the character from the population will result. It will recur only as the result of mutation. If the character occurs only as the recessive homozygote, complete, negative selection will not result in immediate elimination of the character, since the heterozygotes provide a reservoir for the recessive gene. The effective mating population will be limited to the AA- and Aa-type zygotes. What then will be the effect of complete, negative selection against the aa-type zygotes on the gametic frequencies of A and a in future generations?

Assumptions:

1. Complete selection against aa
2. No selection against Aa
3. Very large population
4. Panmixia for AA and Aa.

The gametic frequencies in N_0 may be designated as pA and qa with $p + q = 1$.

The zygotic ratio in N_n will be

$$p_{n-1}^2AA : 2p_{n-1}q_{n-1}Aa : q_{n-1}^2aa.$$

Even though the recessive homozygotes do not reproduce, the frequency of their appearance in future generations will be of interest. This may be computed from the frequency of the recessive gene q in the parental generation $n - 1$. The number of homozygous-recessive individuals, $i.e.$, those manifesting the character, will then be q_{n-1}^2.

The gametic ratio in the nth generation, N_n, will be as follows:

$$pA = \frac{p + nq}{1 + nq}$$

$$qa = \frac{q}{1 + nq}$$

Thus the frequency of aa in N_n will be

$$faa = q_{n-1}^2 = \frac{q^2}{[1 + (n - 1)q]^2}$$

The effect of complete, negative selection on the zygotic and gametic ratios in subsequent generations is shown below. In this example a hypothetical ratio of $.25AA : .50Aa : .25aa$ is assumed at the beginning. The aa individuals do not affect the gametic frequencies of A and a.

If a character is relatively common, as in N_0 above, selection is effective in reducing the frequency of the character. However, as the frequency of the character decreases, the effectiveness of selection also decreases. The explanation for this relationship is based on the ratio of heterozygotes to the recessive homozygotes. Initially, the heterozygotes are twice as frequent as the recessive homozygotes. Ten generations later they are about 22 times as frequent. After 1,000 generations the ratio has increased to 1,999 to 1.

If gene A is subject to mutation, $A \rightarrow a$, it is likely that at some point the frequency of mutation will equal the rate of elimination of a and that the population will assume a state of equilibrium. Natural or enforced complete, negative selection against *aa* will at that point serve only to maintain the *status quo*.

Dahlberg (1948) cites two examples of the effect of selection in human populations, the one negative and the other positive. The first is **celibacy** as practiced in some religious orders in the Roman Catholic Church. This practice often involves persons of exceptionally high talent who leave no offspring and might therefore have an effect of eliminating talent from the population. Since talent is a rare character, the effect of this negative selection might be expected to be slight. Comparison of Catholic and Protestant countries such as France and England reveals little difference in the frequency of talented individuals.

The second example deals with **polygamy** commonly practiced in some regions of the world. In practice only the wealthy can afford several wives. On the assumption that hereditary talent may possibly be measured by social position and wealth, the propagation of talented persons has been favored. Dahlberg points out that it is debatable as to what characters, if any, actually are favored by polygamy. It is also debatable whether the practice has had any great effect.

Formulae have been derived for computing the effect of partial, negative or positive selection. The results will fall somewhere between the limits established by computations for no selection and for complete selection, depending on the extent of the selection pressure.

ASSORTATIVE MATING. There is a tendency in human populations for people with a character in common to marry each other more frequently than would be expected by chance alone. This is a significant departure from the conditions stipulated for application of the Hardy-Weinberg Law. This departure from random mating is termed assortative mating.

Assortative mating results from varied causes, physical, psychical, or social in origin. Women, for example, rather generally select potential husbands who are taller than they. If the male has a choice, he seeks a wife shorter than himself. With the usual exceptions this results in a sorting process whereby tall people marry each other and so on down the line. Albinos are relatively infrequent in the United States population. The reported number of marriages of albinos to each other therefore constitutes a definite departure from randomness. Without citing further specific examples, it may be generalized that for any character regarded as aberrant by the general population, and consequently subject to discrimination, it is likely that random mating will not occur. By choice or necessity the "aberrant" individuals will marry each other more frequently than would be expected by chance alone—a plausible development since we have already indicated that various factors circumvent operation of chance. The tendency of people with a character in common to marry is termed positive assortative mating. It might be emphasized that highly desirable characters are equally as important as undesirable characters in producing assortative mating.

Negative assortative mating may also occur. People with a character in common may tend not to intermarry. An example would be people with domineering personalities. Since continuous association of two dominant personalities leads to frequent clashes, it is a natural development that people with this characteristic generally marry people with less domineering personalities.

Selection and mutation alter the gene frequencies in a population. The other deviations from panmixia do not change the gene frequencies but do change zygotic frequencies. Assortative mating is generally a matter of degree, *i.e.*, partial. Total assortative mating rarely occurs in human populations, but the theoretical effect on zygotic frequencies may be computed. The zygotic frequencies in the n*th* generation may be determined by the following formulae, if the frequency of the recessive gene in N_0 is q (formulae modified from Dahlberg, 1948):

$$p_n^2 = p^2 + \frac{npq^2}{1 + nq}$$

$$2p_nq_n = 2pq - \frac{2npq^2}{1 + nq}$$

and,

$$q_n^2 = \frac{(n + 1)q^2}{1 + nq}$$

As shown in Table XXXV, the initial effects of total positive assortative mating are large. The rate of change decreases until finally the population consists almost entirely of the two homozygous types. Theoretically, with an infinite population, the process would never lead to complete elimination of the heterozygotes. This point however is largely academic.

The frequencies of genes A and a have remained unchanged. In starting with $p = q$, the limit of the process will be achieved when the heterozygotes are actually or for all practical purposes eliminated. At this time the population will consist of the two homozygous types in equal frequencies. For values of q other than 0.5, the initial and final frequencies of the two homozygotes will be unequal. The reader might make the calculations for various generations when $q = 0.1$. The zygotic frequencies in N_0 and N_{100} should be as shown below.

	AA	Aa	aa
N_0	.81	.18	.01
N_{100}	.891818	.016364	.091818

Formulae have been derived for determining the effect of partial, positive or negative assortative mating. The relative extent of the assortative-mating process is an integral feature of such formulae.

INTERMARRIAGE. In considering the effect of intermarriage on a population, it should first be noted that a certain proportion of intermarriage is expected in panmixia. Secondly, the actual frequency of blood marriages is small for most populations. Intermarriage occurs when the frequency of blood marriages exceeds that expected in panmixia.

Table XXXV

THE ZYGOTIC FREQUENCIES IN SUCCESSIVE GENERATIONS
FOR A CHARACTER WITH TOTAL POSITIVE ASSORTATIVE
MATING ($q = 0.5$)

Generation	Zygotic Ratio		
	AA	Aa	aa
N_0	.2500	.5000	.2500
N_1	.3333	.3333	.3333
N_2	.3750	.2500	.3750
N_3	.4000	.2000	.4000
N_4	.4167	.1667	.4167
N_5	.4286	.1429	.4286
N_6	.4375	.1250	.4375
N_7	.4444	.1111	.4444
N_8	.4500	.1000	.4500
N_9	.4545	.0909	.4545
N_{10}	.4583	.0833	.4583
N_{20}	.4773	.0454	.4773
N_{30}	.4844	.0312	.4844
N_{40}	.4881	.0238	.4881
N_{50}	.4904	.0192	.4904
N_{100}	.4951	.0098	.4951
N_{500}	.4990	.0020	.4990
$N_{1,000}$	.499501	.000998	.499501
N_n	$p^2 + \dfrac{npq^2}{1 + nq}$	$2pq - \dfrac{2npq^2}{1 + nq}$	$\dfrac{(n + 1)q^2}{1 + nq}$

The intermarriages of consequence in human populations generally involve relationships no closer than cousins. As such it may be considered inbreeding of low intensity. Intensive inbreeding such as selfing or sibling matings in plants or animals leads to a gradual elimination of the heterozygotes. Thus intermarriage has effects similar to assortative mating.

For a gene that is very rare, for example, one that has arisen as a single mutation, it is apparent that intermarriage is the only mechanism that will allow the homozygous condition of the gene to arise. Such an isolated character will be of little consequence in the population. On the other hand, when a character is common, the small amount of intermarriage occurring in a population will have little significance.

ISOLATES. Geographic and social isolates existing within populations constitute the fifth major departure from random mating. Geographic isolates may result from actual physical barriers such as mountains or bodies of water. More commonly they center around generally recognized communities. It will be immediately recognized that most geographical isolates normally blend together without distinct lines of demarcation. Social isolates are associated with economic strata, religious differences, and tradition.

Developments in transportation, communication, education, and industry have served to eliminate or weaken the geographic and social barriers that produce isolates. It is not necessary for this discussion to elaborate further on types of isolates and changes that have affected them. The reader should be able to visualize numerous examples and their present state of stability.

An important aspect of **isolates** *is that they essentially constitute a separate mating population.* The size of the isolate will determine the extent of inbreeding (cousin marriages). Thus in small isolates it is likely that a rare gene will appear in the homozygous state more frequently than in the general population as a direct consequence of the higher frequency of intermarriage in the isolate. Since panmixia has not occurred in a small isolate, it would be erroneous to assume that the frequency of the recessive homozygote is equivalent to q^2 in the Hardy-Weinberg Law. Such an assumption would lead to too high a frequency of the heterozygotes and a value for q higher than actually exists.

If a recessive gene producing a certain defect is present only in a single isolate, marriage beyond the isolate boundaries will have no harmful effect. Increasing the isolate size will lead to a decrease in the homozygote frequency and an increase in the heterozygote frequency.

The formula below (modified from Dahlberg, 1948) shows the number of persons who will manifest the character if the gene has the frequency q and the isolate is enlarged by a part, x, of itself.

$$aa = \frac{q^2}{1 + x}$$

The frequency of the character decreases in proportion to the expansion of the isolate. If, for example, the isolate is doubled, the number of persons with the character will be one-half the original number.

SUMMARY. This chapter has given a brief introduction to some of the facets of population genetics. The presentation has been intentionally greatly simplified. The genetic constitution of a specified population is obviously dependent on all the factors mentioned, acting and interacting simultaneously with fluctuating intensities. Though this discussion has been limited to single factor characters, the methods are applicable to multiple factor inheritance, but the calculations are necessarily more complicated. The study of the genetics of a population necessitates application of numerous statistical techniques. Determination of the frequency of the recessive homozygote was casually mentioned as a preliminary step in application of the Hardy-Weinberg Law. Consideration reveals that this involves a carefully evolved and executed sampling procedure including allowance for gene penetrance. Similarly, determining the extent of the various factors such as selection, mutation, assortative mating, intermarriage, and size of isolates involves careful and extensive research.

The study of **population genetics** *is* thus *a fascinating but necessarily complex subject.* The reader will find a wealth of detailed information in the literature, but the field is wide-open for further research. Population genetics is singularly important for studying the present and future genetic composition of human populations. The significance and importance of such knowledge can hardly be overemphasized.

References

DAHLBERG, GUNNAR: "Genetics of Human Populations," in M. Demerec, ed., *Advances in Genetics*, New York, Academic Press, Inc., 1948, Vol. II, 67–98.

HARDY, G. H.: "Mendelian Proportions in a Mixed Population," *Science* **28**:49–50 (1908).

STERN, CURT: "The Hardy-Weinberg Law," *Science* **97**:137–138 (1943).

———: *Principles of Human Genetics*, San Francisco, W. H. Freeman and Company, 1949, Chapter 10, 146–169.

WIENER, A. S.: *Blood Groups and Transfusions*, 3rd ed. Springfield, Illinois, Charles C. Thomas, Publisher, 1943, Chapters 11, 12, 173–218.

section 7

Variations and Germinal Changes

Variations are characteristic of all living organisms. They are of two kinds, **heritable** and **nonheritable. Nonheritable variations** *affect the somatic tissues* and *not the cells of the reproductive tract*. Many of them result from environmental and physiological influences, such as good and poor nutrition and maiming accidents in the case of animals. Heat, cold, moisture, and soil conditions may cause pronounced *somatic* effects in plants. **Heritable variations** *have their basis in the germ plasm or reproductive tissues*. Some arise spontaneously from unknown causes in nature, but not all heritable variations are of spontaneous or unknown origin. Many heritable variations have been induced artificially by the use of various types of radiations. The X ray, ultraviolet ray, radium emanations, and neutron bombardments have all affected chromosomes and gene loci. Certain chemicals have also been used to induce germinal changes, especially in chromosome numbers. Many induced germinal changes determine observable phenotypic changes. Some changes in chromosomes and genes occur in purely somatic tissues and are never included in any truly reproductive cells. Such nonheritable variations may occur in the endosperm tissues of seeds, in leaf tissue, or in the tissues of fruits not involving seeds and are lost to the race or species unless propagated vegetatively. To be heritable a change must have occurred in the germ tract or reproductive tissues.

The following germinal changes have been found in, or traced to, the chromosomes: (1) **variation in chromosome numbers,** a condition called **heteroploidy;** (2) numerous **changes in the structure of individual chromosomes** collectively called **chromosomal aberrations;** and finally (3) certain **changes** *at definite loci in the chromosomes* called **point** or **gene mutations.** Many of these changes are microscopically observable; others are ultramicroscopic. Numerous changes are consistently related to variations in the physical appearance or phenotype of the organism concerned.

chapter 17

Heteroploidy or Variations in Chromosome Numbers in Plants and Animals

Chromosome numbers are significant in a consideration of the relationships of organisms and especially as a physical basis for certain types of genetic variations. Plants and animals regularly have a definite number of chromosomes in the nuclei of the cells of each species (pp. 9–11). Races with differing chromosome numbers, however, found in many species of plants and a few animals are known as chromosome races. Closely related species may differ in chromosome numbers and show indications of having been derived from each other or from a common source.

TERMINOLOGY. The total number of chromosomes in a nucleus is called the **chromosome complement.** The number of chromosomes characteristic of the nucleus of the gametes is referred to as the gametic set of chromosomes and collectively with the contained genes as the **genome.** After fertilization the chromosome complement of the zygotic nucleus consists of two sets of chromosomes or genomes. Coordinate with the term **genotype,** designating the gene constitution of an organism, another term, **karyotype,** is used to indicate the *chromosome complement* of an organism. The term comes from the Greek word *karyon* meaning nut, kernel, or nucleus. **Karyotype** has reference to the *number of chromosomes,* the *morphological features,* and all the *structural changes* within individual chromosomes of an organism.

An important conception in the study of chromosome numbers is that of the *basic number* of the species, genus, or group. Usually the number regarded as basic is the lowest found in any race or species of the group. In this connection two terms, homoploidy and heteroploidy, are in common use. **Homoploidy** refers to the condition which may be regarded as normal or basic. In homoploid organisms the gametic chromosome numbers are designated as 1x for the monoploid or haploid and as 2x for the diploid, somatic, or body numbers. **Heteroploidy** *indicates all deviations,* regardless of magnitude, from the presumed normal or basic number of chromosomes which may occur in the nuclei of either somatic or reproductive cells. Heteroploid organisms probably have been derived from organisms with the basic number of chromosomes.

Terms based upon Greek roots also designate many of the deviations in chromosome numbers. The form *-ploid* which occurs in them comes from the Greek meaning -fold, in the old English sense, and is combined with a variety of prefixes. Thus monoploid or haploid means onefold and diploid, twofold. Chromosome numbers of some organisms are exact multiples of the basic monoploid or 1x number. These numbers may be triploid or threefold; tetraploid, fourfold; pentaploid, fivefold; and so on to polyploid

Table XXXVI

KEY TO TERMS INDICATING CHROMOSOME COMPLEMENTS

Exactly the basic chromosome numbers	homoploid
One set of chromosomes, the basic (x) number	haploid or monoploid
Two sets of chromosomes, twice the basic number	diploid
Any other than the basic homoploid chromosome number	heteroploid
An exact multiple of the basic (x) haploid number of chromosomes	euploid or polyploid
Cases in which the heteroploidy is due to the multiplication of the basic monoploid number, that is, the chromosome sets are specifically related but are merely doubled, tripled, quadrupled, etc.	autoheteroploid or autoploid
Exactly 3 times the basic set (3x)	triploid
" 4 " " " " (4x)	tetraploid
" 5 " " " " (5x)	pentaploid
" 6 " " " " (6x)	hexaploid
" 7 " " " " (7x)	heptaploid
" 8 " " " " (8x)	octoploid
" 9 " " " " (9x)	enneaploid
" 10 " " " " (10x)	decaploid
" 11 " " " " (11x)	11-ploid
" 12 " " " " (12x)	12-ploid
" 16 " " " " (16x)	16-ploid
Cases in which the heteroploidy is due to the addition of specifically different chromosome sets as may result from the hybridization between distinct species	alloheteroploid or alloploid (or amphidiploid)
Conditions relating to the members of the pairs of homologous chromosomes	
Numbers of chromosomes of the normal diploid, both members of all pairs present	disomic
Some number of chromosomes other than an exact multiple of the basic (x) haploid set	aneuploid
Numbers of chromosomes more than an exact multiple of the basic (x) haploid number	hyperploid
Conditions in which some of the sets of chromosomes are:	
2x + 1, that is, 3 homologues	trisomic
2x + 1 + 1, that is, 4 homologues	tetrasomic
Numbers of chromosomes less than an exact multiple of the basic (x) haploid number	hypoploid
Conditions in which some of the sets of chromosomes are lacking one or more, as 2x − 1 and 2x − 2	monosomic
Conditions in which both members of a pair of homologues are lacking, 2x − 1 − 1	nullisomic

or manyfold. They may also be designated as 3x, 4x, 5x, etc. Another term, **euploidy,** meaning true doubling or perhaps more exactly true multiples, designates this condition. **Polyploidy** is used as a general term to include all types of euploidy or true multiple numbers. The condition of polyploidy or euploidy is a special kind of heteroploidy.

The designations 1N and 2N used generally for the gametophytic and sporophytic chromosome numbers (pp. 28, 36) do not always indicate the true basic haploid and diploid conditions. In polyploid organisms in which the chromosome number is a multiple of the basic 1x, while the terms 1N-2N represent gametophytic and sporophytic chromosome numbers, they do not represent the true haploid and diploid conditions, which are 1x-2x. The true chromosome formulae may then be represented by 2x-4x, 3x-6x, 4x-8x, or otherwise as the case may be, but the terms *1N* and *2N* may still be used for polyploids to indicate the general number of chromosomes following meiosis and fertilization, respectively. Table XXXVI presents a summary of terminology for many of the chromosome formulae resulting from heteroploidy.

Polyploidy in Plants

Although rare in animals, heteroploidy occurs frequently in plants. Polyploidy, either natural or experimentally induced, has been found in mosses, liverworts, ferns, and in many kinds of flowering plants. Frequently a series of chromosome numbers has been found within a group, species, or genus of plants. This series may consist of normal homoploid plants with the basic haploid or monoploid, 1x, number of chromosomes in the gametic phase and the diploid, 2x, number in the sporophytic phase. In addition there may be sporophytic plants which are themselves monoploid or haploid, that is, with the basic 1x number of chromosomes in the nuclei of their cells. A polyploid series may thus begin with the haploid or monoploid, 1x, and continue with possible gaps through the 2x, 3x, 4x, 5x, 6x, and various other multiples of the basic 1x chromosomes (Tables XXXVI, XXXVII,

Table XXXVII

CHROMOSOME NUMBERS IN WHEAT

Triticum monococcum, where N = 7 and 2N = 14, is
1x − 2x a diploid species.
Triticum durum, where N = 14 and 2N = 28, is
2x − 4x, a tetraploid species.
Triticum vulgare, where N = 21 and 2N = 42, is
3x − 6x, a hexaploid species.

and XXXVIII). In many naturally occurring polyploid series, as well as in those experimentally induced, it has been possible to "fill in" some of the intervening gaps. For example, hybridization between a tetraploid, 4x, and a hexaploid, 6x, may yield a pentaploid, 5x.

Table XXXVIII

SOME POLYPLOID PLANTS WITH THEIR CHROMOSOME NUMBERS

Name of Plant		Chromosome Numbers									Remarks
Scientific	Common	1x Basic	2x Diploid	3x Triploid	4x Tetraploid	5x Pentaploid	6x Hexaploid	7x Heptaploid	8x Octoploid	Higher Numbers	
Cyclamen Several wild species	Cyclamen Several cultivated species	9	1N = 9; 2N = 18		1N = 18; 2N = 36		1N = 27; 2N = 54		1N = 36; 2N = 72	Also an 18-ploid, 2N = 162	Aneuploidy also found 2N = 24, 30, 34, 48, 78, and 130
Chrysanthemum Several wild and cultivated species	Chrysanthemum Many cultivated species and varieties	9	1N = 9; 2N = 18	N = 27	1N = 18; 2N = 36	2N = 45	1N = 27; 2N = 54		1N = 36; 2N = 72	Also a 10-ploid, 2N = 90	
Fragaria Several wild species	Strawberry Many cultivated varieties, some the result of hybridization between species	7	1N = 7; 2N = 14	2N = 21	1N = 14; 2N = 28	2N = 35	1N = 21; 2N = 42		1N = 28; 2N = 56	Also a 9-ploid, 2N = 63. A 12-ploid, 2N = 84. A 14-ploid, 2N = 98	Aneuploidy with 2N = 49 and 77
Pyrus Many wild species	Apple and pear Many cultivated varieties	17	1N = 17; 2N = 34	2N = 51	2N = 68?					1 species 2N = 68	1 variety 2N = 41
Rosa Many wild species	Rose Many cultivated species and varieties	7	1N = 7; 2N = 14	2N = 21	1N = 14; 2N = 28	2N = 35	1N = 21; 2N = 42	2N = 49	1N = 28; 2N = 56		
Rubus Several wild species	Blackberry Raspberry Many cultivated varieties of different species	7	1N = 7; 2N = 14		1N = 14; 2N = 28	2N = 35	1N = 21; 2N = 42	2N = 49			Some 2N = 45
Salix Many wild species	Willow Several ornamental species	19	1N = 19; 2N = 38	2N = 57	1N = 38		1N = 57				
Solanum Many wild species	Potato Eggplant and others Many cultivated varieties	12	1N = 12; 2N = 24	2N = 36	1N = 22; 1N = 44; 2N = 24; 2N = 48	2N = 60	1N = 36; 2N = 72				This genus has been used extensively in experimental work
Tulipa	Tulip Many cultivated varieties	12	1N = 12; 2N = 24	2N = 36	1N = 24; 2N = 48	2N = 60					

Haploid plants called haplonts, that is, sporophytic plants with the true haploid, monoploid, or basic 1x number of chromosomes, have been found in a number of species of flowering plants, including the evening primrose, *Oenothera;* tobacco, *Nicotiana;* tomato, *Lycopersicon;* stock, *Matthiola;* and *Crepis.* They have been found in cultivated rice, in maize, in the Japanese morning-glory, and in wheat hybrids. Darlington has published a list of more than forty haploid plants among species of angiosperms. In addition more than 100 haploids have been reported in the Jimson weed, *Datura.*

A well-known example of a polyploid series occurs in wheat in which one of the species, *Triticum monococcum,* is the true homoploid. It has the basic chromosome number in the true haploid of 7 and the diploid 14; *Triticum durum,* a tetraploid, has 14-28; while the common cultivated wheat, *Triticum vulgare,* with 21-42 chromosomes is a hexaploid.*

Polyploidy appears to be of rather general occurrence among the flowering plants. In fact, some investigators estimate that fully half of all species of flowering plants is polyploid. Situations similar to those in species of wheat have been found in numerous other groups of plants. Table XXXVIII gives a list of polyploids in several genera of flowering plants.

Besides wheat, among crop plants, Stebbins mentions as polyploids alfalfa, banana, coffee, peanut, potato, sweet potato, oats, sugar cane, and a number of the fruits as certain varieties of apples and pears. With these facts in mind, plant breeders are attempting to improve cultivated plants by synthesizing polyploid varieties.

KINDS OF POLYPLOIDS

Two classes of polyploids are recognized, **autopolyploids** and **allopolyploids.** These terms are indicative of the origin of the polyploids and refer to the nature and kinds of chromosomes entering into the chromosome complement of the polyploid. The prefix *auto-* in the term *autopolyploid* comes from the Greek word *autos* meaning within self or from self. Thus the term *autopolyploid* refers to polyploid organisms which originated within a single species. Since chromosome races have developed within the species, the condition may be called intraspecific polyploidy. Usually chromsome races are autopolyploids, and in many cases they form a typical multiple chromosome series. In addition to the scores of cases found in nature, autopolypoids have been artificially induced in experimental cultures.

---

* Besides those mentioned above, the chromosome numbers in several other species of wheat are known. *Triticum aegilopoides* and *T. thaoudar* are also homoploids in which 1N = 7 and 2N = 14. These species are in the einkorn group of wheats. The emmer group, where 1N = 14 and 2N = 28, contains several species of wheat besides *T. durum.* Among these tetraploid species are *T. dicoccum, T. turgidum, T. polonicum,* and others. The vulgare group of species to which the bread wheat, *T. vulgare,* belongs is characterized by the hexaploid number of chromosomes, N = 21 and 2N = 42.

In **autopolyploids** the chromosome complements are regarded as duplications of the set in the original gametic number, because the members of each type of chromosome, regardless of number, are homologous. Homology is revealed in the formation of multivalent rather than merely bivalent associations in meiotic configurations. Although this typical cytological picture is not always found in autopolyploids, high percentages of trivalent chromosomes usually characterize triploids, and high percentages of quadrivalents are expected in autotetraploids. In higher autopolyploids chromosomes may be associated as hexivalents or other multivalents, even though part of the chromosomes may act as bivalents in meiosis.

The prefix *allo-* in the term *allopolyploid* comes from the Greek word *allos* meaning other. Thus allopolyploid refers to polyploids which have originated from combinations of different species. Usually allopolyploids have been derived from hybrids between two species. An allopolyploid plant may originate by a doubling of chromosomes in an F_1 species hybrid, by the fertilization of unreduced gametes of hybrid plants, or otherwise (pp. 336, 337). As contrasted with autopolyploids, which are developed within a species and constitute conditions of **intraspecific** polyploidy, allopolyploidy may be regarded as **interspecific.** In allopolyploids, the chromosome complements consist of different sets of chromosomes. Actually in most cases of allopolyploids, two complete diploid complements are combined in the polyploid which is then a tetraploid. Another term, **amphidiploid,** is used to designate allopolyploids of this type. Since allopolyploids are made up from the chromosome complements of two diploid species, they are really double diploids, which is exactly what the term *amphidiploid* means.

Allopolyploids or amphidiploids may originate from species having the same or different chromosome numbers. In either case, the two species complements of chromosomes in allopolyploids are mostly not homologous. The chromosomes in the complement from one species occur in pairs of homologues or synaptic mates, and those from the second species complement likewise occur in synaptic pairs. The chromosomes in allopolyploids consequently will usually pair as bivalents during meiosis and form relatively few trivalents and quadrivalents. The number of quadrivalents is indicative of the relationship of the two species from which the allopolyploid has been derived. In cytological investigation increasing emphasis is being placed on differences of chromosome behavior in autopolyploids and allopolyploids. One of the problems of polyploidy is to determine how different the chromosomes need to be to justify the designation of an organism as an allopolyploid rather than an autopolyploid.

Although autopolyploids and allopolyploids differ considerably as to the nature and kinds of chromosomes entering into their chromosome complements, these differences may be hard to identify, and it is difficult to draw an absolute line between them. Natural species or genera sufficiently related to hybridize may have many chromosomes and genes which are similar. On a basis of chromosome homology, many allopolyploids are auto-polyploid to a degree and in proportion to the number of homologous chromosomes and genes which they have in common. Müntzing concludes that all **allopolyploid species** *are partially autopolyploid* and that the different chromosome sets or genomes in an allopolyploid are probably never com-pletely distinct. Thus it is now generally accepted that there may be inter-mediate forms of polyploidy not strictly in either of the classes autopolyploid or allopolyploid. **Autopolyploids,** because of the exact doubling of the chromosomes, *may,* however, *be absolutely autopolyploid,* at least at the time of their origin.

Another problem for the student of polyploidy is to determine the pos-sible origin in nature of polyploid races and species. The solution of this problem is approached from many angles among which are: (1) the *experi-mental induction* of both autopolyploids and allopolyploids, (2) *a study of the meiotic behavior of the chromosomes* with special reference to the relative frequency of bivalent and multivalent associations indicating homology of chromosomes, and (3) as will be mentioned later, the *relative fertility* of the polyploid forms.

Aneuploidy in Plants

In contrast with polyploidy, another type of deviation has been found which is known as **aneuploidy** or *not true ploidy,* in contrast with euploidy or true ploidy. In aneuploidy the chromosome number is some other than an exact multiple of the basic number. The deviation may consist of the loss or addition of a single chromosome or of several chromosomes in com-parison with the normal 2N complement. Because their chromosome com-plements consist of even multiples of the basic chromosome set, the mem-bers of true polyploid series have been designated as balanced chromosome forms. Aneuploid plants may be regarded as unbalanced chromosome forms. The presence of a few additional members or the lack of one or more homo-logues for one or more pairs has the effect of disturbing the long-established balance in the chromosome complement. In most cases this unbalance leads to observable phenotypic changes (pp. 360–366). The genera *Carex, Datura,* and *Oenothera* which have been intensively studied show widespread aneuploidy. If researches in *Carex* and certain forage grasses should be confirmed by further studies in other plants, aneuploidy may eventually be regarded as very prevalent.

There are also cases with fewer than the normal number of chromosomes. The term *monosomic* is used to indicate that one chromosome is lacking or that only one member of a certain pair of chromosomes is present in the sporophytic plant. Further, the term **nullisomic** indicates that the organism lacks both members of one pair of homologous chromosomes. Although occasionally reported, the condition of nullisomy is rather rare, because it is possible only in polyploid plants in which each type of chromosome is represented by more than two homologous members. Apparently the loss of both members of a pair of homologous chromosomes would be fatal in a diploid plant. But in polyploids, where there are more than two homologous members of each chromosome type, if two are lost, the other members remain; and in some cases the nullisomic plant is viable, as, for example, nullisomic hexaploid wheat plants reported by Sears. The term *heterosomy* may be used to indicate the condition either of extra chromosomes in a complement or of chromosomes lacking in a normal complement.

Origins of Heteroploidy

Several possible methods of the origin of polyploidy have been recognized. One is the doubling of the chromosomes during early stages in the development of an embryo leading to the production of an entire polyploid plant. Doubling of the chromosomes in a single cell, or a few cells, located in a primordium of a bud or other meristematic tissue might give rise to a polyploid-plant part or to a polyploid tissue. Polyploid branches on, or tissues in, otherwise diploid plants are assumed to have originated in this way. A second method is the occasional origin of a polyploid embryo by the fusion of gametes one or both of which for some reason may be unreduced in chromosome number. Under these circumstances there may be the following two possibilities in fertilization: (1) 2x gamete + 1x gamete = 3x or a triploid zygote and (2) 2x gamete + 2x gamete = 4x or a tetraploid zygote. If doubling of the number of chromosomes in the 2x sporocytes should occur before the meiotic divisions, they would contain the 4x number of chromosomes, and the meiotic divisions would result in 2x gametes. The possibility that two sperms may sometimes unite with a single egg cell has been suggested as a third possible mode of origin. The heteroploid would then contain the 3x number of chromosomes and would be a triploid.

Origins of Haploid Plants

Some of the haploid or 1x plants which have been studied are supposed to have arisen *parthenogenetically*, that is, without fertilization, from otherwise normal 1x egg cells. Normal fertilization of eggs in adjacent ovules may sometimes stimulate an unfertilized egg to undergo parthenogenetic development with a haploid sporophytic plant resulting. Haploid plants may arise in rare instances when both of the male nuclei join with the fusing polar nuclei (endosperm) in the embryo sac; the unfertilized egg cell, stimulated to parthenogenetic development, would then produce a haploid plant. Overdeveloped endosperm tissue, which presumably would be 4N instead of the normal 3N, might indicate the origin of the haploid seedling. A haploid wheat plant was thought to have originated in this manner.

The development of secondary embryos from some of the various haploid cells of the embryo sac such as synergids or polar nuclei has been thought of as a possible origin of haploid plants. This condition of secondary embryos, called *polyembryony*, sometimes accompanies otherwise normal fertilization. Rather commonly in grass plants, including the cereals, a single seed may produce two seedling plants. It is well known that such twin embryos frequently have different chromosome numbers, as one with N = 36 and the other with 2N = 72 in Kentucky bluegrass, *Poa pratensis*. Twin seedlings have been studied in other plants besides the grasses. Haploids have arisen as twin seedlings in cotton, flax, and the Jimson weed. Cooper reported the occurrence of twin embryos, one diploid and one haploid, in about 1 per cent of the ovules of seven species of lily. He concluded that the diploid embryo developed from the fertilized egg and the haploid embryo from a synergid which had been stimulated to growth. Comparative volumes of the diploid and haploid embryos were as 2 to 1. Twin embryos, one triploid and the other haploid, were also found following a cross of *Nicotiana glutinosa* × *Nicotiana tabacum*. The haploid embryo in this case was thought to have developed from a synergid and the triploid from the zygote formed from gametes of the two parent species which differed in chromosome numbers.

Artificial Induction of Heteroploidy

Artificial induction of heteroploidy offers a technique for the plant breeder that may provide new materials basic to further selection and hybridization in crop improvement. Several methods of inducing changes in chromosome numbers in plants are: (1) "decapitation" of young plants to induce the formation of callus tissue, (2) the use of extremes in temperature, (3) the use of chemicals on plant tissues, (4) radiation, and (5) hybridization.

DECAPITATION AND CALLUS TISSUE. In this technique the top of the plant is cut off near the ground surface, and the stem and roots are left to grow. The surface of the cut stem becomes covered with callus tissue in which abnormal mitotic divisions occur. In tomato and related species as much as 6 per cent of polyploidy has been found in branches developing from buds growing from the callus tissue.

TEMPERATURE EFFECTS. Blakeslee observed that naturally occurring heteroploidy in *Datura* frequently followed abnormally cool temperatures in summer. When he subjected plants to lowered temperatures, he obtained some polyploid plants, perhaps because the cold disturbed meiotic divisions and led to unreduced gametes. Fertilization of the unreduced or 2x gametes produced polyploid embryos. Randolph used heat treatment on previously pollinated ears of corn by applying electric heating pads to young growing ears of corn plants. This treatment interfered with the mitotic divisions in the developing embryos and resulted in "somatic doubling" and tetraploidy.

EFFECTS OF CHEMICALS. Among numerous chemicals such as growth substances or auxins, acenapthene, podophyllin, and sulfanilamide, probably most effective in the experimental increase of chromosome numbers has been colchicine applied in dilute aqueous solutions, or in lanolin, to growing meristematic tissues of germinating seeds, root tips, or buds. Colchicine, a poisonous alkaloid, is prepared from the seeds and underground parts of the autumn crocus, *Colchicum autumnale* (Fig. 138). After

FIG. 138. COLCHICUM AUTUMNALE.
Drawing of the meadow saffron from an 18th century engraving showing roots, bulb, and flowers of the plant. This plant is the source of the alkaloid, colchicine. (Courtesy, John Wyeth and Brother, Inc., Philadelphia, Penna.)

Lits in 1934 reported the successful use of colchicine to induce heteroploidy in cells and tissues, other workers perfected techniques of application. In 1937 Blakeslee and Avery reported the induction of polyploidy in *Datura* and several other species of plants. Colchicine interferes with the formation and normal action of the division spindle in mitosis and delays division in the centromeres of the chromosomes (Fig. 139). The net result is that the division of the chromosomes into chromatids is not followed by nuclear division and the cells then have polyploid nuclei.

Plants treated with colchicine are not immediately increased in size, nor do they usually have other conspicuous and desirable qualities. Rather the treatment results in the frequent production of stunted, dwarfed, and greatly deformed plants. Sometimes such plants may ultimately produce a branch having desirable polyploid characteristics.

EFFECTS OF RADIATION ON HETEROPLOIDY. Both radium and the X ray have been effective in the production of polyploidy in the progenies of treated plants. Radiation appears to interfere with pairing and disjunction of the chromosomes during meiosis. Thus heteroploidy is produced not as a primary effect of radiation but as a secondary result of the generally unbalanced chromosome condition in the irradiated parent plants.

HYBRIDIZATION AND HETEROPLOIDY. It has been mentioned that hybridization enters into the production of allopolyploids or amphidiploids (p. 334). Frequently heteroploids have been observed in the progenies of hybrids under experimental control. Ramanujam hybridized two species of rice, *Oryza sativa* × *Oryza officinalis*. When the F$_1$ species hybrid was backcrossed to *O. sativa*, it yielded some triploid plants each with two sets of *O. sativa* chromosomes and one set of *O. officinalis* chromosomes. The triploids were supposedly the product of 2x female gametes, with single sets of both *O. sativa* and *O. officinalis* chromosomes, fertilized by a male gamete from *O. sativa*. Numerous cases have been observed in which

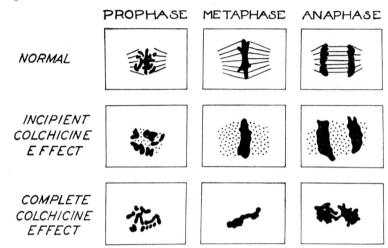

FIG. 139. DIAGRAM OF THE EFFECTS OF COLCHICINE ON NUCLEAR DIVISION.
Normal nuclear spindle forms during prophase, chromosomes appear on the equator of spindle at metaphase, and chromatids separate during anaphase with formation of two new nuclei during telophase. Although the chromosomes undergo normal longitudinal splitting following colchicine treatment, the alkaloid tends to inhibit formation of the nuclear spindle, production of the two nuclei, and development of the cell wall. As a result of colchicine treatment, chromosomes divide but the nucleus does not. The number of chromosomes in a cell is then doubled. (Courtesy Corman, from *Botan. Gaz.* **104**, 1942.)

heteroploidy has followed hybridization. Close approximations of natural species have even been artificially synthesized by hybridization techniques. Thus hybridization may be a method for the induction of heteroploidy.

USING HAPLOIDS AND POLYPLOIDS TO OBTAIN ADDITIONAL HETEROPLOID FORMS. Once some members of a series of polyploid plants are available, it is possible to obtain other members by various techniques. Triploids may be derived by crossing diploid and tetraploid plants. Since triploids (3x) and pentaploids (5x) have uneven chromosome numbers, they frequently give rise to aneuploid progenies, that is, plants with irregular chromosome numbers, such as the well-known "somic" plants. Lindstrom obtained a haploid tomato plant. Using the decapitation technique, he developed completely homozygous diploids by doubling the haploid chromosomes to the 2x number. Following the same method, he developed completely homozygous tetraploids by doubling the diploid chromosomes. Their complete homozygosity makes diploid and polyploid plants developed in this way very useful in genetical studies.

Viability of Hybrid Embryos

It has been known for some time that plants with differing chromosome numbers are to a considerable extent incompatible. Crossing such plants often results in very few or no viable seed. Among investigators in this subject, Cooper and Brink have suggested that the failure to produce viable seeds in such crosses is the result of a disturbance of the endosperm-embryo relationship. The disturbance may be associated with the radical change in the relation of chromosome numbers in the endosperm and embryo. Some years ago Müntzing advanced the theory that incompatibility between plants with differing chromosome numbers was one of the reasons for the extensive survival of polyploids after their origin. After a polyploid has originated in nature by any of the known methods, incompatibility, due to differing chromosome number, prevents its submergence through backcrossing with the parental forms.

FIG. 140. THE COMMON SOW BUG.
Found frequently in moist locations, this bug may become a greenhouse pest. This form may be regarded as representative of a group in which polyploidy was studied. (Courtesy, Weigel, U. S. Dep. Agr. Farmers' Bulletin #1362, Washington, 1923.)

Müntzing discusses the several theories which have been proposed to account for the frequent occurrence of polyploidy in plants and its relative infrequency among animals. He mentions as important the effects of "double fertilization," common in plants, in the production of a favorable endosperm-embryo relationship. He says that disturbances of the relationship cause the death of the embryo. Reference is made to the orchids in which double fertilization is frequently suppressed and endosperm formation is meager. He thinks that polyploidy occurs only rarely in orchids and suggests that there may be a causal relationship between these factors.

Cooper and Brink point out that, even in crosses between species differing widely in chromosome numbers, the zygote may start to function and the hybrid embryo is viable, actually growing at approximately a normal rate during its early stages, even though the endosperm fails to develop. Later with failure of normal endosperm development, the hybrid embryos succumb. Excision and cultivation of such embryos on artificial media are techniques that might extend the study of hybridization in polyploid plants.

Heteroploidy in Animals

Although widespread in plants, heteroploidy is rare in animals. (See list from Vandel, p. 342.) In the social insects, bees and wasps, males normally develop parthenogenetically from unfertilized eggs and are therefore haploid. Females develop from fertilized eggs and are diploids (p. 432). Exceptional triploids and tetraploids have been found in the fruit fly, *Drosophila* (pp. 439–443). Wilson (3rd ed., p. 832) refers to hexaploid and giant octoploid embryos in the bivalens type of *Ascaris megalocephala*,

$1N = 2$, $2N = 4$ (p. 20). Artom found two chromosome races in the shrimp, *Artemia salina*, one $1N = 21$, $2N = 42$ and another $2N = 84$. An octoploid race $2N = 168$ has also been reported in the shrimp. The diploid races reproduced normally, but the tetraploid race with nonfunctional males developed parthenogenetically from unfertilized eggs. Polyploid forms have been discovered among the sea urchins and starfishes. In 1939 Chen described polyploidy in the races of *paramecium*. Also in the sow bug, one of the isopods, *Trichoniscus elisabethae*, Vandel reported a diploid race $1N = 8$,

FIG. 141. SPECIES OF WEEVILS.
Left, the Deubrobium weevil; right, the black Diorymellus. These forms are related to the polyploid curculionids. (Courtesy, Weigel, U. S. Dep. Agr. Farmers' Bulletin #1362, Washington, 1923.)

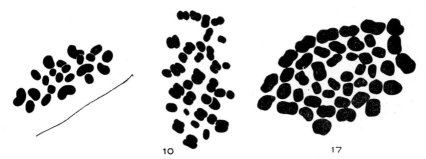

FIG. 142. CHROMOSOME NUMBERS IN WEEVILS.
Left, (7), the diploid number of 22 chromosomes; center, (10), the triploid number of 33 + 1 chromosomes; right, (17), the tetraploid number of 44 chromosomes. (Courtesy, Esko Suomalainen, from *Hereditas*.)

$2N = 16$ and a triploid race $2N = 24$ with females but very few males (Fig. 140). The unreduced 24 chromosome eggs developed parthenogenetically.

Besides those in *Drosophila*, a few instances of polyploidy have been found among other insects, as, for example, in two species of the stick insect, *Carausius*. The moth, *Solenobia triquetrella*, with 30 as the basic $1x$ number, has two races, one with $2x = 60$ and another with $4x = 120$. Zygotes were found with as many as 240 chromosomes. Suomalainen who investigated the weevils belonging to the *Curculionidae* found 11 to be the basic $1x$ chromosome number (Fig. 141). Of 13 species he found 4 diploid, $1x = 11$, $2x = 22$; 5 triploid, $3x = 33$; and 3 tetraploid, $4x = 44$ (Fig. 142). All polyploid forms showed meiotic abnormalities and reproduced parthenogenetically.

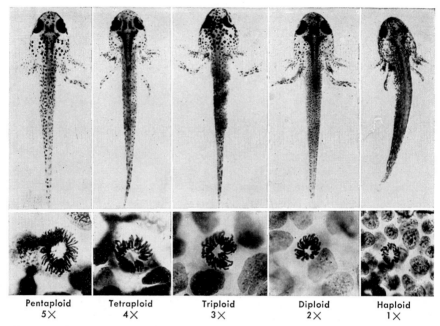

Pentaploid	Tetraploid	Triploid	Diploid	Haploid
5×	4×	3×	2×	1×

FIG. 143. POLYPLOID SERIES OF SALAMANDER LARVAE, TRITURUS VIRIDESCENS.
Pentaploid is at left. Tetraploid, triploid, and diploid in sequence toward haploid at right. Beneath, photomicrographs of metaphase plates showing chromosomes characteristic of each form. These larvae were at the same stage of development, except the haploid which was slightly less advanced. Since the larvae were all about the same size, the changes in cell size due to polyploidy were compensated by a reduction in the number of cells in the higher members of the series. (Courtesy, G. Fankhauser, Princeton University.)

Vandel published the following list of animals in which either natural or induced polyploidy was known.

Hermaphrodite forms
 Helix pomatia (3n and 4n)
Parthenogenetic forms
 Daphnia pulex (6n)
 Cypris fuscata (3n or 4n?)
 Artemia salina (4n and 8n)
 Trichoniscus elisabethae (3n)
 Carausius morosus and *furcillatus* (3n and 4n)
 Solenobia triquetrella and *lichenella* (4n)
 Trachyphloeus (?)
Bisexual forms
 Natural polyploids:
  Ascaris megalocephala and *lumbricoides* var. *bivalens* (4n)
  Artemia salina of Odessa (4n)

Echinus microtuberculatus bivalens (4n)
Asterias forbesii and *glacialis* (4n)
Experimental polyploids:
   Bombyx mori (3n and 4n)
   Many hybrids of *Lepidoptera* (3n)
   Habrobracon juglandis (2n and 3n)
   Drosophila melanogaster (3n and 4n)
   Rana esculenta and *pipiens* (3n)

POLYPLOIDY IN AMPHIBIANS. In frogs $1x = 13$, $2x = 26$, polyploidy was induced by pricking unfertilized eggs. The resulting larvae were found to be haploid $1x = 13$, diploid $2x = 26$, triploid $3x = 39$, and tetraploid $4x = 52$.

Fankhauser using a technique for counting the chromosomes in the tail tips of the larvae of salamanders was able to recognize living polyploid

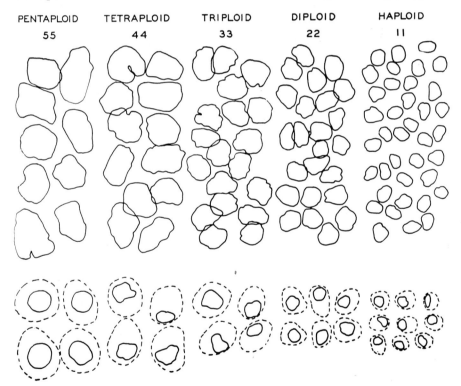

PENTAPLOID	TETRAPLOID	TRIPLOID	DIPLOID	HAPLOID
55	44	33	22	11

FIG. 144. FROM LARVAE OF SALAMANDER, TRITURUS VIRIDESCENS.
Above, outline drawings of the nuclei of epidermis cells from the tail fin. Below, drawings of gland cells also from the tail fin, cell boundaries in broken lines and nuclei in solid lines. From pentaploid at left through series to haploid at right. Nuclear and cell size are roughly proportional to chromosome numbers which are indicated by the numbers 55 to 11. (Courtesy, G. Fankhauser, Princeton University.)

individuals. He found 1 to 10 per cent of spontaneous polyploidy in the natural populations of three species. By using some forms artificially induced, Fankhauser was able to obtain a complete series from haploid to pentaploid in *Triturus viridescens*, 2x = 22 (Fig. 143 and 144). Changes in chromosome numbers were induced by cold treatment of eggs at 0.5° C. to 3.° C. for from 16 to 26 hours.

There was little difference in sizes of the members of the chromosome races. Haploids, however, were a little smaller and polyploids a little larger than the normal diploids. Cell sizes were roughly in proportion to the chromosome number. Organs of the body were slightly smaller in haploids than in diploids. The organs of polyploids were, however, about the same size as in normal diploids. Because the brown-pigment cells or melanophores varied directly with chromosome number, pigmentation of the larvae showed differences. Pigment cells of haploids were smaller and closer together; those of polyploids were larger and more widely spaced than in normal diploids.

Questions and Problems

1. Where is the physical basis of heritable variations located?
2. What is the meaning of the term *heteroploidy?*
3. What are the known extremes of naturally occurring chromosome numbers in plants?
4. Distinguish between the alternating phases in plants, emphasizing particularly the characteristic chromosome numbers. What is meant by the terms $1N$ and and $2N$? How are the haploid and diploid numbers maintained and derived in the life cycles of plants?
5. Differentiate between the terms $1N$ and $2N$ as contrasted with $1X$ and $2X$.
6. What is a chromosome complement? A genome?
7. Explain the distinction between homoploidy and heteroploidy.
8. What is the meaning of the term *polyploidy? Euploidy?*
9. What effects would you expect to find associated with abnormal chromosome numbers in plants? Explain the chromosome constitution of a triploid plant. A tetraploid plant.
10. How widespread is the occurrence of polyploidy in plants? What groups exhibit the phenomenon?
11. What constitutes a polyploid series? Describe the polyploid series in wheat. Name other flowering plants characterized by a polyploid series.
12. What are chromosome races?
13. What kinds of polyploid organisms are recognized?
14. What is aneuploidy?
15. Name some plants in which aneuploidy occurs.
16. What are monosomic plants? Disomic? Trisomic? Tetrasomic? Nullisomic? Which of these is the normal condition? Which is exceedingly rare?
17. What kinds of plants have produced polyploids in nature?
18. What is meant by somatic doubling? Where in a plant could this occur?
19. Explain what is meant by unreduced gametes. How could their fusion result in polyploidy?
20. Suggest several ways in which a triploid zygote might arise.
21. What stages in the life history of a plant should be studied to secure evidence about its chromosome constitution?

22. How can gametes with unusual chromosome numbers arise?
23. What is a haploid plant? Of what importance are haploids in genetical studies?
24. How may haploid plants originate?
25. In the case of twin embryos in plants, why may one of them be a haploid plant?
26. What are the methods which have been used to secure changes in chromosome numbers in plants?
27. Describe the decapitation technique used to induce polyploidy.
28. Speculate on the reported occurrence of polyploid plants in colder climates in relation to the artificial production of polyploidy by cold shocks.
29. How does colchicine tend to induce chromosome doubling?
30. Is it likely that the use of colchicine to induce polyploidy will be of commercial importance? Explain.
31. How can triploid or pentaploid plants be obtained if diploids and tetraploids of a species are available?
32. Are polyploid plants likely to survive in nature? How do you explain the abundance of polyploid plants in nature?
33. Contrast the relative frequency of polyploidy in plants and in animals. What explanations would you offer to account for the scarcity of polyploid forms in animals?
34. Which groups of animals have most of the known polyploid forms?
35. What contribution does recent experimental work with sex determination in polyploid plants make to this topic?
36. Explain why animals which reproduce parthenogenetically should be the ones to show polyploidy most frequently.
37. What are some of the characteristics of polyploidy in animals? Is there a relationship between chromosome numbers and cell size in animals? Is there a general increase in the size of an animal corresponding to increases in chromosome numbers and cell size?

References

BLAKESLEE, A. F.: "Effect of Induced Polyploidy in Plants," *Am. Naturalist* **LXXV**:117–135 (1941).

———— and A. G. AVERY: "Methods of Inducing Doubling of Chromosomes in Plants," *J. Heredity* **28**:393–411 (1937).

BRITTEN, E. J., and W. P. THOMPSON: "The Artificial Synthesis of a 42 Chromosome Wheat," *Science* **93**:479 (1941).

DARLINGTON, C. D.: *The Evolution of Genetic Systems*, Cambridge, England, Cambridge University Press, 1939.

————: *Recent Advances in Cytology*, Philadelphia, P. Blakiston's Son & Co., Inc., 1937.

DE ROBERTIS, E. D. P., W. W. NOWINSKI, and FRANCISCO A. SAEZ: *General Cytology*, Philadelphia, W. B. Saunders Company, 1948.

DOBZHANSKY, THEODOSIUS: *Genetics and the Origin of Species*, 2nd ed. New York, Columbia University Press, 1941, Chapter VII.

FANKHAUSER, G.: "A Pentaploid Larva of the Newt, *Triturus viridescens*," *Proc. Nat. Acad. Sci. U. S.* **26**:526–532 (1940).

————: "Polyploidy in the Salamander, *Eurycea bislineata*," *J. Heredity* **30**:379–388 (1939).

HAYES, H. K., and F. R. IMMER: *Methods of Plant Breeding*, New York, McGraw-Hill Book Company, Inc., 1942.

MORGAN, T. H.: *The Theory of the Gene*, 2nd ed. New Haven, Yale University Press, 1928, Chapters VIII, IX, X, XI, XII, 105–190.

SANSOME, F. W., and J. PHILP: *Recent Advances in Plant Genetics*, Philadelphia, P. Blakiston's Son & Co., Inc., 1939.

SHARP, L. W.: *Introduction to Cytology*, 3rd ed. New York, McGraw-Hill Book Company, Inc., 1934.

SINNOTT, EDMUND W., H. HOUGHTALING, and A. F. BLAKESLEE: "The Comparative Anatomy of Extra-chromosomal Types in *Datura stramonium*," *Carnegie Inst. Wash. Publ.* **451**:1-50 (1934).

STEBBINS, G. LEDYARD, JR.: *Variation and Evolution in Plants*, New York, Columbia University Press, 1950.

SUOMALAINEN, E.: "Polyploidy in Parthenogenetic *Curculionidae*," *Hereditas* **XXVI**:51-64 (1940).

VANDEL, A.: "Chromosome Number, Polyploidy and Sex in the Animal Kingdom," *Proc. Zoöl. Soc. of London* **107**, Series A:519-541 (1937).

WADDINGTON, C. H.: *An Introduction to Modern Genetics*, New York, The Macmillan Company, 1939.

WHITE, M. J. D.: *Animal Cytology and Evolution*, Cambridge, England, Cambridge University Press, 1945.

WILSON, E. B.: The Cell in Development and Heredity, New York, The Macmillan Company, 1925.

chapter 18

Chromosome Numbers in Development of Heritable Traits

As early as 1907 Lutz discovered that a large type of *Oenothera*, or evening primrose, known as the gigas form, had double the usual number of chromosomes and was, therefore, a tetraploid. Later Gates showed that the semigigas form was a triploid. Since then numerous investigators have experimented with plants having "unusual" chromosome numbers. Blakeslee and his associates have made extensive studies of heteroploidy and its effects on form and size of the Jimson weed, *Datura*. In general they found that the plants with increased chromosome numbers were larger than normal. Working with experimentally induced polyploidy in the tomato, Lindstrom also found a size series correlated with chromosome numbers, with triploids and tetraploids larger than the normal diploids (Fig. 145–147). In both the Jimson weed and tomato the haploid or 1x plants are usually smaller, have narrower leaves, bear smaller flowers, and are less vigorous than the normal diploids. In triploids and tetraploids the leaves and flowers are generally larger than those of the diploids (Fig. 148).

Variability of the effects of polyploidy on size, form, and appearance in plants should be emphasized. While greater size may accompany increase in chromosome numbers in plants, there are notable exceptions to this relationship. In some instances monoploid or haploid plants are almost as large as the diploids, and in other cases tetraploids are no larger than the diploids. In the poplar or aspen tree, *Populus tremula* L., x = 19, 2x = 38, 3x = 57, triploid plants were vigorous and often of gigas form. The tetraploids, however, did not exceed them in size or vigor. Leaves of these aspens varied in size; those of the diploids were smallest, triploids larger, and tetraploids largest. In the grass *Dactylis aschersoniana*, artificially induced autotetraploids were not different in size and appearance from the diploid form. Some other grasses, however, show chromosome number and size correlations. In numerous instances there is a definite reduction in size and vigor of plant with increased chromosome numbers. This is found especially in the higher polyploids, as in octoploids, 8x, or higher types.

FIG. 145. SIZE DIFFERENCES RELATED TO CHROMOSOME NUMBERS IN PLANTS.
From left to right, tetraploid, diploid, and haploid tomato plants, *Lycopersicon esculentum*. The haploid plant had low fertility. (Courtesy, E. W. Lindstrom.)

FIG. 146. COMPARATIVE SIZE OF DIPLOID AND TETRAPLOID TOMATO PLANTS, LYCO-
PERSICON PIMPINELLIFOLIUM.
(Courtesy, E. W. Lindstrom.)

FIG. 147. TETRAPLOID AND DIPLOID HYBRID TOMATOES.

Left, the tetraploid hybrid, *Lycopersicon esculentum* × *L. pimpinellifolium*, self-fertile but completely sterile with both parental species. This is a clean-cut case of a new species in the making. *Right*, the diploid hybrid of the same species. (Courtesy, E. W. Lindstrom.)

Polyploidy artificially induced in the garden marigold, *Tagetes erecta*, was accompanied by reduction in height. From the diploid 31 inches tall, the reduction in height was to 12½ inches for tetraploids, to 5½ for octoploids, and in some extreme dwarfs which were thought to be 16-ploid to only 1½ inches. Petunia, cotton, and cultivated cucumber all showed a reduction in size of plant or of plant parts in octoploids. The 8x types frequently showed low vitality, abnormal habit, fragility, and stunted growth.

CELL SIZE. In *Sphaerocarpus*, one of the liverworts, the female gametophytic plants have seven small autosomes and a large **X** chromosome in each cell, and male gametophytic plants have seven autosomes, homologous with those of the female plant, and a small **Y** chromosome in each cell. The sex chromosomes, the large **X** and the small **Y** chromosomes, thus contribute different volumes of chromatin to the cells of the female and male plants. According to Lorbeer, the total volumes of the cells of the female

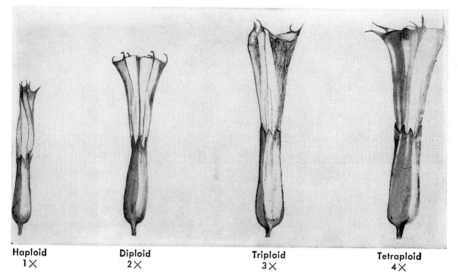

Haploid	Diploid	Triploid	Tetraploid
1×	2×	3×	4×

FIG. 148. FLOWERS OF JIMSON WEED, DATURA.

A series of flowers from polyploid plants showing an increase in size with increase of chromosome numbers. (Modified after A. F. Blakeslee.)

thallus are 1.7 times the volume of the cells of the male thallus, a difference proportional to the difference in the total mass of chromosomes in the cells of the two types of plants.

Polyploidy in the mosses investigated extensively by the Marchals and by von Wettstein shows comparable results but some disparity in measurements. For example, studies of polypoid forms in the moss genus *Amblystegium* by both investigators working independently indicate increase of cell size with an increase in chromosome number (Tables **XXXIX** and **XL**). In one investigation comparisons of the chromosome numbers and cell volumes of the leaves of the moss, *Funaria hygrometrica*, were as follows:

Chromosome numbers	1N	:	2N	:	3N	:	4N
Cell volumes	1	:	2.4	:	4.56	:	6.88

Von Wettstein counted the number of cells across moss leaves from plants with 1x, 2x, 3x, and 4x chromosomes. In general cell size increased in propor-

Table XXXIX

A

MARCHALS' MEASUREMENTS OF CELL SIZES IN THE CHROMO-
SOME RACES OF *Amblystegium serpens*

Race	Cell Measurements in Microns			
Chromosome Number	Length	Width	Thickness	Volume
1N	39	10.0	12.5	4,875
2N	59	11.5	14.5	9,837
4N	76	18.0	20.0	27,360

B

VON WETTSTEIN'S MEASUREMENTS OF CELL SIZES IN THE
CHROMOSOME RACES OF *Amblystegium Serpens*

Race	Cell Measurements in Microns			
Chromosome Number	Length	Width	Thickness	Volume
1N	37.12	8.47	13.50	4,244
2N	51.40	11.12	14.00	8,002
4N	118.32	22.62	21.20	56,739

C

RATIOS OF CELL VOLUMES IN THE CHROMOSOME RACES OF
Amblystegium serpens

Chromosome Races	Marchals' Data	Von Wettstein's Data
1N:2N	1:2	1:1.88
2N:4N	1:2.7	1:5.2

Table XL

RELATIONSHIP BETWEEN NUMBER OF CHROMOSOMES AND NUMBER OF CELLS IN
AN ORGAN

	$1x$	$2x$	$3x$	$4x$
Number of cells across leaf. Mean of 7 moss plants	43.6	51.7		
Number of cells across the leaf of *Funaria hygrometrica*	48.0	49.0	32	13

tion to the number of chromosomes, but the number of cells in an organ decreased.

One comparison of the internal structures of the members of the polyploid series in seed plants is that of Sinnott, Houghtaling, and Blakeslee on the anatomical and histological features of the polyploid forms of the Jimson weed, *Datura stramonium*. In *Datura* haploid, diploid, triploid, and tetraploid sporophytic plants are known (Table XLI).

Table XLI

CELL VOLUMES IN 10–6 Cu. MM. OF POLYPLOID SERIES IN *Datura stramonium*

Plant Tissue	Haploid (12)	Diploid (24)	Triploid (36)	Tetraploid (48)
Epidermal cells	8.16	14.3	18.6	29.4
Subepidermal cells	22.90	27.4	56.4	46.8
Cortex cells	44.40	90.4	134.0	204.0
Pith cells	33.20	62.5	108.0	164.0

Measurements in cubic microns of both nuclear volume and cell volume for two species of *Viola* and their interspecific F_1 hybrid showed a positive correlation with the number of chromosomes.

Table XLII

NUCLEAR VOLUME AND CELL VOLUME IN *Viola* SPECIES AND THEIR HYBRID MEASURED IN CUBIC MICRONS

Structure	V. conspersa	F_1 Hybrid	V. papilionacea
	2N = 20	2N = 37	2N = 54
Nuclear volume	268.1	333.0	523.6
Cell volume	2,277.7	2,743.0	3,607.8

POLLEN GRAINS. Lindstrom studied the correlation of size of pollen grains with chromosome numbers in the polyploid series of the cultivated tomato with the basic haploid chromosome number of 12. Pollen grains with 12 chromosomes from haploid plants had a diameter of 27 microns; those from diploid plants, also with 12 chromosomes, were likewise 27–28 microns in diameter; while pollen grains with 24 chromosomes from tetraploid plants measured 35–38 microns in diameter. In the cultivated cucumber, *Cucumis sativus*, where the diploid pollen grains were as 1, those of the tetraploids were 1.3 in diameter and 1.8 in cross-section area and volume. The correlation of pollen-grain size with the chromosome number has been observed in so many instances that this characteristic is regularly used as a superficial indication of the chromosome number and consequently the position of the plant in a polyploid series.

CHLOROPLASTS. In the mosses, *Physcomitrium* and *Amblystegium serpens*, although the cell volume was greater, the chloroplasts were no larger in polyploid than in diploid plants. The number of chloroplasts, however, increased with the increase in the number of chromosomes. Von Wettstein from his studies of chromosome races in the moss, *Amblystegium*, concluded that increases in number of chromosomes were accompanied by increases in nuclear volume and proportionate increases in cell volume. The number of chloroplasts also increased as the cell volume became greater, but their size remained approximately constant. In both tomato and tobacco

Table LXIII

AVERAGE NUMBER OF CHLOROPLASTS IN RELATION TO THE NUMBER OF CHROMOSOMES IN THE CELLS OF MOSS PLANTS

	$1x$	$2x$	$4x$
Average number of chloroplasts in cells of *Amblystegium*	14.4	26.0	63.4

the chloroplasts in the cells of tetraploid plants were slightly smaller but somewhat more numerous than in those of the diploid plants. In the cucumber chloroplasts were no larger but 1.6 more numerous in tetraploids than in diploids.

PLANT ORGANS AND STRUCTURES. Increase in cell size, characteristic of polyploid plants, also frequently results in a corresponding increase in size of plant organs and of the plant as a whole. For 65 different kinds of flowering plants in which polyploidy had been artificially induced, Blakeslee and his associates mention that the parts of tetraploid plants were more robust than the corresponding structures of diploids and that there was a positive correlation between size of pollen, floral parts, seeds, leaves, and stomata and increased chromosome number. With an increase in size of individual cells, there is, however, a tendency for the number of cells to be reduced in a polyploid plant. Frequently this decrease in cell number tends to decrease the size of plant organs and often of the plant as a whole.

FLOWER SIZE. Parts of the flower, the sepals, petals, stamens, and pistil, and the flower as a whole tend to be greater in tetraploids than in normal diploids (Fig. 148). Babcock reports that the haploids, 1x, of *Crepis* produce smaller flowers than the diploid or 2x forms. Triploids and tetraploids of some species are of gigas type with proportionally enlarged floral parts.

FRUIT SIZE. Fruit size is variable in polyploids. Stebbins states that plants bearing simple fruits with few seeds are frequently larger in the lower polyploids than in the normal diploids. With plants bearing compound fruits and many seeds, there is a tendency for the fruits to be smaller in polyploids, particularly in the higher polyploids. High chromosome numbers may result in a chromosome unbalance, one expression of which is low fertility. Low fertility results in fewer seeds and, with a relationship between number of seeds and fruit size, consequently small fruits. At the same time the shape of fruits of polyploids may be modified from normal.

Genetic Basis of Variability in Polyploids

It is now realized that the effect of an increase in the number of chromosomes depends upon the genetic nature of the plant affected. Often the outstanding features of a plant are dependent upon a large hereditary complex in which there is an interaction of the genes. Size of plant depends upon a multiple factor group or a group of polygenes with possibly all types of factor interactions. If the size genes of a species show cumulative effects that are favorable, polyploidy with a corresponding increase in the cumulative factors may result in increase in size of the plants. However, if in another species the size genes do not show cumulative effects, increase of chromosomes and number of genes may not be followed by an increase in size of the plants. It is even possible that where genes conditioning smaller size are cumulative in their effects, polyploidy would increase the number of genes inhibiting size and result in a smaller plant.

During long periods of time, organisms in nature became morphologically, physiologically, and genetically balanced. An upset in the genetic balance might conceivably follow the induction of polyploidy in a plant and could be followed by unfavorable reactions. These unfavorable reactions may express themselves in the stunted growth, misshaped parts, and infertility traits which are characteristic of many of the higher polyploids that have been artificially induced. In view of the above, explanations of the extremely variable effects of heteroploidy may be sought in a more perfect understanding of the genetics of the plants under investigation.

Autopolyploids by their nature have merely an increased number of the same genes as the original diploid. Their genetic characteristics therefore may not differ greatly from the diploid. Allopolyploids or amphidiploids, which have originated from hybrids of diploid species, combine genes from two distinct species. They may on that account show greater diversity than autopolyploids. Gigas features, if they are found, may be part of the increase of the heterosis in the parental hybrid plants that is carried over into the polyploid.

Physiological Features of Polyploids

VIGOR. Evidence accumulates that each species of plant has become adapted to an optimum number of chromosomes, to certain sizes and numbers of cells and plant parts, and to size of the plant as a whole. Generally little disturbance results from the increase of chromosome numbers in the lower members of a polyploid series such as triploids and frequently tetraploids. Most flowering plants appear to exceed their optimum chromosome number at about the hexaploid, 6x, or the octoploid, 8x, stage. These polyploids then lack vigor, grow more slowly, are no larger, and, in fact, may even be smaller than their normal diploid relatives. It has been found that the rate of cell division in polyploids may either be increased or decreased. In seed plants the rate of growth is generally slower in polyploid tissues than in normal diploid tissues.

VITAMIN CONTENT.   The carotenoid pigments in the endosperm of corn grains, conditioned by the duplicate genes Y_1-y_1, Y_2-y_2, etc., are related to the development of vitamin A. In 1940 Randolph and Hand showed that tetraploid yellow corn produced 40 per cent more carotenoid pigments than diploid plants of the same variety. Endosperm cells (3N) with 3.6 times the volume of diploid cells had 5 times the carotenoid content of the corresponding diploid cells. Mangelsdorf and Fraps have also shown that vitamin content increased with each additional Y gene in the 3N endosperm tissue (p. 251). White corn has the duplicate Y-y genes in the recessive state. An interesting comparison is found in 19-per-cent reduction of carotenoid content of tetraploid races of white corn compared with diploid white corn. This indicates that increasing the number of recessive y genes tends to reduce further the carotenoid pigments and vitamin content that are conditioned by the dominant Y alleles.

MUTATION RATE.   Blakeslee finds that the mutation rate, both that for chromosomal aberrations and gene mutations, is greatly increased in haploid daturas. The natural occurrence of extra chromosomes in the offspring of the haploid plants is nearly 10 times as great as in the progenies of diploids. Spontaneous gene mutations are found to occur at a rate 5 to 30 times greater in haploids than in diploid plants. Apparently there are exceptions to this in other organisms.

ECOLOGICAL FEATURES OF POLYPLOIDS.   Numerous studies have been made to determine the effects, if any, of polyploidy on the ecological distribution of plants. There are some indications that polyploid races and species have a distribution covering a wider range of habitat, including especially lower extremes of temperature and humidity. It has also been suggested that perennial species have higher chromosome numbers than annuals and that winter hardiness is a feature of polyploids. Bowden in 1940 questions the whole theory of the greater adaptability of polyploids over diploids. Stebbins, 1950, tends to regard the problem of the ecology of polyploids as unsolved for the present.

FERTILITY IN POLYPLOIDS.   Polyploid plants show varying degrees of fertility. Autopolyploids are generally less fertile than allopolyploids. Those with uneven numbers of chromosomes such as triploids, 3x, and pentaploids, 5x, especially show low fertility. Auto-, tetra-, and hexaploids, particularly if they are of recent origin, may also have low fertility.

Chromosome behavior, with irregularities in the separation of homologous members in the multivalent combinations during meiosis, is one of the causes of low fertility in autopolyploids. These meiotic irregularities lead to the formation of microspores and megaspores with varying numbers of chromosomes and lowered vitality of these structures. Low fertility or even sterility thus may be associated with chromosome behavior. Examples of experimentally induced autoploids with fertility lower than their diploid ancestors are those in *Datura, Oenothera, Solanum,* and the tomato, *Lycopersicon.* Some plants with low chromosome numbers such as some species of *Crepis* have given rise to fairly fertile autopolyploids. Natural autopolyploids long-established in nature show high degrees of fertility.

Usually allopolyploids or amphidiploids are more fertile than autopolyploids. Although there may be a reduction in fertility in some allopolyploids, they are generally more fertile than the F_1 species hybrid from which they originated by chromosome doubling. The degree of similarity in the members of the chromosome sets entering into the original cross forming the hybrid ancestral to the allopolyploid is a factor in the fertility of allopolyploids. In general, the greater the genetic diversity is and the more unlike the members of the chromosome sets are, the higher the fertility of the allopolyploid. Conversely, the greater the similarity of the chromosomes of the two sets is, the lower the fertility of the allopolyploid. Besides meiotic irregularities a genetic background may exist and form a basis for some of the varying degrees of fertility in both autopolyploids and allopolyploids. There are genes that affect fertility and sterility, compatibility and incompatibility, and even chromosome behavior. These genes are operative in polyploids as well as in diploids.

Comparisons of Natural and Experimentally Induced Polyploids

From his extensive study of data on both experimentally induced autopolyploids and the naturally autopolyploid chromosome races, Müntzing has concluded that there is great similarity in the two categories. He says that the naturally polyploid chromosome races within a species very frequently exhibit the same kinds and degree of gigas characters that occur in induced autopolyploids, with a positive correlation between chromosome numbers, cell size, and gigas characters. Generally higher degrees of polyploidy have been reported in experimentally induced material than normally exist under natural conditions. In nature plants with an excessive chromosome number may be promptly eliminated because of their unfitness for survival. Comparatively the material in experimental polyploids may therefore show greater diversity in size than is found in natural chromosome races.

In a comparison of experimental polyploids and those found under natural conditions, fertility deserves special attention. The reduced fertility accompanying multivalence during meiosis in experimentally induced autopolyploids has already been mentioned and contrasts with the higher fertility of natural polyploid races. In nature there has been a long period for the accumulation of mutations affecting fertility and vigor. The accumulation of the more favorable mutations could have further emphasized the differences in fertility between long-established natural polyploids and those recently induced. Experimental plants are relatively few and of too recent origin to have been subject to much selection. There appears to be, however, some evidence of variation in the fertility of this scanty experimental material. This might be accounted for in part on a purely genetic basis. If experimental polyploids were numbered by the thousands, some of them might be sufficiently fertile to survive in nature.

Allopolyploids occur more abundantly in nature than autopolyploids, but they have perhaps been less frequently induced by artificial means. Allopolyploids as well as autopolyploids are variable in their general characteristics such as size, vigor, and even fertility. From his studies Müntzing concludes that the similarities between autopolyploids and allopolyploids are more important than their differences and that these similarities are due to the fact that on a purely cytological basis many allopolyploids are at least partially autopolyploid. There are probably at least a few similar chromosomes in most allopolyploids within a species.

Genetics of Polyploids

Hybridization between a homozygous-dominant diploid as AA and a homozygous recessive, aa, results in the production of a heterozygous F_1 generation, Aa. Selfing the F_1 or mating the F_1, as $Aa \times Aa$, results in an F_2 ratio of $1AA:2Aa:1aa$. In an autopolyploid, for example an autotetraploid, the allelic genes are doubles, as A-a and A-a, located in two pairs of four homologous chromosomes. Hybridization between a dominant autotetraploid, as $AAAA$, and a recessive, as $aaaa$, will produce a heterozygous F_1 $AaAa$. Random assortment of the quadrivalent chromosomes carrying the genes A-a and A-a will result in the production of the classes of gametes in the ratio of $1AA:4Aa:1aa$. Chance recombination of these gametes may result in a ratio of $35A$-$:1aa$ and the production of a phenotypic ratio of approximately 35 dominants to 1 recessive in the F_2 generation.

The irregularity of chromosome separation previously mentioned naturally leads to interference with the free assortment of the genes. Lack of random separation of chromosomes causes deviations in the expected $35:1$ phenotypic ratio in the F_2 generation of an autotetraploid. The tomato amphidiploid developed from crossing *Lycopersicon esculentum* and *L. pimpinellifolium* yielded several different F_2 ratios. Different gene pairs showed ratios of $31:1$, $28:1$, $25:1$, $22:1$, and $21:1$.

Among suggestions advanced in explanation of the variations in segregation leading to diversities in phenotypic ratios are the following: (1) position of the genes relative to the centromere or kinetochore, the amount of crossing over being influenced by the distance from the centromere, (2) structural changes in the chromosomes of long-established autopolyploids tending to eliminate their autoploid characteristics and causing them to act more like allopolyploids, (3) genetic difficulties as incomplete dominance and gene interactions leading to modified phenotypic ratios, and (4) frequent low fertility of autopolyploids because of meiotic irregularities might modify the phenotypic ratios.

Summary of Variable Effects of Heteroploidy

The effects of heteroploidy in plants are variable. In many cases an increase of the chromosome numbers as in triploids and tetraploids has resulted in an increase in the size of the affected plants. However, an increase in size has not universally accompanied polyploidy, some plants showing little or no difference in size between normal diploids and polyploids and some polyploids even showing reduction in size.

Certain features appear to be characteristic of polyploidy. A general tendency toward stoutness, bluntness, and larger size of parts, such as stems, leaves, stomata, pollen, and flowers, is characteristic of polyploid plants even though the plants may be actually smaller than the normal diploids (pp. 347–349). Increased cell size generally accompanies multiplication of chromosomes through polyploidy with a positive correlation between the chromosome numbers and cell size (pp. 350–353).

A genetic explanation may be offered for the variable effects of heteroploidy in plants. The effects of an increase in the chromosomes with the consequent increase in the number of genes depend upon the action of the genes and the genetic nature of the plant.

Meiotic chromosome behavior *differs* in autopolyploids and allopolyploids and within the two groups. The variations are dependent upon the degree of homology among the chromosomes composing the polyploid complement, that is, the similarity or dissimilarity of chromosomes contributed by the original diploid plants. Such differences at meiosis constitute a physical basis for the phenotypic ratios presented in the progenies of polyploids.

Aneuploidy or Polysomy

The normal condition of two homologous members in each type of chromosome is designated as **disomy**; the two members of each pair are disomes, and the plant is a **disomic plant.** Minor deviations in chromosome numbers probably arising through irregularities in nuclear divisions and constituting the condition known as aneuploidy have been found in some varieties and species of plants. Blakeslee investigated aneuploidy in the Jimson weed, *Datura*. He found that *Datura* commonly had twelve pairs or twenty-four chromosomes, that is, $1x = 12, 2x = 24$. Sometimes one of the twelve chromosome types was represented by three homologous members instead of the normal two. A plant with one chromosome type consisting of *three* homologues is a **trisomic plant,** and the condition is termed trisomy. The chromosome formula of a trisomic *Datura* may be indicated as $2x + 1$ or $24 + 1 = 25$ chromosomes. An otherwise normal diploid plant with one extra chromosome is called a trisomic diploid. If a normal diploid *Datura* plant with twelve pairs of chromosomes is *a balanced form*, a trisomic diploid, or any other aneuploid type, may be designated as an *unbalanced chromosome form*. With twelve pairs of homologous chromosomes in *Datura*, twelve forms of trisomic diploid, $2x + 1$, plants are possible. All of them have been found, and each of the unbalanced $2x + 1$ plants differs markedly from the normal diploid plant and from the others. Among the characteristics influenced by the extra chromosomes are the size and form of the fruits or capsules, the development of spines on the capsules, and the ultimate size, form, and branching type of the whole plant. The study of polysomic plants has enabled investigators to locate in the chromosome groups of genes influencing the development of certain characteristics. Besides trisomic diploids, $2x + 1$, plants with extra chromosomes have been found in the haploid, triploid, and tetraploid members of the polyploid series of *Datura*. The term **polysomy** is used to designate the general condition in which plants have varying numbers of extra chromosomes from one to many. Each of the several polysomic forms or types found in *Datura* is indicated by a distinctive term. Aneuploid plants lacking one or more chromosomes were also found in *Datura*. Plants lacking two members of a chromosome pair are called nullisomics. Nullisomic diploid embryos probably never live, and even tetraploids lacking two members of one type of chromosome are small and weak.

POLYSOMIC TYPES IN DATURA, 1x = 12 CHROMOSOMES

Kinds of Plants	Nature of Chromosome Complements	Chromosome Formulae	Chromosome Numbers
Balanced haploid	one member of each type	1x	12
Unbalanced disomic haploid	one member of each type plus one extra	1x + 1	12 + 1 = 13
Balanced diploid	two members of each type	2x	24
Unbalanced trisomic diploid	two members of each type plus one extra	2x + 1	24 + 1 = 25
Unbalanced tetrasomic diploid	two members of each type plus two extra members of one type	2x + 2	24 + 2 = 26
Unbalanced double trisomic diploid	two members of each type plus one extra of two types	2x + 1 + 1	24 + 1 + 1 = 26
Unbalanced monosomic diploid	two members of each of eleven types but only one member of the twelfth type	2x − 1	24 − 1 = 23
Unbalanced double monosomic diploid	two members of each of ten types but only one member in each of the two other types	2x − 1 − 1	24 − 1 − 1 = 22
Unbalanced nullisomic diploid Not viable	two members of each of eleven types but both members of twelfth type lacking	2x − 2	24 − 2 = 22
Balanced triploid	three members of each type	3x	36
Unbalanced tetrasomic triploid	three members of each type plus one extra	3x + 1	36 + 1 = 37
Balanced tetraploid	four members of each type	4x	48
Unbalanced pentasomic tetraploid	four members of each type plus one extra	4x + 1	48 + 1 = 49
Unbalanced hexisomic tetraploid	four members of each type plus two extras of one type	4x + 2	48 + 2 = 50
Unbalanced septisomic tetraploid	four members of each type plus three extras of one type	4x + 3	48 + 3 = 51

The twelve pairs of chromosomes in *Datura* are designated by letters: the type with the largest chromosome members, **L**; other large types, **l**; medium large, **M**; medium small, **m**; the next to the smallest type, **S**; and the very smallest pair, **s** (Fig. 149). As a further means of identification, the Blakeslee associates also numbered each end of the twelve pairs of chromosomes. The ends of the largest chromosome **L** were numbered **1 · 2**; the next largest, type **1**, was numbered **3 · 4**; the largest **M** type, **5 · 6**; and so on to the smaller chromosomes. The next to the smallest chromosome was numbered **21 · 22,** and the very smallest was designated **23 · 24.**

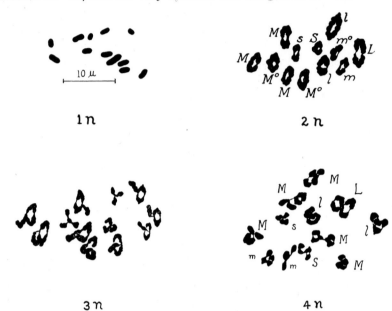

FIG. 149. CHROMOSOME COMPLEMENTS OF 1N, 2N, 3N, 4N DATURAS. (Courtesy, A. Dorothy Bergner and Carnegie Institution of Washington.)

CHARACTERISTICS OF POLYSOMIC PLANTS

The first polysomic plant studied in *Datura* was a trisomic diploid called "Globe," because of its rounded or globose capsules. It differed further from the normal diploid in having stout spines on the capsules and in the form of the leaves which were broad with slight marginal identations (Fig. 150–152). It had three instead of the normal two of the next to smallest chromosomes designated **21 · 22** with the chromosome formula 2x + **21 · 22.** Later a tetrasomic diploid, 2x + 2(**21 · 22**), was found which showed the Globe characteristics to a greater degree than the trisomic diploid. Evidently the extra dosage of genes carried by the one extra chromosome **21 · 22** had the effect of conditioning the development of shorter, broader, and more globose capsules with stouter spines than were found in the normal disomic diploid. When the total gene dosage was further increased with two extra **21 · 22** chromosomes in the tetrasomic diploid, there was a correspondingly greater gene unbalance, intensifying the phenotypic Globe characteristics.

The Globe character was also studied in tetraploid *Datura.* Among these were a pentasomic tetraploid 4x + **21 · 22,** a hexisomic tetraploid 4x + 2(**21 · 22**), and a septisomic tetraploid 4x + 3(**21 · 22**). All showed the

FIG. 150. CAPSULE TYPE IN DATURAS.

The capsule type of a normal *Datura* plant with the normal 24 chromosomes. Following, arranged in 3 rows, are the capsule types of the possible 12 trisomic plants. These plants each have one extra chromosome. The extra chromosomes are all different, ranging from 1·2 to 23·24 as indicated below in each case. (Courtesy, A. F. Blakeslee.)

FIG. 151. NORMAL DIPLOID, 2N, PLANT OF DATURA.
(Courtesy, A. F. Blakeslee.)

FIG. 152. GLOBE, 2N + 21 · 22, A TRISOMIC PLANT OF DATURA.
(Courtesy, A. F. Blakeslee.)

Globe characteristics more markedly than in normal balanced diploids and balanced tetraploids. The Globe character was greatest in the plants with highest number of extra $21 \cdot 22$ chromosomes and with the correspondingly greatest gene unbalance. Thus, $4x + 1(21 \cdot 22)$ showed the least of the Globe characteristics, $4x + 2(21 \cdot 22)$ a little more, and $4x + 3(21 \cdot 22)$ most of all.

In the course of the investigation in *Datura*, trisomics with an extra chromosome from each of the twelve pairs were studied. These trisomic plants were all distinctly different, because the extra dosage of genes from

FIG. 153. COCKLEBUR, $2N + 11 \cdot 12$, A WELL-KNOWN TRISOMIC PLANT OF DATURA.
(Courtesy, A. F. Blakeslee.)

each of the twelve pairs of homologous chromosomes as $1 \cdot 2, 3 \cdot 4, 5 \cdot 6$, etc., tends to condition specific forms of trisomic Jimson-weed plants. These new kinds of plants were each given type names indicating their outstanding characteristic (Fig. 153).

DESIGNATION OF PLANTS	CHROMOSOME COMPLEMENT OF PLANT
Normal disomic diploid	2x
Trisomic diploid Globe	$2x + 21 \cdot 22$
Tetrasomic diploid double Globe	$2x + 21 \cdot 22 + 21 \cdot 22$
Pentasomic tetraploid Globe	$4x + 21 \cdot 22$
Hexasomic tetraploid Globe	$4x + 21 \cdot 22 + 21 \cdot 22$
Septisomic tetraploid Globe	$4x + 3(21 \cdot 22)$
Trisomic diploid Ilex	$2x + 23 \cdot 24$
Trisomic diploid Cocklebur	$2x + 11 \cdot 12$
Trisomic diploid Poinsettia	$2x + 17 \cdot 18$
Double trisomic diploid Ilex-Globe	$2x + 21 \cdot 22 + 23 \cdot 24$
Trisomic diploid Rolled	$2x + 1 \cdot 2$

Questions and Problems

1. Explain the terminology associated with that phase of heteroploidy known as polysomy.
2. How do polysomic plants originate?
3. If a trisomic diploid plant 2x + 1 shows certain outstanding traits, what may be expected in a tetrasomic diploid 2x + 2; in a pentasomic tetraploid 4x + 1; in a hexasomic tetraploid 4x + 2; in a 4x + 4 plant?
4. Explain the difference between plants of the formulae 2x + 2 and 2x + 1 + 1.
5. What are trisomics? How many trisomics may be expected in *Datura?* Why? What are their phenotypic characteristics? How are their phenotypic characteristics explained on the basis of their chromosomal features?
6. Why are nullisomics generally confined to polyploid plants? What are the phenotypic effects of nullisomy?
7. What are some of the most striking characteristics associated with polyploidy in plants?
8. What effect does polyploidy have on flower size? Name some plants in which this relationship has been studied.
9. In general, how does polyploidy affect cell size? What is the relationship of polyploidy to volume of chromatin?
10. Name some lower plants in which polyploid series have been found and compare chromosome numbers and cell volumes in the series.
11. How have the lower plants been useful in the study of polyploidy?
12. What data have been found on relationship of cell size and chromosome number in the Jimson weed?
13. How has size of pollen grains been used in diagnosing polyploidy in some of the flowering plants?
14. Is increased number of chloroplasts associated with polyploidy?
15. Which plant parts are particularly affected by changes in chromosome numbers?
16. What relationship has been thought to exist between geographical occurrence and polyploidy in plants? Is this invariably true?
17. Tell of the relationship between polyploidy and vitamin development in corn.
18. Are physiological features of plants generally affected by polyploidy?
19. How general is the association of increased fertility with polyploidy?
20. What is the biological value of inducing polyploidy? Can induced polyploidy be expected to be of economic importance?
21. How may chromosome behavior influence fertility in autopolyploids and allopolyploids? Why does chromosome behavior differ during meiosis in the two kinds of polyploids?
22. What is the comparative fertility of natural and induced polyploids?
23. What factors work to increase fertility in long-established polyploids?
24. In general are there great differences between natural and induced polyploids?

References

BLAKESLEE, A. F.: "Cryptic Types in *Datura* Due to Chromosomal Interchange and Their Geographical Distribution," *J. Heredity* **20**:177–190 (1929).

———: "New Jimson Weeds from Old Chromosomes," *J. Heredity* **25**:81–108 (1934).

———: "Variations in *Datura* Due to Changes in Chromosome Number," *Am. Naturalist* **56**:16–31 (1922).

——— and JOHN BELLING: "Chromosomal Mutations in the Jimson Weed, *Datura stramonium*," *J. Heredity* **15**:194–206 (1924).

DE ROBERTIS, E. D. P., W. W. NOWINSKI, and FRANCISCO A. SAEZ: *General Cytology*, Philadelphia and London, W. B. Saunders Company, 1948.

DOBZHANSKY, THEODOSIUS: *Genetics and the Origin of Species*, 2nd ed. New York, Columbia University Press, Chapter IV, 94–150.

SHARP, L. W.: *Fundamentals of Cytology*, New York and London, McGraw-Hill Book Company, Inc., 1943, Chapters XIII, XIV, 193–215.

———: *Introduction to Cytology*, 3rd ed. New York and London, McGraw-Hill Book Company, Inc., 1934.

SINNOTT, EDMUND W., L. C. DUNN and Th. Dobzhansky: *Principles of Genetics*, 4th ed. New York, McGraw-Hill Book Company, Inc., 1950, Chapter VIII, 192–197.

WHITE, M. J. D.: *Animal Cytology and Evolution*, Cambridge, England, Cambridge University Press, 1945.

chapter 19

Chromosomal Aberrations—Changes in the Structure of Chromosomes

Chromosomes are generally regarded as rather constant units with genes arranged in linear order within them. Occasionally, however, spontaneous or induced breaks in the chromosomes result in derangements of the genes from their normal positions. Fusions of the broken ends of the fragments generally follow the breaks and may then result in the loss of some genes with the rearrangement of others into new alignments. The gene content of a chromosome and the positions of genes within a chromosome are only relatively permanent, not absolutely fixed. Breaks in chromosomes and fusion of the broken ends may result in changes in the chromosome structure called chromosomal aberrations. Structural changes in chromosomes may be relatively large and are called gross aberrations, or they may be ultramicroscopic when they are referred to as minute changes or aberrations. Structural changes may be confined to a single chromosome, may extend to both members of a pair of homologous chromosomes, or may involve members of two or more pairs of homologous chromosomes. The following summary indicates the terminology of these relationships.

Breaks and Structural Changes	Are Designated by the Term
confined to a single chromosome are	homosomal
involving the two members of one pair of homologous chromosomes are	allelosomal
involving two or more nonhomologous chromosomes are	heterosomal
homosomal aberrations confined to one arm or branch of a chromosome are	homobrachial or intraradial
homosomal aberrations involving both arms of a chromosome are	heterobrachial or interradial
allelosomal aberrations involving the corresponding arms or branches of a pair of homologous chromosomes are	allelobrachial
allelosomal aberrations involving noncorresponding arms or branches of the two members of a pair of homologous chromosomes are also	heterobrachial

THE IMPORTANCE OF THE CENTROMERE. The essential function in nuclear division of the structural feature of the chromosome,

366

the **centromere,** has been mentioned (p. 16). The centromere is also important in connection with structural changes in chromosomes. A chromosome normally containing a single centromere is said to be a *monocentric* chromosome, while a fragment of a chromosome without a centromere is an *acentric* fragment. Abnormally, two centromeres may occur in a chromosome which is then *dicentric*. Abnormal chromosomes such as acentric and dicentric chromosomes are at a disadvantage during nuclear divisions. Acentric fragments of chromosomes often fail to pass to either of the poles of a mitotic spindle and are thus soon lost from the nucleus. Dicentric chromosomes may become stretched across the division spindle as the two centromeres move toward different poles and thus form the chromatid bridge or chromosome bridge. Such chromosomes tend to break irregularly.

The terms *acrocentric, metacentric,* and *telocentric* refer to the positions centromeres may occupy in the chromosomes. These terms have Greek derivations; thus, acrocentric from *akros* meaning tip refers to centromeres located near the tips of chromosomes; metacentric from *meta* meaning after or beyond refers to centromeres farther away or distant from the tips; and telocentric from *telos* meaning end refers to rare cases in which following X-ray treatment fragmentation of a chromosome has occurred directly at the centromere, leaving a piece of chromosome with a terminal centromere. Acrocentric chromosomes, with the centromere located very near the tip, have arms of greatly different lengths. At anaphase acrocentric chromosomes appear hook-shaped or almost rod-shaped. In metacentric chromosomes with the centromere located closer to the middle portion, the arms are more nearly the same length. Metacentric chromosomes appear as V-shaped structures at anaphase.

Breaks and other structural changes in a chromosome may always be located relative to the centromere. Breaks may occur between the centromere and one end of the chromosome, and the structural changes may thus be confined to one arm. The term *paracentric* may be applied to breaks and structural changes of this type. The Greek derivative *para* means beside or, in this case, actually to one side of the centromere. The term *intraradial* or within one arm is also used to designate changes restricted to one arm of a chromosome. Breaks may occur on both sides of the centromere, and the resulting structural changes then will involve both chromosomal arms. Breaks and structural changes of this nature are called pericentric changes. The Greek word *peri* means around, and pericentric means around the centromere. Structural changes involving both arms of a chromosome are also called interradial changes.

Kinds of Structural Changes in Chromosomes

BREAKS IN CHROMOSOMES. *Fragmentation.* Breaks in chromosomes may occur spontaneously in nature. They can be artificially induced by radiation of various types such as X-ray and atomic radiation and also by certain chemical treatments. Spontaneous or induced breaks are basic to structural changes in chromosomes. Usually breaks are followed by fusions of broken ends of either the same or different chromosomes. When breaks are not repaired by fusions, the broken chromosome remains broken into two or more large or small pieces which may be called **fragments.** Because a centromere is essential for the continued existence of a chromosome, perhaps only pieces of chromosomes lacking a centromere should be designated as fragments. Chromosomes suffering loss of parts through breakage but still containing a centromere should be designated as *deficient* chromosomes regardless of their size. Though a single break in a chromosome might lead to the loss of a terminal piece or segment of a chromosome, this type of fragment is seldom found. Breaks directly involving the centromere are also rare.

STRUCTURAL CHANGES IN CHROMOSOMES. Structural changes or chromosomal aberrations are of several kinds. There may be losses of parts of a chromosome or gains of some parts from another chromosome. The changes may be entirely within a single chromosome or they may involve two or more chromosomes. *Changes* occurring *within a single chromosome* may be called **transpositions.** Among transpositions are *inversions,* in which the genes occur in reverse order, and *shifts,* which consist of segments moved or shifted from their normal position to a new location in the same chromosome. These are rather simple structural changes. In more complex structural changes, pieces or segments may be exchanged between two different chromosomes. Structural changes of this type are **translocations.**

CHROMOSOME FRAGMENTS, DELETIONS, AND DEFICIENCIES. Fragmentation following from two breaks anywhere between the ends of a chromosome may release an intercalary segment, that is, a piece from between the ends (Fig. 154). Segments released in this way from the main body of the chromosome may retain their rod shape, or they may assume a ring shape if the broken ends come into contact and fuse. This structure, may or may not contain the centromere. If a centromere is present in the piece, it can pass through succeeding nuclear divisions and survive as a small but deficient chromosome. If no centromere is present in the broken-out piece, it is said to be a *deleted fragment,* or a *deletion,* which is soon lost in the nuclear divisions. A chromosome which has suffered the loss of a fragment becomes a *deficient* chromosome, that is, it is deficient for a segment and its block of contained genes. Deletions may be large and involve microscopically visible segments, while others are ultramicroscopic. The importance of any loss is that the chromosome becomes deficient for a certain number of genes.

CYTOLOGICAL EFFECTS OF DELETIONS. In the meiotic prophase of a *deletion heterozygote* (see below), chromosome pairing proceeds normally at parts of the chromosomes. In the region of the deletion where a string of

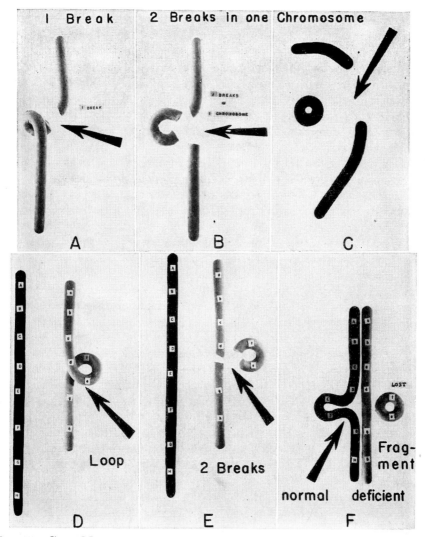

FIG. 154. CLAY MODELS ILLUSTRATING BREAKS, FRAGMENTATION, AND DELETION IN CHROMOSOMES.

C, one of the possible results of two breaks. In this case there are a ring-shaped or "doughnut" chromosome and two rod-shaped pieces. Since there is normally only one centromere, of these rod-shaped pieces one may contain the centromere and the other represent an acentric fragment. D, a pair of homologous chromosomes. D and E represent a possible method of forming a deletion or the loss of an intercalary segment from a chromosome. F, conjugation of a normal chromosome and its aberrant homologue. The latter has suffered an intercalary deletion and is deficient. Since pairing is between allelic genes, the normal chromosome forms a loop in the region corresponding to the deleted region in the aberrant deficient chromosome.

genes is lacking in the rebuilt chromosome, the corresponding segment in the normal intact chromosome has nothing with which to pair. The section of the normal chromosome opposite the deleted segment is then pushed out into a loop (Fig. 154), the size of which depends upon the size of the deleted segment in the rebuilt chromosome. Deficiencies tend to reduce the amount of crossing over in deficiency heterozygotes.

GENETIC AND PHENOTYPIC EFFECTS OF DELETIONS AND DEFICIENCIES. Because of the loss of genes, perhaps the most significant effect of deficiencies is their **lethality.** This lethal effect is evident in organisms which have become homozygous for the deficiency. Usually the segment is lost from only one member of a pair of homologous chromosomes in an organism, which then is a *deficiency heterozygote.* Among the progenies of such an organism, however, it is possible that individuals may occur in which the two members of a pair of homologous chromosomes both have the deficiency. Organisms which are thus homozygous for a deficiency are called *deficiency homozygotes* and they seldom survive. The lethal effects of deficiencies also manifest themselves in the haploid gametophytes of plants, especially in the microspores, pollen, and pollen tubes. Although generally the female gametophytes are injured by deficiencies, some of them seem to be able to survive and function.

Apparently in rare cases very small segments of chromosomes may be absent without causing the death of the homozygous organism. *Drosophila* furnishes an example of an organism which may lose one entire chromosome and still be viable. The mostly inert Y chromosome may be lacking in the male Drosophila without causing death. In the haplo-IV *Drosophila*, one small IV chromosome may be lacking and the fly still be viable. Possibly sometimes, as in the case of nullisomics (pp. 335-336), the organisms persist only if they are polyploids. Another possibility for viability might be the representation of the lost genes as duplications in other loci (pp. 379-380). Even in the heterozygous state, the loss of large segments from a chromosome may often result in death.

The loss of a very small segment of a chromosome by deletion behaves like a Mendelian unit in inheritance. While this deficiency in the homozygous condition may be lethal, it may persist in the heterozygous state. The deficiency heterozygote crossed with a normal gives a 1:1 ratio exactly as is found in the case of mutant genes. Thus very small deficiencies might be mistaken for gene mutations. The variation known as "notch" in the Drosophila is associated with this type of deficiency. It is generally recognized that some lethal mutations in the Drosophila have been due to small deficiencies.

It is the genes which remain and not the deleted ones that condition the visible phenotypic effects in a viable organism bearing a deficiency. With well-known allelic genes, where the dominant allele is eliminated by the deletion, the recessive gene remains in the deficiency heterozygote and expresses itself. This condition is similar to the hemizygous state noted in males carrying recessive genes in their single **X** chromosome and has been called pseudodominance.

In the case of genes with an *additive* effect, if one of the pair were deleted, the effect of the remaining gene would be less than if both had been present. Goldschmidt suggested that in some cases the effects of genes is proportional to their quantity. If a gene conditions a chemical reaction such as oxidation to form a pigment, there would be less oxidation and hence less pigment with one than two of these genes. If a recessive-mutant gene manifested itself phenotypically by a reduction in color as eosin eye in the Drosophila, a deletion of one such mutant gene would produce a lighter eosin eye, which would then be further from the normal than a normal homozygous eosin fly. The deletion would actually tend to increase the action of the mutant gene, that is, a further reduction in color away from normal. In the case of mutant genes having a retarding or an inhibiting effect on some development, two genes might cause more disturbance than a single one, and a deletion by removing one gene might result in a more nearly normal action of the remaining allele in the deficiency heterozygote than in the normal homozygote.

TRANSPOSITION. *Inversions.* Two breaks in a single chromosome, subsequent rotation of the separated section through 180 degrees, and fusion of the broken ends result in an inversion, that is, an inversion of position (Fig. 155). Inversions are generally if not exclusively intercalary, that is, they do not involve the extreme chromosome ends. There is no loss of chromatin nor deficiency of genes in simple inversion. The genes are all present, but they are in changed positions relative to the accepted normal.

The breaks in connection with an inversion may be confined to one arm of the chromosome, that is, they may be intraradial or *homobrachial* or one of them may be in each arm of the chromosome and involve the centromere; in this case they are interradial or *heterobrachial*. The presence of one inversion in a chromosome does not preclude the occurrence of another or even of several inversions or other structural changes in the same chromosome. The succeeding inversions may be entirely independent, that is, in different parts of the chromosome, or they may occur within the same region of the chromosome. If two or more inversions occur in the same region, they may partly overlap, or a small inversion may occur entirely within a larger one. In the Drosophila the presence of inversions, like deletions, may be microscopically observed in the giant salivary chromosomes, where the dislocation of the bands in an inverted segment may be detected.

CYTOLOGICAL EFFECTS OF INVERSIONS. Inversions manifest their presence cytologically by such meiotic irregularities as loops in the chromosomes during the prophase or in the appearance of chromatin bridges and fragmented chromosomes in later division stages. Although other factors may also influence the rate of crossing over, a definite reduction in the cross-

over value is one indication of the presence of an inversion. In organisms
heterozygous for an inversion, crossing over near the region of the aberration may give rise to a dicentric chromosome. During the succeeding anaphase, as the two centromeres approach the opposite spindle poles, the
chromosome is stretched between them and forms a chromatin bridge
(chromosome or chromatid). Finally this bridge may break with ensuing

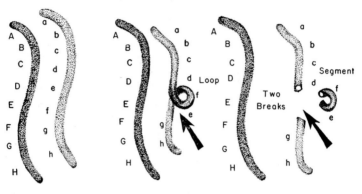

One Pair of Homologous Chromosomes

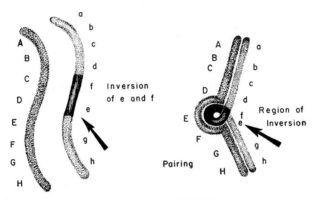

INVERSION

FIG. 155. DIAGRAM OF THE INVERSION OF AN INTERCALARY SEGMENT OF A
CHROMOSOME.
Pairing in meiotic configuration at lower right.

structural changes in the chromosome. It has been shown that a chromatin
bridge may be the beginning of a series of deficiencies, duplications, and
reduplications, which are then extended through the entire mitotic cycle of
the gametophytes of plants and even to the mitoses of the endosperm of
the seed.

THE GENETIC EFFECTS OF INVERSION. Organisms may be heterozygous
for an inversion, or they may become homozygous for the structural change.
Thus there are inversion heterozygotes and inversion homozygotes. The

principal genetic effect of inversions is their tendency to cause a reduction in the amount of crossing over. Pairing between the two homologues concerned in an inversion heterozygote can only be accomplished if chromosomes form loops at the inversion point (Fig. 155). In inversion homozygotes where there is no interference with the conjugation process, pairing and crossing over proceed at the normal rate. Other genetic effects of the presence

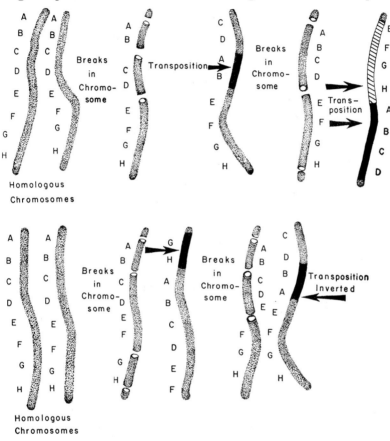

TRANSPOSITIONS

FIG. 156. DIAGRAM OF TRANSPOSITIONS OR CHANGES OF POSITION OF SEGMENTS IN A SINGLE CHROMOSOME.

of inversions have been observed. Anderson reports that long inversions cause considerable pollen and ovule sterility in maize.

TRANSPOSITIONS. *Shifts.* Another type of transposition is the shift which requires a minimum of three breaks in a single chromosome, with the minimum formation of four pieces, two intercalary segments and two end pieces. If any intercalary segment changes place with any other intercalary segment, the resulting structural change is called a **shift** (Fig. 156).

The shifted segment may or may not be inverted in its new position. Shifts may be confined to one arm of the chromosome in which case they are said to be intraradial or homobrachial, or they may involve both arms of the chromosome and then are interradial or heterobrachial.

CYTOLOGICAL AND GENETIC EFFECTS OF SHIFTS. Although the shift is a relatively simple aberration, it interferes with the normal pairing of chromosomes at synapsis because of the changed position of a certain block of genes. Normal crossing over is also reduced in the region of the shift. Since all of the genes of the rebuilt chromosome are present when a shift has occurred, little phenotypic effect results. There is a certain amount of abnormal crossing over in organisms heterozygous for a shift.

TRANSLOCATIONS. Surely the most complex and perhaps the most important of all structural changes in chromosomes are those in which a deleted segment is moved from its normal position in one chromosome to a new location in a different chromosome. Exchanges of this type are called **translocations** (Fig. 157 and 158). Translocations require a greater number of simultaneous breaks than simple deletions or inversions. When translocations involve two members of a pair of homologous chromosomes, they are called allelosomal translocations, fraternal interchanges, or interchanges between homologous chromosomes. When the interchanges involve non-homologous chromosomes, they are called external interchanges or heterosomal translocations. In translocations there may be an exchange or interchange of segments of approximately equal or unequal lengths. That is, if a chromosome loses a segment to another chromosome, it may also receive a segment of similar but not necessarily of identical size. Interchange of segments between chromosomes constitutes a mutual or reciprocal translocation. Besides the reciprocal translocation in which pieces or segments of chromosomes are exchanged, a doubtful type called a "simple" translocation has been postulated. In the simple translocation a segment is detached from one chromosome and transferred to another chromosome without reciprocation of the latter. It is suspected that translocations described as simple were in fact reciprocal but that one of the translocated segments was very small. The occurrence of still another rare type of aberration, the lateral translocation, has been noted. In a lateral translocation the translocated segment is attached to the side of the receiving chromosome, forming a sort of branched chromosomal structure.

Schemes for designating the chromosomes involved in translocations have been proposed. For example, in maize where the 10 pairs of chromosomes are numbered in the order of their size from 1, the largest, to 10, the smallest, translocation may be designated T2–8 or T1–9 indicating that a translocation has occurred between chromosomes 2 and 8 or between chromosomes 1 and 9, respectively. Sometimes subletters indicate the genes involved.

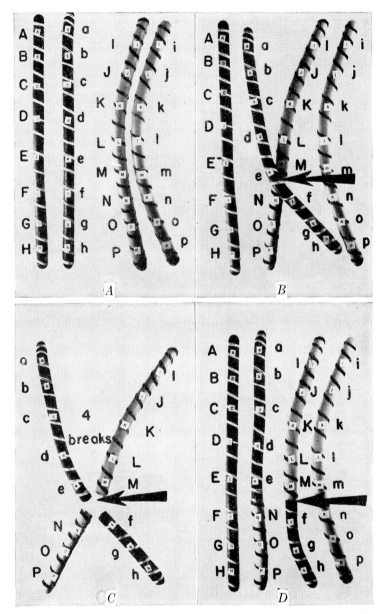

FIG. 157. CLAY MODELS OF TRANSLOCATION OR THE EXCHANGE OF SEGMENTS
BETWEEN MEMBERS OF TWO PAIRS OF CHROMOSOMES.
A shows two pairs of homologous chromosomes with genes. B, C, and D illus-
trate the reciprocal translocation between members of the two pairs of chromosomes.
Note arrow at D.

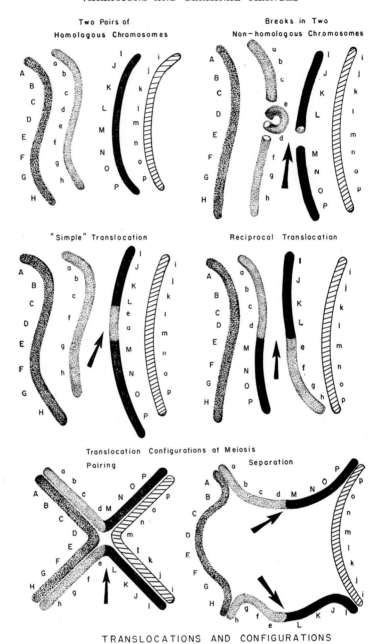

FIG. 158. DIAGRAM OF TRANSLOCATION OR TRANSFER OF SEGMENTS BETWEEN MEM-
BERS OF TWO PAIRS OF CHROMOSOMES.

Cross configuration follows pairing of homologous segments of translocation and
normal chromosomes. Ring configuration at lower right is a later stage.

THE NATURE OF TRANSLOCATIONS. In early studies of translocations, their formation was referred to as illegitimate crossing over. This term, currently not in common use, emphasized some of the similarities between translocation and crossing over. The principal *resemblance* is in the breakage of chromosomes and the fusion of the broken ends with an exchange of pieces of the chromosomes. Another similarity is the occurrence of both reciprocal translocations and crossing over between chromatids. There are *important differences between crossing over and translocations.* Crossing over takes place naturally by a normal and regular exchange of similar-sized pieces of the chromatids derived from homologous chromosomes. From known behavior the amount of crossing over may be predicted in most instances. The breaks necessary for the crossing over of segments occur at identical loci in the chromatids, giving rise to new alignments and new combinations of genes in the chromosome. Since crossing over is restricted to homologous chromosomes, no new genes are introduced into the linkage group. While interchanges of segments may occur between homologous chromosomes as in allelosomal translocation, the typical translocation is a reciprocal exchange of segments between *nonhomologous* chromosomes, *heterosomal* translocation. In the latter way genes from the outside are introduced into a linkage group. Another dissimilarity is that translocations are never predictable, because they occur irregularly and follow no set rules. As contrasted with crossing over, even in reciprocal translocations, the exchanged segments may not be of equal size and may even differ markedly. While crossing over normally rarely disturbs the relative position of the centromere, reciprocal translocations may include the centromere in one segment and leave it out in another.

CYTOLOGICAL EFFECTS OF TRANSLOCATIONS. Translocated segments may be found in a single member of a pair of homologous chromosomes with the other member normal. This constitutes a translocation heterozygote. In the translocation heterozygote the interchanged segment introduces a block of new genes into the system, which are not allelic with those occupying corresponding positions in the normal chromosome. Introduction of non-allelic genes into a linkage group will tend to interfere with linkage and crossing over in the group. Disturbance of conjugation in the chromosome pair involved in the translocation leads to unusual chromosome configurations or cytological abnormalities and genetic effects.

If reciprocal translocation has occurred between the members of chromosome pair 1 and chromosome pair 2, the new or interchanged chromosomes would consist in one case of a part of chromosome 1 attached to a piece of chromosome 2 and in the other case of a part of chromosome 2 attached to the reciprocal segment from chromosome 1. In a plant heterozygous for this reciprocal translocation, there would be a normal number 1 chromosome, a normal number 2 chromosome, and in addition the two interchange chromosomes. The presence of interchanged segments in the chromosomes of a translocation heterozygote interferes with normal side by side pairing of genes of homologous chromosomes. In a structural hybrid of this nature, the rebuilt or interchange chromosome 1-2 would pair with the normal number 1 chromosome up to the point of the interchange segment from chromosome 2, and part 2 of this interchange chromosome would pair with the corresponding part of the normal chromosome 2. In the same way the other interchange chromosome, 2-1, would be expected to synapse with the normal chromosome 2 to the point of interchange, and from there the interchanged portion from chromosome 1 would pair with the normal chromosome 1. For complete pairing of allelic genes then, four chromosomes instead of the normal two must be involved in one chromosomal configuration. This configuration of four chromosomes, two normal and two interchanged, taking the form of a cross at synapsis is characteristic of translocation heterozygotes (Fig. 158 and 160). As meiosis progresses the chromosomes forming the cross open up to form a ring or chain of chromosomes attached at their ends. Characteristic ring or chain configurations have been found in the later prophase and early metaphase of the first meiotic division in *Oenothera, Datura*, maize, and other organisms. Besides the ring and chain configurations, occasionally acentric fragments and dicentric chromosomes may arise as structural abnormalities following translocations.

In some cases both members of the pair of homologous chromosomes may have similar translocated segments, constituting a translocation homozygote. Because of the presence of the interchanged segment in both of the new or rebuilt chromosomes, the introduced genes are allelic, and the interchange chromosomes are homologous throughout their length. Meiosis in a translocation homozygote may proceed regularly with no evidence of cytological abnormalities in contrast with the condition in the translocation heterozygote described above.

THE GENETIC AND PHENOTYPIC EFFECTS OF TRANSLOCATIONS.   Reduced viability and fertility are the principle effects of translocations in *Drosophila*. Viability may be as low as 15 per cent with the surviving flies often weak, of abnormal appearance, and low fertility. Many homozygous translocations are lethal in the fruit fly. In *Drosophila* translocations have caused phenotypic effects such as slight modifications of eye and body colors. Apparently phenotypic effects are more marked in translocation homozygotes than in heterozygotes which more nearly approach normality in these respects, and even they are frequently subnormal in some way.

A few phenotypic variations in plants have been interpreted as the results of translocations. Roberts made a careful study of 13 induced translocations involving 8 of the 10 pairs of chromosomes in an inbred line of maize. By statistical study of heights of plants, diameter of stalks, length of leaves, width of leaves, maturity of silks, and maturity of pollen, relatively slight but significant differences were found between the pure inbred line of plants and the homozygous and heterozygous translocation progenies.

The general conclusion, however, was that "no conspicuous phenotypic changes could be detected in any of the translocation progenies." This is in accord with Blakeslee's data on the phenotypic effects of segmental interchanges in the chromosomes of *Datura*. In more than 90 strains or "prime types" homozygous for segmental interchanges, the large majority showed

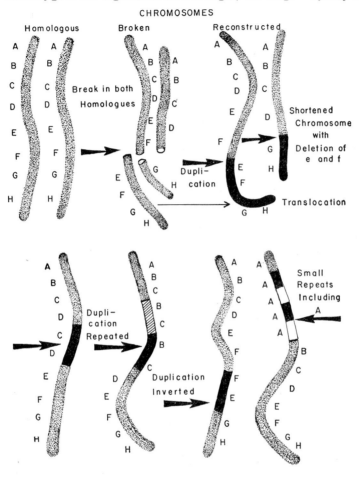

DUPLICATIONS AND REPEATS

FIG. 159. DIAGRAM OF DUPLICATIONS AND REPEATS IN CHROMOSOMES.

no deviation from the normal appearance. In only a few cases were the prime types abnormal. Some of the translocations in *Datura* observed by Blakeslee and his associates did lead to the production of recognizable phenotypic forms.

DUPLICATIONS.   Many individuals and even races have been found with large or small pieces or segments of chromosomes containing extra blocks of genes which duplicate those normally present. The occurrence of additional segments with their blocks of genes is assumed to have resulted from structural chromosomal changes such as translocations between homologous chromosomes. These additional segments are called **duplications.** Their important feature is that a certain number of genes or a block of genes is reduplicated or repeated in the organism so that it has additional genes over its normal number (Fig. 159). Duplications that are very small segments containing only one or a very few genes that frequently may be reduplicated have been called repeats.

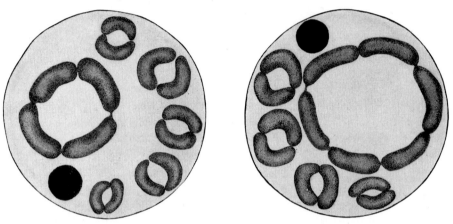

FIG. 160. CHROMOSOME CONFIGURATIONS IN OENOTHERA.
At left, a ring of four chromosomes and five pairs of bivalents in nucleus of a microsporocyte. Nucleolus shown as dark body in lower part of sporocyte. At right, a ring of six chromosomes and four pairs of bivalents. Nucleolus shown as dark body in upper part of sporocyte.

THE CYTOLOGICAL EFFECTS OF DUPLICATIONS.   The cytological effects of duplications are not so pronounced as those of some other chromosomal aberrations. Some duplications or repeats such as those conditioning bar eye in *Drosophila* are observable microscopically. They show up as repeated bands in the salivary chromosome but seem to cause little disturbance in the chromosome behavior. Organisms heterozygous for larger duplications, if they are viable, may show abnormal chromosome pairing at synapsis, since there will be no loci with which the duplicated portion can pair, and the duplication segment will be pushed out in loop formation. Duplications may be heterozygous with certain genes present in triplicate or homozygous with certain genes present in quadruplicate. Greater cytological disturbances occur in the germ cells of organisms heterozygous for duplication than in duplication homozygotes where the meiotic processes may proceed in a normal manner.

THE GENETIC AND PHENOTYPIC EFFECTS OF DUPLICATIONS.   The phenotypic effect on the characteristics of the organism depends in a large degree on the specific actions and interactions of the duplicated genes. Thus if the action of the genes is additive, as the Y gene in yellow endosperm of corn or the R gene in red color of wheat grains, a duplication might tend phenotypically to intensify the characteristic. Should the duplicated gene or genes have a retarding or inhibiting effect on the development of a character, reduplication of these genes might increase the retarding effect.

Many phenotypic effects besides bar eye are produced by duplications. Numerous variations in the wing, eye, and other characters of *Drosophila* are conditioned by duplications. Large duplications as well as large deficiencies tend to have *lethal effects*. Lethality in the case of either deficiencies or duplications may be the result of disturbing long-established genetic balances dependent upon a normal number of genes in an organism. Decreasing the number of genes in an organism through deletion or increasing them through duplication abruptly disturbs the genic balance normally existing. Organisms subjected to these disturbing influences may die prematurely. Cytological studies indicate that many supposedly true diploid organisms have in fact a number of small duplications. In some cases the salivary chromosomes of *Drosophila* have revealed small duplications involving a few bands. These duplications have apparently been long-established, and their effects if any have been regarded as normal.

Structural Hybrids

The term *hybrid* applied to an organism indicates that it has been derived from two parents which differ genetically. In general, the term *hybrid* is used to designate organisms heterozygous for one or more pairs of Mendelian units or genes. A hybrid then in this strict sense is a Mendelian hybrid. When two species are crossed, the offspring is a species hybrid. Likewise, the offspring of individuals from two genera is a generic hybrid. Perhaps, unfortunately, the term *hybrid* has been extended to cover still other situations. An organism which arises from the union of two gametes differing in chromosome numbers, as from heteroploid organisms, is designated as a numerical hybrid. Chromosome aberrations lead to the production of organisms which are heterozygous for chromosome changes. That is, the heterozygotes have one normal chromosome and one structurally changed chromosome. There may be inversion heterozygotes, deficiency heterozygotes, or translocation heterozygotes. To these kinds of heterozygotes, the term *structural hybrid* has been applied—actually it is a chromosome structural hybrid. Structural hybrids may have large or extremely minute changes, and the changes may be few or very numerous. The term *undefined structural hybrid* has been used to designate one in which the exact nature of the structural changes has not been determined.

Position Effect of Genes

Chromosome aberrations such as inversions, translocations, and duplications cause changes in the linear order of genes. These rearrangements bring some of the genes into new locations and into contact with a new set of neighboring genes. Observation of the phenotypic effects of these changed genes has led to the idea that the behavior of a gene is determined not only by its own properties but by those of all the genes in the genotype and especially by its near neighbors. This changed behavior called position effect has not been observed in many organisms, but its existence appears to be well-established in the fruit fly, *Drosophila melanogaster*. The phenomenon was first discovered by Sturtevant in 1925.

In *Drosophila* certain individuals have been found in which the eye has changed from the normal round eye to a narrow vertical bar. This variation, called bar eye or barred eye, has a reduced number of facets. The germinal modification conditioning bar is located in the region of 57.0 in the **X** chromosome and is inherited as a dominant. Bar eye is conditioned by the duplication of a very small segment. When the chromosome is normal, the gene or genes in this region condition the normal wild-type round eye. Individuals which have a small duplication of the segment in their chromosomes develop the barred-eye character. This structural abnormality may exist as a heterozygous duplication, with one **X** chromosome normal and in the case of females the other **X** carrying the duplication, or there may be homozygous duplications with both **X** chromosomes in the female carrying the duplication. In males, with only one **X,** it is always hemizygous.

Sturtevant found that sometimes an exchange of unequal-sized segments occurred in the region of the bar locus during crossing over. This abnormal transfer resulted in a complete transfer of the bar duplication from one chromosome to another. Thus the duplicated bar region was reduplicated in one **X** chromosome, and the other **X** chromosome was left without that small segment. By breeding flies with this reduplication, he found that the presence of two bar regions, both located in one chromosome, exerted more influence on the reduction of size of the bar eye than the presence of two single-bar duplications each in one of the homologous chromosomes such as occur in the homozygous bar flies. With two bar segments located in sequence in one **X** chromosome, about 45 facets were developed in the bar eye, but in the case of the ordinary homozygous bar flies, where each of the two bar duplications was in one of the two homologous **X** chromosomes, 68 facets were developed in the bar eye. The effect of the genes in the bar segments on the number of facets in the eye was influenced by the relative positions in the chromosome. The influence of location was called **position effect.**

Besides the case of bar eye in *Drosophila*, several other instances of position effect have been reported in the fruit fly. Among these may be mentioned the genes conditioning *cubitus interruptus*, a vein modification in the wing, and roughest, a modification of the eye surface. The scute series of multiple alleles affecting the bristles on the body have also shown position effect.

In plants this phenomenon has been observed in a series of multiple alleles affecting pigmentation in the flower buds of the evening primrose, *Oenothera*. Phenotypic effects attributed to changed positions of genes in the chromosomes have also been noted in the leaf characters of the Jimson weed or Datura, in the endosperm of maize, and in fertility in vetch, *Vicia*. Investigations of this topic in plants have been limited in number, and according to some critics, those reported are not absolutely free from alternative interpretations.

THE POSSIBLE NATURE OF POSITION EFFECT. Goldschmidt has raised the question of the existence of the gene as an actual entity. Without committing himself definitely to the proposition, he suggests the possibility of explaining all the effects of the gene on the basis of the position of the material in the chromosomes. This suggestion, however, has not met with general acceptance among geneticists.

The influence of position effect is thought to depend on the exact point of attachment of the disturbed segment in the rebuilt chromosome and upon the nature and quality of the genes near the rearrangement. Muller suggested that possibly position effect is an expression of the same forces which cause the close association of the members of a pair of homologous chromosomes. Such forces acting between unlike genes might tend to deform them, and then the deformation might affect the nature and quantity of the products of the genes concerned.

Genes may be pictured as organic molecules united with each other in the longitudinal direction to form micellae, after the fashion of the cellulose micellae. Breakage of such a micella and the formation of a new micella may involve modifications of the intergenic bonds which may or may not be reversible.

The Nature of Structural Changes in Chromosomes

Two ideas have been current regarding the breaking and fusion of chromosomes leading to structural changes. One of these is the *contact hypothesis*, according to which the chromosomes come in contact and adhere. Then, at some point of contact, the chromosomes break and fuse simultaneously, changing the chromosome structure. The other is the *breakage first hypothesis* which assumes that the chromosomes are first broken. Following breakage there are several possibilities. The broken chromosomes may remain as fragments, or the broken ends may reunite to restore the original chromosome structure; they may fuse with other broken ends of the same or other chromosomes. While positive proof for either is lacking, the breakage first hypothesis appears to have most support among cytologists.

To learn about the nature and causes of the breaks in the chromosomes, biologists have subjected the cells of living organisms to changes in temperature and exposed them to chemicals and to ultraviolet rays, X rays, radium emanations, fast neutrons, and even to cosmic rays. While all of these have yielded results of one kind or another, the X ray has been very productive of induced chromosome changes. Fast neutrons also have been found to be effective in producing chromosomal aberrations. The terms x_1, x_2, etc., and R_1, R_2, etc., are used to indicate the first, second, and succeeding generations following X-ray and radium treatments, respectively.

X-RAY HITS, BREAKS, AND FUSIONS IN CHROMOSOMES. In radiation work it is generally assumed that a direct X-ray *hit* will cause a *break* in a chromosome. Thus hits and breaks have come to be used almost synonymously in the literature. The simpler aberrations that require fewer breaks naturally follow the lighter X-ray treatments, and the more complex structural changes in chromosomes result from the heavier dosages. The latter are dependent upon more numerous breaks and thus require a greater amount of X-ray treatment.

Single X-ray hits causing single breaks may result in the following aberrations in chromosomes: a fragment and a terminal deficiency or possibly a small deletion involving a single gene or very few genes. Two X-ray hits confined to a single chromosome and causing two distinct breaks may result in an intercalary deletion or an inversion. Two X-ray hits causing breaks in different chromosomes may result in translocations or interchanges (Fig. 157 and 158). It is fairly well established that the frequency of all types of chromosomal aberrations like fragments, small deficiencies, and others is in proportion to the X-ray dosage measured in r units. The occurrence of surviving structural changes is in proportion to a little less than the square of the X-ray dosage.

It is generally thought that a wide range of structural changes results from radiation treatments. Perhaps some of them are minor breaks in the irradiated chromosomes that are quickly repaired by prompt rejoining and fusion of the broken ends. If the injured chromosome is restored to its original structure, the change is never observed. In other cases breakage may be so extensive and the structural changes so radical in the irradiated chromosome that death of the cell results. These also are seldom noted. It is suspected that the observed chromosomal aberrations are but a few of all those that may occur following radiation treatments. Recognized aberrations are the survivors between the two extremes of injury.

Questions and Problems

1. Contrast the meaning of the terms *genotype* and *karyotype*.
2. What are chromosomal aberrations?
3. What do you understand by the term *chromosome break?* May chromosome breaks be induced?
4. Why does mere fragmentation generally fail to increase the number of chromosomes in an organism?
5. What is meant by the term *inversion* as applied to a chromosome?
6. How does an inversion probably occur? How many breaks in the chromosome are thought to be involved?
7. Distinguish between a transposition and a translocation.
8. What are reciprocal translocations? How do they occur?
9. Distinguish between the process of crossing over and reciprocal translocations.
10. What is the important feature of a duplication?
11. Distinguish between the contact hypothesis and the breakage first hypothesis as applied to chromosomal aberrations.
12. Discuss some of the recognized causes or contributing factors in the production of spontaneous chromosomal aberrations.
13. What evidence has been accumulated to indicate genetic control of spontaneous chromosomal aberrations?
14. What is a structural hybrid? Are structural hybrids all of the same specific nature? In general, how do structural hybrids manifest themselves cytologically?
15. What is the primary cause of the abnormal meiotic behavior of the chromosomes of a structural hybrid?

16. What is the reason for the difference in the meiotic behavior of an aberration heterozygote and an aberration homozygote?
17. What is the most usual phenotypic effect of chromosomal aberrations?
18. Why are nullisomics rare? In what type of organism are they most likely to be found?
19. When viable, do chromosomal aberrations generally show pronounced phenotypic effects? Cite some of the evidence.
20. What is position effect? Cite some cases of inheritance apparently the result of position effect.
21. Why do biologists and plant breeders try to induce chromosomal changes?
References at the end of Chapter 20.

Mutations

The Theory of Mutation, formulated in 1902 by Hugo de Vries, was based on his studies of heteroploid plants and structural aberrations of the evening primrose, *Oenothera*. Heritable variations have been variously called *sports*, *saltations*, and *mutations*. The word *mutation* is derived from the Latin *mutare*, meaning to change. The fundamental feature of the mutation theory is the occurrence of some permanent change in the germ plasm preceding the appearance of the heritable variation. The term **mutation** has been widely applied to cover visible or *phenotypic variations* resulting from germinal *changes in chromosome numbers, chromosomal structural changes*, or *invisible changes within individual genes*. Currently it is generally restricted to an invisible change, physical or chemical, within a single gene or locus in a chromosome, that is, a gene mutation. Geneticists are accepting Stadler's suggestion that *gene mutations are the residue* of germinal changes remaining *after all types of distinctly visible chromosomal changes* such as heteroploidy and definite structural changes *have been excluded.*

Although mutations may occur in the chromosomes and genes of either reproductive or somatic cells, most heritable mutations have been found to have occurred in the reproductive tract or reproductive cells, as meiocytes or gametes. Mutant genes do not immediately express themselves phenotypically because most of them are recessive. One or more generations must intervene between the occurrence of a recessive-gene mutation and its recombination with another similar recessive to effect its phenotypic appearance in a population.

Occurrence of Spontaneous Gene Mutations

Gene mutations occur both *spontaneously* in nature and as artificially *induced changes*. Spontaneous gene mutations, however, have supplied most of the material for the great mass of Mendelian studies undertaken during the last five decades. In the study of heredity since 1900, spontaneous mutations in a great number of organisms have been recognized. Of these the various species of *Drosophila* have contributed the greatest number of gene mutations. Hundreds of normal or wild-type genes and their mutant alleles are known in these flies. Among the first recognized and best-known gene mutations in *Drosophila* are those conditioning white eyes, pink eyes, black-body color, yellow-body color, and vestigial wings in contrast to the normal wild-type characteristics, red eyes, gray-body color, and long wings, respectively (pp. 59, 123). In the common Indian corn or maize plant, perhaps the second best-known organism genetically, the effects of more than 400 genes are recognized. They include the contrasting characteristics of starchy and sweet endosperm, colored and colorless aleurone, white and yellow endosperm, and many other alternate hereditary traits.

In mice and other rodents as rats, rabbits, and guinea pigs, gene mutations determine black coat, white coat, brown coat, and several spotted types in all color variations, in contrast to the normal self-colored wild-type gray or agouti rodent. The heritable color variations of domesticated farm animals, while neither so numerous nor so well known genetically as those of rodents, are conditioned by the action and interaction of gene mutations and their normal alleles. Likewise in human beings, many of the alternative characters as hair-color types, eye-color types, skin pigmentation, and many body deformities are conditioned by mutant genes. Besides their importance in the development of these more or less superficial traits, genes and gene mutations are thought to be basic to the fundamental features of size and many physiological functions of animals and plants. It is quite likely that gene actions and gene mutations are influential in the development of many of the general and special mental traits characteristic of human beings.

Gene mutations have been found in many types of organisms besides those mentioned and presumably may be found in any organism subjected to close and continued observation. Gene mutations vary in their influence from effects on structural and physiological characters so profound as to result in death to changes so slight they can scarcely be recognized. Between these limits there are many gradations in the effects of mutant genes. In both plants and animals, although a few are dominant, the great majority of known gene mutations, whether spontaneous or artificially induced, are recessive to the normal or wild-type gene. In organisms in which a number of mutations have occurred at one locus, forming a series of multiple alleles, most of the new mutant genes are recessive in inheritance to the normal gene from which they arose (pp. 195–199). A few dominant mutations, however, are known in *Drosophila* and other organisms, including some of the larger farm animals.

Induced Mutations

After the announcement of de Vries' mutation theory, biologists became actively interested in the nature and causes of mutation. For many years experimenters have attempted to induce mutations artificially through the use of radiation, chemicals, and other agents. Investigation in this field received great stimulus in 1927 from Muller's report of success in the artificial production of mutations in *Drosophila* through the use of X rays. By the use of a special technique, he was able to compare the frequency of mutations following X-ray treatments with the normal frequency of spontaneous lethal mutations in *Drosophila* cultures. After exposure of one hour to an X-ray dosage of 10,000 r units, there were 100 times as many lethal gene mutations as occurred normally. If the time of exposure of one hour or less was compared with the whole life span of two weeks for a generation of *Drosophila*, the mutation rate was about 3,500 times as great as that for spontaneous mutations.

At about the same time, Stadler, equally successful with plant material, announced the production of mutations in the cereal plants barley, oats, wheat, and maize through radiation techniques. He used both X ray and ultraviolet on cereal plants by exposing pollen and seeds to radiations. In one case he found 53 mutations in 2,800 plants grown from exposed seeds with none in the 1,500 plants from unexposed seeds left as controls.

All types of radiations have been used to induce gene mutations as well as chromosomal aberrations. Besides the X-ray and ultraviolet waves, radium emanations, cosmic rays, heat, and cold have been used to induce germinal changes in a great variety of organisms. Blakeslee and his associates reported success in the production of gene mutations in *Datura* following treatments with radium emanations and with X rays. Apparently true gene mutations have been induced by various investigators in tomato, cotton, snapdragon, and possibly in tobacco.

Treatment of seeds and seedlings of plants and of eggs of *Drosophila* with solutions of organic and inorganic chemicals, such as iodine and its compounds, copper sulphate, ammonia, and hydrochloric and acetic acids, has been undertaken to induce gene mutations. Some of these techniques appear to have yielded positive results. Many experiments have been carried on with the lower forms of life, including various fungi and bacteria for which it is possible to modify the culture media. Mustard gas has been used successfully to induce mutations in bacteria and in the fungus, *Neurospora*.

THE RELATION OF MUTATION RATE TO X-RAY DOSAGE   To determine the relation between the radiation dosage and the rate of mutation, organisms have been treated with 200 r units as the lower limit and 10,000 r units as the upper extreme. For comparisons the treatments were continuous in some cases until the whole dosage had been applied. In other cases the treatments were interrupted at intervals of minutes or hours. In one series of experiments with *Drosophila*, Muller applied extremely low dosages of X ray as $\frac{1}{20}$ and $\frac{1}{100}$ r units per minute over a month's time. In all of these experiments, the mutational effect in irradiated organisms was in direct proportion to the total X-ray dosage regardless of the manner or length of time in which the treatments were given.

TEMPERATURE CHANGES IN RELATION TO INDUCED MUTATIONS. Variations in temperature have been assumed to influence the rate of spontaneous mutation (pp. 390, 391). Changes in temperature, however, appear to have little effect on the rate of induced mutation when combined with radiation. A possible explanation of the dissimilarity in response to temperature changes of spontaneous and induced mutation rates may be sought in the vast difference in the potency of short-wave radiation and slight temperature changes. The X radiation is so powerful that the effects completely overshadow the slight effects of a few degrees' change in temperature. In the case of spontaneous mutations, however, the effects of radiation are minor, and the effects of slight changes in temperature may be more easily seen.

COMPARATIVE EFFECTS OF ULTRAVIOLET AND X RAYS. Stadler considers that the X ray tended to cause structural changes in the chromosomes of maize that were frequently lethal, especially in the 1N gametophytic structures. X-ray treatments result in extensive structural changes and even total destruction of chromosomes. When the chromosomes are injured, some genes may be destroyed. Accordingly, Stadler thought the apparent gene mutations might be deficiencies in the chromosomes so minute that they involved only the locus of one or very few genes. The aberrations in many cases might be too small for microscopic observation, and since they would be inherited according to Mendelian principles, they might be regarded as genes. When induced mutations, however, mutated back to the normal-type gene, a true original gene mutation and not a deficiency at a locus would be inferred.

Ultraviolet rays are less penetrating and apparently less damaging to chromosomes than X rays. Ultraviolet rays produce only a relatively few of the more minute structural changes and possibly none of the grosser aberrations but a surprisingly large number of apparently true gene mutations.

Spontaneous Gene Mutations

Although most mutant alleles studied in Mendelian heredity have arisen spontaneously in nature, their origin is still among the unsolved problems of biology. Many factors may be concerned in the process. Comparison of the infinitesimal amounts of radiation to which organisms may be exposed in nature with the heavy dosages used in radiation experiments suggests, however, that spontaneous mutations are dependent on factors other than radiation. Dobzhansky states that a summary of computations by independent investigators would indicate that less than 1 per cent of all spontaneous mutations may be attributed to the effects of natural radiation.

RATES OF SPONTANEOUS MUTATION. Rates of spontaneous mutation vary in different organisms, in the chromosomes of each organism, and even in the loci of a chromosome in a given organism. There is no general rate of mutation for any gene, chromosome, or organism, much less for all organisms. Under particular genetic, physiological, and environmental conditions, rates of mutation are specific for definite loci in chromosomes. The mutation rate varies for each gene locus.

Because of their abundance and their ready detection by a disturbance of expected ratios, lethal genes have been extensively used, especially in *Drosophila*, for studies of mutation rates. In a study of the rates of spontaneous mutations in the **X** chromosome of *Drosophila*, 48 lethal mutations, or 0.18 of 1 per cent, were found in 26,000 flies. The rates in 11 series of experiments varied from 0.07 to 0.69 of 1 per cent, indicating considerable variability in stocks of *Drosophila* grown under diverse laboratory conditions. A summary by Plough of 19 separate investigations involving different chromosomes and distinct loci within the chromosomes in more than 56,000 flies showed an average of 0.62 of 1 per cent spontaneous lethal mutations in unselected stocks of *Drosophila*. However, the general range of spontaneous lethal mutations may be from a fraction of 1 per cent to about 3 per cent for each chromosome. While mutations affecting visible characters may occur as frequently as lethals, many of them may escape detection. Possibly in *Drosophila* 1 or 2 visible mutations of spontaneous origin might be found in from 3,000 to 5,000 flies.

Stadler studied the rate of spontaneous mutation in *Wx*, *Sh*, *Y*, and *Su*, the normal alleles, of the waxy, shrunken, yellow, and sugary genes determining endosperm characters, the dominant-color genes *Pr* and *R*, and the color inhibitor *I* of the factor complex for aleurone coloration in maize. Of these genes *Wx*, *Sh*, *Y*, and *Su* mutated at a very low rate and *R* at a high rate. *R* mutated to the recessive allele *r* at the rate of 492 per million gametes as compared with only 1 mutation of *Sh* to *sh* and no mutation of *Wx* to *wx* in similar numbers. The rates of mutation for *Pr* and *I* were intermediate between those of the more stable and the more mutable genes.

EFFECTS OF TEMPERATURE ON SPONTANEOUS MUTATION RATES.   With *Drosophila* grown at temperatures between 4° C. and 40° C., an increase of from 6° C. to 7° C. resulted in a two- or threefold increase in the number of mutations. When the flies were grown at continuous low temperatures, the rate of spontaneous gene mutations was conspicuously lowered. Since the increased mutation rate follows the Van't Hoff law of temperature effects on the rate of chemical reactions, it suggests that the mutation process is of a chemical nature. Temperature shocks from brief exposures of an hour or a few hours to either heat or cold also tended to increase the rate of mutation. Plough thinks that the effects of temperature shocks must be in response to something else besides the temperature, for the time of exposure was very short. He suggests that the intergenic or chromatic material between genes rather than the intragenic material is affected by temperature shocks, while continuous exposure to increased temperatures influences the chemical reactions within the gene itself.

UNSTABLE OR MUTABLE GENES. Some extremely unstable or highly mutable genes are known in both plants and animals. Although not restricted in occurrence to somatic tissue, they frequently show their effects by variegation in the colors of such tissues as the pericarp, endosperm, or aleurone of maize or in the petals of some plants. Mutable genes have been reported in a variety of plants. Demerec mentioned more than 60 cases of unstable genes mostly associated with variegation in colors in a wide range of plants as the larkspur or *Delphinium*, snapdragon or *Antirrhinum*, sweet pea or *Lathyrus*, four-o'clock or *Mirabilis*, *Dahlia*, *Petunia*, and *Ipomoea*, the morning-glory. Besides affecting coloration in the flowers, some unstable genes have influenced the production of chlorophyll, leading to variegation in the leaves. As an example of the action of unstable genes, the case of the larkspur may be mentioned. One of the color genes has shown its high degree of mutability in the formation of many small purple dots in the otherwise lavender or rose-colored petals.

The factor complex conditioning aleurone coloration in maize has the basic complementary-color genes A-a, C-c, and R-r. Among the supplementary genes are Dt-dt which in the presence of the complementary basic-color genes, ACR, determine dotted or uniformly colored aleurone, respectively. Ordinarily the genes aa in the factor complex would be expected to result in colorless aleurone regardless of whether Dt or dt is present in the genotype, because the latter merely influence the distribution of color. Rhoades found, however, that when the factor Dt was introduced into the genotype, replacing its recessive allele, dt, gene a of the A-a pair became unstable and highly mutable. It mutated with considerable frequency to the dominant A. Cells containing the mutant genes were scattered through the aleurone tissue and became capable of producing aleurone color because of the interaction of A with the other complementary genes, C and R. The presence of the mutant gene was manifested phenotypically in variegation of the aleurone by small colored dots in an otherwise colorless-aleurone layer. The cells without color were those containing the unmutated genes aa.

In cases of unstable genes, such as the color factors in the larkspur petals and the aleurone tissues of maize, the period of mutability may vary, the mutation occurring at different developmental stages. When large sectors show the effects of a mutated gene, the mutation is assumed to have occurred early. When small sectors are affected, the mutation is thought to have occurred at a later stage in the development of the tissue.

Since the endosperm and aleurone layer of maize grains are 3x tissues, it was possible to test the frequency of mutation with a, aa, and aaa in the genotypes by varying the parentage. It was found that the number of mutations was directly in proportion to the number of a genes present. Grains with aa had twice as many and with aaa three times as many mutations as those with only one a. Rhoades found that increasing the Dt alleles also increased the mutation rate of a. One Dt gene gave 7.2 mutations, two Dt gave 22.2 mutations, and three Dt alleles gave 121 mutations per seed. Besides the effects of additional Dt genes on the mutation rate of a, still other genes modifying the mutation rate were found to be present in certain genotypes. This case is especially clear in showing the importance of the genetic environment in the process of mutation.

Although unstable or highly mutable genes occur frequently in plants, relatively few have been found in animals. Demerec, however, has reported studies of four such genes in *Drosophila virilis*. These genes are reddish-a, the action of which results in a golden-body color, mt-3 and mt-5, both determining the development of small or miniature wings, and m, conditioning purplish-red eyes. As is the case in plants, the mutability of unstable genes in animals varies with the genetic environment. With an ordinary mutation rate of from 3 to 14 per cent, some of the unstable genes in *Drosophila* mutated as frequently as 80 per cent when stimulated by proper genetic environment.

Although mutability of unstable genes was generally influenced by the genetic environment, it was found to be remarkably unresponsive to external environmental factors such as changes of temperature, carbon-dioxide concentration, and even radiation. It has therefore been postulated that internal chemical and genetic factors of undetermined nature are influential in modifying the mutability of some of these unstable genes.

MULTIPLE ALLELISM.   Instability of certain loci in some organisms has been indicated by the occurrence of series of mutant genes known as multiple alleles, which arise spontaneously at the same locus and at various times. Multiple alleles may therefore be regarded as multiple mutations. The number of alleles in a series varies with different organisms and in the different loci in which they have been discovered.

General Considerations of Mutations

Evidence indicates that mutation is confined to only one of the members of an allelic pair of genes and that the simultaneous mutation of the two members of a pair of allelic genes even under optimum radiation dosages would actually be an extremely rare event. There may possibly be a slight tendency for the genes in a certain region of a chromosome to mutate together as a group under the influence of X-ray treatments. In general, however, mutation in nature may be regarded as a local occurrence rather specifically restricted to one locus at a time.

The comparative rates of spontaneous mutation have been studied in haploids, diploids, and polyploids. Blakeslee found that spontaneous mutations in haploid *Datura* occurred more frequently than in diploid plants of the same species. Goodspeed, however, found that X-ray-induced mutations were more frequent in the polyploid forms of tobaccos than in the diploids. In general, the rate of mutation is roughly proportional to the number of genes carried by a chromosome. The rate of mutation is higher in the two larger chromosomes of *Drosophila* than it is in the smaller ones. The rate of mutation, however, is considerably higher in chromosome III than it is in chromosome II, even though the number of genes is probably only slightly greater in III than in chromosome II. Plough calls attention to a disparity in this relationship and suggests that possibly the mutability of all genes in chromosome III is higher than in chromosome II or that certain genes in III have a higher rate of mutation. On the general basis that the rate of mutation is proportional to the total number of genes, it would be expected that its rate in the different members of a polyploid series might well be in direct proportion to the number of chromosomes and consequently to the number of genes present in each member of the series. More mutations might be expected in a polyploid form of a species, with its duplication of genes at homologous loci, than in the corresponding diploid form simply because there would be more genes of each kind to mutate.

The difficulty of recognizing mutations, however, is greater in polyploids, because with their increased chromosome numbers there are more dominant alleles to mask the effects of a new mutant gene. If a recessive mutation occurs in one locus in an autotetraploid, there would be three normal unmutated genes at each locus to mask the new recessive allele. In a diploid organism with one allele at each locus in each of the two members of the pairs of homologous chromosomes, a recessive mutation in one of them would be more quickly recognized than in the polyploid form. In a haploid organism, with its single set of chromosomes, there is only one gene at a locus. Then, with no normal alleles present to mask them, the effects of a recessive mutation would be evident in the first generation following a germinal change. Mutations should therefore be most easily found in haploid organisms. Mutations in haploids may not really be more numerous, as Blakeslee thought them to be in *Datura* but merely more easily detected.

Somatic Variations, Bud Sports, and Chimeras

When germinal changes occur in the nuclei of somatic tissues, most of them are lost because these cells have no part in reproduction. If, however, a germinal change occurs in the early development of the growing point of a stem tip or a bud, it may be included in most of the tissues, reproductive as well as somatic, developing in the branch. Should flowers and seeds be produced on the branch, a somatic mutation of this type might become heritable.

BUD VARIATIONS

The occurrence of somatic, vegetative, or bud variations has been observed in many different kinds of plants. The variations include different form and habit of plant, changed leaf types, form and colors of tissues, flavor, textures, and time of maturity of fruits. Shamel and Pomeroy in a study of bud variations in apple, peach, and plum from the fruit-growing regions of the United States listed 173 bud variations in the apple alone. These occurred on the trees, frequently as single branches bearing fruit atypical in color, size, flavor, and date of maturity. Sometimes an entire tree in a planting was markedly different from others of its variety. Such trees were assumed to have been propagated from an earlier bud sport. These investigators concluded that bud variations offered excellent material for the development of improved varieties of fruit trees. Many striking bud variations or bud sports have been propagated and developed into new commercial varieties.

Emerson found 25 somatic variations in the endosperm tissue of 500 seeds of maize, that is, at the rate of about 1 in each 20 grains. He was sure that only a single chromosome with its contained genes was involved in this case. With the endosperm of corn having 30 chromosomes, great numbers of these variations are possible provided the rates of change are the same for each chromosome. Because chromosomes vary in their rates of mutability, the rates of change in each of the 30 might not equal that observed by Emerson.

ORIGINS OF BUD VARIATIONS. On the assumption that most somatic variations have originated as germinal changes, three possibilities are recognized: (1) numerical mutations including any of the forms of heteroploidy, (2) chromosomal aberrations or structural changes in individual chromosomes such as deletions, inversions, duplications, or translocations, and (3) true gene mutations occurring in somatic tissue.

Elimination of chromosomes in somatic tissue has been observed in well-known cases in *Drosophila* that resulted in somatic mosaics which resemble the gynandromorphs in that organism. This type of germinal change occurring in plants might be a means of origin of bud variations and in the case of heterozygous plants could lead to distinct phenotypic changes in the affected parts. Structural changes in somatic chromosomes have been demonstrated in plants. Navashin and Gerassimova studied them in the aging seeds of *Crepis* and found them more abundant in the upper part of the embryo than in the root portion. Jones also found chromosomal aberrations in the endosperm of maize. While these types of germinal change may well occur as bud variations, in general, structural changes in chromosomes have few pronounced phenotypic effects. The occurrence of apparent gene mutations in somatic tissue has been observed in various plants.

CHIMERAS

Another type of somatic variation is a mixture of plant tissues of different species, varieties, or genetic antecedents growing in one plant body. Abnormalities of this sort, called chimeras, have occurred both as spontaneous abnormalities in nature and in artificially induced structures in experimental material. The term *chimera* has its origin in mythology where it refers to a monstrous animal.

Plant chimeras are of different kinds. Structures consisting of two different tissues growing side by side and occupying distinct sectors of varying sizes in the plant are called sectorial chimeras. In a second type the two kinds of tissues are disposed one within the other. That is, one kind of tissue occupies the center of the plant structure as a core, and the second kind of tissue grows around it as a thin covering layer like a skin or a cortex. These are called periclinal chimeras. The word *periclinal* has its origin in the Greek words *peri* meaning around and *klino* or bend. The term *periclinal* means a tissue bent around or, more exactly in this case, growing around. A third type called a mericlinal chimera has one kind of tissue of limited extent placed in a peripheral position. A mericlinal chimera is actually an interrupted periclinal structure with a large or small segment of the outside or periclinal tissue covering a central core.

ORIGIN OF CHIMERAS.   Chimeras occur (1) as autogenous or spontaneous abnormalities and (2) as experimentally induced structures. It has been suggested that spontaneous chimeras originate as somatic variations and continue afterward as anatomical abnormalities. The artificial induction of chimeras by grafting techniques has been demonstrated by Winkler, Baur, Jorgensen, Crane, and others. In this method two species or varieties of plants, as **A** and **B,** were grafted. After the stock and scion had united, the top was cut off at the point of union leaving tissues of both plants **A** and **B** in the stem stub. Later, as callus tissue covered the wound, adventitious buds arose. Some of these buds and the branches that grew from them were found to be of both kinds of tissues, **A** and **B,** from the original stock and scion. If the two kinds of tissues from the stock and scion grew together side by side in the bud and branch, they formed a sectorial chimera. But if one tissue was inside the stem and the other surrounding and covering it, the chimera was periclinal.

HETEROPLOID TISSUES IN CHIMERAS.   Attempts to double the number of chromosomes in some plants have resulted in chimeras. Some plants, composed of tissues differing in chromosome numbers, have these tissues arranged in all sorts of ways, both sectorial and frequently as some type of periclinal chimera. Triploid and tetraploid cells are larger and haploid cells smaller than those of the normal diploid tissues. Because of this relationship and the differences in cell size, the kinds of cells and the extent of the tissues may be determined very exactly. Working with *Datura*, Blakeslee and his associates, especially Satina, have studied this type of structural abnormality which may be called a chromosomal chimera. In grasses portions of 1 plant may have the original diploid chromosome number and others have the induced tetraploid number. These diversities may appear in the flowers as well as in the vegetative parts. This type of variation may be partly chimera. The term *mixoploid* may also be used to designate such structures.

CHARACTERISTICS OF CHIMERAS.   When sectorial chimeras produce leaves, flowers, or fruits, they are mostly identical with one or the other of the two kinds of plants entering into the composition of the chimera. In a few cases the sectorial feature may be extended into the individual leaves, flowers, or fruits, forming exactly on the border line between the two kinds of tissue. In periclinal chimeras, generally the leaves, buds, flowers, and fruits are typical of the external layer of tissue, because these structures all arise exogenously, that is, from the external layers of tissue. For the same reason, in plants propagated from stem cuttings, buds or scions taken from periclinal chimeras generally resemble the external part of the chimera.

It has been found, however, that plants propagated from root cuttings taken from periclinal chimeras generally resemble the plant furnishing the tissue of the central core of the chimera. This is because the adventitious buds developing on root cuttings arise endogenously, that is, from the internal tissues, in this case, the central core of the chimera.

Some cultivated potato plants are periclinal chimeras with an external layer of tissue of one kind and an internal core of another. By shaving off the external parts of the eyes of potato tubers, it has been possible to induce buds to grow from the deeply located central core. In some cases the plants induced by this technique were distinctly different from those normally developed. The Rural variety of potato normally produces russet tubers. By shaving the eyes as described above, a plant developed producing lighter-colored tubers without the normal russeting. This was introduced as a white Rural variety and had a limited vogue as a commercial crop. Sectorial chimeras also occur in potatoes. In these cases a portion of a tuber may be of one color and the remainder of the tuber of another color. Propagation from eyes cut from the two parts has given rise to two distinct types or varieties of potatoes.

Chimeras are observed in apples and citrus fruits, in which somatic variations in colors may involve from one-half to one-third of a fruit. Often a red-type apple may be found with a prominent stripe of darker or lighter hue or possibly entirely lacking in color. Similar color variations are also found in citrus fruits where there are sectors either lighter or of more intense color than the normal yellow. In most cases these variations involve purely vegetative tissues and are not continued in the propagation of the plants.

Chimeras are of popular interest and arouse a certain curiosity, but they are of minor importance in genetic investigations. They may be of interest and value to the plant propagator as the source of new varieties.

Questions and Problems

1. Why are the variations acquired through action of environmental factors generally regarded by biologists as nonheritable?
2. What is a gene mutation? What is Stadler's idea of the relation of gene mutations to other germinal changes?
3. Review the historical development of the idea of mutation from its beginning to its restriction to gene mutations. Explain the possible relationship of mutation to the evolution of new forms of plant and animal life.
4. What organisms have furnished most of the known gene mutations? What is the relationship of gene mutations to Mendelian studies?
5. What techniques have been most effective in the production of induced gene mutations?
6. Is there any apparent relationship between radiation dosage and experimentally induced mutation rate?
7. What kind of gene mutation has been most frequent in radiation techniques used to induce germinal changes?
8. Why are temperature changes of little importance in influencing the mutation rate in X-ray treatments?
9. Compare the effects of X rays and ultraviolet rays as agents in the production of gene mutations. Why should one be more effective than the other as an agent for inducing gene mutations?

10. What is the possible action of radiation in causing changes in the gene?
11. What are spontaneous gene mutations? Are the causes of spontaneous gene mutations known?
12. Can any definite statement be made concerning the rate of spontaneous gene mutations?
13. Is the rate of spontaneous gene mutation the same for all organisms? All chromosomes in an organism? All loci in a chromosome?
14. Which would be easier to detect, a dominant or a recessive mutation? Why?
15. If an investigator suspected the occurrence of a recessive-gene mutation, what breeding technique might be used to demonstrate its presence?
16. About what rate of spontaneous mutation has been found in *Drosophila?*
17. Do all gene loci mutate at the same rate in the same organism? Cite a specific experiment to support your argument.
18. As compared with results obtained with experimentally induced gene mutations, what explanation may be given of the fact that the rate of spontaneous mutations is affected by temperature changes?
19. What is meant by the terms *mutable* or *unstable gene?* Cite some example of mutable genes. In what kind of tissue have these unstable or mutable genes been found?
20. Does the genetic background in which they operate have any influence on the rate of mutation shown by unstable genes?
21. Have mutable or unstable genes been found in any considerable range or variety of organisms? Name organisms in which they have been found.
22. Considering a pair of allelic genes, with one member in each of a pair of homologous chromosomes, may mutation occur in both loci simultaneously or is it restricted to a single gene?
23. In general, are mutations actually more frequent in haploids, diploids, or polyploids?
24. Even though mutations may be more frequent in polyploids than in haploids or diploids, why are they more difficult to recognize in organisms with multiple chromosome numbers?
25. Explain what is meant by an allele. What is multiple allelism? Give examples of multiple alleles. To what germinal behavior is multiple allelism due?

References

Biological Symposia, Vol. VI. *Temperature and Evolution. Isolating Mechanisms. Genetic Control of Embryonic Development*, Lancaster, Pennsylvania, The Jaques Cattell Press, 1942.

CATCHESIDE, D. G.: "Effects of Ionizing Radiations on Chromosomes," *Biol. Rev. Cambridge Phil. Soc.* **20**:14–28 (1945).

Cold Spring Harbor Symposia on Qualitative Biology, Vol. IX. *Genes and Chromosomes*, Cold Spring Harbor, Long Island, New York, The Biological Laboratory, 1941.

DARLINGTON, C. D.: *The Evolution of Genetic Systems*, Cambridge, England, Cambridge University Press, 1939.

DOBZHANSKY, THEODOSIUS: *Genetics and the Origin of Species*, 2nd ed. New York, Columbia University Press, 1941.

GOLDSCHMIDT, RICHARD: *Physiological Genetics*, New York and London, McGraw-Hill Book Company, Inc., 1938.

McCLINTOCK, BARBARA: "The Production of Homozygous Deficient Tissues with Mutant Characteristics by Means of the Aberrant Mitotic Behavior of Ring-shaped Chromosomes," *Genetics* **23**:315–376, (1938).

SANSOME, F. W., and J. PHILP: *Recent Advances in Genetics*, Philadelphia, P. Blakiston's Son & Co., Inc., 1939, Chapter IX, 252–296.

SHARP, L. W.: *Fundamentals of Cytology*, New York and London, McGraw-Hill Book Company, Inc., 1943, Chapter XIII, 193–203.

Symposium. Cytology, Genetics and Evolution, Philadelphia, University of Pennsylvania Press, 1941.

WADDINGTON, C. H.: *An Introduction to Modern Genetics*, New York, The Macmillan Company, 1939.

section 8

Development of Heritable Characters

The earlier students of genetics were concerned with segregation, assortment, and recombination of genes in the inheritance of qualitative and quantitative characters of living organisms. The manner in which the gene, the indivisible unit of heredity, is passed from generation to generation, the chromosomal relationships of genes in Mendelian heredity and in linkage, has been summarized as the mechanism of heredity. This older, but still fundamental interpretation, has come to be referred to as *classical genetics*. In some of the *newer aspects of genetics*, consideration is given to the specific effects of genes and of specific "organizers" in the development of morphological features as expressed in form and structure, *developmental* genetics; the effects of genes in the control of physiological functions, *physiological* genetics; and the specific biochemical actions of genes, *biochemical* genetics.

chapter 21

Gene Action in Development
of Heritable Traits

In any consideration of heritable traits, whether under the heading of developmental genetics, physiological genetics, or biochemical genetics, *the central problem is the nature of gene action.* Accumulating data indicate that gene action is related to the production of catalyzing enzymes influencing biochemical reactions.

THE RANGE OF CHARACTERISTICS UNDER GENE CONTROL. The list of characteristics known to be under gene control is much more extensive than is indicated by the relatively few cases cited in the earlier sections of this text. Characteristics under gene influence include: (1) variations in size and form of organism; (2) the vast array of colors in plants and animals; (3) physiological processes such as earliness and lateness of development, milk production in cattle, egg production in fowls, and the yields of fruits and seeds in cultivated plants; (4) many specific metabolic processes in domesticated animals and in man; (5) blood groups in domesticated animals and in human beings; (6) disease resistance; (7) sex determination in plants and animals, self-sterility in plants, and sex phenomena in animals; (8) psychological characteristics in man such as differences in taste reactions, musical abilities, some types of feeble-mindedness and nervous disorders, some types of subnormal vision, and possibly the entire range of variation in mentality in human beings; and (9) certain genetical and cytological phenomena, such as variation in mutability of unstable genes in different genetic environments, "stickiness" of chromosomes under the influence of the "sticky" gene, variations in amount of genetic crossing over, and certain abnormal chromosome behavior during meiosis.

THE NATURE OF GENE ACTION. In considerations of gene action, the catalyzing effect of a gene or of its products has been stressed. When a gene acts to duplicate itself, forming an exact copy, it is said to be autocatalytic. Genes also have heterocatalytic properties. Data from numerous investigations indicate that, through their heterocatalytic activities, genes form enzymes which catalyze biochemical reactions.

401

Beadle lists more than 20 definite biochemical reactions that are under known gene control in about a dozen different organisms. The organisms range from the yeast plant to man and include some of the algae, fungi, flowering plants, insects, dogs, and rabbits. The biochemical reactions include those concerned in the production of color variations in plants and animals, splitting of sugar molecules, protein and amino-acid metabolism, and nitrate reduction. In each case the gene is thought to initiate enzyme production that influences or controls a definite reaction in the general metabolic process. Later another gene with its enzyme becomes active in the reaction. In one organism, *Neurospora*, studies have been made of more than 100 induced mutations, each one influencing a definite biochemical reaction in the metabolism of that plant.

Gene mutations seem to affect the catalytic properties of the gene. Muller has suggested that if a mutation *destroys*, or abolishes, the *autocatalytic* power of a gene, it cannot reproduce itself and therefore it ceases to be a gene. If the autocatalytic power remains *unimpaired*, but the *heterocatalytic* property is *lost*, following a mutation, the gene remains a gene, because it can reduplicate itself. But with its heterocatalytic power lost, the gene becomes inactive, as far as any effect on an organism is concerned, and it becomes an *amorph*, a negative form. If a mutation *impairs*, but does not destroy, the heterocatalytic power of the gene, it becomes less effective and may be called a *hypomorph*, that is, a lesser form. If a mutation *increases* the heterocatalytic property of the gene, it may have a greater phenotypic effect on the organism. A gene of this type is called a *hypermorph*, that is, a super form. And finally if a mutation *changes* the heterocatalytic action of the gene from one specific process to another, the gene may then be called a *neomorph*, that is, a new form.

Examples of variations in catalyzing power of genes may be found in the members of some multiple allelic series. Multiple allelic series originate through a number of presumably unrelated mutations forming mutant genes which all affect the development of the same trait but to different degrees (pp. 195–199). Some of these genes then may act as *hypermorphs*, *increasing the character;* some as *hypomorphs*, *decreasing* the trait; and still others as *amorphs* with apparently total elimination of the characteristic.

Genetic and Chemical Basis of Coloration in Plants and Animals

The inheritance and development of color variation in plants and animals afford good examples of specific gene actions. In general, coloration in both plants and animals is based on the presence of a definite organic chemical compound; this is the chromogen or precursor of color, itself usually a colorless material, that may be changed chemically to form the color.

GENE ACTION IN THE DEVELOPMENT OF FLOWER COLORS. The principal coloring matters in flowers are the anthocyanins, anthoxanthins, and carotenoids. Variations in flower color depend upon the presence or absence of one or more of these chemical substances, upon structural changes in their molecules, upon variations of the quantities of the substances, upon combinations of the basic substances, and finally upon the acidity or alkalinity, the pH, of the cell sap in the flower parts. The anthocyanins responsible for the red and blue colors in flowers are water-soluble glycosides formed by the chemical union of the basic coloring matter, one of the anthocyanidins, and one or more molecules of a simple sugar.

In many plants the production of anthocyanin coloration is dependent genetically upon the interaction of two or more dominant complementary genes as in the sweet-pea flowers and in the aleurone layer of maize seeds (pp. 202–206). Besides the production of anthocyanin color, the specific color is determined by chemical changes. In general, the greater the number of hydroxyl or OH groups that are added to the molecules, the more intense the blue color.

Three prominent anthocyanin molecule types, pelargonidin, cyanidin, and delphinidin, differ in the number of —OH groups added to the prime ring and in the position in the ring at which the hydroxyl is added. Specific genes are concerned with the molecular changes. The dominant alleles tend to determine increased oxidation as, CD, interacting to produce the greatest degree of oxidation and highest development of blue pigmentation as shown in delphinidin; Cd, with a lesser oxidation and less intensity of blue as in cyanidin; and the double recessive, cd, with only slight oxidation and still less blue pigment as in pelargonidin.

Besides the oxidation, the number of sugar molecules incorporated in the anthocyanin molecules appears also to be under gene control. Hydrogen-ion concentration or the degree of acidity, influencing the anthocyanin colors, likewise is dependent upon the genotype of the plant and is thus hereditary.

GENE ACTION IN DEVELOPMENT OF COLORS IN ANIMALS. Coloration in mammals appears to depend upon the presence of chromogens, colorless compounds that may be chemically changed through the action of oxidizing enzymes to form pigments. Tyrosine, an amino acid, is probably the basic chromogenic material which through a series of enzymatic oxidations forms two general types of melanic pigments, the dark eumelanic pigments that are either black or brown and the phaeomelanic or xanthic pigments that are red or yellow. Specific colors depend largely upon the relative amounts and distribution of these two types of pigments. Color types of rodents are known to be under gene control with modifications resulting from hormones and environmental factors. Oxidation of the chromogens to form the colors may be influenced by two general enzymes or enzymatic systems, enzyme I and enzyme II. Through the work of Wright and his associates, the action of genes in the biochemistry of color formation in the coats of animals is best known in the guinea pig. The genetic basis of color inheritance in the guinea pig is a complex of seven pairs of major genes

and numerous minor ones that have modifying actions. Among the major
genes the following have actions that determine the quality and intensity of
the pigments.

C-c and their alleles—*the albino series,* influence the production of
both the dark or eumelanic pigments and the red-yellow or phaeomelanic pigments. Wright says that this series of alleles is concerned
with the quantity or activity of the two enzymes affecting the reactions that lead to the formation of the two types of pigments. In
the allelic series the lowest member, c^a, in the homozygous state,
$c^a c^a$, acts as an amorph and determines the almost complete lack of
pigment characteristic of the albino guinea pig.

F-f—a pair of alleles acting as *intensity factors* for the red-yellow
pigments. With *F-* present in the genotype, the red-yellow or phaeomelanic pigments have full intensity. With *ff* present, the intensity of
these pigments is reduced. The *ff* genes have no effect on the black
pigments. Apparently *F-f* influence the concentration or activity
of the enzyme system necessary in the production of phaeomelanin.
The *f* gene, therefore, acts as a hypomorph.

P-p—*the pink-eye alleles,* acting as intensity factors for the black
and brown pigments. With *P-* present in the genotype, the eumelanic
pigments have full intensity. With *pp* present, these dark pigments
are reduced in intensity in the hair and almost completely eliminated
in the eyes, making the animal a pink-eyed guinea pig. The *pp* genes
have no effect on the red-yellow pigments. It may be assumed that
the *P-p* genes act to influence the quantity of the enzymes concerned
with the chemical reactions leading to the formation of melanic
pigments. With *P* present, the amount of the enzyme or the enzymatic activity is increased. With *pp* the amount or the activity of
the enzyme is decreased, *p* acting as a hypomorph.

B-b—*the black-brown alleles,* act on the eumelanic pigments and
determine the difference between black and brown guinea pigs. The
B-b genes have no effect on the red-yellow pigments. With *B-* present
in the genotype, the eumelanic pigments are transformed, and the
animal has black fur and black eyes. With *bb* present in the genotype, the pigments are transformed into brown, and the fur and
eyes are brown. Evidently the *b* form of the gene acts as a hypomorph. Besides the genes listed above that act to influence the
quality and intensity of the pigments, Wright classifies the following genes concerned with the distribution of pigments.

E-e—the extension alleles, act to determine the extension of the dark eumelanic pigments. With *E-* present in the genotype, the eyes and fur are black. With *ee* present in the genotype, the eyes are black, but the fur is red or yellowish. Wright suggests that the genes *B-b* and *E-e* act on the hair follicles. *E-* determines that the follicles contain the eumelanic or dark pigments and *ee* that they contain only the red-yellow or phaeomelanic pigments. The *B-b* pair acts only on the follicles that contain the dark or eumelanic pigments, determining whether they are black or brown.

A-a—the agouti alleles, act on the eumelanic pigments. *A-* in the genotype determines the presence of a light-colored band just below the tip of each individual hair. *A* may be considered as acting to block the development of the eumelanic pigment in this subterminal band. With *aa* in the genotype, the hairs are fully pigmented, black or brown, throughout their length.

S-s—the spotting factors, act to determine the distribution of color over the body, regardless of the color type. With *S-* in the genotype, the animal is self or solid color, while *ss* determines that the animal is spotted with white. Russell has shown that white-spotted areas on colored guinea pigs lack the necessary enzymes to transform the colorless chromogens into the color pigments.

Gene Action in Physiological Processes

Among a few well-known cases in which specific metabolic processes are associated with the action of a definite hereditary unit is a variation in the metabolism of dogs. In some mammals purine, a nitrogenous compound, may be excreted in the urine as uric acid. In other mammals, as in most breeds of dogs, the uric acid, through the action of the enzyme uricase, may be further broken down to allantoin. In the Dalmatian coach dog, however, the nitrogenous material is excreted as uric acid. Trimble and Keeler studied the inheritance of this metabolic variation in dogs. They concluded that the inability to excrete the more completely broken-down material, allantoin, is inherited as a simple recessive Mendelian character. Since it has been found that Dalmatian dogs actually produce the enzyme uricase necessary for the production of allantoin, its formation must result from some cause other than the lack of the proper enzyme. Possibly there may be some interference with the normal action of the uricase in the homozygous-recessive Dalmatian dogs.

In human beings the disease known as *alcaptonuria* (p. 405), a metabolic disorder, is characterized by blackening of the urine on exposure to air. Because of its long-recorded history, Beadle refers to this metabolic abnormality as a classic in biochemical genetics. The substance responsible for the characteristic blackening of urine is alcapton or homogentisic acid (2,5,-dihydroxyphenylacetic acid). Normal human beings have an enzyme that acts to break down homogentisic acid, but persons with the disease lack the enzyme. This metabolic disorder is definitely inherited. Possibly the responsible gene fails to produce the proper catalyzing enzyme.

Gene Action in the Metabolism of Neurospora. Beadle, Tatum, and others, working with the red bread-mold fungus, *Neurospora*, have accumulated some exceptionally clear evidence for a one-gene, one-specific biochemical reaction. *Neurospora* with male and female plants has both sexual and asexual methods of reproduction. Investigators treat the asexual spores with X rays or with ultraviolet rays to induce gene mutants in the fungus. The treated spores are grown, and the resulting mycelium is crossed with normal untreated fungus plants of opposite sex. The ascospores resulting from the cross are formed, eight in each ascus or spore sac. If a mutation has occurred, the mutant gene and its normal allele will be segregated, and the spore sac will contain four mutant and four normal genes. The ascospores are next isolated and grown separately on a complete culture medium. For growth, *Neurospora* requires (1) carbon supplied from sugar, starch, or fat; (2) nitrogen from either inorganic or organic compounds of nitrogen; (3) certain chemical elements such as calcium, phosphorus, sulphur, and other minor elements provided by inorganic salts; and (4) biotin of the vitamin-B group. The complete culture medium is fully supplied with the above essential materials and, in addition, with an abundance of vitamins and various amino acids such as arginine, ornithine, etc.

After the cultures to be tested for mutations have become well established on the complete culture medium, they are transferred to a medium containing only the minimum essentials for growth of the normal or wild-type *Neurospora*. One type of minimum medium contained only (1) sugar, (2) mineral salts, (3) inorganic compounds of nitrogen, and (4) biotin to satisfy the minimum requirements for growth. Use of inorganic nitrogen compounds instead of organic compounds of nitrogen and omission of all nitrogen in the form of amino acids enabled the investigators to test the strains of fungi for their abilities to catalyze the synthesis of the amino acids. Any strain of the fungus able to grow on the minimum medium was considered to be normal or wild type and therefore able to catalyze the synthesis of all the amino acids necessary for growth. Any strain of the fungus unable to grow on the minimum medium was recognized as a biochemical mutant, unable to catalyze the synthesis of certain amino acids. To determine the nature of the mutation, further attention was directed to the mutant strains. In one laboratory where 85,000 single-spore cultures of *Neurospora* were tested, between 500 and 600 mutant strains were found which were unable to synthesize the compounds necessary for growth of the fungus. Among the mutant strains were many duplicates, but more than

100 were distinct and therefore the result of gene mutations at different loci in the chromosomes.

From biochemical researches of this type has come the hypothesis that there is a definite relation of gene action to chemical reaction. This is expressed as a one-gene to one-primary-function relationship. Possibly this primary function may be accomplished through a one-gene to one-enzyme relationship. Beadle, 1951, in a brief summary of advances in chemical genetics emphasizes that at present no clear case of direct gene-enzyme production–chemical reaction has been proved.

The relationship of gene to chemical reaction is the presumed ability of the gene to form a pre-enzyme or an enzyme that acts as a catalyst in the chemical reaction. The gene-enzyme–chemical reaction is brought out in *Neurospora* in the ornithine-citrulline-arginine cycle among the amino acids. Ornithine and citrulline are precursors of arginine and enter into its synthesis. The investigators found four genes that are necessary for the synthesis of ornithine. Building up citrulline from ornithine, carbon dioxide, and ammonia seems to occur in two steps. Under the influence of two specific genes, molecules of CO_2 and NH_3 are added to the ornithine molecule. The next step, the addition of an NH_3 molecule to that of citrulline, seems to be controlled by another specific gene forming arginine. Gene control is exercised through its heterocatalysis of an enzyme which acts as a specific catalyst in each separate chemical reaction of the synthesis. After arginine has been synthesized, it may act as a building stone in the development of proteins, or it may break down under the catalyzing influence of the enzyme arginase and form urea and ornithine.

The mutant strains which are unable to grow on the minimum medium contain a mutant gene that blocks one step in the complex chemical reaction and thus prevents the arginine synthesis. Perhaps the mutant gene forms an enzyme that is incapable of catalyzing the specific step in the chemical reaction, or it forms an enzyme that actually prevents a specific step in the reaction. Another possibility is that the mutation has changed the gene into an amorph that is incapable of forming an enzyme. The necessary step in the synthesis then fails because of the lack of the catalyst.

In the synthesis of vitamins, such as nicotinic acid of the vitamin-B group also studied in *Neurospora*, the specific biochemical reactions were found to be under a step-by-step control of definite genes. While the one gene–one enzyme–one biochemical reaction hypothesis still has supporters and probably holds true in certain cases, it is not universally accepted at present among investigators. Perhaps this is too simple for many other cases. Current among many investigators is the thought that two or more genes may be involved in the production of a single enzyme. Then there is the further possibility that a single gene may influence the production of more than one enzyme.

GENE ACTION IN DEVELOPMENT OF SIZE AND FORM. Geneticists have been interested in the development of size in both plants and animals. In most cases differences in size are characterized by many features: difference in chromosome numbers, differences in rates of cell division, the number of successive divisions, rates of growth, and general vigor. Size in living organisms is generally dependent upon a large complex of multiple genes. It is well known that organizers, hormones, or growth substances have great influence on the development of form and size. Among these substances hormones from the sex glands, thyroid, and pituitary glands are pronounced in their effects on size and form and on psychological characteristics in human beings. Although the development of these glands and the production of hormones are under gene control, specific gene action is definitely known in only a few cases.

GENE ACTION AND THE INFLUENCE OF HORMONES IN DEVELOPMENT. Among the ductless or endocrine glands, the pituitary is normally especially active. Hormones of the pituitary gland influence growth and development. An inactive or underactive pituitary in the human being, resulting in a deficiency of certain hormones, causes subnormal size and development of the body. If this inactivity starts early in development, a child fails to grow to normal size and remains childlike through life. This condition is called infantilism. Overactivity of the pituitary gland in human beings, producing an excess of certain hormones, results in the production of giants. This condition is called giantism. Although development and activity of the pituitary gland are thought to be hereditary in the human being, exact data on the inheritance have not been worked out.

Inheritance of pituitary development and hormone production in the case of a dwarf mouse is better understood. It has been found that the size of a normal mouse and a dwarf mouse results from the influence of a single pair of genes. Further studies have shown that the gene for dwarfness exerts its influence by determining subnormal development in the anterior lobe of the pituitary gland. The resulting hormone deficiency expresses itself in dwarfism in the mouse.

GENE ACTION IN THE DEVELOPMENT OF PLANT HORMONES. Certain substances active in promoting growth in plants are called *growth substances* or plant hormones or, specifically, auxins. In a few cases the action of genes on the influence of plant hormones has been studied. In corn a strain of mutant plants, called nana, is much smaller than the normal types. Normal and dwarf maize plants are determined by the action of a single pair of genes, *Na-na*, the dwarf being homozygous recessive, *na-na*, and the normal, *Na-*. Van Overbeek found that in the dwarf nana plant the normal amount of one of the growth substances, the plant hormone auxin, was actually produced. The *na* gene, however, determines the formation of an enzyme which catalyzes the abnormal oxidation of most of the growth substance. The result is that there is a reduction of growth hormones in the nana plants. The deficiency in the hormone is thought to be the cause of dwarfness in the nana plants.

Another variation in corn is found in a strain in which the plants show an inherited tendency to grow horizontally on the ground. These plants are called "lazy" corn plants. Normal and lazy plants are determined by the gene pair *La-la*, with *la-la* plants of the lazy type and *La-* normal. A normal corn plant, if bent down, soon grows upward again. Lazy plants, if bent down to a horizontal position, continue in that position. Van Overbeek found that the *la* gene disturbed the normal distribution of the growth hormone, auxin, and this resulted in the lazy habit. When normal corn plants are bent to a horizontal position, the growth hormones tend to move away from the upper side and to concentrate in the lower side of the stem. The presence of excess growth substance on the underside of the stem stimulates a greater amount of growth on the underside than on the upper side where growth is slowed down and causes the stem to turn upward again. In *la-la* plants the downward movement of the growth hormone is inhibited by the *la* gene, and the plants continue to grow horizontally. Lazy corn is thus an inherited character developed through hormone action that is definitely under gene control.

GENE ACTION IN THE DEVELOPMENT OF FORM.   The shape of the fruits of cucurbits such as squash, gourds, and melons varies. Some fruits are round, some disk-shaped, others bottle-shaped, and still others elongate. In most cases the shape is determined by one or two or, at most, by a few pairs of genes. Sinnott has demonstrated that form in these fruit types is independent of dimensions and of size and is developed as a result of different rates of growth in length and diameter. In spherical forms the rate of growth is about the same in all directions. Differences in the rates of cell division in the different primordia and the orientation of the mitotic-division spindles, the direction of greatest cell elongation, all under gene control are also involved in the development of form in the fruits of the cucurbits. From data on other studies of development, possibly the genes determining fruit shapes exert their influence through control of distribution or amounts of growth substances of the plant.

DIFFERENTIATION OF ORGANS AND TISSUES IN ANIMALS. In the early development of the animal embryo, the various organs and tissues appear to be under the control of organizers. Beadle, referring to organizers, suggests that they may be regarded as the "hormones" of early development, although the name is not usually applied to them. Because the various species develop different sorts of organs, organizers may be considered to be under the influence of genes. Holtfreter has suggested that in the Amphibia the developing embryo comes under the influence of a succession of organizers, the *primary, secondary, tertiary*, etc. The primary organizer, active in the very early stages of development, influences the differentiation of the larger parts or regions of the embryo, such as the head and its grosser parts, the notochord and lateral plate. A series of secondary, tertiary, etc., organizers next influence the gills, mouth, teeth from the head endoderm; the midbrain, eye lens, cornea from the head mesoderm; the ectodermal layer and skin from the lateral plate; and the lumen of the gut and neural tube from the notochord.

The influence of the organizers has been studied through tissue transplantation. In the early stages of embryonic development, small portions of tissue may be removed entirely or transplanted from one part of the embryo to another without interfering with the normal development. After the organizers have had time to exert their influence, removal of a piece of tissue will leave its mark in the production of an organ deficient for that amount of tissue. Transplantation experiments show the lasting effects of the organizers. A piece of tissue or a developing organ that has been under the influence of an organizer for a certain time is fixed and will develop into a specific organ, regardless of its position in the embryo. For example, the developing eye of the amphibian embryo may be removed from the head and transplanted to some other region of the body where it continues its development, forming a lens much as it would have done in its normal position.

References

BEADLE, G. W.: "Biochemical Genetics," *Chem. Rev.* **37**:15–96 (1945).

———: "Genetic Control of the Production and Utilization of Hormones," *Proc. 7th Int. Genet. Cong.*, No. 19, Edinburgh, 1939, 58–62.

BONNER, DAVID: "Biochemical Mutations in *Neurospora*," *Cold Spring Harbor Symposia* **XI**:14–24 (1946).

Cold Spring Harbor Symposia, Vol. **XVI**. Cold Spring Harbor, Long Island, New York, The Biological Laboratory, 1951.

CRANE, M. B., and W. J. C. LAWRENCE: *The Genetics of Garden Plants*, 2nd ed. London, Macmillan & Co., Ltd., 1938, Chapter V, 69–88.

DUNN, L. C.: *Genetics in the 20th Century*, New York, The Macmillan Company, 1951, 221–239.

RUSSELL, W. L.: "Investigation of the Physiological Genetics of Hair and Skin Color in the Guinea Pig by Means of the Dopa Reaction," *Genetics* **24**:645–647 (1939).

Symposium. "Genes as Physiological Agents," *Am. Naturalist* **79**:289–363 (1945).

WADDINGTON, C. H.: *Organizers and Genes*, Cambridge, England, Cambridge University Press, 1940.

WRIGHT, S.: "Estimates of Amounts of Melanin in the Hair of Diverse Genotypes of the Guinea Pig, from Transformation of Empirical Grades," *Genetics* **34**:245–271, (1949).

———: "Physiological Aspects of Genetics," *Am. Rev. Physiol.* **7**:75–106 (1945).

———: "Physiological Genetics of Melanin Pigmentation of the Guinea Pig," *Biol. Symposia* **6**:337–355 (1942).

———: "A Quantitative Study of the Interactions of the Major Colour Factors of the Guinea pig," *Proc. 7th Int. Genet. Cong.*, No. 326, Edinburgh, 1939, 319–329.

——— and LORA IVASKA BRADDOCK: "Colorimetric Determination of the Amounts of Melanin in the Hair of Diverse Genotypes of the Guinea Pig," *Genetics* **34**:223–244 (1949).

chapter 22

Extra Nuclear Inheritance

Special Parental Influences in Development of Embryos

Observations of early stages in the development of the fertilized eggs of animals suggested the possibility of *cytoplasmic inheritance*. The unfertilized egg has definite polarity, stratification, and to some extent differentiation of the cytoplasm. Polarity to a great extent determines the early cleavage lines in the fertilized egg. Certain differentiated regions of the cytoplasm of the animal egg develop into definite parts of the embryo. There is evidence that in plants also the early cleavages of the zygote are to a large extent predetermined by the polarity of the unfertilized egg cell.

MATERNAL INFLUENCES. Following specific and generic crosses in lower animals, as in sea urchins and some of the lower fishes, the fertilized egg develops into the embryo under maternal influence. At first this seemed like a type of cytoplasmic inheritance. However, it is now known that polarity of the unfertilized egg, determining the position of the early cleavage planes of the zygote, stratification and differentiation of the egg cytoplasm marking out the parts of the young embryo, and the rate of growth of the embryo are all predetermined under the influence of the genes of the female parent. In many other cases the similarity of the embryo and the juvenile forms of the F_1 hybrid to those of the maternal species has been accounted for by the extrusion of the paternal chromosomes from the zygote. The embryonic development was therefore actually under the influence of maternal chromosomes and genes, and there is no real evidence of cytoplasmic inheritance in these cases. There may be a prolonged *maternal influence but not maternal cytoplasmic inheritance*.

Another instance of maternal influence is the classical case of the shells of snails. Following reciprocal crosses between the dominant dextral, *DD*, and recessive sinistral, *dd*, of the coiling types of snails, the F_1 is heterozygous dominant, *Dd*. Nevertheless, it always develops according to the maternal type of coiling. The type of coiling is dependent upon the position or tilt of the mitotic spindles in the early cleavage stages, and this orientation of the mitotic spindles is determined by the maternal genes. Interestingly enough all F_2 individuals in reciprocal crosses develop the dextral type of coiling. This occurs because all F_1s are heterozygous dominant, Dd, and orientation of spindles is under the influence of the dominant-dextral gene, D, present in the F_1 females. Not until the F_3 generation is there segregation into the expected 3 dextral : 1 sinistral coiling forms. Phenotypic expression of the genotypes is thus delayed because of the relationship between coiling and the early cleavages that are predetermined by the maternal genotypes. While these cases show maternal influences, they are in no wise nongenic phenomena but, quite the contrary, are good examples of Mendelian heredity under special conditions.

Plastid Inheritance

Most plant cells contain small protoplasmic bodies called *plastids*. Some of the plastids contain carotenoids that are associated with the development of the yellow and orange-red colors of plant parts. Others, containing the green material, chlorophyll, are of primary importance in the synthesis of carbohydrates. The leucoplasts, young stages of both types, are colorless. Plastids are presumably derived by division of pre-existing plastids and have been regarded as an illustration of nongenic inheritance.

Since plastids constitute a distinct and possibly an independent system of entities within the cytoplasm, the influence of nuclear genes on their behavior merits discussion. Many instances are known of the influence of genes in the production of the yellow, orange, and orange-red colors of flowers and fruits as are a hundred or more in which the production of sugar, dextrins, and starch is under the control of identified genes. In chlorophyll development or deficiency other hundreds of cases are known to be under gene control. Against this array of gene-controlled plastid behavior, a relatively few instances appear to be exceptions to regular Mendelian heredity and gene control.

Many of the suspected cases of nongenic inheritance of chlorophyll deficiencies have been found in plants with variegated leaves and stems, the *albo maculata* types of botanical literature. In these plants the leaves show irregular patches of green and white. Some plants are all green, some all white, and others variegated (Fig. 161). In variegated types such as occur in maize, there are alternating stripes of dark- and light-green, yellow, or white tissue in the leaves. Crosses among certain variegated or albo maculata types have seemed to furnish evidence confirming nongenic inheritance. The inheritance of the albo maculata condition is apparently through the female parent only. As M. M. Rhoades has said, "These chlorophyll variegations, transmitted through the female line only, constitute the most compelling evidence for cytoplasmic inheritance."

Some investigators have interpreted this apparent non-Mendelian inheritance as a third type of heredity in which the plastids themselves act as hereditary units, hence the idea of the plastidome or plastome in heredity. Writing of the clear evidence of nuclear control in plastid behavior in some instances and not in others, Darlington said, "It is equally clear in other cases that the plastid is as autonomous and permanent as any gene." Others also, as, for example, Renner, are of the opinion that plastids are themselves hereditary units and might show changes like mutations of genes.

FIG. 161. A VARIEGATED PLANT.

MATERNAL TRANSMISSION OF THE ALBO MACULATA TYPE OF CHLOROPHYLL ABNORMALITY. Reciprocal crosses between normal green plants and the variegated or albo maculata types have yielded unlike F_1 generations. When normal green plants were used as the female parents and variegated plants as the pollen parents, the F_1 plants were normally green. The reciprocal cross produced a mixture of green, variegated, and occasionally even completely white plants showing an apparent predominant female influence on the offspring. This kind of maternal influence may be determined by the transmission of the cytoplasm and the contained plastids into the zygote almost exclusively through the egg cell, because the male gamete contributes little or no cytoplasm and few if any plastids.

THE INHERITANCE OF CHLOROPHYLL ABNORMALITIES IN MAIZE. Anderson reported maternal transmission of an abnormality in maize expressing itself as pale-green stripes on the otherwise dark-green leaves. When the plant was self-pollinated, seeds yielded normal green, pale-green-striped, and pale-green seedlings. Because of chlorophyll deficiency, the pale-green seedlings died. Pollination of abnormal plants with pollen from normal plants again produced seeds which yielded green-striped and pale-green seedlings (Fig. 162). Tests of pollen, however, from the original striped plants on unrelated normal plants failed to produce the

Fig. 162. Chlorophyll Deficiency Shown by Alternate Green and Nongreen Stripes in Leaves of Maize.
(Courtesy, E. G. Anderson, from *Botan. Gaz.* **76**, 1923.)

abnormality in either the first or second generation. These tests were interpreted as indicating that the plastid primordia from the maternal plants transmitted the chlorophyll abnormality.

A similar chlorophyll abnormality was explained by Demerec on the assumptions of gene control of plastids and the influence of specific genes that showed exceptional frequency of mutation in somatic tissue.

THE INHERITANCE OF GENE-INDUCED CHLOROPHYLL ABNORMALITY. Because of its clear relationship with the well-known recessive iojap gene, *ij*, in maize, a third case of maternal transmission of chlorophyll abnormalities assumes considerable importance. In the homozygous state, the iojap gene manifests itself by producing green and white stripes. Within the light areas, the plastids are smaller than normal and develop no chlorophyll. The dominant allele, *Ij*, conditions normal-sized green plastids throughout the plant. Rhoades in 1943 reported that the abnormality conditioned by the recessive-mutant iojap gene, *ijij*, was trans-- mitted through the maternal cytoplasm where it appeared to persist regardless of the genotype and independent of genic control.

Table XLIV

RECIPROCAL CROSSES INVOLVING VARIEGATED PLANTS

Normal green plant × Variegated plant F₁ normal green	Variegated plant × Normal green plant F₁ In various proportions of— Normal green Variegated Some pure white

Rhoades found that F₁ progenies, *Ijij*, of crosses between green plants, *IjIj*, and mutant-striped plants, *ijij*, were phenotypically normal green when the female plant was normal but showed a variety of chlorophyll types when the female parent was the mutant-striped plant (Table XLV). His explanation of these unexpected results was based on the assumption that

Table XLV

RECIPROCAL CROSSES INVOLVING A CHLOROPHYLL DEFICIENCY

Normal green × Mutant striped IjIj ijij F₁ *Ijij* All normal green	Mutant striped × Normal green ijij IjIj F₁ *Ijij* Variety of chlorophyll types Normal green Striped green and white Completely white

egg cells arise from different tissues of the maternal plant. In the variegated female parent, egg cells originating from normal green areas supposedly contained normal green chloroplasts and when fertilized would give rise to normal green plants. Egg cells originating, however, from an area of white tissue with the mutant type of small colorless plastids when fertilized might be expected to give rise to white plants. An egg cell originating from some of the variegated tissue might contain both normal and abnormal plastids and give rise to a variegated plant by separation of the two types of plastids during the somatic development of the embryo.

Further data were obtained from backcrosses of a heterozygous F₁, *Ijij*, to the homozygous P₁, *IjIj*. Normally the backcross would be expected to yield genotypes *IjIj* and *Ijij* in a 1:1 ratio with phenotypic expression, because of dominance of the *Ij* gene, in a progeny of normal green plants. This phenotypic condition, however, was not realized (Table XLVI); again there was a variety of types, including white seedlings.

Rhoades emphasized that these white seedlings constituted the best evidence of plastid transmission through the cytoplasm contributed by the female gamete and of plastid development independent of genic control. In each of the genotypes, the presence of at least one dominant *Ij* gene would be expected to condition the development of chlorophyll in the plastids. Here is a case in which a change in the plastids was induced by the action of the recessive allele of *Ij-ij*. But after the change, the modified plastids seemingly had a genetic continuity uninfluenced by the nuclear genotype. Even in cells homozygous for the normal chlorophyll gene, *IjIj*, the plastids continued to multiply in their changed state which became permanent.

Table XLVI

BACKCROSS PROGENY INVOLVING CHLOROPHYLL
DEFICIENCY

F₁ Variegated plants × Normal green plants
    Ijij   *IjIj*
Backcross-progeny genotypes *IjIj* and *Ijij*
Backcross-progeny phenotypes
    Normal green plants
    Variegated plants with green and white stripes
    Completely white seedlings in which the plastids
    lack chlorophyll regardless of the genotype

Relationships of Genes and Plasmon

Sonneborn in a discussion of chromosomal genes and cytoplasmic units of the plasmon (1951) distinguishes five interrelationships. Under (1) he includes changes induced by genes in plastids, such as mutation to a form incapable of producing chlorophyll as reported by Rhoades and discussed above. (2) Genes control concentration of cytoplasmic particles as *kappa,* or plastid numbers as in polyploids compared to diploids and haploids, and finally the mitochondria that are likewise more numerous in diploids than in haploids. (3) Genes are suspected of acting as selective agents on self-duplicating cytoplasmic structures, such as different types of plastids, mitochondria, and *kappa* and *sigma* particles. (4) A cooperation of genes with the plasmon has been assumed in cases in which neither alone apparently determines a trait. There may be an interaction between the two or possibly the development of the hereditary trait in response to a change in either the chromosomal genes or in the cytoplasm, such as some types of chlorophyll development. (5) In a final class is included a relationship in which chromosomal genes determine alternative phenotypic traits but, once established, the trait is perpetuated by the cytoplasm through a period of multiplication. Possibly environmental factors such as temperature may be involved in a change of phenotypic expression which then tends to persist. This is a type of interaction between genes and cytoplasm that may be basic to the phenomena of: (a) *Dauermodifikationen* or persistent modifications, (b) plastid variegation in plants, (c) some types of sex determination found in algae, and (d) possibly cell differentiation. Sonneborn points out that Correns, interpreting plastid inheritance in plants, approached the conception of this fifth type of relationship and interaction between genes and cytoplasm.

Cytoplasmic Inheritance

Besides the plastids there are visible mitochondria, also possibly hereditary units of the plasmon. In some cases it is known that both plastids and mitochondria are under genetic control. Polyploid series are known in which their numbers vary proportionately with the chromosome numbers. Among the ultramicroscopic entities which may possibly be concerned with cytoplasmic inheritance are viruses and the hypothetical plasmagenes or cytogenes which some investigators locate in the cytoplasm. The hereditary materials of the plasmon carried in the cytoplasm are designated by Greek letters, as *alpha, beta, kappa, sigma,* etc.

Evidence for cytoplasmic inheritance is found in the classical experiments of von Wettstein, of Renner, and of Lehmann, drawn from the unusual phenomena of unlike reciprocals in wide species and generic crosses in plants. Reciprocal crosses usually produce similar F_1 generations.

RECIPROCAL CROSSES BETWEEN SPECIES OF MOSSES. From 1920 to 1930 von Wettstein studied the problem of cytoplasmic inheritance. Reciprocal crosses between various strains or races within a species of moss showed no F_1 differences, but reciprocal crosses between species and genera were frequently unlike, with a tendency for the F_1 to resemble the female parent. Von Wettstein placed diploid F_1 hybrid sporophytes in culture media and by the process of regeneration grew protonemata, the early gametophytic stages. These were 2N like the diploid structures from which they grew and developed into diploid gametophores or "moss plants" which in turn produced 4N or tetraploid sporophytes following fertilization. One series of experiments dealt with the moss genus *Funaria*, which shows species differences in both gametophytic and sporophytic structures. *Funaria mediterranea*, for example, has a gametophyte bearing leaves which taper greatly, become filamentous at the apex, and have midribs which end abruptly beneath the apex. In this species the paraphyses, the sterile structures among the sex organs, consist of spirally arranged oval cells. The sporophytes bear small capsules which have tall sharp caps or opercula. Another species, *Funaria hygrometrica*, has a gametophyte bearing leaves which end in a broad flat apex, the midribs extend into the apex, and the paraphyses are composed of spherical cells arranged in straight rows. The sporophytes in this case bear large capsules with broad flat caps.

Reciprocal hybridization of these two species of mosses produced 2N, or diploid, sporophytes which were unlike. In the combination *Funaria mediterranea* with *F. hygrometrica*, the F₁ sporophyte capsules were very similar to those of the female parent. In the reciprocal combination the F₁ sporophyte capsules were also like those of the female parent *Funaria hygrometrica*.

To learn the effects of reciprocal crossing on the gametophytic structures, von Wettstein applied the technique of regeneration, producing protonemata from the hybrid sporophytes. As the protonemata and the mature gametophytic structures developed, these too showed the resemblances to the female parent in reciprocals. Von Wettstein attributed the matroclinous tendencies to the effects of the cytoplasm derived in quantity from the female parent. Accordingly the development of some of the plant characteristics was conditioned by the *plasmagenes* or *cytogenes* as others have designated the hereditary units in the cytoplasm. This conditioning effect is compared with the effects of the genes of the chromosomal genome in ordinary Mendelian inheritance. The *plasmon* is then to be regarded as the material basis of cytoplasmic inheritance.

FIG. 163. UNLIKE RECIPROCAL HYBRIDS IN EPILOBIUM.

a, *Epilobium roseum* × *Epilobium hirsutum*. b, *Epilobium hirsutum* × *Epilobium roseum*. (Courtesy, B. M. Duggar, from Lehman in *Proc. Intern. Congr. Plant Sci.* **I,** 1926.)

RECIPROCAL CROSSES IN EPILOBIUM. Species of *Epilobium*, commonly known as the willow herb, were extensively investigated by Renner and by Lehmann and their associates. Crosses between varieties within one species of *Epilobium* produced F₁ generations that were alike in reciprocals, but when certain species were crossed reciprocally, the F₁ plants differed as in the mosses described above (Fig. 163). When the cross *E. roseum* with *E. hirsutum* was made, the F₁ plants were tall, erect, had an open habit of growth, scanty branching, and bore fertile flowers. From the reciprocal combination the F_1 plants were short, bushy, profusely branched, and bore reduced and nearly sterile flowers. In each case the F_1 plants resembled the female parent.

Here, too, it was assumed that the cytoplasm of the maternal parent had a predominant influence in the development of the F_1 embryos. Renner explained the unlike reciprocal hybrids on the basis of action of certain hereditary units in the plasmon, located in the cytoplasm. Lehmann, however, postulated that different nuclear constitutions reacted variously in different cytoplasms and that the cytoplasm influenced the reaction of the chromosomal genes. Later studies by other workers appear to confirm Lehmann's interpretation. Michaelis remarks that possibly these matroclinous tendencies are not confined to crosses in *Epilobium*. They may also occur in other plants.

THE CYTOPLASMIC INHERITANCE OF MALE STERILITY IN MAIZE. In 1933 Rhoades reported on an extensive investigation of male sterility in maize. This case stands today as one of the most thoroughly investigated instances of extra nuclear transmission among plants. The abnormality expressed itself in extensive degeneration of the microspores, resulting in scant viable pollen. A few plants, however, produced some good pollen. The abnormality was transmitted entirely through the female parent. The scantily produced normal and viable pollen from male sterile plants did not transmit the abnormality to the progeny.

Rhoades failed to find any gene conditioning this abnormality. In the male sterile plants chromosome behavior was normal during meiosis and a quartet of spores was formed from each microsporocyte. Soon, however, degeneration of the microspores was observed. Comparisons of microspores from normal fertile plants and the abnormal male sterile plants showed a marked difference in the number, size, and shape of the cytoplasmic elements which were considered to be plastids or plastid primordia (Fig. 164). Some normal-appearing microspores were found among the degenerating ones. Furthermore, cytoplasmic differences were reported in the somatic cells of normal and male sterile plants.

Rhoades was careful to point out that, regardless of marked difference between the cytoplasmic elements in normal and male sterile plants, the abnormal cytoplasmic elements could not be assumed to cause degeneration in the microspores. The abnormal cytoplasmic elements merely represented a stage in the degeneration of the microspores, and whatever caused male sterility also caused changes in the cytoplasmic elements in the cells of the abnormal plants. The transmission of this type of male sterility appears to depend entirely upon nonnuclear factors. Rhoades emphasizes, however, that some types of male sterility are conditioned by recessive genes.

This investigation has furnished some of the strongest evidence for nongenic heredity, and Rhoades himself realized that the results might be interpreted as supporting the hypothesis of cytoplasmic inheritance. He was careful to point out that there was little evidence regarding the nature of the causal cytoplasmic elements. Rhoades states that the idea of a diseased cytoplasm, proposed by Correns, offers a more logical explanation of this case of male sterility than the hypothesis of hereditary units in the cytoplasm.

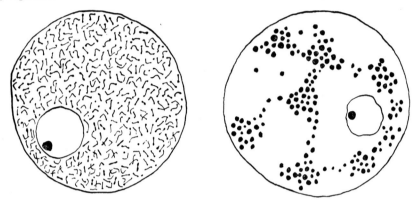

FIG. 164. MICROSPOROCYTES OF MAIZE.
The cell to the right shows appearance of bodies normally in the cytoplasm. The cell to the left shows an abnormal microsporocyte characteristically produced in plants showing male sterility. (Courtesy, M. M. Rhoades, from *J. Genet.* **XXVII**, 1933.)

THE ACTION OF THE KAPPA MATERIAL IN PARAMECIUM.

A race of the ciliate, *Paramecium aurelia*, which makes the fluid in which it lives poisonous to most other races of paramecium, has been called a "killer." Sonneborn has investigated the inheritance of the killer *vs.* the nonkiller traits and has concluded that the alternative characteristics are determined by the alleles K-k plus a cytoplasmic material called *kappa*. The *kappa* material appears as extremely small but microscopically visible particles in the cytoplasm. The number of *kappa* particles depends directly upon the number of K genes in the genotype. A genotype of KK determines that there will be about 400 *kappa* particles in the cytoplasm of each paramecium, Kk determines about 200 particles, and with the homozygous recessive, kk, there are eventually none.

Races are killers only when both the dominant gene K and the cytoplasmic material *kappa* are present; they are nonkillers, regardless of the genotype, when *kappa* is absent. Genotypes kk with *kappa* present in the cytoplasm remain killers through several fission generations, then they lose their *kappa* material and their killer quality and thereafter remain nonkillers. In these cases apparently *kappa* is completely and permanently lost, for even with the introduction of the K gene through mating $kk \times KK$, there is no killer effect. If, however, the mating $kk \times KK$ is made before the *kappa* material is lost, the introduction of K maintains the killer effect and does this even if the KK parents, lacking *kappa*, are themselves nonkillers. These results are regarded as evidence that the cytoplasmic material, *kappa*, alone is responsible for the killer quality. Further it is thought that *kappa* is not self-perpetuating and its continued presence is dependent upon the action of the *K* gene. This is apparently the only function of *K*, as experimental evidence indicates that a *K* genotype cannot initiate the production of *kappa*. If, however, some *kappa* material is present in the cytoplasm, the introduction of the *K* gene maintains and increases *kappa*. Sonneborn suggests that the gene *K* works through the cytoplasmic *kappa* to produce a killer substance, *paramecin*, that kills paramecia lacking *kappa*. The *kappa* material is only in the cytoplasm; paramecin is only in the fluid in which killers have lived. Sensitive organisms are actually killed by paramecin, not by *kappa*.

The following summary has been offered. The *kappa* material is: (1) absent from the migratory gamete nucleus, (2) present in the cytoplasm of killers, (3) essential for the development of paramecin, the killing agent of killers, (4) physiologically active even in the absence of the gene *K*, (5) dependent upon the gene *K* for its increase and unable to persist when *K* is replaced by the allele *k*, and (6) not initially produced by gene *K* or any other gene in the killer race. (7) Paramecia with genotype *KK* have twice as much *kappa* as heterozygotes *Kk*.

The dominant gene *K* is (1) unable to initiate the production of the *kappa* material and (2) controls the increase and maintenance of *kappa* when that material is already present. *KK* or *Kk* plus *kappa* = killers; *KK* or *Kk* plus *kappa* may also = nonkillers. The latter group though genetically and cytologically killers are phenotypically nonkillers. This raises a question, why are they nonkillers when they have all of the equipment to make them killers?

In certain cases autogamy or conjugation in a nonkiller *KK* plus *kappa* race restored the killer function. This suggested that even though *KK* and *kappa* are both present, whether the race is a killer or a nonkiller may depend in some cases upon the concentration of the *kappa* material present. It was thought that the killer quality was restored in these nonkiller *KK* plus *kappa* races through autogamy, because autogamy doubled the amount of *kappa* thus increasing it to the killer level.

In some cases killer races gave rise to killer and nonkiller lines through fission multiplication alone, presumably because there was an unequal division of the *kappa* material during fission. It has also been found that fertilization between nonkiller and nonkiller as *KK* plus *kappa* × *KK* minus *kappa* may also yield killer types. This was accounted for on the theory that through slow or delayed separation of the conjugants, some cytoplasm containing *kappa* was passed into the nonkiller *KK* minus *kappa* organism, which then through autogamy could produce killers.

The gene *K* is regarded as a self-duplicating physiological agent. *K* reduplicates itself and the *kappa* material which is supplied to the cytoplasm.

Combining with *kappa*, *K* is able to catalyze the synthesis of more *kappa* material, which is apparently able to function only in its detached location in the cytoplasm.

References

Advances in Genetics, Vol. I (1947) 264–358, Vol. II (1948) 1–66. New York, Academic Press, Inc.

ANDERSON, E. G.: "Maternal Inheritance of Chlorophyll in Maize," *Botan. Gaz.* **75**:411–418 (1923).

Cold Spring Harbor Symposia on Quantitative Biology, Vol. IX. *Genes and Chromosomes. Structure and Organization*, Cold Spring Harbor, Long Island, New York, The Biological Laboratory, 1941.

———, Vol. XI. *Heredity and Variation in Microorganisms*, Cold Spring Harbor, Long Island, New York, The Biological Laboratory, 1946.

DARLINGTON, C. D.: *The Evolution of Genetic Systems*, Cambridge, England, Cambridge University Press, 1939, Chapter XX, 114–122.

———: *Recent Advances in Cytology*, Philadelphia, P. Blakiston's Son & Co., Inc., 1937, Chapters II, III, IV.

DEMEREC, M.: "A Second Case of Maternal Inheritance of Chlorophyll in Maize," *Botan. Gaz.* **84**:139–155 (1927).

DUNN, L. C.: *Genetics in the 20th Century*, New York The Macmillan Company, 1951, 291–314.

EAST, E. M.: "The Nucleus-Plasma Problem," *Am. Naturalist* **68**:289–303, 402–439 (1934).

GOLDSCHMIDT, RICHARD: *Physiological Genetics*, New York, McGraw-Hill Book Company, Inc., 1938, 267–281.

JENNINGS, H. S.: *Genetics*, New York, W. W. Norton & Company, Inc., 1935.

LINDEGREN, C. C.: "A New Gene Theory and an Explanation of Dominance to Mendelian Segregation of the Cytogene," *Nat. Acad. Sci. U. S.* **32**:68–70 (1946).

MORGAN, T. H.: *The Physical Basis of Heredity*, Philadelphia, J. B. Lippincott Company, 1919, Chapter XVI.

———: *The Theory of the Gene*, 2nd ed. New Haven, Yale University Press, 1928.

RHOADES, M. M.: "The Cytoplasmic Inheritance of Male Sterility in Zea Mays," *J. Genet.* **XXVII**:71–93 (1933).

———: "Genic Induction of Inherited Cytoplasmic Differences," *Proc. Nat. Acad. Sci. U. S.* **29**:327–329 (1943).

SCHRADER, FRANZ: *Mitosis*, New York, Columbia University Press, 1944.

SHARP, L. W.: *Fundamentals of Cytology*, New York and London, McGraw-Hill Book Company, Inc., 1943.

———: *Introduction to Cytology*, 3rd ed. New York, McGraw-Hill Book Company, Inc., 1934, Chapters VIII, IX, X, XVI, XVII.

SIRKS, M. J.: "Plasmatic Inheritance," *Botan. Rev.* **4**:113–131 (1938).

SONNEBORN, T. M.: "The Dependence of the Physiological Action of a Gene on a Primer and Relation of Primer to Gene," *Am. Naturalist* **79**:318–339 (1945).

SPIEGELMAN, S., and M. D. KAMEN: "Genes and Nucleoproteins in the Synthesis of Enzymes," *Science* **104**:581–584 (1946).

WADDINGTON, C. H.: *An Introduction to Modern Genetics*, New York, The Macmillan Company, 1939.

WILSON, E. B.: *The Cell in Development and Heredity*, New York, The Macmillan Company, 1925, Chapter VI.

WRIGHT, S.: "Genes as Physiological Agents," *Am. Naturalist* **79**:289–303 (1945).

———: "The Physiology of the Gene," *Physiol. Rev.* **21**:487–529 (1941).

section 9

Sex Determination and Sexual Types

Among sex types in animals are: (1) monosexual individuals, normal males and normal females; (2) bisexual individuals, the normal hermaphrodites in lower animal forms; and (3) several types of sex deviations and sex intergrades. In monosexual individuals the normal male has only one kind of sex glands or gonads, the testes producing only male gametes, the sperms. Normal females have only the female gonads, the ovaries producing only the female gametes, the ova or eggs. Besides the primary function of gamete production, in many instances male and female animals are distinguished by secondary sexual characters, such as differences in horns in sheep, deer, and other animals, plumage in fowls, or beard and the lack of it in the human being (Fig. 165–169). The development of these secondary sexual characters is influenced by the sex hormones from the sex glands.

The sex of an individual, a vastly more significant character than the coat color of an animal, the flower color, or color of some cellular layer in a seed, may be assumed to be determined by a genetic basis of genes and chromosomes. An adequate consideration of sex determination and sex differentiation must include the interaction of the following three groups of factors:

1. The hereditary basis, genes and chromosomes in the genotype and karyotype
2. The influence of the physiological conditions within the developing organism including various kinds of hormones from ductless glands other than the sex glands
3. The influence of the environment surrounding the developing organism.

The *final expression of the sexual characteristics in an organism is* the *resultant of the influences of all the genetic, physiological, and environmental factors* concerned in their development.

chapter 23

Sex Determination and Sex Differentiation in Animals

The processes of sex determination and of sex differentiation are correlated in the development of sexual types. Sex determination is cytologically and genetically based upon the mechanisms of meiosis and fertilization. During meiosis sex chromosomes, carrying the basic sex genes, are distributed to the gametes. Fusion of the gametes then brings to the zygote the fundamental genetic basis of sex determination. Sex differentiation involves the further development of the differences between the male and female. In the process of sexual differentiation, physiological and sometimes environmental conditions have a part. The sexual development of the individual is influenced by hormones produced in the ductless glands of the animal body. The development of many of the secondary sexual characteristics is fundamentally influenced by the hormones from the sex glands. In the developing embryos of the higher animals, the primordia of the sex characteristics apparently remain completely neutral for a considerable period. After a time these primordia one after another come under the influence of the sex-determining genes and other differentiating factors, and eventually either a male or a female is developed. Goldschmidt refers to a *turning point* in the growth of the embryo at which the genetic factors become operative and direct the development toward either male or female characteristics.

SEX CHROMOSOMES AND AUTOSOMES. Two kinds of chromosomes are recognized: (1) **the sex chromosomes,** also called the **X** and **Y** chromosomes, accessory or odd chromosomes, idiosomes, heterosomes, and allosomes, that carry the genes primarily concerned in sex determination; and (2) **the autosomes** that contain many genes concerned with the production of somatic characters but in some animals also carry genes which directly influence sex.

In the common fruit fly, *Drosophila melanogaster*, there are four pairs of homologous chromosomes (Fig. 170). Three pairs are the autosomes and are identical in male and female flies. In the female, the sex or **X** chromosomes

FIG. 165. HORN DEVELOPMENT IN MOOSE.

Top, bull moose, Hoodoo Lake, Lola National Forest, Idaho, showing characteristic horn development of male. *Bottom,* characteristically hornless cow moose, Portage, Alaska. (Bull moose courtesy, K. D. Swan and U. S. Forest Service; cow moose courtesy, J. Malcolm Greany and U. S. Fish and Wild life Service.)

FIG. 166. HORN DEVELOPMENT IN ELK.
Two bull elk, right, characteristically horned and one cow, left, hornless, from Jackson Hole, Wyoming. (Courtesy E. P. Haddon and U. S. Fish and Wildlife Service.)

FIG. 167. BISON OR AMERICAN BUFFALO.
Right, the larger horns and extreme burliness of the male of this species are characteristic. *Left,* bison cows and calves in contrast with the male. (Male courtesy, Kenneth Weaver; cows and calves courtesy, E. P. Haddon and U. S. Fish and Wildlife Service.)

are also alike, but in the male the sex chromosomes are unlike. One is an **X** chromosome like the two **X** chromosomes in the female. Its homologue, slightly larger with a curved portion at one end, is known as the **Y** chromosome. The female flies therefore have **XX** + 6 autosomes and the male flies **XY** + 6 autosomes.

The contrasting **XX** and **XY** chromosome pairs are the basis of sex determination in the fruit fly. In the formation of egg cells in the female, the meiotic process results in the distribution of 1**X** chromosome and 3 autosomes to each egg or female gamete. The male gametes, however, are of two kinds, one with the **X** chromosome and the other with the **Y** in addition to the complement of 3 autosomes in each case. Since eggs have equal chances of being fertilized by sperms with the **X** or with the **Y** chromosome, zygotes will be of two kinds. One kind, having 6 autosomes plus **XX** chromosomes,

FIG. 168. PLUMAGE DIFFERENCES IN THE SEXES OF PEAFOWLS.
The females are the smaller birds with the short tail feathers. In contrast, note the spectacular length and spread of the cock's tail feathers. (Courtesy, Eugene L. Pearce, Seville Pea Fowl Farm, Clearwater, Florida.)

will develop into female flies, and the other with 6 autosomes plus **XY** will develop into male flies.

Because of the occasional failure of the members of the sex-chromosome pairs to separate during meiosis, abnormal gametes may be formed. Bridges found that as a result of this nondisjunction of the sex chromosomes in *Drosophila*, some eggs were formed with **XX** and others which contained no sex chromosomes at all. If an **XX** egg was fertilized by a sperm bearing a **Y** chromosome, the resulting zygote contained **XXY** + 6 autosomes. Such exceptional flies were female regardless of the presence of the **Y** chromosome. If an egg with no **X** chromosome was fertilized by a sperm bearing an **X** chromosome, the resulting zygote contained only one **X** chromosome, **XO** + 6 autosomes or **X** *zero* + 6 autosomes. These exceptional **XO** flies were male regardless of the lack of the **Y** chromosome ordinarily present in males. It appears likely that the **Y** chromosome has little effect upon the actual determination of sex. There are indications that in *Drosophila* it is also a blank as far as other hereditary somatic traits are concerned. The **XO** (**X** *zero*) male flies have all the expected somatic traits of normal males and apparently differ from them only in being sterile. Since the number of **X**

FIG. 169. SEX DIFFERENCES IN TURKEYS.
Note the particularly larger size of the cock at right. (Courtesy, A. O. Schilling.)

chromosomes present in the genotype constitutes the fundamental genetic feature of sex determination in *Drosophila*, **XX** + 6 autosomes provide the genetic basis for the development of a female, while the **X** + 6 autosomes with or without a **Y** chromosome condition the development of a male.

The type of sex determination known as the **XX-XY** type is the genetic basis of sex determination for a large number of animals of diverse types, including *Drosophila* and other insects (Fig. 170), some of the fishes, and possibly all mammals including man.

TYPES OF SEX DETERMINATION. Within the wide range of living organisms, several distinct methods of sex determination, each with a different genetic basis, have been found, as follows:

1. Sex chromosomes apparently undifferentiated and therefore not identified. It may be supposed that the genes determining sex are located in certain autosomes

2. The sex-determining mechanism essentially the **XX-XY** type though with certain deviations as follows:

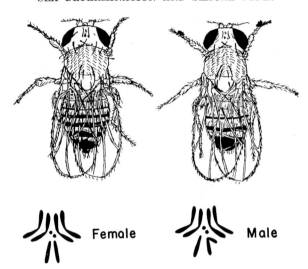

FIG. 170. MALE AND FEMALE FRUIT FLY, DROSOPHILA MELANOGASTER.
Chromosome complements below each sex. A difference in the sexes is the shape of abdomen, broad and pointed in the female, at left; narrower and blunter in the male, at right. The width of the dark bands is different in the two sexes. The male is further differentiated by the presence of sex combs on the forelegs.

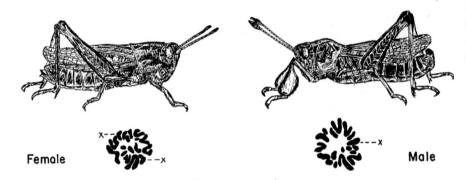

FIG. 171. THE ALPINE GRASSHOPPER, GOMPHOCERUS SIBIRICUS.
The sexes vary but little. The male has peculiar swellings on the forelegs. Left, female with 18 chromosomes including 2 **X** chromosomes. Right, male with only 17 chromosomes including 1 **X**. In this organism sex is determined on the **XX-XO** basis. (Modified after Witschi, from *Sex and Internal Secretions*, Edgar Allen, ed., Baltimore, The Williams & Wilkins Company, 1932.)

a. The true **XX-XY** type as in *Drosophila*, in which the female is the homozygous or homogametic sex and the male is the heterozygous or heterogametic sex. **XX** = female, **XY** = male

b. Certain cases in which the **X** and **Y** chromosomes are attached to a pair of autosomes and, because of this attachment, follow the autosomes through the maturation and fertilization processes

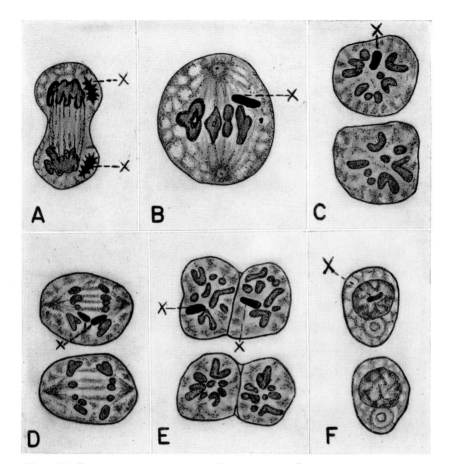

Fig. 172. Spermatogenesis in the Grasshopper, Gomphocerus sibiricus.

A. Telophase of last mitotic division in spermatogonia. The conspicuous **X** chromosomes show a tendency to form separate chromosome vesicles.

B. Metaphase of first meiotic division in primary spermatocyte. The single **X** chromosome passes undivided to one pole. Two nuclei are formed one having nine chromosomes including the **X** and the other, with only eight, lacks an **X** chromosome. The behavior of these two types of nuclei may be seen in C, D, E, and F which follow.

C. Polar views of metaphase of second meiotic division in the secondary spermatocytes. The upper plate shows an **X**, while the lower plate lacks the sex chromosome.

D. Anaphases of second meiotic division. Upper one shows an **X** passing to each pole of the spindle. The lower spindle has been derived from the nucleus lacking an **X**.

E. Result of second meiotic division. Above, two cells each with nine chromosomes including an **X**. Below, two cells each with eight chromosomes and lacking an **X**.

F. Two types of spermatids formed as a result of the meiotic divisions. One, above, has an **X** and when united with an **X**-bearing egg will determine a female. The other, below, lacks the sex chromosome. Upon union with the **X**-bearing egg, it will produce a zygote with only a single **X**, which will determine a male. (Modified after Witschi, from *Sex and Internal Secretions*, Edgar Allen, ed., Baltimore, The Williams & Wilkins Company, 1932.)

431

c. Other cases in which the **Y** chromosome is broken into fragments, two to several, forming the **Y-complex** which acts as a synaptic mate for the single **X** chromosome

3. The **Y** chromosome is entirely absent, possibly permanently lost in the evolution of the species. This results in the **XX-XO** (**X** *zero*) type of sex determination (Fig. 171 and 172)

4. The female is the heterozygous or heterogametic sex, and the male is the homozygous or homogametic sex. **XX** = male, **XY** = female. This type of sex determination is found in birds of all types including domestic fowls, in some fishes, and in certain moths and butterflies. This was termed the **ZZ-ZW** type of sex determination but is now generally indicated as **XX** and **XY**, with **Z** = **X** and **W** = **Y**

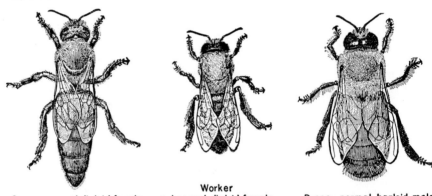

Queen—normal diploid female   Worker subnormal diploid female   Drone—normal haploid male

FIG. 173. THE HONEY BEE.
(Courtesy, Phillips, U. S. Dep. Agr. Farmers' Bulletin #447, Washington, 1911.)

5. The females are *diploid* organisms, and the males are *haploid*, as found in bees, wasps, and other social insects. Among bees there are three types of individuals: (a) the diploid queen bees which are fully developed functional females that produce eggs, (b) the diploid workers which are underdeveloped nonfunctional females and never produce eggs, and (c) the haploid drones which are functional males and produce sperms (Fig. 173).

Sex Ratios

The numerical proportion of males and females in any sample of a population is called the **sex ratio**. The sex ratio is generally written to indicate the number of males to each 100 females, thus 105:100 means a ratio of 105 males to 100 females. The sex ratio may also be expressed as the percentage of males in any given sample of the population. Thus a sex ratio of 52 per cent would indicate that 52 per cent of the number of individuals studied were males. There are primary, secondary, and tertiary sex ratios based upon the proportion of the two sexes at the time of conception, birth, and maturity, respectively. For a number of reasons, these three ratios differ.

With statistics on human births in the United States indicating a secondary sex ratio of 106:100 in the white and 103:100 in the Negro population, Crew has suggested that the primary sex ratio in human beings may be 170 males to 100 females. Witschi, reviewing the literature, gives the secondary sex ratio in swine as 112:100 but suggests 150:100 as a probable primary sex ratio. Numerous suggestions have been advanced to explain the excess of male-forming zygotes over the female-forming zygotes. Among them are: (1) that the Y sperms swim faster and that more of them reach the eggs than of the X-carrying sperms, (2) that because of meiotic irregularities more Y sperms are produced than X sperms, thus increasing the chance of more XY embryos, and (3) reduced viability of XY or male embryos in the prenatal period. Accumulated evidence indicates reduced viability of male embryos.

While the approximate secondary sex ratio is known for a fairly large number of animals, few data are available on the tertiary sex ratios at maturity and after for any group of animals other than human beings. Census reports of human populations establish clearly that more males than females die in most of the age groups. Since the infantile and juvenile death rates may be unequal in the two sexes, the tertiary sex ratio based upon the proportions of the two sexes at maturity may not be the equivalent of either the primary or the secondary sex ratios.

Crew, commenting on the tertiary sex ratios in man, uses the census reports of Great Britain to show that there are more deaths in males than females throughout most of the life span. In only two age groups, 10–15 years and 40–45 years, periods of great physiological change, is female mortality higher than the male. From secondary sex ratios of 106:100 for the white population of the United States and 104:100 in Great Britain, the proportion of males to females is constantly reduced (with the exceptions above noted). In the 5–10 year period the sex ratio becomes almost equal, 99.9 males to 100 females. At age 85 in England, there are only 55.2 males to 100 females in the population. The sex ratios of human beings in the total human population in the United States has been calculated from 1940 census figures to be 101.1:100. This is the lowest excess of males in the history of the country and represents a continuous decline from a high in 1910 of 106 males to 100 females. Two factors are thought to have contributed to this change. One is the great decline of foreign immigration which had been predominantly male. The other is the aging of the population, which allows a longer period for the operation of sexual differences in mortality favoring females.

Sex Abnormalities and Theories of Sex Determination

Deviations from the normal male and female types of animals have long been of popular interest. This interest has been especially keen when sex deviations were observed among the higher domestic animals or human beings. The degree of deviation in such animals varies greatly. Some are only slightly subnormal while others are sex intermediates which show features of both sexes and are neither truly male nor truly female. Among abnormal or intermediate sexual types there are: *sex reversals, anatomical abnormalities, hermaphrodites, gynandromorphs,* and *intersexes.* Intermediate sexual types may owe their origin to one or several of the following causes: (1) an unbalance of the purely genetic factors, (2) pathological conditions, (3) physiological factors, (4) anatomical abnormalities, and (5) environmental factors. The biological importance of intermediate sexual types lies in the information about the nature of normal sex types which they may yield and the nature of sex determination that has been obtained from their study.

ABNORMAL SEXUAL TYPES

SEX REVERSALS. Sex may be partially or completely reversed during the life span of an organism. In some species of lower animals, it is apparently normal for individuals to change their sex. In these cases the factors which influence the change in sex may be *environmental* or may accompany *aging* of the individual. Sex reversals have been found in some lower forms of animal life such as certain isopods, which are parasitic on fishes. There is also evidence of sex reversal in amphibians such as frogs in which it has occurred in nature and has also been experimentally induced. Since sex reversal in the higher forms of animal life is rare, it is regarded as abnormal. Though the occurrence of crowing hens has been observed and partial sex reversals have been noted in fowls, seldom if ever has the reversal been complete from one sex to the opposite.

Most instances of partial sex reversals in fowls are caused by *diseased conditions of the ovaries* of the female. After tumors and tuberculous conditions have destroyed the active tissues of the ovaries, tissues resembling those found in the testes begin to develop male hormones, and the animal may show at least partial sex reversal. In fowls and higher animals, the reversal is generally from female to male. In human beings occasional occurrence of partial sex reversal, incorrectly called hermaphroditism, has frequently been attributed to a diseased condition of the ovaries of a genetic female.

THE FREEMARTIN. A sex inversion called **freemartinism,** though reported as possibly occurring in other domestic animals, is best known in cattle. This condition may sometimes though not always appear in the female member of a pair of twins of opposite sex. Animal breeders have long been aware that the heifer twin to a bull calf is frequently sterile. The heifer is called a *freemartin*. The scientific explanation of freemartinism is that the fetal membranes of the opposite-sexed twins become fused in such a manner that there is a common circulation of blood of the two embryos. It is thought that the male hormones have an inhibiting influence on the developing female sex glands and, in addition, promote the partial development of male secondary sexual characteristics. The resulting female, or freemartin, is a type of sterile intersex with some male traits.

Experimentally induced freemartinism has been demonstrated in amphibians, such as frogs. Embryos of these amphibians were grafted together in such a manner that there was a cross circulation of blood or *parabiosis*. In some instances reversal of the sex and formation of types of intersexes resulted from these operations.

ANATOMICAL ABNORMALITIES. *Cryptorchidism.* Frequent in the males of mammals is the abnormal retention of the testes in the abdominal cavity. This condition *is not of an intersexual nature*. Normally in mammals, the testes start development within the abdominal cavity and descend into the scrotum during the embryonic period. Because of some abnormality, the testes may fail to make the descent into the scrotum and are retained within the abdominal cavity. Males of this type are scientifically termed **cryptorchids**. They are known as ridglings by animal breeders. The term *cryptorchid* is derived from the Greek words *kryptos*-hidden and *orchis*-testicle, hence literally *hidden testicle*.

Individuals with both testes retained are completely sterile and produce nonfunctional spermatozoa. Their secondary sexual characters and reactions, however, are completely male, because the male hormones are produced by cryptorchids regardless of the position of the sex glands. Individuals with one normally descended testis may produce functional spermatozoa and be fertile. Investigations have shown that the failure of the retained testis to produce functional sperms may be associated with the higher temperature within the abdominal cavity, which renders the gametes nonfunctional.

OTHER ABNORMALITIES IN SEX ORGANS. Considerable newspaper publicity is often given to surgical operations performed on certain intermediate individuals who purport to have changed their sex, established their masculinity or feminity as the case may be. According to these accounts, the individuals were males genetically but on account of certain malformations had been regarded as females or possibly as some type of sex intermediate.

HERMAPHRODITISM.   In the higher animals **hermaphroditism** is known in many of the domestic animals and occurs occasionally in man. The term comes from *Hermaphroditus*, the fabled son of Hermes and Aphrodite, combining both sexes in one body. In some strains of animals, there is apparently an hereditary basis for the development of this type of sex deviation. Though in swine one hermaphrodite might be expected among 100,000 taken at random, Baker found 11 per cent of hermaphroditism in a herd where the trait was apparently transmitted by the male parent.

The term *hermaphrodite* or, in the vernacular of animal breeders, *'maphrodite* incorrectly applied to numerous sex deviations in higher animals, should be restricted to organisms which develop the primary and secondary organs of both the male and female sexes. There is considerable range in the degree and type of abnormalities found. Although many hermaphrodites have sex organs more or less resembling both ovaries and testes, the organs are generally imperfect, and extremely few hermaphrodites produce both eggs and sperms. In fact, in many cases the individuals are completely sterile and produce no functional gametes. The evidence in most of the critically investigated cases indicated that usually hermaphrodites are genetically females in which development of the female sex organs has been interrupted and the development of male characteristics initiated but not completed. In some instances the so-called hermaphrodite has male sex organs, testes, and no female sex glands but shows a number of female secondary sex characters.

Anatomically hermaphrodites may have an ovary on one side and a testis on the other (Fig. 174) and sometimes a combination of ovary and testis, the *ovotestis*, which may occur on one or both sides. Usually neither of the

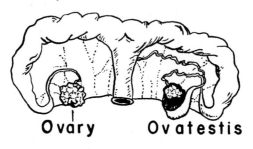

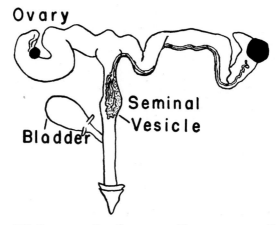

FIG. 174. INTERNAL SEX ORGANS OF HERMAPHRODITE PIG.
In each case there is an ovary on one side and a testis or an ovatestis, on the other side. (Upper drawing courtesy, Witschi, modified after Crew; the lower, Witschi, modified after Gould, from *Sex and Internal Secretions*, Edgar Allen, ed., Baltimore, The Williams & Wilkins Company, 1932.)

sex glands produces functional gametes, but both may secrete sex hormones that influence the development of secondary sexual characteristics. Occasionally the ovary produces eggs, but the production of sperms is very rare.

In 1942 Asdell summarized the literature on hermaphroditism with special reference to the influence of hormones on the development of the accessory reproductive tract in mammalian hermaphrodites. He found descriptions of 73 cases of hermaphroditism, 9 in rodents, 1 in the Insectivora, 1 in the domestic cat, 4 in domestic cattle, 1 in Indian cattle, 6 in goats, and 51 in swine. In addition, cases were cited in the primates, including man, for which no numbers were given. Asdell concluded that hormones from the ovaries, ovotestes, and testes exert a considerable influence on the development of the accessory reproductive structures of mammalian hermaphrodites.

HERMAPHRODITISM IN HUMAN BEINGS. Few biological topics have excited so much popular curiosity as that of occasional or supposed hermaphroditism in man. Many cases called hermaphroditism have been types of sex reversals or other abnormalities. Medical literature differentiates between intersexes, sex reversals, and *pseudohermaphroditism*. True hermaphrodites are rare in human beings, with possibly not more than 20 cases in the medical records. It is extremely unlikely that any human hermaphrodite could possibly function bisexually in reproduction.

GYNANDROMORPHS. *Gynandromorph* and *gynander* are names given to a type of sex deviation in which the body of the organism is composed of *distinct* male and female parts. The terms come from combinations of the Greek words *gyne*, meaning woman, and *aner*, meaning man, with *morphe* meaning form. Sometimes one-half of the body, either the left or right side, shows distinctly female secondary sexual characteristics, while the opposite side shows distinctly male characters. Sex intermediates of this type are called *bilateral* gynandromorphs. Gynandromorphs have been found in a number of insects, Drosophila, the silkworm, bees, and some wasps. Because normal female Drosophila are slightly larger than males, the larger size of the female portion of the body of bilateral gynandromorphs gives them a characteristic crooked shape (Fig. 175). Though some gynandromorphs have both male and female primary sex organs, generally they do not. In many gynandromorphs the portion showing the sex deviation is less than one-half. It may be only one-fourth, one-eighth, or even a smaller part of the body as in the *sex piebalds* in which females have spots of male tissue scattered over the body. There are instances in which only a few cells of the body show the sex deviation. The gynandromorph type of sex deviation has been termed a *sex mosaic* or a *sex composite*, because the body of the organism is composed of pieces of tissue which are of different sexes, analogous to a table top composed of different kinds of wood.

True identifiable gynandromorphs are largely confined to insects, although a few more or less doubtful cases have been reported in birds. Perhaps the term *gynandromorph* should be confined to organisms in which the secondary sexual characters are not under the influence of the sex hormones secreted by the primary sex glands. When, as in the higher animals, secondary sexual characters are greatly influenced by sex hormones, those characters will respond to the hormone from the sex glands, and a selected portion of the body cannot be isolated from their influence. The secondary sexual characters would then be difficult to change from female to male, and the animal would not show the features of a gynandromorph. A cytological gynandromorph might occur in a mammal, but it would be difficult to identify.

In insects, the secondary sexual characters are influenced by sex hormones only slightly or not at all. The tissue, therefore, responds to the sex chromosomes present, and insects may be gynandromorphs if the tissues in question have the proper sex chromosomes to develop two sex types in one

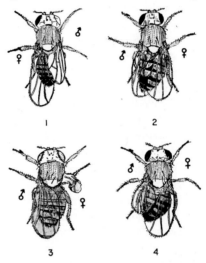

Gynandromorphs

FIG. 175. GYNANDROMORPHS OF DROSOPHILA.

Note the differences in wing lengths, wing structure, and eye color on the two sides of the individual flies. Since their linkage relations are known, these characteristics serve as markers. Besides the markers the sex combs and abdominal markings also indicate the sex of the parts of the bodies. The markers, white eye and short wing, sex-linked characters, indicate a difference in the chromosome complement in the two halves of the body. Male flies are slightly smaller than females. Thus flies half male and half female are crooked or bent to one side.

Sex combs on the two gynandromorphs below indicate that the left side is male and the right side female. Wing characters as markers indicate different genotypes on right and left sides. (Modified after Morgan by permission of Carnegie Institution of Washington.)

body. With an extended knowledge of the action of the genes in the Drosophila, it has been possible by genetic analysis to determine with certainty the presence or absence of any specific chromosome in a tissue which showed deviation from the normal. In heterozygous flies it was therefore possible to determine by the action of these genes if there were two **X** chromosomes or only one **X** chromosome present in any given tissue.

THE ORIGIN OF GYNANDROMORPHS. Gynandromorphs are thought to originate after the elimination of an **X** chromosome from one of the somatic cells at an early stage in the development of an **XX** zygote. Gynandromorphs have been found in which one portion, the female, had **XXX** and the other portion had only **X** and was entirely male. Found more frequently were only two **X** chromosomes in the female portion and a single **X** in the male portion, which indicated that one of the **X** chromosomes had been entirely lost or eliminated in an early cleavage division. Elimination of an **X** chromosome at a division other than the first would give rise to **X** tissue in a portion of the body less than one-half. A second method of the origin of gynandromorphs is by the presence in rare cases of two nuclei in an egg cell. If two nuclei, each containing an **X** chromosome, were fertilized, one by a sperm with an **X** chromosome and another by a sperm with a **Y** chromosome, a zygote with two nuclei would be formed, one **XX** and the other **XY**; such a zygote would develop into female and male portions of the embryo, producing a gynandromorph. This is regarded as a possible but unusual method of origin of gynandromorphs in the Drosophila.

SOMATIC MOSAICS. Occasionally an autosome may be eliminated from the developing embryo. When this happens, a part of the fly, one-half, one-fourth, or a smaller portion, will lack an autosome and its contained genes. If appropriate marker genes are carried in the autosomes, tissues deficient for this chromosome may be identified from their phenotypic characteristics. These organisms, called somatic mosaics, are not gynandromorphs because no sex characters or secondary sexual traits are involved, but the mixture of tissues is developed in a manner similar to that in the sex mosaics. The sex mosaics are possibly more easily recognized and probably occur more frequently than somatic mosaics.

INTERSEXES AND THE BALANCE THEORY OF SEX DETERMINATION IN DROSOPHILA

An extremely interesting group of sex deviations found in the progenies of a triploid female Drosophila was reported by Bridges. Mating a triploid female, **XXX** + 3 sets of autosomes, to a normal diploid male, **XY** + 2 sets of autosomes, yielded variable progenies including **intersex types** and **sex deviates** called *supermales* and *superfemales*. The eggs of the triploid female were assumed to have had unusual chromosomal constitutions, **X** + 1 set of autosomes, **X** + 2 sets of autosomes, **XX** + 1 set of autosomes, and **XX** + 2 sets of autosomes. Random fertilization of the four types of eggs by normal sperms resulted in normal sexual types and the sex deviates observed.

The genic balance theory of sex determination is an attempt to account for the development of sex in Drosophila on the basis of the action of many genes scattered through all the chromosomes. The principle interaction, however, is supposed to be between the predominately female-producing genes carried by the **X** chromosome and the predominately male-producing genes carried in autosomes, with the **Y** chromosome an inert or blank homologue of the **X**.

Table XLVII

PROGENIES OF TRIPLOID FEMALE DROSOPHILA

Parents   Normal Diploid Male × Triploid Female 3N
                   XXX + 3 sets of autosomes

XY + 2 sets of autosomes

During maturation 2 types of normal viable sperms are produced

During maturation 4 types of viable eggs are produced

	1N egg normal type X + 1 set of autosomes	2N egg unusual type XX + 2 sets of autosomes	Egg unusual type X + 2 sets of autosomes	Egg unusual type XX + 1 set of autosomes
1N sperm normal X + 1 set of autosomes	XX + 2 sets of autosomes Normal diploid female Fertile	XXX + 3 sets of autosomes Triploid female Partially fertile	XX + 3 sets of autosomes Intersex Infertile	XXX + 2 sets of autosomes Superfemale Infertile
1N sperm normal Y + 1 set of autosomes	XY + 2 sets of autosomes Normal diploid male Fertile	XXY + 3 sets of autosomes Intersex Infertile	XY + 3 sets of autosomes Supermale Infertile	XXY + 2 sets of autosomes Female with extra Y Partially fertile

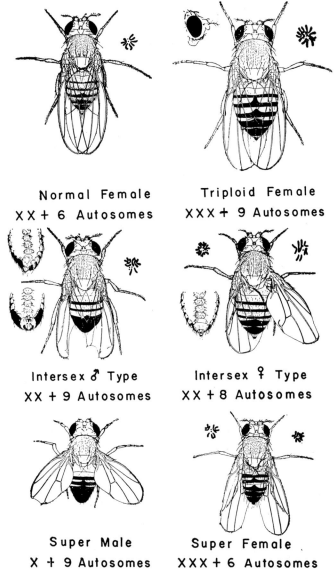

FIG. 176. SEX TYPES AND CORRESPONDING CHROMOSOME TYPES IN DROSOPHILA.
Presence or absence of the Y chromosome has little influence. With the autosomes tipping the balance toward intersexuality, the presence or absence of the small extra IV chromosome is just sufficient to determine the male or female type of intersex, respectively. Supersexes as well as all intersexes are sterile. Diploids, triploids, and tetraploids show varying degrees of fertility. (Modified after C. B. Bridges.)

The normal diploid female in *Drosophila* has a complement of 8 chromosomes, which may be written as **XX** + 2 sets or 6 autosomes. The female-producing genes in the 2 **X** chromosomes overbalance the male-producing genes in the 2 sets of autosomes, and the net result of the genic balance is the production of a normal female fly. When there is only 1 **X** chromosome as in a zygote with **XY** + 2 sets or 6 autosomes, the female-producing genes in **X** are insufficient to overbalance the action of the male-producing genes in 2 sets of autosomes, and the net result of the genic balance is a normal male fly. Females are produced in all cases in which the proportion is in multiples of **X** to 1 set of autosomes as in the normal female with **XX** + 2 sets of autosomes; in the triploid female, **XXX** + 3 sets of autosomes; and in the tetraploid female, **XXXX** + 4 sets of autosomes. The same proportion exists in the haploid mosaics in which a part of the body is composed of cells with only the haploid number of chromosomes, that is, **X** + 1 set of autosomes. These regions are female.

Characteristics of the intersexes and other sex deviations are apparently determined by a disturbance of the equilibrium between the action of the

Table XLVIII

SEX TYPES IN DROSOPHILA

		Intersexes			
Superfemale	Females	Female types	Male type	Male	Supermale
XXX + 2 sets of autosomes 300/200	**X** + 1 set of autosomes haploid mosaic 100/100 **2X** + 2 sets of autosomes normal diploid 200/200 **3X** + 3 sets of autosomes triploid 300/300 **4X** + 4 sets of autosomes tetraploid 400/400	**XX** + 3 sets of autosomes **XXY** + 3 sets of autosomes 200/300	**XX** + 3 sets of autosomes (IV chromosone) 200/300	**XY** + 2 sets of autosomes normal diploid 100/200	**XY** + 3 sets of autosomes 100/300
Index = 1.5	Index = 1.0	Index = 0.67	Index = 0.67	Index = 0.50	Index = 0.33

predominately female-producing genes in the **X** chromosome and the predominately male-producing factors in the autosomes as in the intersexes with **XX** + 3 sets of autosomes.

Superfemales developed from zygotes with chromosome complements of **XXX** + 2 sets of autosomes, or an extra **X** with its female-producing genes in addition to the normal number. *Supermales*, on the other hand, were developed from zygotes with chromosome complements of **X** + 3 sets of autosomes, having thus one extra set of autosomes with their male-producing genes. Both kinds of supersexes proved to be sterile (Fig. 176).

To arrive at a numerical sex index for the normal sexes and all the sex deviations in *Drosophila*, arbitrary values of 100 each were assigned to the female-determining genes in the **X** chromosome and the male-determining genes in each set of autosomes. Thus, **X** + 1 set of autosomes, equalling 100:100 or 100/100, established an index of 1. All normal females in *Drosophila* have an even balance of **X** chromosomes to autosomes. Thus, the sex ratio of a normal diploid female 200:200 or 200/200 = 1. Likewise, the triploid female with **XXX** + 3 sets of autosomes and the tetraploid with **XXXX** + 4 sets of autosomes have, respectively, a ratio of 300/300 = 1 and 400/400 = 1. Bridges then calculated the sex index for all the sexual forms from the superfemale, **XXX** + 2 sets of autosomes, 300/200 = 1.5 to the supermale, **X** + 3 sets of autosomes, 100/300 = 0.33; the intersexes with **XX** + 3 sets of autosomes have a ratio of 200/300 = 0.67, and a normal male has **X** + **Y** + 2 sets of autosomes = 0.50 (Table XLVIII).

chapter 24

Sex Determination in Plants

As contrasted with animals, the problem of sexuality and of the determination of sex in plants is complicated by the presence in the life cycle of a
haploid phase of much longer duration. The haploid or gamete-producing
phase, the *gametophyte*, includes a spore, a thallus, and finally the production
of gametes, followed by their union at fertilization, eventual meiosis, and
the production of meiospores. In the life cycle the two processes of fertilization and meiosis keep the chromosome numbers in equilibrium and are
therefore both essential.

Among seed plants in both the gymnosperms or cone-bearing plants and
the angiosperms or flowering plants, distinct male and female tendencies
may be found. Although the sporophyte or diploid phase, which is recognized
as the "plant" in the gymnosperms and the angiosperms, produces only
spores and never gametes, as animals do in the corresponding diploid phase,
the term *male* has come to be associated with the stamens and the anthers
in the flowers of these plants. The anthers produce the microspores that
develop into pollen grains and pollen tubes with sperms or male gametes.
The terms *male flower* and *male plant* have been applied to flowers and plants
producing only stamens since they give rise to the male elements in reproduction. Similarly, because they give rise to the female elements in reproduction, the terms *female flower* and *female plant* may be used to designate
flowers and plants that produce only pistils. The connection here is through
the ovules in the ovaries of the pistils. Megaspores are produced in the ovules
with female gametophytes or embryo sacs, structures containing the eggs
developed from megaspores. Flowers which have only stamens or only pistils
are called imperfect flowers, that is, they are sexually imperfect.

Gradations of sexuality occur in the numerous families and genera of
flowering plants. Among the angiosperms, the willow, poplar, spinach,
cultivated hemp, and others are regularly *monosexual* or *dioecious*, producing
separate male and female plants, usually with only minor degrees of differentiation between the sexes. Certain minor differences, however, occur in
some plants. The female plants of hemp, hop, and willow begin blooming

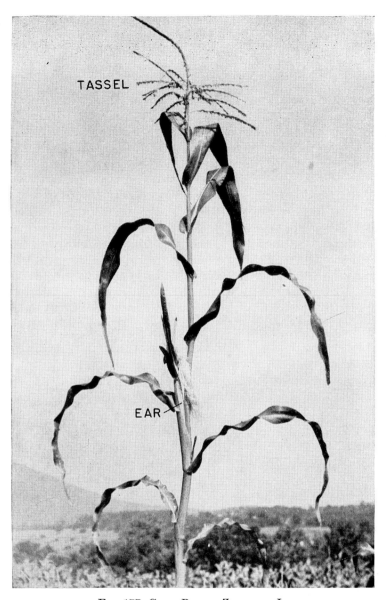

FIG. 177. CORN PLANT, ZEA MAYS L.

The plant is in full bloom; the anthers in the tassel or male inflorescence are shedding pollen. The stigmas or silks on the ear or female inflorescence are receptive to the pollen at this stage. The normal corn plant is an excellent example of the monoecious condition, that is, male and female flowers in different parts of the same plant. (Courtesy, Dr. H. W. Thurston, Jr.)

before the male plants. Differences between male and female plants, some of which appear even in the seedling stages of hemp and others, include those of size of plant, length of internode, and intensity of green color. Although there are distinct male and female plants among the angiosperms, the *bisexual* or *monoecious* condition in which both stamens and pistils occur on the same plant is most usual. In fact, many of the angiosperms bear perfect flowers which contain both stamens and pistils. While the conifers, such as the pine, among the higher gymnosperms are regularly bisexual or monoecious, many of the lower gymnosperms such as the ginkgo tree and the cycads are typically monosexual plants and therefore dioecious.

Terminology

The terms *homothallism* and *heterothallism* may be more appropriately applied to the haploid phase of the lower plants than the terms *bisexual* and *monosexual* or their equivalents. A plant which produces both male and female gametes has only one type of thallus and is, therefore, *homothallic*. Species in which the plants are distinctly male or female, producing two types of thalli, are said to be *heterothallic*.

Hall* has suggested the following use of terms applied to the several conditions of sex:

A. Among sexual organisms there may be individuals which show characteristics of both sexes.

1. *The hermaphrodite* is an organism, either an animal or gametophytic plant, in which both eggs and sperms are normally produced. Examples are the earthworm, some flat worms, and the gametophytes of some mosses and ferns. This stresses the normal hermaphroditism in many of the lower organisms.

2. Certain sex abnormalities and sex deviations previously discussed are included in the outline at this point (pp. 434–443).

B. In the spore-bearing generation of the higher plants, in which two kinds of spores are produced, the terms *monoclinous* and *diclinous* may be used.

1. The term *monoclinous*, coming from the Greek words *mono* and *kline*, meaning one and bed, respectively, may be applied to those plants in which both *microspores* and *megaspores* are produced in the same structure, that is, in perfect flowers. Examples of these are the lily, the rose, and the pea. The terms *hermaphroditism*, *hermaphrodites*, and *hermaphroditic flowers* when applied to perfect flowers are incorrectly used. They should be reserved for the gamete-producing structures.

2. The term *diclinous*, from the Greek words *di* and *kline*, meaning in two beds, may be applied to those plants which bear the two types

---

* Professor Henry F. Hall of Sir George Williams College, Montreal, Canada.

of spores (*micro-* and *megaspores*) in different structures. That is, the staminate (male flowers or cones) and the pistillate (female flowers or cones) structures are borne separately in imperfect flowers. Diclinous plants may be further classified into two groups, *monoecious* and *dioecious*.

a. *Monoecious* plants produce the *two types of imperfect flowers*, staminate and pistillate *on different parts of the same plant*. A common example of this type is the Indian Corn, *Zea mays* (Fig. 177), which produces a group of staminate flowers, the tassel, at its apex and a group of pistillate flowers on one or more side branches. The common squash, pumpkin, watermelon, and other cucurbits are additional familiar examples of monoecious plants.

b. *Dioecious* plants produce the *imperfect staminate* or male flowers and the *imperfect pistillate* or female flowers *on different plants*, the so-called male and female plants, respectively. Many well-known trees such as the poplar, the willow, and the ginkgo are examples of dioecious plants. In some cases the distinction between the male and female plants in these dioecious forms is definitely associated with the mechanism of the **XX-XY** chromosome. This has been demonstrated in the cultivated asparagus, hemp or *Cannabis*, *Lychnis* or *Melandrium*, and in the water weed, *Elodea*. Some palms also are dioecious.

Mechanisms for Sex Determination in Plants

A chromosome basis for sex determination in plants was first discovered in 1917 by Allen in the dioecious liverwort, *Sphaerocarpus donnellii*, in which the sporophyte has 7 pairs of autosomes, a large **X** chromosome, and a much smaller **Y** chromosome, making a total of 16 chromosomes. During meiosis, the chromosome number is reduced to either **X** + 7 autosomes, determining a female gametophyte, or **Y** + 7 autosomes, determining a male gametophyte. Similar sex-determining chromosome mechanisms have been found in other species of *Sphaerocarpus*, in *Pallavicinia*, *Riccardia*, *Pellia*, *Marchantia*, and in some species of mosses. Large **X** chromosomes in the female gametophytes and smaller **Y** chromosomes in the male gametophytes have been found in the common moss, *Polytrichum*, and in other mosses. In 1945 Allen, in a summary of the investigations of sex determination, stated that a sex-determining chromosome mechanism consisting of an **X** and a **Y** has been found in about 40–45 of the dioecious species of bryophytes. In about an equal number of species, investigation revealed no recognizable sex chromosomes.

THE **XX-XY** TYPE OF SEX DETERMINATION. In 1923 Santos first definitely recognized an unequal pair of chromosomes, the **X-Y** or sex chromosomes, in male plants of one of the species of flowering plants, the water weed or ditch moss, *Elodea gigantea*. Further recognition of sex chromosomes was reported in some of the species of *Rumex* or dock, *Lychnis* (*Melandrium*) or campion (Fig. 178), *Salix* or willow, *Populus* or poplar, and *Humulus* or hop. During succeeding years the **XX-XY** type of sex-determining mechanism has been found in plants of several other genera.

In the common cultivated hemp, *Cannabis sativa*, there are distinct male and female plants, each characterized by 20 chromosomes as the 2N or diploid number (Fig. 179–181). In 1939 Mackay reported that the cells of the female plants *in addition* to the complement of 9 pairs of autosomes contain a pair of **X** chromosomes and those of the male plants an **X** and a smaller **Y** chromosome (Fig. 182). The female plants, **XX** + 18 autosomes,

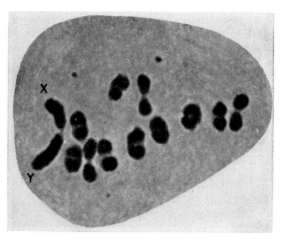

FIG. 178. THE FIRST MEIOTIC DIVISION AT METAPHASE OF A DIPLOID MALE PLANT
OF MELANDRIUM.
There are 11 pairs of autosomes with an unequal pair of sex chromosomes at left. Although there has been some difference of opinion as to the relative size of the **X** and **Y** chromosomes, this illustration shows that the **Y** is the larger. (Courtesy, Warmke and Blakeslee, Carnegie Institution of Washington.)

produce a single type of megaspore with **X** + 9 autosomes. The male plants, **X** + **Y** + 18 autosomes, however, produce two types of microspores, one of which has **X** + 9 autosomes and the other **Y** + 9 autosomes. Gametophytes and eventually gametes are produced from these mega- and microspores. The random union of the two types of sperms with the single type of egg cells would determine the development of diploid male and female plants in the theoretical ratio of 1:1, but sometimes the theoretical sex ratio may not be realized.

In 1940 Allen summarized the data on sex determination in 117 species of flowering plants. Of these, **X** and **Y** chromosomes have been demonstrated in 55 species. In 16 additional species, some definite chromosome mechanism other than the **X-Y** basis has been demonstrated. For 46 species in

25 families, no sex-determining chromosome mechanism had then been recognized.

Among the deviations from the **XX-XY** type of sex determination in plants, the following have been described:

1. *Chromosome Complexes.* In species of *Rumex* or dock and of *Humulus* or hop, the homologue of the **X** chromosome is a chromosome complex con-

FIG. 179. MALE AND FEMALE PLANTS OF THE HEMP, CANNABIS SATIVA.
The male plant, shown at the left, is slenderer and matures earlier than the female plant. The male plants at maturity are light yellowish green in color. The female plant shown at the right is more robust and denser than the male plants. Female plants at maturity are dark green in color.

sisting of 2 **Y** chromosomes which act together in pairing with the **X**. During meiosis, the **Y**-*complex*, acting as a unit, separates from the **X**, and both **Y** chromosomes go to the same pole of the division spindle.

2. *The* **XX-XO** *Type.* This method of sex determination, found in some of the insects, has also been reported in one of the species of yams. The female plants presumably have 36 chromosomes including **XX**. The

male plants have only 35 which include an **X** but no **Y** chromosome or other homologue of **X**.

3. *An Unpaired Y Chromosome.* An extra unpaired chromosome, presumably a **Y**, has been described in two species of mistletoe. In these plants the female has 20 chromosomes and the male 21, including the single unpaired **Y**. If correctly interpreted, this is a unique condition for any organism.

Fig. 180. Branches from Plants of Hemp in Full Flower.
Left, male; right, female.

Location of Sex Determiners in the X and Y chromosomes

The occurrence of *structural aberrations* in the sex chromosomes has made possible a new approach to the solution of the problem of sex determination. This technique revealed the roles of the different parts of the **X** and **Y** chromosomes in sex determination. Warmke and also Westergaard, working independently, partially analyzed the nature and location of the sex-determining genes of *Melandrium*, which has the **XX-XY** sex-determining mechanism. Plants with aberrant **Y** chromosomes which had suffered

Staminate Flowers

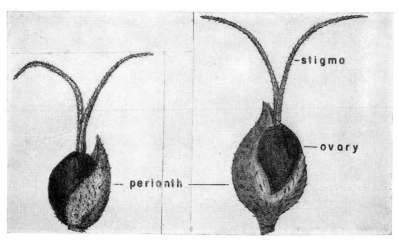

Pistillate Flowers

FIG. 181. MALE AND FEMALE FLOWERS OF DIOECIOUS HEMP, CANNABIS SATIVA.
Above, two male or staminate flowers. These flowers consist of a stalk and receptacle bearing delicate light-green perianth parts and six pendant anthers. Below, two female or pistillate flowers. The female flowers consist of a stalk and receptacle bearing thin light-green perianth parts and a pistil. The perianth parts envelop the dark-green ovary. The two-parted stigma protrudes from the bracts. Male and female flowers are normally produced on separate plants.

FIG. 182. CHROMOSOMES OF HEMP PLANT, CANNABIS SATIVA.
Left, a polar view of first meiotic metaphase showing 10 pairs of chromosomes. Right, showing members of each of the 10 pairs separating. The sex chromosomes X and Y are of unequal size. This chromosome group is from a meiotic division in a male plant. (Courtesy, Elizabeth L. Mackay, from Am. J. Botany.)

deletions and were therefore *deficient* for certain blocks of genes were studied for effects on the development of sex. In another case a *translocation* had occurred between the **Y** and **X** chromosomes. The presence of the aberrant **Y** in the karyotype tended to make plants *intersexual* instead of definitely male and female.

A gene or block of genes in one arm of the **Y** chromosome may act as a "male promoter." Warmke's analysis indicates that this male promotion may be taken in two steps under the influence of *two separate factors, one* that initiates the development of stamens with their anthers and carries the development to meiosis, and the *second* that completes development in the anthers and leads to pollen production. Besides these male promoting factors the **Y** chromosome is thought to contain a *female suppressor* that inhibits the development of pistils in potentially perfect flowers. Westergaard considered the possibility that the **X** chromosome may contain a *male suppressor* and that *male promoters* may be carried in the autosomes. He further suggested an epistatic-hypostatic relationship among the various suppressors and promoters.

The use of structural aberrations in the study of sex determination opens up the possibility of an analysis of the sex chromosomes in many different kinds of organisms and the determination of the location of the principal genetic factors involved. This type of analysis also may be helpful in the proper interpretation of environmental influences in sex determination in plants.

Sexuality in the Gametophytes of Flowering Plants

Difference in the size of pollen grains, observed in some dioecious species of angiosperms, may be an expression of differences in the chromosome complements in the pollen grains, some of which have an **X** and some a **Y** chromosome. With the **X** and **Y** sex chromosome of different size, volumes of the pollen grains may be influenced by the relative chromatin masses. In *Rumex* and *Melandrium* the growth rate of the pollen tubes containing an **X** chromosome is greater than of those with the **Y**. The pollen tubes containing the **Y** are longer lived than those containing the **X** chromosome in *Melandrium*.

Notwithstanding these differences, generally pollen tubes or *male gametophytes* that are identical in structure and function are produced by microspores containing either an **X** or a **Y** chromosome. This fact indicates that the **X** and **Y** chromosomes in the flowering plants *do not function as the sex-determining mechanism for the gametophytes.* The pollen tubes may contain either an **X** chromosome or a **Y** chromosome, but they *are always male structures* and eventually produce the *male* gametes, the sperms. The embryo sac, or female gametophyte developing from the megaspore, containing an **X** chromosome *is always female* and produces the *female* gamete, the egg. These much reduced thalli arise from haploid spores, megaspores producing female gametophytic structures and microspores producing male gametophytic structures. The sex of the gametophytic structures appears in general to be determined when the mega- and microspores are produced or even earlier.

The sex of the gametophytes in angiosperms apparently is irreversibly determined with the preceding development of stamens and pistils by the sporophyte. The female line has the carpel, nucellus, megasporocyte, megaspore, female gametophyte, and finally the egg cell. The male line consists of stamen, anther, microsporocyte, microspore, male gametophyte, and finally the sperms. Sex expression may begin with the production of pistillate or staminate flowers. In other cases, as in cultivated corn, it begins even earlier with the development of the inflorescences. Normally the ear and the tassel are differentiated sexually. Jones says that there is a physiological gradient in maize from femaleness at the base of the plant toward maleness at the top. In the dioecious or monosexual angiosperms, the whole sporophytic plant is sexually differentiated during the development of the embryo.

Artificial Synthesis of Sexual Forms in Plants

In maize, genes have been identified that specifically influence the development of the flowers. Certain recessive genes designated as *tassel seed*-1, *tassel seed*-2, and *tassel seed*-4, or ts_1, ts_2, and ts_4 have similar phenotypic effects. In the homozygous state they all condition development of pistillate flowers on the tassels in place of the normal staminate ones. Hence the name, tassel seed. Maize plants which are homozygous for any of the tassel-seed genes, *ts-ts*, are essentially female.

Similarly, certain other mutant genes determine the development of maize plants which are essentially male. One of these genes is designated as *silkless*, *sk*. When the plants are homozygous, *sksk*, the ovaries abort. Jones found that hybridization between homozygous silkless, *sksk*, and tassel seed, *tsts*, produced F_1 plants which were heterozygous for both allelic pairs, *Sksk* and Ts_2ts_2. Because of the dominance of *Sk* and Ts_2, the F_1 plants were, therefore, normal monoecious plants, producing male flowers in the tassels and female flowers on the ears.

In the F_2 and later generations, recombinations of the silkless and tassel-seed genes resulted in the production of a dioecious strain of maize. The purely female plants of this strain were genetically homozygous for the two recessive genes *sksk* and ts_2ts_2. In these plants which were monogametic, the *ts* gene completely nullified the action of *sksk*. The purely male plants were genetically $skskTs_2ts_2$. That is, they were homozygous for the silkless gene, *sksk*, which conditioned the production of aborted ovaries. They were heterozygous for the tassel-seed gene, Ts_2ts_2, which in this state had no visible effect on the production of pollen. Because the male plants were heterozygous for one pair of the conditioning genes, Ts_2ts_2, they were heterogametic. That is, they produced two types of pollen and eventually two types of male gametes. These types were $skTs_2$ and $skts_2$. Emerson also obtained dioecious strains of maize involving other specific genes. These investigations with maize demonstrated the production of a *dioecious* strain of plants *from a normally monoecious strain* by the recombination of genes that act in fundamental expressions of sex. Genes influencing sex are thought to be common in plants. In corn at least nine of the ten pairs of chromosomes contain genes influencing the expression of sex.

Genetic and Environmental Factors in Sex Expression

Schaffner and other investigators attempted to show that the sex of plants is determined by physiological and ecological factors, with the sex chromosomes merely an indication of the sexual condition. Accordingly factors of nutrition and varying degrees of light intensity might influence the expression of sex in plants even to a complete reversal of sex. Bearing upon this topic are other suggestions that the several genotypes basic to sexuality in plants may have various phenotypic expressions. Sexuality, just as many other characters, is the resultant of both genetic and environmental factors. Frequently insufficient consideration has been given to the possibility that a factor complex consisting of many genes may be fundamental in sex determination in plants. There might also be multiple allelism in the sex factors. Multiple allelism as an explanation of strong and weak sexuality would accord genetically with similar situations in some insects.

The importance of structural aberrations in the sex chromosomes also deserves consideration when the possible effects of environmental factors in sex determination are studied. Some apparently environmental influences on sex determination might have been the result of structural changes in chromosomes which created a genetic unbalance. Environmental effects in the control of sex expression would be more striking in forms with a weak or critically unbalanced genotype for sex determination.

Questions and Problems

1. What is the normal sexual condition in the higher animals?
2. Where in the animal kingdom is hermaphroditism the normal condition?
3. What is the genetic basis for the development of sexual differences in animals?
4. Is sex determination genetically simple or complex? Discuss the chromosomes and genes involved.
5. List the three groups of factors which interact in the production of sexual characteristics.
6. Distinguish between sex determination and sex differentiation.
7. How do sex chromosomes and autosomes differ? In appearance? In their effects? What are some of the other names for sex chromosomes?
8. Explain the **XX-XY** chromosome basis of sex determination. How do unusual sex types in *Drosophila* originate?
9. What is the genetic basis of sex determination in man?
10. How does the **XX-XO** type of sex determination differ from the **XX-XY** type?
11. What is a **Y**-chromosome complex?
12. What sexual types are recognized in bees? What is the chromosomal basis for sex determination in bees?
13. How is a sex ratio obtained? Distinguish between the sex ratios obtained at various times in the life history of animals.
14. Why is the proportion of the sexes unequal? Explain some of the probable reasons for unequal numbers of males and females.
15. What are the secondary and tertiary sex ratios in human beings? What are possible causes of differences in these ratios?

16. What accounts for the change in sex ratio determined from the 1940 census data as compared with previous census data?
17. What is meant by sex reversal?
18. What is frequently the cause of sex reversal?
19. How is free martinism in cattle explained? Has there been any experimental demonstration of freemartinism?
20. Explain what is meant by hermaphroditism?
21. Describe the anatomical basis of cryptorchidism.
22. What is a gynandromorph?
23. Describe the characteristics of gynandromorphs which have been found in *Drosophila*.
24. How is the elimination of an **X** chromosome related to the origin of gynandromorphs in *Drosophila?* How also can gynandromorphs originate?
25. What is the chromosomal constitution of intersexes and supersexes in *Drosophila?* Account for the occurrence of these types.
26. How have supersexes been produced experimentally?
27. What is the genic balance theory of sex determination? Illustrate with data from *Drosophila* studies.
28. How was a numerical sex index worked out?
29. Name some other factors, genetic or environmental, besides those already discussed, which influence expression of sex in animals.
30. Are plants as sharply differentiated sexually as animals are?
31. To what plants are the terms *homothallism* and *heterothallism* applied?
32. Explain the use of the terms *monoclinous* and *diclinous* as applied to plants.
33. What are monoecious plants and dioecious plants as applied to flowering plants?
34. In what plant was a sex chromosome first discovered?
35. What is the sex-determining mechanism in lower plants such as the liverworts and mosses?
36. State the important facts concerning the discovery of **X** and **Y** chromosomes in the flowering plants.
37. Describe the chromosome situation in the common cultivated hemp plant, with special emphasis on the sex-determining mechanism.
38. What species of plants have a **Y**-chromosome complex?
39. Do the **X** and **Y** chromosomes influence sexuality in the gametophytes of the flowering plants?
40. If, as seems possible, the sex chromosomes are without influence on the gametophytic tissues of flowering plants, where and how are these structures differentiated sexually?
41. Cite some evidence to show that the genetic basis of sex in plants is complex.
42. Is there any possible relationship between the nature of the genetic basis for sex determination and the influence of the environment on sex expression in plants?
43. What types of sexual forms have been found in the progenies of polyploid animals?
44. Besides the fact of unbalance between the **X** chromosomes and the sex genes on the autosomes, has any abnormal cytological behavior been observed in polyploids? Describe.

References

ALLEN, C. E.: "The Genotypic Basis of Sex Expression in Angiosperms," *Botan. Rev.* **6**:227–300 (1940).

ALLEN, E.: *Sex and Internal Secretions*, 2nd ed. Baltimore, The Williams & Wilkins Company, 1939.

CREW, F. A. E.: *The Genetics of Sex in Animals*, Cambridge, England, Cambridge University Press, 1927.

JONES, D. F.: "Sex Intergrades in Dioecious Maize," *Am. J. Botany* **26**:412–415 (1939).

KNAPP, E.: "Heteroploidie bei *Sphaerocarpus*," *Ber. deut. Botan. Ges.* **54**:346–361 (1936).

MORGAN, T. H.: *Heredity and Sex*, New York, Columbia University Press, 1913.

———: *The Theory of the Gene* 2nd ed. New Haven, Yale University Press, 1928, Chapters XIV, XV, XVI, XVII, 199–291.

———, C. B. BRIDGES, and A. H. STURTEVANT: "The Genetics of *Drosophila*," *Bibliographia Genetica* **II**:1–262 (1925).

MURRAY, M. J.: "Colchicine Induced Tetraploids in Dioecious and Monoecious Species of the *Amaranthaceae*," *J. Heredity* **31**:477–485 (1940).

———: "The Genetics of Sex Determination in the Family *Amaranthaceae*," *Genetics* **25**:409–431 (1940).

WARMKE, H. E., and A. F. BLAKESLEE: "The Establishment of a 4n Dioecious Race in *Melandrium*," *Am. J. Botany* **27**:751–762 (1940).

WILSON, E. B.: *The Cell in Development and Heredity*, New York, The Macmillian Company, 1925 Chapter X, 742–825.

section 10

Twins and Human Heredity

Reoccurrence of family traits has led to general acceptance of heritability of some of the obvious physical characteristics of human beings. There is nevertheless a too general reluctance to believe that more *obscure* physical characteristics, and particularly those expressing themselves in *mental attributes,* are also determined by inheritance. Biologically considered, however, man is an animal with organs functioning as those of the lower animals. The hereditary background of man's characteristics, though often undetermined, must resemble the genetics of similar traits in other animals. Experimentation to determine inheritance of traits in man is obviously impractical. There are, however, other methods of studying human inheritance. *Analysis of family histories,* comparative studies of *identical* and *non-identical twins,* and *statistical techniques of population genetics* have all been used in gathering information about heritable traits in human beings. *A science of* **human genetics** *is developing.*

chapter 25

Twins and Multiple Births

Popular interest in human twins centers around the close resemblance of identical twins or the lack of it in nonidentical pairs. Story and drama make frequent use of the theme of twins whose similarity is confusing even to intimate associates. The subject of twinning and multiple births is not only of universal popular interest but is of scientific importance. Studies of twins have been undertaken for their contributions to the subject of heredity as well as for their immediate interest. In human beings the distinction between identical and fraternal twins, based on their origin, makes possible a comparison of the relative importance of heredity and environment in the development of individuals. Identical twins reared apart have been especially good subjects in these studies.

Lower animals generally produce large numbers of young. Insects, spiders, fish, Amphibia, reptiles, and birds vary in the number of offspring they produce, but in general they have larger numbers than mammals. As the complexity of organisms increases, there appears to be a corresponding increase in the care given to the young and along with this a decrease in the number of young produced. Among mammals rodents generally have large litters, and cats and dogs likewise may produce as many as 8 or 12 young at one time. An English setter in Saint John, New Brunswick, was credited with producing and nursing 16 pups.

Farm animals, with the exception of swine, usually produce small numbers of offspring. In swine, which commonly produce a number of young, twins which were presumably identical have been observed along with other young in a single litter. Cattle, swine, and dogs are known to exhibit the phenomenon of *superfetation* or the production of *two or more* young at one time by *two sires*. This may be used as a control in studies of heredity of several breeds. A Guernsey cow, for instance, produced twin calves which were not full sisters (Fig. 183). The sires were an Angus and a Hereford. If breeds differing in color and other prominent characteristics are being studied, the young of two different sires in a single litter can serve as valuable material in the study of inheritance under presumably similar prenatal physiological conditions.

TWINS AND MULTIPLE BIRTHS IN FARM ANIMALS. In sheep and goats *twinning* is not unusual, and it may occur with about equal frequency in both types of animals. Some strains of sheep have been established in which twin births may occur more frequently than single births. In ordinary strains fewer than one-fifth of all births are twin births. The economic advantages in increased meat and wool production of the frequently twinning races are readily apparent. Their per-

FIG. 183. GUERNSEY COW AND HER HALF-SISTER TWIN CALVES.
The cow had been bred to both an Angus and a Hereford bull. One of the calves, right, has the typical Hereford markings, though the amount of white is a little less than average. The other calf, left, shows the Angus characteristics. The sire of each calf thus could be identified in this rare case. (Courtesy, E. L. Vieth, from *J. Heredity*.)

petuation is dependent, however, on sufficient milk production by the ewes for nourishment of both lambs. Twinning in sheep was studied from the anatomical viewpoint by Henning who found evidence of occasional monovular origin of two fetuses.

Sheep and goats are known to produce *multiple* births as well as twins. Wilson and Gregory reported the birth of sextuple lambs (Fig. 184), of which five survived for several weeks (at least to the time of the writing of the report). In a herd of dairy goats in Pennsylvania, one doe was reported as having given birth to a set of *triplets* in each of three consecutive years. This was followed by sets of *quintuplets* in 1937 and in 1938 (Fig. 185). Roscoe F. Patt, the herd owner, observed this unusual fertility with great interest but reported in 1941 that the fecundity of the herd had not risen noticeably above that of the breed. Multiplets in goats have also been reported from California. The *Journal of Heredity*, October 1946, had an account of fraternal quintuple calves born on a farm near Fairbury, Nebraska. This set consisted of four males and a modified female with intersex or freemartin characteristics. The calves differed in color, color markings, hair-whorl patterns, weight at birth, and rates of growth, indicating their fraternal rather than identical nature.

FIG. 184. A LITTER OF SIX LIVING LAMBS WHICH IS REGARDED AS HIGHLY EXCEP-
TIONAL.
(Courtesy, J. F. Wilson and D. W. Gregory, from *J. Heredity*.)

In larger domestic animals *twinning occurs less frequently* than in the cases above, as may be noted from the following comparisons based on data from the United States Department of Agriculture:

Dairy Cattle	98%	are single births
	2%	twins and multiple births, but mostly twins
		1 in 100 are triplets
		1 in 14,000 quadruplets
Beef Cattle	95.5%	are single births
Goats	19.4%	are single births
	61%	are twins
	22%	are triplets
	0.6%	are quadruplets
Horses	98.5%	are single births

FIG. 185. QUINTUPLETS AMONG GOATS.
(Courtesy, W. N. Patt, 2nd, from *The Reading Eagle*.)

Twins in Human Beings

Probably the rarity of the occurrence of twins in human beings accounts for the interest their appearance universally excites. Available statistics reveal that twins occur in the human population of the United States about once in 88 births. Also in the United States, twinning is found to occur most frequently in an area in the South and in the northern plains regions and is more frequent among Negroes than among whites. Twinning among the

Japanese and other Asiatics generally is rare. Among Japanese, twin births occur about once in 301 births compared with once in 87.3 births for the white race in the United States and once in 82–85 births for Germany, Italy, and Scotland. It has been found that the frequency of surviving twins in the adult population is about 80 per cent of the frequency among the newborn, indicating higher mortality among twins than in the general population.

FIG. 186. FRATERNAL TWINS.
(Courtesy, Pearl and Ruby Lee.)

THE NATURE AND ORIGIN OF TWINS. The terms *identical* and *fraternal* are used to distinguish between twin pairs or members of multiple birth groups which are very similar and those which are no more alike than any other brothers and sisters (Fig. 186). Members of twin pairs may or may not be identical, and among multiple births some or all of the individuals may be either identical or not identical. From a record of 279,237 sets of twins, about 93,827, or slightly over 33 per cent, were reported by Hamlett as identical. Distinction between identical twins and ordinary or fraternal twins is based on degree of resemblance and their origin.

Identical twins are considered to be monozygotic, that is, they have originated from a single ovum or egg fertilized by a single sperm. Subsequent division of this fertilized egg forms two identical embryos. Identical twins, therefore, have identical genotypes, and because of the chromosomal differentiation between the sexes in human beings, it is assumed that identical twins must be of the same sex. Fraternal twins are dizygotic, that is, they are the product of two distinct ova or eggs which have been separately fertilized by different sperms. Fraternal twins each have a distinct inheritance. Their genotypes are different. In fact, a pair of fraternal twins might actually have two fathers. This possibility was recently featured in a news item concerning the claim of two men to the paternity of a pair of twins. Fraternal twins differ from each other as much as any other brothers and sisters (siblings) born at different times and may be of like or unlike sex.

A significant basis for postulating distinct origin of two kinds of twins is apparent in the sex ratios found among twins; that is, twin pairs of male-male, female-female, and male-female occur in the ratio of 1:1:1. On the assumption that approximately one-third of all twin births are identical twins and thus of the same sex, there would be about 16 per cent males and 16 per cent females; of the remaining two-thirds, it would be assumed that $\frac{1}{4}$ would be males, $\frac{1}{4}$ females, and $\frac{1}{2}$ would be male-female or 16 per cent males, 32 per cent male-female, and 16 per cent females. Or, if the identical (like-sexed) twins show a ratio of 1:1 and form $\frac{1}{3}$ of all twins, and fraternal twins show a ratio of 1:2:1 and form the other $\frac{2}{3}$ of all twins, the combined ratios will be approximately a 1:1:1 ratio of twin pairs. Data on the sex ratios confirm this assumption. If there were only one type of twins as to origin, the sex ratio ought to be 1:2:1.

MONOZYGOTIC ORIGIN OF TWINS. The idea of the *monozygotic origin* of twins among vertebrates including man has been developed by analogy from an interesting study of a small hard-shelled animal, the *armadillo*. According to Newman and Patterson, in embryological studies made on armadillos, the actual process of division of a single egg into four or more embryos was observed (Fig. 187). Monozygotic origin of twins has also been established in observed cases in sheep and swine. Newman reports further that the occurrence of an early one-egg human twin embryo has been actually demonstrated by Streeter.

The stage in the development of the fertilized egg or zygote (or embryo) at which the division occurs which results in twin embryos has been a subject of speculation by embryologists and students of twinning. The exact nature of the very early stages in the development of the human embryo, that is, from 10 to 12 days, has been entirely unknown until recently. Some information about the very early development of human ovarian eggs has been accumulated. In 1944 Rock and Menkin published an account of the fertilization and early cleavage of human eggs cultured in vitro. They observed two eggs in the two-cell stage 40.5 and 45 hours, respectively, following contact with spermatozoa. Two others were seen in the three-cell stage 46 hours after exposure to spermatozoa. While these observations do not give a full account of the early embryology in human beings they furnish some background for the assumption that events proceed in human beings much as they do in other mammals.

FIG. 187. ARMADILLO WITH HER MONOZYGOTIC QUADRUPLETS.
These animals customarily produce four identical quadruplets. (Courtesy, The Armadillo Farm, Comfort, Texas.)

CRITERIA OF IDENTITY IN TWINS. In studies of twins to determine whether they are fraternal or identical, a combination of characteristics is required. Usually when twins are so similar that most people frequently mistake their identity, further study proves them to be identical. If twins are to be considered identical, they should show great similarity in most of the following respects: *stature, weight, facial features,* and type and *proportion of hands and fingers.* The *hair* of each should be alike, not only in color but also in texture and form, such as degree of fineness and curliness. The *eyes* should be alike in the pigment pattern on the iris, in addition to general color; *complexion,* too, unless notably modified by exposure, and distribution of *body down* or *hair* should be similar. Finally, the *teeth* and any irregularities in dentition prove to be alike in identical twins. *Blood groups and types* are also studied in determinations of the nature of twin pairs, and identical twins will have the same characteristics of the blood.

The microscopic character of the friction ridges of fingers and palms has also been studied, and often the patterns show a stronger cross-resemblance in the members of a twin pair than on the two hands of one of the twins. This phenomenon has been called mirror imaging or *reversal of symmetry*. In extreme cases reversal has been observed in inversed orientation of digestive organs or of the heart. A minor character that may show mirror imaging is the whorl of the hair of the head, that is, in some twin pairs one may have a clockwise and the other a counterclockwise whorl. The reversal of symmetry has also been found in other features, such as facial asymmetries, dental irregularities, and left- or right-handedness. Left-handedness occurs nearly twice as frequently (11 per cent) in twins of both kinds as among the single born (6.5 per cent). Reversed symmetry is sometimes used as an additional indication of monozygotic origin of twins, but its absence does not deny it.

INHERITANCE OF THE TENDENCY TO TWINNING. It is rather generally supposed that the tendency to twinning and multiple births in man is inherited in some families. One interesting study which was recently reported centered about Swiss quadruplets who had attained the age of 60 years. There were several multiple birth relatives. Twinning was demonstrated in both maternal and paternal lines in 8 of 18 cases and in one or the other line in 10 of the cases. The author assumed a recessive gene for twinning. When this is present in the homozygous condition, he thinks either the male or female has the capacity to be the parent of identical or fraternal twins. Study of the families in which twins and multiple births occur suggests that the *tendency for the production of twins may be inherited*. It has even been thought that this tendency may be inherited through the male line, but the mechanism of inheritance is at present unknown. In connection with the production of fraternal twins, it is quite possible that ovulation of two or more eggs at one time may occur frequently. A physical basis for multiple ovulation has been determined by actual studies of certain cases, and physical structures in general are hereditarily determined. Since the fertilized egg contains genes from the male and the female parents, both lines may be equally involved in the determination of any of its subsequent behavior.

A possible method by which the male line may determine twinning is suggested in the hypothesis, advanced first by Danforth and later supported by Curtius and Greulich, that the sperm of some men may cause the ovum to form two cells. Both of these cells could then be fertilized, each by a different sperm. Twins so produced would have the identical maternal inheritance coupled with distinct paternal inheritance. They might be of like or unlike sex and would presumably be *intermediate* between identical and fraternal twins in their degree of likeness of most physical characteristics. A recent study by Southwick involving 919 pairs of twins in 85 kindreds showed that identical twins are much more frequent in kindreds with other twins than in those without. One author concluded that two genetically linked genes on an autosomal chromosome condition the production of monozygotic and dizygotic twins. According to this investigation, which included 1,131 pairs of twins, there would be no basis for the assumption that twinning is determined by the male parental line.

Physical and Mental Characteristics of Twins

Studies of twins dealing with physical characteristics and with mental traits have assumed importance as a new technique in the study of human heredity. The contrasting origins of identical and fraternal twins are now known to imply an identical genotypic constitution for members of identical twin pairs as compared with distinct genotypes for fraternal twins. Large-scale comparative *studies of the two kinds of twins*, therefore, can be expected to yield data concerning *the relative importance of heredity and environment*.

Several investigations have been made of *heart activity* in twins by comparative studies of the electric currents which accompany it. The records of these currents are known as electrocardiograms. One author, using 106 pairs of twins, 53 of them monozygotic and 53 dizygotic, concluded that the monozygotic twins showed a great preponderance of similar electrocardiograms in comparison with the dizygotic twins. Such a conclusion, if well founded, would strengthen the case for heredity, since the monozygotic twins presumably have an identical inheritance. Another cardiographic study of 50 pairs of twins, however, pointed to the individuality of the activity of the heart and thereby adds nothing to the case for heredity.

One student of the *ossification* or hardening of bones concluded that genetic factors control the chronological order of ossification. Some of the evidence was supplied in the roentgenograms of the hands of the Morlak quadruplets who are identical. Pictures of the bones of the hands of these four girls were so nearly alike in comparison with expectations based on previous studies that hereditary control is assumed to determine the order in which the bones of the hand are ossified. Another study is concerned with the *structure of the brain*. Brains of monozygotic and dizygotic pairs of twins who died soon after birth were compared. Since there was much greater similarity in the complexity and frequency of the convolutions of the brains of the monozygotic than of the dizygotic twins, brain patterns are thought to be heritable. A study of acne and similar skin afflictions showed great similarity and only slight differences in 36 pairs of monozygotic twins, while 12 pairs of dizygotic twins showed marked differences in these traits.

INCIDENCE OF DISEASE IN TWINS

Tuberculosis in twins has been studied by Diehl and Verschuer, who found a high degree of concordance in identical or monozygotic twins. In identical twin pairs, when one was reported as having tuberculosis, the other also had the disease in 70 per cent of the cases. Among fraternal twins the pairs in which both members were tuberculous were only 25 per cent of the group. There was also a high degree of concordance in the nature of the tuberculosis, that is, the organ affected and the length of the illness. One unusually striking case of similarity of identical twins revealed that both members had developed the disease at almost the same time and showed the infection in nearly identical regions in the upper lobe of the left lung. These data are interpreted as indicating a genetic background for the development of tuberculosis, though the exact factors are not yet known.

Another physical characteristic studied in twins is the *development of tumors*. Dr. Madge Macklin has assembled data from medical literature and added a number of new cases of monozygotic and dizygotic twins with tumors. Of these 105 pairs of twins, 62 were identical and 43 fraternal. Of the identical twins, more than 60 per cent were both affected, and nearly 60 per cent showed the tumor to be of the same type and at the same site. The difference in age of onset varied from 0.6 to 1.5 years. In the fraternal twins, both members were affected in fewer than 38 per cent of the cases, the tumor was of the same type in about 20 per cent of the cases, and the age of onset in the twin members varied from nearly 3 to nearly 8 years. Concordance was, therefore, much greater in the identical than in the fraternal twin pairs. On this basis, Dr. Macklin concludes that "hereditary factors play a strong role in determining not only the presence of the tumor and its type, but also the time of its appearance."

Normal and Abnormal Mental Conditions in Twins

Twin pairs showing abnormal mental states have also been investigated. In general, these show that when one member of a pair of twins has a mental abnormality or *psychosis*, both of them are much more frequently affected when they are identical than when they are fraternal twins. In cases of *dementia praecox* in identical twins, its onset was usually found to be at the same age. In a study of the type of insanity known as *schizophrenia*, of identical twins, both members were affected in 68 per cent of the cases and, of fraternal twins, only 14 per cent showed the abnormality in both members.

CRIMINALITY AMONG TWINS.   Criminals among twins have been the subject of a recent study which indicated that, of fraternal twin pairs, slightly more than half showed concordance or both members as criminals. Among identical twins this concordance rose to two-thirds; this percentage may be modified by the authors' observation that often in discordant identicals the noncriminal had really a criminal career but had escaped conviction. Since the identical twins, who by definition have an identical heredity, so often have similar criminal careers, various students assert that genetic factors are important in the determination of criminal behavior.

THE RELATIVE ABILITIES OF TWINS.   Miscellaneous characteristics which are important in personality and in mentality have been isolated for study. Gottschaldt studied some of these in a number of identical and fraternal twins. Suitable tests were devised to measure responsiveness, motives, ability to find objects, etc., and these showed 94 per cent of concordance in identical twins and only 26 per cent of concordance in nonidentical twins. Various experiments which were carried on with pairs of twins in concentration camps are interpreted as showing the predominant potency of hereditary factors over environment in determining character.

There is some basis for the common belief that members of twin pairs may be unequal in their abilities. When such an inequality exists, it may be readily explained on the basis of an imbalance in the placental blood exchange. The imbalance may be minor or sufficiently great to result in the death of one twin. One author has suggested the possibility that many single-birth individuals may actually have had a twin at an early stage in prenatal development. There is probably no valid reason to believe that the average level of capacity, physical or mental, of twins is either less or greater than that of the general population of the single born.

THE INFLUENCE OF HEREDITY AND ENVIRONMENT IN TWINS. Many phases of inheritance in twins are being studied, not only for their bearing on knowledge about twins but also in the interest of a wider knowledge of inheritance in general. Among these are the interesting cases of twins reared apart and reported by Newman, Freeman, and Holzinger. Identical twins which had been reared apart from infancy were sought over a number of years, and comparisons were made between these and pairs of identical and fraternal twins who grew up in the same environments. The authors conclude that the identical twins are much more alike than the fraternal twins in most of the traits measured. When differences are found between identical twins reared together, biologists are likely to attribute them largely to prenatal factors. They point out, however, that if there are any early differences leading to greater assertiveness on the part of one twin over the other, this feature may become accentuated with time as both twins consistently react toward each other in the same way. Personality differences of identical twins may then become greater with age.

An important role is attributed to the environmental factor in producing differences in the case of identical twins reared apart. In the case of separated identical twins, the environmental factor can produce differences as great or greater than those produced when both hereditary and environmental factors operate within twin families as in the case of fraternal twins reared together. Small differences in environment, however, have no effect in producing significant differences in identical twins reared apart. In some of the tests, significant *correlations* were found between the differences between identical twins reared apart and the estimated amount of difference between their respective environments. Correlations, it may be pointed out, are statistical measures of relationship. A perfect correlation is expressed by the whole number 1. Fractions of the number 1 indicate less perfect correlations. Various involved statistical methods are employed to test the significance of correlations. The closest correlation was between schooling and educational achievement (0.91). It was somewhat less close between schooling and intelligence (0.46 to 0.79) and least between social environment and intelligence (0.42 to 0.53).

Differences in the environment as shown in separated identical twins were judged sufficient to have produced differences in weight, ability, and behavior large enough to overshadow the genetic differences which occur between siblings (brothers and sisters). The authors have suggested that different levels of behavior are differently modifiable by environment. In general, abilities organized to meet specific demands and answer specific problems are measurable and show correlations with environment. The differences in personality measures of separated twins had negligible correlation with the differences in environment so far as they could be ascertained.

The solution of the question of the relative share of environmental and genetic differences may only be approached under a given set of circumstances. No general answer can as yet be given. Educators will be interested in the conclusion that identical twins reared under extreme differences in educational and social environments showed significant changes in intelligence and educational achievement as measured by the tests the authors employed. The general conclusion is that the share of environment in determining traits which are susceptible to environmental influences is large when the environment differs greatly as compared with heredity. But when the genetic difference is large and the environmental difference is small, the share of heredity is relatively large. The reader must remember, however, that environment cannot effect changes exceeding the genetic potentialities of the individual.

Multiple Births in Human Beings

The birth and development of the Dionne quintuplets in Canada focused attention on the phenomenon of multiple births in human beings. The publicity accorded the Dionne "quints" made "news" of all multiple births. A newspaper report in 1941 referred to the birth of quintuplets in Brazil, but three of these died. Possibly authentic was the report of the birth of quintuplets to the Diligenti family in Argentina on July 15, 1943. Other even less reliable reports mention a set of sextuplets consisting of four boys and two girls born to a family named Esquivel in Potosi near Rivan, Nicaragua, and a set of septuplets, six boys and one girl, born to a de Lopez family living near Zamora, in the state of Michoacán, Mexico. There is an older report concerning sextuplets born September 6, 1866, to a family named Bushnell in the United States. The Bushnell sextuplets are said all to have survived with at least some of them reaching maturity.

Frequency of Multiple Births in Human Beings

As mentioned previously, twins occur about once in 88 births in the white race in the United States. This figure has been used in calculating the possible number of multiple births such as triplets, quadruplets, and quintuplets in the population. One well-known analysis sets the relative frequency of multiple births as follows, on the basis of the occurrence of twins once in n number of times. Triplets are thought to occur once in n^2 number of births and quadruplets once in n^3 births. In calculating the theoretical possibilities of the frequencies of multiple births, it must be realized that biologically multiple births such as triplets, quadruplets, and quintuplets are not merely twins multiplied. The substitution of 88 for n in the calculation is a means of approximating the possible frequency and may indicate expectations as follows:

$n^2 = 7,744$; that is, triplets 1 in 7,744 births
$n^3 = 681,472$; that is, quadruplets 1 in 681,472 births
$n^4 = 59,969,536$; that is, quintuplets 1 in approximately 60,000,000 births
$n^5 = 959,512,576$; that is, sextuplets 1 in nearly a billion births
$n^6 = 8,443,710,704$; that is, septuplets 1 in eight and one-half billion births.

FIG. 188. THE DIONNE QUINTUPLETS AT THE AGE OF 5 YEARS.
Left to right, Emilie, Annette, Cecile, Marie, and Yvonne. These girls have been judged to be identical quintuplets and thus presumably of monozygotic origin. (World Copyright, 1939, NEA Service, Inc.)

Other investigations, however, furnish data that vary from these estimates. Hamlett has gathered statistics which show that actually triplets occur 14 per cent less frequently than once in 7,744 and quadruplets 19 per cent more frequently than once in 681,472 births. There seems also to be a racial difference in the frequency of multiple births much as has been found in twinning. Strandskov estimated that quadruplets are born in Negro families once in 273,897 births or twice as frequently as in the white population of the United States.

QUINTUPLETS. The figures on occurrence of multiple births emphasize how unusual the Dionnes of Canada and the Diligenti children of Argentina really are. They also indicate the unlikelihood of the occurrence of septuplets or even sextuplets. Extreme caution in accepting any reports of these higher multiple births is justified. The reports of sextuplets in Nicaragua and septuplets in Mexico must be regarded as unsubstantial until more data have been obtained. The Dionne quintuplets have been thoroughly studied by scientists. Members of the medical profession have been interested in their physical condition and development, psychologists have studied their mental reactions, and geneticists have been concerned with their resemblances and their biological origin. No children in the world have been more intensively analyzed than the "quints." Aside from their number the most interesting feature about the Dionne quintuplets is that they are identical (Fig. 188). Many studies emphasize their close similarity and confirm the assumption of their monozygotic origin, that is, from a single fertilized egg.

FIG. 189. THE KEYS QUADRUPLETS.

Mona and Roberta have been judged to be identical twins, thus of monozygotic origin, and Leota and Mary as fraternal. This set of quadruplets was probably trizygotic. (Courtesy, J. R. Franchey and the Keys Quadruplets.)

QUADRUPLETS. Hamlett reported that there were 48 sets of quadruplets born in the United States between 1915 and 1930. In a study of multiple births, Gardner and Newman were able to locate only 7 sets of quadruplets in which all 4 members were surviving in 1942. Thus, even quadruplets are not very common. Besides the 7 sets with all members living, there are other sets with part of the membership surviving, and other sets of quadruplets have been born since 1942. In a series of articles, these observers state that quadruplets may be as good material for scientific studies on multiple births as quintuplets and, because of their frequency, offer a greater variety of zygotic origins than the higher multiple births.

Among quadruplets are the Kaspars, born in New Jersey. These are of unlike sex, three boys and a girl, and therefore not identical. More recent studies of the Kaspar quadruplets indicate that the set is of dizygotic or two-egg origin, consisting of a set of identical monozygotic triplets, all males, and a single-egg member, the girl.

The well-known Keys quadruplets (Fig. 189), while all girls, are nevertheless not alike. One of these girls has blonde, wavy hair, and the other three are dark and straight-haired. Since Newman judged two of the four as identical monozygotic twins and the other two as fraternal, they are thought to be trizygotic, that is, of three-egg origin. Another set of girls, the Morlak quadruplets, is considered to be identical and thus monozygotic or of one-egg origin. However, the Perricone quad-

Table XLIX

THE FIVE THEORETICALLY POSSIBLE METHODS OF ZYGOTIC ORIGIN OF QUADRUPLETS

Type	Method of Origin		Possible Sexes	Example
I	Monozygotic or one-egg sets	Cases in which all four of the identical quadruplets have developed from one zygote or fertilized egg	All four of one sex either (1) four males or (2) four females	The Morlaks
II	Dizygotic or two-egg sets	A. Cases in which the quadruplets are composed of a set of identical triplets, all three developed from one zygote, and a single member developed from a second fertilized egg	(3) four males (4) four females (5) three males and one female (6) three females and one male	The Badgetts The Kaspars
		B. Cases in which the quadruplets consist of two pairs of identical monozygotic twins, each pair developed from a single fertilized egg. There are genetical reasons to indicate that this combination may never develop	Probably never occurs	
III	Trizygotic or three-egg sets	Cases in which the quadruplets consist of one pair of identical monozygotic twins developed from one zygote and the other two members each from a single fertilized egg	(7) four males (8) four females (9) three males and one female (10) two males and two females (11) one male and three females	The Keys
IV	Tetrazygotic or four-egg sets	Cases in which each of the four members of the quadruplets developed from a single zygote, that is, from four distinct eggs each separately fertilized	(12) four males (13) four females (14) three males and one female (15) two males and two females (16) one male and three females	The Perricones The Schenses

ruplets, all boys, have been diagnosed as of tetrazygotic origin, that is, they were developed from four distinct and separately fertilized ova or zygotes.

Another set of quadruplets, somewhat younger than the Perricone quadruplets, is the Schenses of South Dakota. This set consisting of two boys and two girls is also regarded as tetrazygotic or four-egg quadruplets. They resemble each other no more than ordinary brothers and sisters born at different times. The all-girl set of Badgett quadruplets of Galveston, Texas, is thought to consist of one set of monozygotic or one-egg identical triplets and one single member.

Methods of Origin of Quadruplets and the Inheritance of the Tendency for Multiple Births

Gardner and Newman emphasize that twins and multiple births have been noted in the ancestry and collateral kindred of families producing quadruplets. This is especially noted in the Badgett family in which the mother of the quadruplets is herself one of a pair of identical twins and the father has a pair of twin brothers. Besides these, there are at least four pairs of twins and a set of triplets in the collateral branches of the mother of the quadruplets.

Newman is inclined to regard the tendency to one-egg twinning as weakly inherited and the two-egg twinnings as dependent upon the first method or at least favored by it. According to this theory, the first embryo to reach the uterus is implanted. This implantation tends to render the membrane of the uterus temporarily resistant to further implantation. Thus, if there are additional fertilized eggs, their implantation is delayed for a time. This delay may give the second or additional zygotes time to divide, as Rock and Menkin show that the human ovarian egg may undergo cleavage within 40 to 48 hours. Later, before or after cleavage into twin primordia or even into quadruplex or multiple primordia, second or additional implantations may occur. In this way, two-egg twinning or multiple embryos may originate.

According to Newman and Gardner, there are only five theoretically possible methods of zygotic origin of quadruplets. These are shown in Table XLIX.

Questions and Problems

1. Discuss the occurrence of multiple births in the lower animals. Cite some instances of unusually large litters in the domestic animals.
2. What is superfetation? Of what value is this in the study of animal husbandry?
3. Are twinning and multiple births in farm animals of any economic value?
4. Does anatomical evidence favor the idea of single-egg origin of twins in sheep?
5. What is the evidence concerning possible inheritance of the tendency toward multiple births in sheep and goats?
6. What is the frequency of twinning in sheep and goats? In cattle? In horses?
7. What is the frequency of twinning in human beings? Are there geographical and racial differences in the rates of twinning? Discuss.
8. What are identical and fraternal twins? How do they originate biologically? What is meant by monozygotic origin of twins? By dizygotic origin?
9. What is the significance of the occurrence of male-male, female-female, and male-female twins in a 1:1:1 ratio?
10. Describe some of the ideas associated with embryonic development in connection with the monozygotic origin of twins.
11. What are some of the criteria of identity in human twins?
12. Is the tendency to twinning in human beings inherited?
13. Since the development of identical twins is dependent upon the division of the ovum or egg cell, a purely female structure, how is it possible for the male parent to influence the production of twins?

14. What is the evidence indicating greater coincidence of tuberculosis among identical rather than fraternal twins?
15. What evidence is there concerning the concordance of tumors in identical and fraternal twins?
16. Cite some of the evidence indicating the coincidence of abnormal mental states in identical and fraternal twins.
17. What is the concordance of abilities in fraternal and identical twins?
18. What have been some of the approaches to the solution of the relative importance of heredity and environment in the development of twins?
19. What general conclusion if any can be drawn regarding the relative influence of heredity and environment from the study of twins?
20. What may be said concerning the probability of high multiple births such as quintuplets, sextuplets, and septuplets in human beings?
21. When it is said that the Dionne quintuplets are identical, what biologically significant fact is implied in that statement?
22. Relative to quintuplets, what is the frequency of quadruplets? How abundant are quadruplets in the United States?
23. What are the possible methods of origin of quadruplets?

References

DAVENPORT, C. B.: *How We Came by Our Bodies*, New York, Henry Holt & Company, Inc., 1936.

GARDNER, IVA C., and H. H. NEWMAN: "The Keys Quadruplets" (Studies of Quadruplets I), *J. Heredity* **31**:419–424 (1940).

——— and ———: "The Perricone Quadruplets" (Studies of Quadruplets II), *J. Heredity* **31**:307–314 (1940).

——— and ———: "The Badgett Quadruplets" (Studies of Quadruplets IV), *J. Heredity* **33**:345–350 (1942).

——— and ———: "The Kaspar Quadruplets" (Studies of Quadruplets V), *J. Heredity* **34**:27–32 (1943).

——— and ———: "The Morlak Quadruplets" (Studies of Quadruplets VI), *J. Heredity* **34**:259–263 (1943).

——— and ———: "The Schense Quadruplets" (Studies of Quadruplets VII), *J. Heredity* **35**:83–88 (1944).

GREULICH, W. W.: "Fraternal Twins," *J. Am. Med. Assoc.* **110**:559–563 (1938).

HAMLETT, G. W. D.: "Human Twinning in the United States," *Genetics* **20**:250–258 (1935).

JORDAN, H. E., and J. E. KINDRED, *Embryology*, New York, D. Appleton-Century Company, Inc., 1932.

MACARTHUR, J. W.: "Diagnosis of the Dionne Quintuplets as a Monozygotic Set," *J. Heredity* **29**:323–329 (1938).

MACKLIN, MADGE: "The Role of Heredity in Disease," *Medicine* **14**:1–75 (1935).

NEWMAN, H. H.: *Multiple Human Births*, New York, Doubleday, Doran & Company, Inc., 1940.

———: *Physiology of Twinning*, Chicago, University of Chicago Press, 1923.

———, F. N. FREEMAN, and K. J. HOLZINGER: *Twins: A Study of Heredity and Environment*, Chicago, University of Chicago Press, 1937.

——— and IVA C. GARDNER: "Types and Frequencies of Quadruplets" (Studies of Quadruplets III), *J. Heredity* **33**:311–314 (1942).

SOUTHWICK, W. E.: "Association of Identical and Fraternal Twins in Kindreds," *Am. Naturalist* **73**:44–68 (1939).

chapter 26

Inheritance of Physical Traits
in Human Beings

Many physical traits of man are obvious whether considered as racial or individual characteristics. The races of men are distinguished by different skin colors, black, brown, red, yellow, and white. Head shape and facial features, eye characters, hair color and form, and stature in some cases are also racially distinctive. Variability in many physical features besides color is characteristic in human beings. Families and individuals as well as races differ in hair form and color, eye colors, facial features, and in many other normal physical characters. Besides the normal traits man has many physical abnormalities that are heritable. Studies of inheritance attempt to account for the resemblances and differences among related human beings as they do in the lower organisms.

Genetic Basis for Inheritance of Stature and Body Form

Studies of *stature* in man indicate that it is probably inherited on a *multiple factor* basis, with the genes for shortness dominant over those conditioning tallness. This means the children of exceptionally tall parents are likely to be taller than average. If genes for tallness are recessive, tall persons may be homozygous for them. Because homozygous-recessive organisms breed true, the offspring of homozygous tall parents therefore inherit the genes for tallness and are likely to be phenotypically tall. There is usually more variation in the children of short parents than in matings of tall × tall, because the dominant genes for short stature may cover up the recessives, which subsequently appear in phenotypes when pairs of recessive genes are recombined. Galton's observations of the tendency of children to be less tall than their tall parents or less short than their short parents led him to formulate the theory of regression. Regression is the tendency of offspring to revert or regress to the condition of the race. This tendency is now attributed to the multiple factor determination of many characters, including size (pp. 257–270).

Davenport and Steggerda who studied racial crossing in Jamaica concluded that lengths of body segments and appendages are independent genetic traits. But Castle who has investigated size inheritance in lower

476

animals has stated, "The genetic agencies affecting rabbits are general in their action, influencing in the same general direction all parts of the body." Body form in man is dependent upon hereditary and environmental factors, including the physiological environment conditioned by hormones, which in turn may be genetically determined. At the present, these interrelations are still largely speculative and based on research with lower animals. The secretions of the endocrine glands or hormones are known to show definite effects on body build in human beings. Nutritive conditions likewise effect recognized changes. Davenport, however, has stated that two sets of genes may be involved in the genetic background for fleshiness, with the genes for fleshiness dominant.

Studies of inheritance of some abnormalities in stature have shown the following relations:

CONDITION	GENES

Achondroplastic dwarfism
  Shortened extremities
  Fairly normal trunk
	Dominant, usually
	Recessive, occasionally

Ateleiotic dwarfism Entire body small	The interaction of two complementary dominant genes explains occurrence of dwarfs among children of normal parents, possibility of single recessive genes fortuitously combined
Cretinism Physical stunting accompanied by defective mentality	Genetic subnormal functioning of the thyroid

Inheritance of Malformations

Besides stature and general form of body in human beings, minor physical abnormalities are also inherited. Among them are the following:

CONDITION	INHERITANCE
Split hand or lobster claw With variations in fusing and disproportionate development of digits	Commonly dominant in inheritance, perhaps a gene complex
Split foot, lobster-claw foot	Perhaps a single dominant gene plus modifying genes
Syndactyly Fingers fused	Dominant
Brachydactyly, brachyphalangy Shortening of fingers and toes	Dominant characteristics, affected individuals usually heterozygous

Polydactyly
  Extra fingers and toes
  Variable in expression
	Probably dominant gene influenced by modifying genes; perhaps low penetrance and poor expressivity in some families (pp. 180, 207)

Clinodactyly Curved fingers	Slight curvature dominant over straight type
Clubfoot	Homozygous-recessive state of single pair of genes with modifying genes on X chromosome. Possible prenatal influences involved
Harelip and cleft palate	Two pairs of recessive genes, one is sex-linked (more severe abnormality), other is autosomal

Inheritance of Head Shape and Facial Features

Numerous studies of shape of skull indicate that Mendelizing hereditary units are involved, with genes for broadening probably dominant and a number of genes cooperating in determining the shape. Nutritive conditions, however, also influence the development of head form. Again, in the study of race crossing in Jamaica, Davenport and Steggerda found greater inter-pupillary distance in Negroes than in white persons. The variability of the "intermediate browns" would suggest that a number of genes are involved.

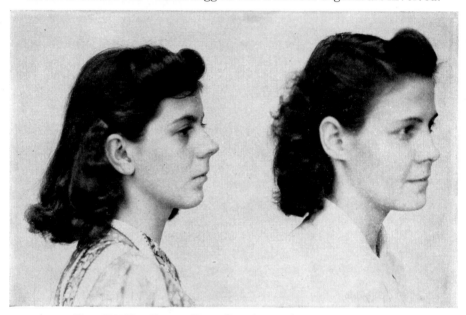

FIG. 190. EAR LOBES: FREE (LEFT) AND ADHERENT (RIGHT).
These characteristics are inherited.

One interesting approach to a study of facial expression was an analysis of photographs of 1,610 persons belonging to 394 families. On the basis of excess of similarity between siblings over the similarity between parents and children, the authors concluded that facial expression is heritable. Another study of facial features indicated that the characters long face, prominent nose and ears, and cleft in the chin showed segregation in harmony with simple Mendelian interpretations. A pictorial pedigree of 42 individuals in seven generations illustrated this segregation. Heritable variations of this nature should interest orthodontists, who attempt to reconstruct jaw structure.

Size and shape of ear, a relatively insignificant character, may be determined by a number of genes, while a single pair of genes may be involved in the condition of adherence or freeness of the lobule of the ear. The adherent ear lobe appears to be a pure recessive (Fig. 190). Possibly sex linkage is involved, too, in other ear characteristics, some of which appear more frequently in males than females.

Inheritance of Skin Color in Man

Among characteristics of human beings which have long attracted the attention of geneticists is the obvious one of skin color. Not only are the races of man differentiated by skin color, yellow, red, black, brown, and white, but individuals in these races likewise differ as to the depth of coloring. Though the genetic basis for this character is not yet determined with certainty, there is rather general agreement that multiple genes must be involved.

FIG. 191. NORMAL AND WHITE INDIAN CHILDREN.
In stature and facial characteristics, the albinos resemble the other members of the tribe. The reduced tolerance to light is indicated by the squinting of the two albinos. (Courtesy, Harry V. Harlan, modified after R. O. Marsh, Science Service, from *J. Heredity*.)

ALBINISM IN MAN. *Albinism*, which occurs in man as well as in many other animals, is characterized by absence of color in hair, skin, and eyes. The eyes and sometimes the skin may appear pinkish, since blood vessels produce this tinting in the absence of obscuring pigments. The basis of inheritance of albinism in man is assumed to resemble that known for lower animals and to depend on a recessive gene. Albinism occurs in several races of man. In Panama where a tribe of Indians was found to have an unusually frequent occurrence of albinos, the condition has been recorded since 1681 (Fig. 191). Among the Indians, the formation of black pigment seems to be inhibited, but the yellow-red pigments are only partially suppressed, because the albino Indians have yellowish hair. There is some evidence that a series of multiple allelic genes for albinism in human beings may function similarly to the series for coloration in rabbits and cats (pp. 195–200).

INHERITANCE OF LIGHT AND DARK SKIN COLORS. Light skin color, although conditioned by supplementary genes, is presumed to be

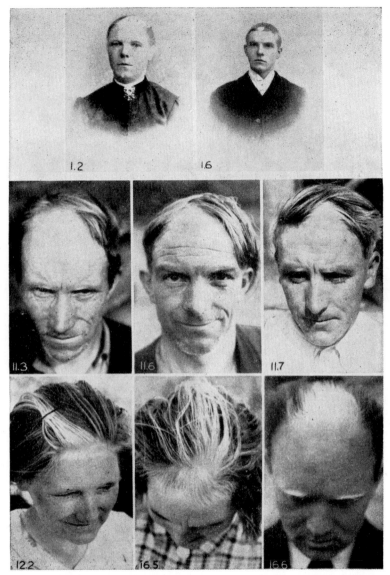

FIG. 192. FRONTAL BLAZE IN SECOND AND THIRD GENERATIONS.
Photographs from two generations of a Norwegian family which for four generations has shown white forelocks and skin spotting. (The numbers refer to a pedigree chart not reproduced here.) The eyebrows of 16.6 as well as the large triangular forelock are white. (Courtesy, Hans Sundför, from *J. Heredity*.)

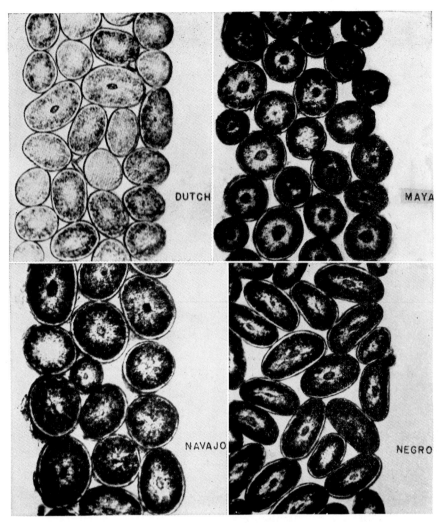

FIG. 193. HAIR FORM OF FOUR RACES, DUTCH, MAYA, NAVAJO, NEGRO, SHOWING STRIKING DIFFERENCES IN SHAPE AND STRUCTURE, GREATLY MAGNIFIED. Note correlation with straightness and curliness. (Courtesy, Morris Steggerda, from *J. Heredity*.)

recessive to darker skin color. According to Davenport, Negro skin color may be due to two additional pairs of genes affecting the production of the enzyme tyrosinase. Perhaps duplicate cumulative genes are involved in skin coloration. Gates, who has recently published analyses of numerous pedigrees from racial crosses, has proposed three pairs of genes with unequal but cumulative effects as basic to the possible ten recognizable color variations that he scored. The darkest skin color according to Gates's scheme would be determined by the homozygotic-dominant state of all three genes and the skin color of fair white persons by the homozygotic recessive of all three.

The Inheritance of Hair Characters in Man

The genetic basis for various aspects of hair characteristics in man has not been determined with the precision achieved for similar characteristics

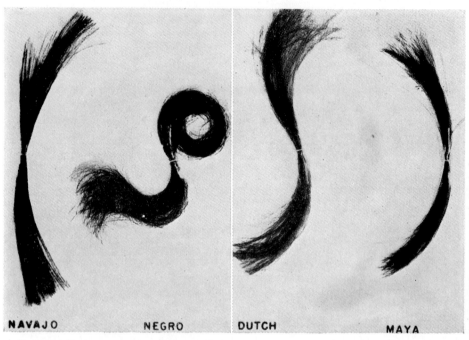

NAVAJO   NEGRO   DUTCH   MAYA

FIG. 194. LOCKS OF HAIR FROM FOUR RACES SHOWING MACROSCOPIC APPEARANCE OF THE TYPES IN FIG. 193.
The Dutch was finest; Negro and Mayan samples were coarse. (Courtesy, Morris Steggerda, from *J. Heredity*.)

in some of the lower animals. Perhaps again some of the most likely assumptions may be tabulated as indications of the inheritance.

CHARACTERISTIC	INHERITANCE
Hair colors	Extensive genetic basis, dominant state of basic gene determines color
Dark hair	Supplementary genes for production of melanin
Red or gold hair	Additional supplementary genes for production of a carotinlike substance
Frontal blaze	Similar to skin spotting and doubtlessly is inherited (Fig. 192)
Graying of hair	Premature graying inherited as a dominant
Hair form (Fig. 193 and 194)	
Straight hair from straight follicles, circular in cross section	Assumption of gene C effects curliness

CHARACTERISTIC	INHERITANCE
Curly hair, oval in cross section	Genes Cc effect wavy hair
Woolly hair from curved follicle, flat-tened in cross section	Second gene S is complementary and inter-acts with C
Straight hair	$ccss$
Very closely curled hair	$CCSS$
Intermediate conditions	Various combinations of the genes
Baldness	Most kinds are hereditarily determined patterns centered in families (Fig. 195), inherited as an autosomal dominant, sex-limited expression perhaps related to hormones
	BB = baldness in both sexes
	bb = normal full head of hair
	Bb = males bald, females not bald

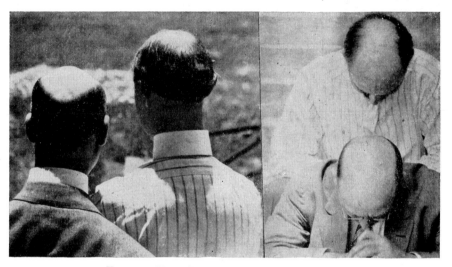

FIG. 195. TWO CASES OF PATTERN BALDNESS.

Two views of the same individuals. The man at the right (upper in second view) had heavy, coarse, curly hair in his youth. He began to lose it very gradually. His father had the same pattern of baldness; his mother's family had thin hair but no baldness. The other man has thin, straight hair; baldness appeared at the age of 19, and his son developed the same pattern at the same age. His maternal grandmother was bald. (Courtesy, Dorothy Osborn, from *J. Heredity*.)

Inheritance of Eye Characters

Variations in appearance and vision of the eyes are extremely numerous and have long been studied by geneticists. Probably more is known about the inheritance of eye characters than about any other organ of the human body. The shape of the eyes is generally considered to be a racial character-istic. Oblique eyes which are typical of the members of the Mongolian race are considered recessive to straight eyes.

INHERITANCE OF EYE COLOR. Eye color is usually fairly stable after infancy but perhaps never absolutely stable. Though blond hair and blue eyes and brown hair and brown eyes are commonly associated, the genes determining eye color are thought to be independent of those for hair color. Color of the iris is dependent on a twofold pigmentation. The back of the iris has a double layer of deeply colored cells which exclude light from the interior of the eye. The front of the iris (anterior layers) may or may not be pigmented. When pigment is lacking altogether in the anterior layers, the eyes may be light or dark blue, depending on the color of the posterior layers. Conditioned by the pigmentation of the anterior layer, eyes are brown, light brown, green, or gray.

Variations in eye color would therefore be dependent on at least two genes and possibly on a factor complex of two pairs of genes with some pattern factors. Brown eyes, then, may be assumed to be the expression of cumulative action of both dominant genes, blue eyes of the double recessive, and intermediate colors of the heterozygous condition, with differential enzyme activity perhaps involved. Eye color is one of the characters in human beings probably entirely dependent on the inherited genotype.

INHERITANCE OF ABNORMALITIES OF VISION.   An abnormality of vision that has been studied genetically is color blindness. Various types of color blindness are red, green, red-green, blue-yellow, and complete color blindness. In the latter the afflicted person has difficulty distinguishing any color. Total color blindness is very rare. The four kinds of partial color blindness are conditioned by recessive genes carried at distinct loci in the sex chromosomes. The genes for red, green, and blue-yellow are located in the nonhomologous portion of the X chromosome (Fig. 201 and pp. 499, 501). These genes are X-linked and are transmitted from an afflicted man to his daughter, who is generally normal, to a grandson who again shows the defect. Total color blindness is conditioned by a recessive gene at a locus in the homologous parts of the X and Y chromosome. Total color blindness may be inherited through both sexes. Women may transmit it in the X chromosome through the eggs. Men may transmit it in either the X or the Y chromosome through the two types of sperms. Total color blindness is another of the conditions probably associated with inbreeding, as occurs in cousin marriages.

GENETICS OF COLOR BLINDNESS.   The red-green types of color blindness are more common than the other kinds. As in the inheritance of hemophilia (pp. 492–494), the red-green types of color blindness are most frequently found in men and boys. They are transmitted by women who may be genetic carriers of the defects even though they seldom show them (Fig. 196). Since the female has two X chromosomes, usually the dominant gene in one of them will prevent the expression of the recessive gene for color blindness carried in the other X chromosome. In males there is one X chromosome and one Y chromosome. Since the Y chromosome is largely ineffective or inert, the recessive gene for color blindness carried on the single X chromosome expresses itself in the development of the defect.

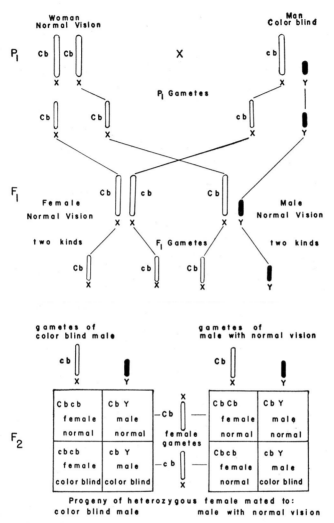

FIG. 196. DIAGRAM OF THE INHERITANCE OF COLOR BLINDNESS IN HUMAN BEINGS.
P_1 Normal female $CbCb$ mated to a color-blind male cb Y.

F_1 Both males and females have normal vision, but female is heterozygous.

F_2 Diagrammatic representation of union of gametes of female heterozygous for color blindness: at left with those of color-blind male; at right with those of normal male.

Actually, there are several types or degrees of red and green color blindness, each presumably determined by its own gene, perhaps at a different locus in the X chromosome. Possibly multiple alleles are involved in the different degrees of defect in each case. There are cases of red-blindness and others of green-blindness, the sense for both colors, however, being somewhat impaired in the two types. Color blindness is more rarely found

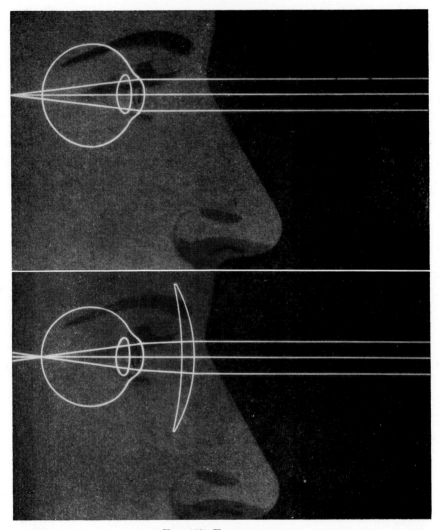

FIG. 197. FARSIGHTEDNESS.

Hyperopia or farsightedness is that condition in which the rays of light come to a focus behind the retina of the eye. Farsightedness is illustrated above. The correction of farsightedness is accomplished by wearing a convex lens before the eye. This lens brings the rays of light into sharp focus on the retina, as illustrated below. (Courtesy, Bausch & Lomb Optical Company, from *The Educational Focus* **XII**:4, 1941.)

in females than in males, but there are recorded cases of females presumed to have been homozygous. The percentage of color blindness in women has been found to be probably not more than 1 per cent, while the percentage of color-blind white males is from 5 to 8 per cent. Studies show that the amount of color blindness in populations varies with different races. In general, the defects are more frequent in white than in the colored races.

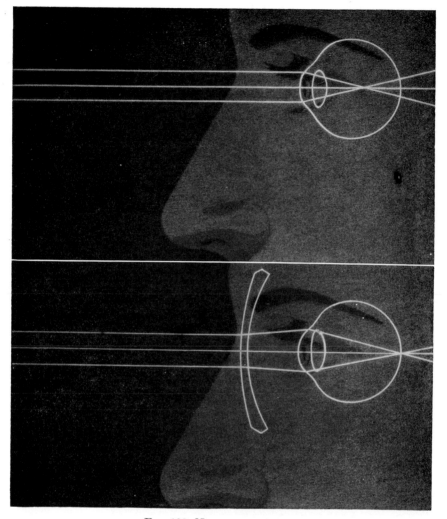

FIG. 198. NEARSIGHTEDNESS.

Myopia or nearsightedness, illustrated above, is that condition in which images of objects are brought to a focus in front of the retina of the eye. The correction of nearsightedness is accomplished by wearing a concave lens before the eye. This lens brings the rays of light into sharp focus on the retina as illustrated below. (Courtesy, Bausch & Lomb Optical Company, from *The Educational Focus* **XII**:4, 1941.)

OTHER COMMON ABNORMALITIES OF VISION. Genetic studies have also been made of shortsightedness or myopia, farsightedness or hyperopia, astigmatism, and cataract. For myopia, the best-grounded hypothesis considers two recessive genes with possibly some sex linkage as determiners. Two different anatomical features are involved in myopia, one the increased length of the axis of the eyeball and the other the curvature of the cornea. There is some evidence of dominance here. Perhaps various combinations of the genes in dominant and recessive states may determine the varying myopic phenotypes. In farsightedness the axis of the eyeball is too short for proper focusing of nearby objects; the shortened axis is probably dominant over the longer axis of normal vision (Fig. 197 and 198).

The genes involved in astigmatism, an error of refraction caused by unequal curving of the anterior surface of the cornea, are as yet unknown, but the condition is definitely hereditary and probably is dominant. Also with various types of cataract, the exact genetic background is unknown, but they are generally attributed to dominant inheritance.

Inheritance of Ear Characters

Much of the well-established variability in hearing ability is known to be hereditary, though some of it follows as the aftermath of various diseases, such as scarlet fever and meningitis.

HEREDITARY DEFECTS OF THE EAR. Of the many kinds of deafness, from one-fourth to one-third are hereditarily determined.

CONDITION	INHERITANCE
Atrophy of auditory nerve may begin at about 40 years of age and progress more or less rapidly	Dominant
Otosclerosis change in bony walls of ear, occurs in twice as many women as men	Attributed both to dominant and to recessive genes and to combinations of a dominant autosomal and a dominant sex-linked gene
Deafness following inflammation of the middle ear	Appears to run in families but may ensue as an outcome of a variety of infections
Deaf-mutism	Inherited but difference of opinion as to method exists

chapter 27

Inheritance of Physiological
Conditions in Human Beings

Inheritance of various physical and physiological abnormalities has been generally noted when these have reappeared in successive generations. From such observations a peculiar fatality has come to be associated with inheritance. Normality, however, is determined by genes and thus by heredity, equally with abnormality. Defects which are found frequently in more than one child in a family are dependent upon relatively few recessive genes. When they are seldom found in more than one child in a family, they may be dependent upon a complex grouping of genes. That is, the frequent occurrence of a trait in a family is an indication that its inheritance is relatively simple, and infrequent occurrence of a trait may indicate that its mode of inheritance is probably more complex. And again, it cannot be pointed out too often that the organism is the product of both hereditary and environmental factors, as Hogben states, of "the interaction between a certain genetic equipment contained in the fertilized egg and a certain configuration of extrinsic agencies."

An example taken from poultry may illustrate the meaning of this statement. A certain kind of chicken when fed on yellow corn or given green food rich in carotenoid pigments will develop yellow shanks; others in the same group will develop white shanks, and the ratio in the flock will be a typical 3 : 1 Mendelian ratio of three with yellow shanks to one with white. If the same kind of chicken is fed on white corn, which is deficient in carotenoids, they will all have white shanks. The genetic potentiality for yellow shanks must have a given environment for its expression. Other kinds of genic potentialities will express themselves in any environment in which the organism can maintain life. In human heredity, it is not always known which kind of potentiality is involved. Eye color would seem to be a characteristic determined solely by the hereditary background. The development of certain physical abnormalities, such as goitre, may depend not only on a given genetic complex but also on conditions in the environment, in this case the amount of iodine in the diet.

Inheritance of Resistance and Susceptibility to Disease

Inheritance of resistance or of susceptibility to disease in human beings is a controversial subject for which there is insufficient evidence. Though it is a matter of common observation that some families appear to show predispositions to some diseases, that some racial differences in immunity or susceptibility are apparent, it remains for the future to establish the genetic basis. Acquired immunities established by vaccination or inoculation are of course environmental conditions which cannot be inherited. Whatever may be inherited, it is not a disease but the genic potentiality that makes an individual or a race resistant or susceptible.

Relation of Heredity to Various Physical and Physiological Abnormalities

The list of all known hereditary physiological and physical abnormalities is far too long to consider here. Not only the abnormal but the normal condition will have an hereditary background. A predisposition to normal good health as well as a normal body is generally inherited. While modern scientific treatments of disease and hygienic measures are decreasing the number of deaths from infectious diseases, they increase the number of persons who survive and later die of other hereditary diseases. At the same time knowledge of the nature of inheritance of these defects and diseases becomes increasingly important.

Some conditions appearing rather regularly in certain families may be based on an hereditary predisposition but without exact determination of its nature. A rachitic constitution expressed in lowered calcification of bones and teeth is in this category. Any marked deviations from normal functioning of the glands of internal secretion or an unbalance of the hormones may be expressed in various physical and sometimes mental disturbances. The thyroid gland is subject to variations in functioning. Among conditions resulting is goitre that prevails in some families and not in others. Studies of twins indicate a genetic background, because pairs of identical twins have shown much greater concordance of expression of goitre than pairs of fraternal twins. The fraternal twin members were found no more likely both to show goitre than any other pair of children from one family. It has been suggested that the genetic basis for goitre consists of two pairs of genes, one perhaps in the X chromosome. Dominance in the male may be variable, with a possibility of influence of sex hormones in differential development of goitre in the two sexes.

Allergies, expressed in unusual sensitivity to certain foods, animals, pollen, or other substances, may show themselves in a variety of ways. An hereditary basis is generally assumed to be present, but investigators are not agreed as to its nature, some postulating dominant genes, others recessives. Possibly a pair of basic genes, when present as homozygous recessive, *aa*, determines sensitivity. Then nonallergic heterozygotes $Aa \times Aa$ may produce allergic children.

TUBERCULOSIS. Early investigations led to the belief that tuberculosis "ran in families." After Koch's discovery of the tubercle bacillus as the causative agent, medical opinion veered to the side of environment and infection as the only cause of tuberculosis. More recently with genetic studies of tuberculous families, the hereditary basis is again gaining ground; not the disease is inherited but "the soil necessary for its development." Many studies of family histories have been made, and twin studies, too, are important in this connection. In general, susceptibility may be determined by recessive genes, while other genes may prevent their expression.

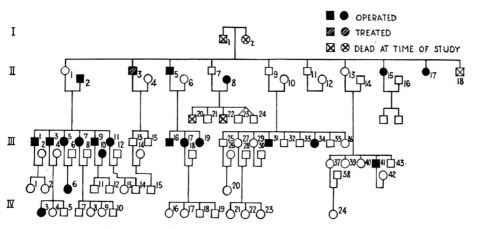

FIG. 199. A FAMILY PEDIGREE OF APPENDICITIS.

An illustration of family pedigrees as they are charted to depict incidence of various conditions under investigation. Squares are used as symbols for males and circles for females. Solid black indicates affected individuals. In this pedigree, among the children of II-1 and II-5, the incidence of appendicitis has been 100 per cent. II-2 is the brother of II-6. Eleven progenies having the same ancestors had appendicitis. The fourth generation is very young, and other cases may yet occur. (Courtesy, Sister M. Flavia, from *J. Heredity*.)

OTHER CONDITIONS. *Hypertension* which manifests itself in abnormally high blood pressure has been ascribed to a dominant hereditary determination, though some cases fail to show an hereditary background. *Diabetes,* a condition resulting in lowered nutrition of the body and excretion of sugar in the urine, was originally thought to be based on a dominant gene or several genes with similar effects expressed in varying degrees of severity of the disease. Snyder, however, proposed a recessive gene for diabetes from a study of 675 family histories. There may be several types of diabetes. Gates has suggested that a dominant gene may condition a mild form of the disease which may usually be easily controlled, and the recessive type may be more severe. Affecting from 16 to 20 per cent of the population, *appendicitis* is another condition which appears to be genetically determined, but whether by a single gene or multiple genes is not known (Fig. 199). *Tumors and cancers*, too, have been the subject of considerable genetic investigation. Macklin, famous for her investigation of problems of cancer in mice, concluded that susceptibility to cancer in mice is based on a simple recessive. Macklin stated that "if evolution means anything at all, it means that if cancer is inherited in mice, it is inherited in other mammals, at least in those who show it." It may prove futile to seek an identical genetic basis for all tumors, because cancer is not one disease but many. When family histories deal with specific kinds of cancer, statistics may reveal the hereditary basis. It may be dependent on recessive genes, since it frequently appears in families that have no knowledge of previous cases. The increasing average population age may also be giving opportunities for the phenotypic appearance of cancer that may have failed to be manifested in earlier generations, though genotypically present.

POSSIBILITY OF LETHAL GENES IN MAN. Lethal genes in man have not been isolated as definitely as in some of the lower animals (pp. 188-195). Baur, Fischer, and Lenz suggest, however, that the preponderance of deaths of male infants over female infants must be accounted for by inherited lethal genes. Perhaps even the differential birth rate can be explained on the basis of lethal genes inherited by the male zygote.

Other investigators regard several fatal childhood and juvenile diseases as based upon hereditary lethal genes. Besides definitely lethal ones there are several sublethal or borderline cases. Early death, leaving no offspring, adds difficulties to the genetic analysis of many suspected lethal characters.

Hemophilia

Hemophilia, a condition in which the blood fails to clot normally after an injury, has been studied genetically. The condition has been found in numerous isolated communities in Europe where it has been possible to construct pedigrees of fairly large numbers of persons through several generations. The occurrence of hemophilia in some European royal families has also aided in studies of its inheritance. An early observation in regard to hemophilia was its consistent restriction to males. Because it appeared to be transmitted through females, hemophilia came to be regarded as a sex-linked trait (pp. 159-169).

Sex-linked recessive inheritance of hemophilia is based on the heterogametic nature of the male sex. Of the 48 (diploid) chromosomes in human beings, the members of the pair of sex chromosomes are of unequal size in males. In females the 2 sex chromosomes are alike in size. Males therefore have only one large chromosome called the **X** chromosome, which is associated with a much smaller one called the **Y** chromosome, and females have **XX** chromosomes. On the basis of known inheritance, the gene for hemo-

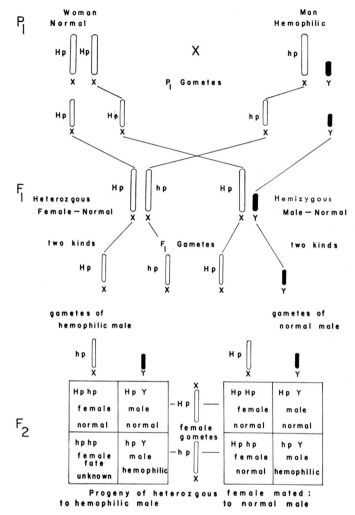

FIG. 200. DIAGRAM OF INHERITANCE OF HEMOPHILIA.

P₁ Normal female mated to hemophilic male.

F₁ Both male and female are normal, but female is heterozygous.

F₂ Diagrammatic representation of union of gametes of female heterozygous for hemophilia: at left with those of hemophilic male; at right with those of normal male.

philia is assumed to be located on the **X** chromosome, manifesting its presence in the male where no corresponding normal gene on the **Y** chromosome exerts an influence (Fig. 200).

Snyder, who has made very extensive studies of this condition, feels that data are as yet insufficient to settle the question of the existence of females which are homozygous for hemophilia. The assumption would normally be that if hemophilia in males is owing to a gene in the simplex condition on the **X** chromosome, it should appear also in females where the **XX** chromosomes would be expected to carry it in the homozygous state. Brinkhous and Graham have recently reported the occurrence of hemophilic female dogs with the genotype *h-h*; these dogs could be treated and reared to maturity. Physiologically their condition is similar to that in hemophilic human beings, because both lack a plasma factor in the blood. The evidence from dogs indicates that the *h-h* genotype is not otherwise lethal. Hogben has offered three possible explanations for the failure to find well-authenticated cases of hemophilic females. Perhaps they have not been found because the disease is very rare, perhaps the gene is lethal in duplicate (homozygous recessive), or perhaps it cannot manifest itself in the duplicate condition owing to the physiological environment of the female soma.

Although true hemophilia is normally inherited as a recessive sex-linked character as indicated above, several features deserve mention. Some investigators, as, for example, Haldane, consider the possibility of *different* mutant genes, *probably alleles*. Accordingly the mutant alleles condition different degrees of hemophilia, and affected persons show varying severities of the disease. Since the alleles, designated as H, h, and h', occupy the same loci, they are inherited in the same crisscross sex-linked manner. The allele h may be regarded as conditioning a severe type and h' a milder form of bleeding.

True hemophilia may be confused with other diseases which produce various types of "bleeders." The difference in inheritance of the several diseases has led to the diversity of opinion about the exact manner of inheritance. Faulty diagnosis of bleeders' diseases and sometimes a failure to recognize true hemophilia have added to the confusion.

Inheritance of the Human Blood Groups

Because of their importance in the practice of medicine, considerable study has been devoted to the characteristics of human blood. Among the topics considered have been blood groups and hemophilia. Their physiology and genetic determination, unknown until recently, are still under investigation. Although transfusion experiments were attempted in France as early as the 17th century, the reason for their frequent failure was unknown. The basis of incompatibility of blood between some persons was not known until the isoagglutination reaction of blood was discovered by Landsteiner in 1900. Based on this reaction, four blood groups were identified which were later shown to be hereditarily conditioned. These are designated as O, A, B, and AB. Later, with Levine, Landsteiner discovered three blood types, M, N, and MN, independent of the A-B-O groups, as well as a third system determined by an agglutinogen P. More recently distinguished is a fourth blood-group system independent of the A-B-O, M-N, and P groups, namely, the variations of Rh-Hr. Investigations indicate existence of a variety of blood types in other animals besides the human being. Stormont and Cumley report recognition of more than 80 different blood factors in cattle. By blood tests every animal in a herd except identical twins may be differentiated. With these tests it is possible to obtain information about the parentage and to identify breeding animals from which identification tags have been lost.

The differentiation of blood types in human beings is primarily important in the field of medicine where transfusions must be used, but a knowledge of their characteristics and inheritance is significant also in law, studies of racial migrations, population genetics, and linkage in human genetics. For transfusions blood types of donor and recipient must be mutually compatible. When incompatible types are mixed, the red corpuscles may clump or disintegrate. In the animal body such clumping and hemolysis are attended by shock and kidney damage and may terminate in death.

Antigen is the term applied to any foreign substance which, when injected into an animal, stimulates the formation of a specific reacting substance. An antibody is the specific reactive substance produced by the body in response to the injection of an antigen. An agglutinogen is a special antigen. In the case of the O-A-B and Rh blood types, the agglutinogen is present on the surface of the red blood cells. Agglutinins are antibodies found in immune blood sera which when added to the corresponding agglutinogen, in this case a suspension of the blood to be tested, cause the blood cells to adhere to one another or to agglutinate. Agglutination, when it occurs in the animal body, may cause shock or even death, because the clumped masses cannot pass through the capillaries. The degree of agglutination depends upon the proportion of antibody or agglutinin to agglutinogen. Agglutinins may be characteristically present in the case of some blood groups. In others they may develop in response to the introduction of agglutinogens by transfusions or otherwise.

Blood-group determination may be one of the tests for identical twins (pp. 462–465), and knowledge of its inheritance is being accepted in some states as evidence in disputes involving doubtful parentage and interchanged children. Wiener (1950) reported that the use of the A-B-O, M-N, and Rh-Hr tests gives a 50 per cent chance of excluding paternity of a man falsely accused and that more than 90 per cent of cases of interchange of children can be solved with the combined use of the tests for the three most important blood-group systems for the two sets of parents and children. The combined determination of all blood groups for an individual is expected eventually to provide extreme precision of identification. Recognition of identification by means of blood-group information and other characteristics of blood is accepted by some courts in criminal cases. In addition to the best-known medical application of information about blood groups in transfusions, the treatment of the disease *erythroblastosis fetalis* which is a cause of fetal and infant deaths is also based on information about blood types.

Knowledge about blood groups has been applied as a tool in anthropological studies of racial relationships. According to one theory, the O group was the original type characteristic of primitive man. This type is very largely found in certain tribes of American Indians. Since group A predominates in central and western Europe and group B in Asia, it has been assumed that A and B arose by mutation in these localities. But the occurrence of all four types, A, O, B, and AB, in most regions of the earth is regarded as evidence of the mingling of the races of man which has been going on since prehistoric time. Recently blood types of tribes of American Indians have been compared with those of Asiatic races in studies of racial migration.

Continued studies of blood groups and types is expected to aid in obtaining information about linkage groups in human beings. Eventually as such data accumulate, they may lead to perfection of human chromosome maps.

Table L

O, A, B, AND AB BLOOD GROUPS

Phenotypes	Genotypes
O	ii
A	$I^A I^A,\ I^A i$
B	$I^B I^B,\ I^B i$
AB	$I^A I^B$

INHERITANCE OF THE O, A, B, AND AB BLOOD GROUPS. A series of multiple alleles has been postulated by Bernstein as the genetic determinants of the O, A, B, and AB blood groups. These genes have been designated in various ways, but Strandskov, to emphasize their allelic relationship, has proposed the substitution of symbols such as have been applied to allelic genes in other organisms, accordingly: I^A, the gene for isoagglutinogen A; I^B, the gene for isoagglutinogen B; and i, the allele determining the isoagglutinogen O. I^A and I^B are each dominant over i, but neither is dominant over the other. This lack of dominance accounts for the genotype $I^A I^B$ expressed in the AB blood group. In addition to the four blood groups, O, A, B, and AB, two major subgroups of A are called A_1 and A_2. Another subgroup, A_3, is very rare. To avoid complexity, these and their combinations $A_1 B$ and $A_2 B$ have not been included in Tables L and LI.

INHERITANCE OF THE M-N BLOOD TYPES. The M-N blood types are determined by the incompletely dominant genes $M\text{-}m$. Phenotypes MM, MN, and NN corresponding to genotypes MM, Mm, and mm have been identified.

INHERITANCE OF RH-HR BLOOD TYPES. A significant addition to knowledge of human inheritance was made by Landsteiner and Wiener in 1940 when they announced the discovery of agglutinogen Rh. Blood of the rhesus monkey, *Rhesus macacus*, was being used in the experimental work which led to identification and naming of the Rh series of blood types and corresponding series of genes in man. The Rh-Hr types of human blood can be demonstrated by serological techniques involving the use of Rh and Hr antisera derived from human beings. Anti-Rh or Rh antibody is used for distinguishing between the presence of the corresponding agglutinogen (antigen) Rh-positive and its absence, Rh-negative.

Table LI

O, A, B, AND AB BLOOD GROUPS

Parental Combinations		Possibilities for Progeny				
Phenotypes	Genotypes	Genotypes	Phenotypes—Blood Groups			
O × O	ii × ii	ii	O	..	..	..
O × A	ii × I^AI^A ii × I^Ai	ii, I^Ai	O	A	..	..
O × B	ii × I^BI^B ii × I^Bi	ii, I^Bi	O	..	B	..
O × AB	ii × I^AI^B	I^Ai, I^Bi	..	A	B	..
A × A	I^AI^A × I^AI^A I^AI^A × I^Ai I^Ai × I^AI^A I^Ai × I^Ai	ii, I^Ai, I^AI^A	O	A	..	..
A × B	I^AI^A × I^BI^B I^AI^A × I^Bi I^Ai × I^BI^B I^Ai × I^Bi	ii, I^Ai, I^AI^B, I^Bi	O	A	B	AB
A × AB	I^AI^A × I^AI^B I^Ai × I^AI^B	$I^AI^A, I^Ai, I^AI^B, I^Bi$	..	A	B	AB
B × B	I^BI^B × I^BI^B I^BI^B × I^Bi I^Bi × I^BI^B I^Bi × I^Bi	I^Bi, I^BI^B, ii	O	..	B	..
B × AB	I^BI^B × I^AI^B I^Bi × I^AI^B	$I^Ai, I^Bi, I^BI^B, I^AI^B$	..	A	B	AB
AB × AB	I^AI^B × I^AI^B	I^AI^A, I^BI^B, I^AI^B	..	A	B	AB

Filling in blanks in last column, as, for example, A, B, and AB at top, would provide the blood groups which could not be obtained from the matings

Since the discovery of these blood types, it has been determined that a series of 8 or more allelic genes* is concerned in the inheritance of the Rh blood types (Table LII). Three types of Rh antisera, anti-Rh, anti-rh' and anti-rh", and two reciprocally related Hr antisera, anti-hr' and anti-hr", are used to identify the various Rh-Hr phenotypes and genotypes. Additional antisera have been produced by some workers. As new antisera become available, additional phenotypes may be identified. Eight Rh phenotypes can be distinguished with the three "standard" Rh antisera.

---

* Some workers have proposed a theory of closely linked genes for the Rh series.

With the two additional Hr antisera to identify the homozygous and hetero-zygous genotypes, 18 Rh-Hr phenotypes corresponding to 36 possible genotypes could be distinguished. With anti-hr', Rh_1 and rh' may each be divided into the presumably homozygous and heterozygous subtypes, and with anti-hr'', Rh_2 and rh'' may be similarly divided.

Table LII

SIMPLIFIED SCHEME TO SHOW THE RELATIONSHIP OF ALLELES AND
PHENOTYPES IN THE RH BLOOD TYPES
(After Wiener)

Genes	Phenotypes (Agglutinogens) International Nomenclature Designations	21 Most Common Genotypes*
r	rh	rr
r'	rh'	$r'r'$ and $r'r$
r''	rh''	$r''r''$ and $r''r$
r^y	rh_y (rh'rh'')	$r'r''$
R^0	Rh_0	R^0R^0 and R^0r
R^1	Rh_1	$R'R'$, $R'r'$, $R'r$, $R'R^0$, and $r'R^0$
R^2	Rh_2	R^2R^2, R^2r'', R^2r, R^2R^0, and $r''R^0$
R^z	Rh_z (Rh_1Rh_2)	R^1R^2, $R'r''$, and $r'R^2$

* Not including the rare alleles or the Rh variants

Much of the study of blood types has been carried on in hospitals, where physiologists customarily refer to Rh-positive and Rh-negative blood types. Wiener proposed a system to harmonize physiological and genetic designa-tions, as indicated in Table LII. The 8 allelic genes may be recombined to form 36 genotypes which condition different phenotypes and express them-selves in the variations of the Rh agglutinogens. As indicated above, ad-ditional refinements may allow for identification of a larger number of types; and, as with the O, A, B, AB series, in the Rh series some intermediate forms called Rh variants have also been discovered.

In human beings the Rh agglutinin is formed as a result of isosensitiza-tion by red blood cells from blood transfusion or as a result of certain pregnancies. Anti-Rh sera are produced by immunizing animals, by indi-viduals receiving transfusion of Rh incompatible blood, and also by Rh-negative women who have been immunized by blood cells from an Rh-posi-tive fetus during pregnancy. The agglutinogens of the Rh types of blood would react with the agglutinins or anti-Rh bodies of the rh type and thus cause the clumping of the red blood cells when these two blood types come together.

The distribution of genes for the Rh blood types varies in the races of human beings. Tests indicate that 85–87 per cent of white persons in New York City has one of the dominant Rh blood types or, expressed in reverse, that the Rh-negative types are found in 12–15 per cent of the white individuals. The Rh-negative types, however, are very rare in Mongolians and occur in but 5–8 per cent of the Negro race.

The rh character of human blood is important in *erythroblastosis fetalis* (p. 495) which is attributed to differences in the antigenic composition of the erythrocytes (red blood cells) of the two parents. If the mother is Rh-negative and the father has one of the types with the Rh blood factor, the mother's blood may react with the fetal blood which, because of dominance, is characterized by the effects of the *R* gene in some form. The maternal anti-Rh agglutinins may then affect the susceptible fetal blood, and still-birth or severe anaemia may result. The importance of blood reaction in connection with obstetrics is the basis for much of the investigation of Rh blood types now undertaken in clinical laboratories, because *erythroblastosis fetalis* may show a mortality of 50 per cent. The presence of the *rr* genes in 12–15 per cent of the white population accounts for the more frequent occurrence of the disease than among Chinese and Japanese where the *rr* genes are more rare.

CONCLUSION. In conclusion it should be emphasized that all the work on differential blood types and their inheritance is fairly new and therefore in a state of rapid change. Points now regarded as established may later prove to be unfounded.

Linkage in Human Beings

Although knowledge of linkage in man has been of slower development than in plants and lower animals, *sex-linked* characters in man have long been recognized. In 1779 Michael Lort in England noted the peculiar inheritance of color blindness in man and reported his observations to the Royal Society of London. Forty years later C. T. Nasse in Germany connected the disease hemophilia with sex-linked inheritance in man. Sex-linked characters are determined by genes in the sex chromosomes, both the **X** and the **Y**. It is important to emphasize the *three types of sex-linked genes* in human beings (pp. 500–501). There are (1) genes carried in the *nonhomologous part* of the **X** chromosome which are completely **X**-linked and have no corresponding allele in the **Y** chromosome. There are (2) completely **Y**-linked genes carried in the *nonhomologous part* of the **Y** chromosome which have no corresponding alleles in the **X** chromosome. Then (3) there are genes in the *homologous parts* of both the **X** and **Y** chromosomes. Because these regions of **X** and **Y** are homologous, each gene has a corresponding allele in the opposite chromosome exactly as is found in normal autosomes. Genes in the homologous parts of the **X** and **Y** chromosomes are never completely linked to one chromosome but normally show crossing over from the **X** to the **Y** and *vice versa* exactly as in autosomally linked genes.

Genetical work by Haldane based on the cytological investigations of Koller and Darlington has shown relationship of various sex-linked genes

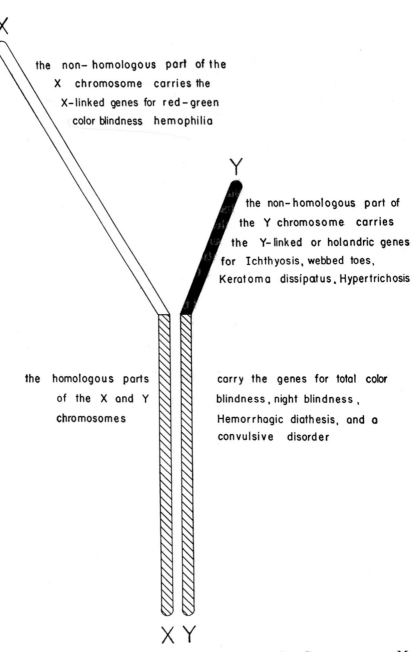

X

the non-homologous part of the
X chromosome carries the
X-linked genes for red-green
color blindness hemophilia

Y

the non-homologous part of
the Y chromosome carries
the Y-linked or holandric genes
for Ichthyosis, webbed toes,
Keratoma dissipatus. Hypertrichosis

the homologous parts
of the X and Y
chromosomes

carry the genes for total color
blindness, night blindness,
Hemorrhagic diathesis, and a
convulsive disorder

X Y

FIG. 201. DIAGRAM OF THE POSSIBLE RELATIONSHIP OF SEX CHROMOSOMES IN MAN.
Because crossing over occurs in the homologous segments of **X** and **Y,** the genes
carried in these parts show incomplete linkage as is typical of autosomal genes. Since
there is no crossing over in the nonhomologous **X** and **Y** segments, their genes show
complete **X**- and **Y**-linkage, respectively. (Diagram based on the researches of Koller
and Darlington, Snyder and Palmer, and Kaliss and Schweitzer.)

to the parts of the **X** and **Y** chromosomes in human beings (Fig. 201). Additional work by Snyder and Palmer and more recently by Kaliss and Schweitzer has extended knowledge of sex-linked genes in man. Evidence now clearly indicates that among others the alleles determining red color blindness, green color blindness, and hemophilia are definitely located in the nonhomologous part of the **X** chromosome. These genes and their conditioned sex-linked traits, since they are completely **X**-linked, follow the course of the **X** chromosomes through the generations. Thus the red-green types of color blindness and hemophilia exhibit the characteristic crisscross inheritance of ordinary sex linkage (pp. 159–160).

Among the few completely **Y**-linked characters, the skin abnormality known as *Ichthyosis hystrix gravior* is probably best established as a holandric, completely male, trait. Since such *holandric* characters, or more correctly their conditioning genes, follow the course of the **Y** chromosome, they are inherited through the male line only, that is, the affliction passes from father to son. The inheritance of this character was traced through six generations of males. Snyder lists three other traits showing evidence of complete **Y**-linkage. These are one type of webbed toes; *Keratoma dissipatum*, another skin abnormality; and hypertrichosis of the ears of mature males.

Evidence indicates that probably eight hereditary defects in human beings are now recognized as traits conditioned by genes located in the homologous parts of the **X** and **Y** chromosomes (Fig. 201). Among these are total color blindness in which no color is distinguished; a form of night blindness known as Oguchi's disease; two skin abnormalities, *Xeroderma pigmentosum* and a recessive *Epidermolysis bullosa;* an eye defect, *Retinitis pigmentosa*, in which pigments are deposited in the retina of the eye. In 1943 Snyder and Palmer described a convulsive disorder and Kaliss and Schweitzer, a case of hereditary *hemorrhagic diathesis* characterized by spontaneous bleeding from the nose, uterus, and mucous membranes, both of which were regarded as conditioned by genes located in the homologous parts of the **X** and **Y** chromosomes. The genetical importance of this group of genes lies in their incomplete linkage to either the **X** or the **Y** chromosome. They show crossing over from the **X** to the **Y** and *vice versa* in the same manner as autosomally linked genes.

Besides the three types of sex linkage mentioned above, a fourth kind of inheritance has been postulated for human beings in which the transmission is from mother to daughter, not to her sons. This type, called **hologynic** *or wholly female inheritance*, has been indicated in a few human pedigrees. The explanation is based upon some cases found in *Drosophila* in which the two **X** chromosomes were joined and failed to separate at meiosis. In such cases the two **X** chromosomes both passed into an egg as **XX**. Since these two sex chromosomes determine femaleness, **XX** eggs, whether fertilized by **X** or by **Y** sperms, develop into females with hologynic inheritance.

A POSSIBLE CASE OF AUTOSOMAL LINKAGE IN HUMAN BEINGS. Burks studied families showing hereditary deficiency in the number of teeth which was apparently associated with hair color in human beings. In this investigation 212 pairs of sibs were compared for similarity in tooth deficiency and hair color. From the statistical treatment of the data, Burks concluded that there was linkage of these two characteristics with about 10 per cent crossing over between these autosomally linked genes. This is the first instance of autosomal linkage so far discovered in man, although other studies suggest the possibility of autosomal linkage relations between myopia and eye colors. Haldane has considered Burks's data and conclusions and suggests with extreme scientific caution that although the case for autosomal linkage is strong, possibly more evidence is needed before the fact can be established. Investigation of other traits may be expected to indicate other instances of autosomal linkage in man.

LINKAGE OF HEMOPHILIA AND COLOR BLINDNESS WITH CROSSING OVER OF THE DETERMINERS IN THE X CHROMOSOME. Red-green color blindness and hemophilia are conditioned by X-linked genes and are therefore well-known examples of ordinary sex-linked characters. Each of these traits with its contrasting normal state is presumably determined by a single pair of genes, although there is a possibility that multiple alleles may be involved in each case.

A history of a German family showing both hemophilia and green color blindness in some members has been presented by Rath as the first clear-cut evidence of crossing over in the chromosomes of human beings. A phenotypically normal mother had four sons. The oldest was hemophilic and color blind, the second was also hemophilic but had normal color vision, the third had normal blood and was color blind, while the fourth had normal blood and normal color vision. The mother is regarded as an undoubted carrier for both green color blindness and hemophilia. If both genes were in one of the X chromosomes, the male offspring either would be green-color-blind bleeders or have normal color vision and normal blood. The occurrence of both a normal-visioned bleeder and a green-color-blind son with normal blood required the assumption of crossing over. On the other hand, if the genes had been distributed to the two X chromosomes, one in each, the sons either would be normal-visioned bleeders or have healthy blood and be green-color-blind. The meeting of the two abnormal characters as well as of the two normal characters could again be explained only by the assumption of crossing over. It is fundamentally immaterial which of the possibilities is assumed, since either requires crossing over as an explanation. A confirmation of the meeting of the two abnormal characters, hemophilia and color blindness, and the two normal characters, healthy blood and normal color vision, in a Japanese family was reported by Murakami, et al., in 1951, who assume that crossing over in the germ cell of the woman of the first generation brought sex-linked genes into the same chromosome.

Riddell from a six-generation pedigree of a hemophilic × color-vision-defective family reported the case of a woman who was heterozygous for both hemophilia and color blindness. These traits were derived from different parents. An only son of this woman did not show crossing over of these traits. In considering linkage relations and crossing over in the sex chromosomes, the synaptic situation should be kept in mind. Completely X-linked genes in the nonhomologous part of an X chromosome do not cross over with the holandric genes which are completely Y-linked and located in the nonhomologous part of the Y chromosome. X-linked genes may, however, cross over with other X-linked genes, since a female has two complete X chromosomes *including the nonhomologous parts*. Thus the genes for color blindness and hemophilia may cross over in the female, because they are located in the nonhomologous parts of the X chromosome.

White believes that Rath's case of crossing over of the genes for hemophilia and green blindness, while it constitutes definite evidence, is insufficient for an estimation of the frequency of crossing over between the genes for these two defects. Haldane, however, has published an estimate of the amount of crossing over between the loci of red-green color blindness and hemophilia. From data in seven distinct studies of these two X-linked genes, including the work of Rath and Riddell, Haldane estimated crossing over between these genes at between 5 and 15 per cent with 10 per cent as a close approximation. Haldane, with the help of other statisticians, devised mathematical techniques for use in the study of linkage relations in human beings where genetic experimentation is impossible.

The fundamental analyses were made of data from lower animals, including numerous species of insects and particularly the Drosophila. Information so obtained gave a basis for knowledge about the frequency of occurrence of mutations and the preservation in a population of mutant genes under various known and assumed types of mating. Knowledge about changes in genes and their continued existence has come to be called the science of gene dynamics. Gene dynamics is now also being applied in human genetics to explain the occurrence of gene mutation in man.

Another study by White concerned congenital stationary nightblindness with myopia and color blindness in several members of a pedigree which extends over seven generations. Of 183 direct members of this family, 87 were males and 96, females. Of the females 13 produced affected sons or grandsons and are thereby known to have been transmitters. Of the males 20 showed ocular defects, 5 being night-blind, myopic, and green-color-blind; 7 night-blind and myopic; 6 color-blind; and 2 night-blind and myopic with condition of color vision unknown. Altogether 76 per cent of the males for whom data were available had defects. This excess of 26 per cent over the expected 50 per cent may be due to lack of complete data and a high degree of crossing over. Empirical calculations indicate a crossover ratio within the limits of from 39.1 to 47.4 per cent, with a mean of 43.25

per cent ±4.15 per cent. The gene determining green color blindness is assumed to be 43.25 plus or minus 4.15 units distant from the gene (or genes) determining the occurrence of night blindness with myopia.

From these facts, White in agreement with Haldane concludes that the human **X**-chromosome map will be a long one. White located the genes for green color blindness and night blindness with myopia on the nonpairing segment of the **X** chromosome. Night blindness and myopia are either governed by the same gene or by two genes in positions so close together that the crossover ratio between them is very small. Recently the gene determining night blindness has been located in the homologous part of the **X** chromosome. This fact, indicating incomplete **X**-linkage, might tend to complicate the results in studies involving linkage with the gene for color blindness. Naturally it may be at considerable distance from the locus of red-green color blindness in the nonhomologous part of the **X** chromosome.

Such investigations of sex linkage provide the basis for the preparation of a map of the sex chromosomes in human beings. On this map the relative positions of a number of genes may be indicated although the exact position of the loci has not been determined. Future work may yield data to complete an accurate map of the sex chromosomes.

The numerous blood types studied in connection with other traits may suggest linkage relationships. One of these undertaken by Snyder and co-workers used the blood groups, O, A, AB, and B; the blood types, M, N, and MN; and the presence or absence of taste for the chemical phenyl-thiocarbamide. The data indicated that there is no linkage between the genes involved in the determination of these traits. The large number of chromosomes in man, 48, makes the study of autosomal linkage difficult. Gates recently published a list of all known linkages and suspected linkages in human beings. His list includes

> 45 **X**-linked characters
> 7 **Y**-linked characters
> 48 combinations of possible autosomal linkage and
> 7 cases of hologynic inheritance.

chapter 28

Inheritance of Mental Traits
in Human Beings

Unwillingness to believe that human characteristics are heritable is often particularly insistent where mental traits are concerned. The geneticist, however, believes that hereditary genes determine the potentialities of all biological characteristics. Their expression is modified by the interaction of the genes among themselves and with various aspects of the environment in which the organism finds itself.

All the tests which have been used in a large number of cases reveal that human beings differ in intelligence just as they do in many more simply measurable characteristics. They have been found to be distributed in accordance with a normal frequency curve. When a large group of men is measured for height, these measurements can be arranged on a graph. If the group is a fair random sample, the measurements will be found to form a normal frequency curve (Fig. 136). Measurements of intelligence when arranged on a graph will form a similar curve indicating that very high intelligence and very low intelligence are about equally rare, with average intelligence most frequent.

According to Terman who made very extensive studies of intelligence in children, 60 per cent of the population will fall within 10 points on either side of the average and have an I. Q. between 90 and 110. Fourteen per cent will be found between 80 and 90 on one side and between 110 and 120 on the other, and about 5 per cent in the next range of 10 points, to 70 below and 130 above. Finally 1 per cent will be found with an I. Q. lower than 70 and another 1 per cent higher than 130. Those below 70 are rated as feeble-minded, and the exceptional 1 per cent with an I. Q. higher than 130 is considered as geniuses or near-geniuses. Adverse critics of these and other intelligence tests feel that they do not measure intelligence but only the things learned in the environment of the individual. Defenders of the tests maintain that they find and measure the potentiality for learning from the environment. All these measures have been used in genetic studies planned to determine the heritability of intelligence.

Inheritance of Intelligence

As with physical traits, where studies of twins and studies of inheritance of abnormalities have illuminated the inheritance of normal traits, so also with intelligence. Much of the research having to do with mental traits has been concerned with abnormal or unusual characteristics, and much of it is based on comparative studies of identical and fraternal twins. Most of the studies of the inheritance of intelligence have been of groups rather than of individuals. That is, groups of children have been compared, such as children in orphanages *vs.* children living with their parents, orphan children of laborers *vs.* orphan children of professional parents, sons of university graduates of proved success *vs.* sons of university graduates of less success, etc. Many of the studies are open to a variety of interpretations. Some of them will be considered at this point.

CORRELATION OF INTELLIGENCE AMONG RELATIVES. Schuster and Elderton published a correlation of academic reports of Oxford University undergraduates between fathers and sons which lags only a little behind the correlation of physical characters. This may mean that the fathers and sons have a highly correlated mental endowment. Critics point out that the important factor would be the environment provided by the fathers, such as scholarly attitudes resulting in academic application or indifferent attitudes resulting in very indifferent application by the sons. Those who believe inheritance important in the cause of such correlation say that the fathers and sons inherited a similar innate mental make-up, which expresses itself in them and in the environment which fathers provide for their sons.

To determine by intelligence tests the effect of uniformity of environment, Pearson studied children in orphanages in California. Between siblings, that is, brothers and sisters, he found a correlation of 0.508 in intelligence which is statistically significant. A similar study of children under the more varied conditions of school life was made in Great Britain, and the correlation in intelligence between siblings was found to be very similar, viz., 0.515. From this study it was concluded that environment has little effect in modifying the intellectual similarity of brothers and sisters. Wingfield also found that the long-continued equal environment of an orphanage did not reduce the differences in intelligence of the unrelated children.

One of the striking studies of the kinships of celebrated men was Galton's statistical analysis of the relatives of 415 unusually noted men. They were found to belong to 300 families which had produced about 1,000 men of exceptional distinction. Galton's standard of exceptional talent was so high that he considered it as appearing once in every 4,000 persons, or at the rate of 250 per million. In the selected kinships he found that among 100 celebrated men 31 had noted fathers, 41 noted brothers, 48 noted sons, 17 noted grandfathers, and 14 noted grandsons. If talent were not hereditary, only 0.025 celebrities should be found among the fathers of 100 celebrated men. Actually, as indicated above, he found 31. The expectation for noted grandfathers if talent were not hereditary would be 0.05, but there were actually 17. The figures incidentally also show that a man has a smaller proportion of his total inheritance in common with either of his grandfathers than with his father. F. A. Woods made a similar study of the kindred of 3,500 noted Americans. He estimated that the probability that any American citizen taken at random would be related to one of these celebrated men was 1 in 500. He found that the probability that one of his 3,500 noted Americans would be related to another was 1 in 5, or a hundred times the calculated probability for the general population.

One of Woods's original studies was concerned with the occurrence of mental abilities and moral superiority among members of royal families. He studied more than 800 individuals from the 12th to the 19th centuries for whom attainments and virtues were known. They were classified and arranged in a series of grades from 1 to 10 on the basis of their abilities, class 10 being reserved for individuals showing the highest attainments. Such noteworthy characters as Frederick the Great, Queen Isabella of Spain, William the Silent, and Gustavus Adolphus were in the highest class. In a great chart groups of other class 9 and class 10 characters would be found clustered about these outstanding individuals. Woods concluded that there is a distinct correlation in royalty between mental and moral qualities and that they are hereditary.

The author stated that the majority of eminent men come and always have come from families well above the average. In Great Britain the ratio of notable men from the "lower classes" has actually declined. From the *Dictionary of National Biography* he found that, previous to the 19th century, 11.7 per cent of the most eminent men listed was born of skilled or unskilled laborers. By the early 19th century this percentage declined to 7.2 per cent, and the second supplement, dealing with a more recent period, shows a further decline to 4.2 per cent. Perhaps these figures may be interpreted as indicating that the better talents which were once latent have been removed from the class of untrained laborers by the better educational opportunities afforded during the past century. If this is correct, socially important contributions are less and less likely to come from the so-called underprivileged classes. These and other similar studies all indicate that unusual ability tends to run in families, but they do not prove that ability is inherited. On the other hand, there must be some explanation for the unusual preponderance of exceptional ability in the kinships of noted persons. It is hard to believe that a mere chance of better environment, independently of the superior ability to furnish a superior environment, could be the explanation. A superior environment alone cannot make a noted or highly celebrated person out of an individual lacking in superior capacities. A superior environment can only assist in the expression of the potentialities an individual has.

USE OF TWINS IN THE STUDY OF THE HERITABILITY OF INTELLIGENCE. A number of comparative studies of identical (or monozygotic) and fraternal (or dizygotic) twins have been made to determine the hereditary basis of intelligence. One of these in 1933 established that the difference in I. Q. of monozygotic or one-egg twins was only half as great as the difference in pairs of dizygotic or two-egg twins. Since monozygotic twins by their nature have identical hereditary constitutions (pp. 463–465), this finding shows the influence of heredity in intelligence. Examinations of twins in European concentration camps, reported by Gottschaldt, included tests of word-logic and abstract thinking. On the basis of comparisons of pairs of the two kinds of twins, the hereditary factor is considered to be from two to five times more potent than environment. Tests of practical intelligence and motor tests also showed that the dizygotic twins reached their maximum performance discordantly, while the monozygotic twins were concordant. In other words, the best performances of members of dizygotic twin pairs were at unequal levels, while those of members of monozygotic twin pairs were at more nearly the same levels. Such results are interpreted as lending additional support to the hereditary determination of the abilities so measured, or the so-called functional side of learning. Studies have also been made of brains of twins on the assumption that brain structure is related to intelligence. A recent comparison of brains of monozygotic and dizygotic twin infants appears to establish the heritability of cerebral patterns. The complexity and frequency of the convolutions of the brains of the monozygotic twins were much more similar than those of the dizygotic.

GENETIC BASIS OF INTELLIGENCE. Authors who have given thought to the hereditary background of intelligence have postulated multiple genes as the determinants (pp. 260 265). Harrison Hunt proposed a series of possibly five genes, suggesting that the dominant homozygous condition of two of them might be thought of as effecting average intelligence (Table LIII). The number of genotypes possible in the range of

Table LIII

SUGGESTED GENOTYPIC BASIS FOR DEGREES OF MENTALITY

Degree of Mentality	Dominant Factors	Possible Genotype
Idiot	0	aabbccddee
Imbecile	1	Aabbccddee
Moron	2	AaBbccddee
Low average	3–4	AaBbCCddee
Average	5–6	AaBbCCDdee
High average	7–8	AaBbCCDDEe
Eminent	9	AABBCCDDEe
Genius	10	AABBCCDDEE

average mentality is evident and might be used to account for the wide difference in ability in the normal population.

Thorndike suggested a similar theory on the assumption of variation in the quantitative effects of a number of genes. At present it may be said that the expression of intelligence may be subject to environmental influences. Its potentialities, however, are not modifiable, and it is probably dependent on a combination of hereditary factors.

Inheritance of Special Abilities

In addition to studies of general intelligence, a number of investigations have been concerned with special talents. Terman has said that intellect by its very nature is highly general and that achievement in any of numerous fields is possible to one who is intellectually superior, provided the necessary interests and drives are present.

Without determinations of specific genetic bases, there are numerous examples of the appearance of some special talents in certain families. Titian, the eminent painter, came from a family including nine other painters. Mathematical ability appears in some families. The Bernoullis were a family, originally from Antwerp, which numbered eight outstanding mathematicians in three generations. Training is thought to modify mathematical ability only slightly. One recent study ascribed 97 per cent of this ability in adults to original nature. Among special talents perhaps musical ability has received most attention from students of heredity. Population studies of the singing voice among children from Jutland to Sicily showed a consistent decrease in occurrence of the bass-soprano combinations from north to south. Tenor-alto voices were far more numerous in Italy than in northern Europe. In the study of racial crossing in Jamaica, application of the Seashore tests for 26 measurable factors in musical ability found Negroes to have a definite inherited background for musical ability. Exceptional musical endowment expressing itself creatively as well as in performance has been traced in 28 musical families through three or more generations. The Bach family showed this special talent in an unbroken line through five generations. Probably numerous genes must be combined to effect the development and expression of any of the special talents, a group of multiple genes furnishing the basis of general intelligence and additional genes producing special talents. Everyone has either the dominant or recessive gene of each of these pairs of alleles.

Inheritance of Abnormal Mentality

The foregoing aspects of the inheritance of elements involved in intelligence have to do with normal and desirable traits. Unfortunately, abnormal mental conditions likewise have an hereditary background. In fact, a great deal of genetic study has been devoted to feeble-mindedness and insanity. Much information concerning inheritance in general has come from such studies together with some more or less definite conclusions about the abnormal states.

GRADES OF ABNORMAL MENTALITY. Low-grade mentalities can be arranged in a series downward from degrees of feeble-mindedness through imbecility and idiocy. Though there are various causes of idiocy, probably including prenatal maternal disturbances of a nutritional nature, injuries at birth, and glandular abnormalities, some forms of idiocy are definitely hereditary. One of these, called amaurotic idiocy, is known to be conditioned by a recessive factor. It appears in offspring of consanguineous marriages of persons whose ancestors have had affected relatives. Mongolian idiocy, which is a type of mental deficiency owing probably to abnormal secretion of the thyroid gland, may also have an hereditary basis. Its inheritance has not been definitely determined, but it may be due to a recessive gene. A relationship to maternal age at the time of birth and a possibility of unknown environmental influence on the thyroid gland have also been suggested. The mental condition can be improved, if not definitely restored to normal, by glandular treatment provided it is applied continuously from a very early age; this would be without effect on the presumed hereditary background of the glandular defect.

Feeble-mindedness has been studied in many attempts to determine whether it is based on inheritance. One study revealed an impressive number of feeble-minded children in families when one or both parents showed various mental or nervous defects. Another investigator in comparing the sibs, that is, brothers and sisters, of feeble-minded and the general population found 31.5 per cent feeble-minded among the former and only 0.59 per cent in the general population. Studies of feeble-mindedness in twins add further support to the hereditary determination of this mental condition. In one study, 200 twin pairs were tested. Among 100 of these, which were members of monozygotic twin pairs and thus had the same genetic constitution, there was a feeble-minded twin in 88 cases and a normal twin in the remaining 12. This shows a high degree of conformity. In 100 dizygotic twin pairs, in which a feeble-minded member was reported, 7 had a feeble-minded twin and 93 had a normal twin. This difference in the incidence of feeble-mindedness in the two kinds of twins is interpreted as indicating that heredity is a potent source of feeble-mindedness.

INHERITANCE OF FEEBLE-MINDEDNESS. It is likely that no single type of heredity determines all kinds of feeble-mindedness. One hereditary factor, sometimes two or more, sometimes dominant and sometimes recessive factors, and even sex-linked genes have been suggested by various students as conditioning feeble-mindedness. The grade of feeble-mindedness is not always the same in families. Slightly defective parents may have imbecile or idiot children. Where the inheritance is recessive, the likelihood of the appearance of the condition is perpetually present. A heterozygous carrier of the recessive gene will be likely to have feeble-minded children when mated to another heterozygous carrier of the same gene. But, from a mating to a normal person without the recessive state, the children are likely to be normal. These recessive genes, however, are carried on through successive generations, ready to express themselves at any time when they are paired with other recessive genes for the conditions.

INHERITANCE OF EPILEPSY. A common impairment of the central nervous system is expressed in epilepsy. A study by Lennox indicated that 0.5 per cent of the American population has temporary lapses or fits. Twelve per cent are thought to carry genes for epilepsy without showing the symptoms. Some students distinguish between genuine and symptomatic epilepsy, implying that some epileptic conditions may have their origin in nongenetic causes such as embryonic injury, infantile illness, or various toxins or traumatisms. Because no simple Mendelian ratios have been confirmed in epilepsy and because mortality among epileptics is high, the conditions may be related to recessive genes, perhaps several.

INHERITANCE OF INSANITY. Though this subject, too, has been largely investigated, much remains to be learned. The manic-depressive psychosis, showing itself in alternating phases of extreme excitation or even violence and severe depression, is attributed to a single dominant gene. The type of insanity described as schizophrenia is also said to have a genetic basis. Explanations vary from postulates of a single recessive gene with partial penetrance to a two-gene theory, a single dominant or a multiple gene base. Possibly in the case of dementia praecox, certain environmental factors may act with a genetic base to evoke the condition.

Conclusion on Human Heredity

The real difficulty in the way of securing adequate information about human heredity is the lack of controlled experiments and the extreme complexity of heredity in organisms so diverse and specialized as man. In most genetic research with the lower animals and with plants, the experiment is set up to yield a certain type of data. In human beings such experiments are impossible. Data must be taken from families found in the general population (Fig. 202). The generations must be read backward. The current generation may be regarded as the F_2, in which case the immediate parents are the F_1 and the grandparents the P_1 generations. Or the current generation may be considered the F_1 resulting from the mating in the past generation of two parents with contrasting traits. In this case the F_2 would be sought in the following generation, 25 or more years in the future. Population genetics provides a most hopeful technique for further research in human genetics (pp. 312–326).

The complexity of heredity must be stressed. Most human beings are heterozygous for a great many genes. When it is realized that the number of genes known in certain of the lower organisms has been expanded to two or three thousand in some cases and that these do not comprise all the

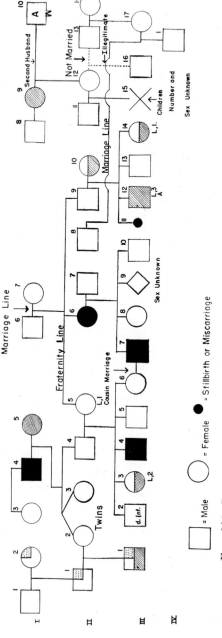

FIG. 202. PEDIGREE CHART TO SHOW MANNER OF CONSTRUCTION AND USE OF SYMBOLS.

Roman figures indicate generations; Arabic figures locate individuals. Placement of letters in or around a symbol standard for certain traits: A, alcoholic; B, blind; D, deaf; E, epileptic; F, feeble-minded; I, insane; M, migraineous; N, normal; Ne, neurotic; P, paralytic; S, syphilitic; T, tuberculous; W, wanderer. Specially designed for this chart: solid black = successful leader in politics; quarter-dotted = extra thumb on right hand; L,1 = highly successful author; L,3 = little or no literary ability; crosshatched = superior in vocal music. (Modified after International Commission on Eugenics, from J. Heredity.)

genes, it can be understood that there must be thousands of genes determining human characteristics. Even 10 pairs of alleles can produce 3^{10} or 59,049 different recombination types, according to Haldane. Thousands of genes can, therefore, produce a staggering number of variations. To clear up the background of these variations is a stupendous task. Nevertheless, a start has been made. As mentioned above, more than a hundred pairs of alleles are recognized in human beings, but the total number almost certainly runs into thousands, perhaps even tens of thousands.

Questions and Problems

1. Name some of the physical traits in human beings for which inheritance has been studied.
2. What kind of factors enter into the determination of stature in man? Do these factors have any relation to the type of graph which can be developed from height measurements in human populations?
3. What explanation can be offered for the facts that short parents sometimes have children taller than themselves?
4. Would you advise any of your friends to marry into a family in which dwarfism has appeared? Explain your answer.
5. Is stature in man dependent upon inheritance alone? What other factors may be considered?
6. From what is known of its inheritance in man and that of similar anatomical abnormalities in the lower animals, what may be the expectations in the immediate progenies should two achondroplastic dwarfs marry and have children?
7. What is the genetic basis of the occurrence of ateleiotic dwarfs?
8. If a man having six digits on each hand and foot should marry a normal woman, what would be the possibilities as to digit number in their children?
9. How is the trait of shortened fingers or brachydactyly inherited?
10. How is albinism inherited? How do you account for the fact that a normally pigmented man may marry a normally pigmented woman and have albinotic children? Why may an albino have normally pigmented children?
11. What is the genetic basis of the pigmentation characteristic of the Negro race?
12. In racial crosses between white and Negro races, what are the expectations as regards color in the F_2 generation?
13. Can racial characteristics of skin and hair be expected to reappear in children of mixed marriages? Why?
14. Why may the progenies of white and Negro crosses sometimes be nearly white as to pigmentation but show distinctly kinky hair and Negroid facial features?
15. Why is it difficult to offer simple genetical explanations of the inheritance of hair colors in man? Compare with coat colors in animals.
16. What is the mode of inheritance of hair form resulting in straight, curly, and kinky hair?
17. A popular statement is that civilized man has brought baldness upon himself by wearing tight hats. Evidence cited for this is that few women are bald. What may be said about this situation?
18. Describe the factor complex underlying the inheritance and development of eye colors in human beings.
19. How are the genes conditioning red-green color blindness carried from one generation to another? Why is it more likely that a man inherits color blindness from his mother's family than from his father's side of the house?

20. Diagram the situation showing the progenies of a color-blind father and a woman with normal vision. What is the genetic condition in their sons and daughters? Assume that these sons and daughters each marry persons with normal vision. What results may be expected in their children?

21. Name other defects of vision known to have a physical basis in heredity.

22. What ear conditions may be expected in the children of deaf parents?

23. Are first-cousin marriages a fundamental cause of deaf-mutism? Explain.

24. Distinguish between tolerance, resistance, and immunity in reference to disease.

25. Is a disease actually inherited?

26. What evidence concerning the inheritance of a tendency to the development of goitre can be gained from the study of fraternal and identical twins?

27. Is tuberculosis inherited? What is the relative incidence of tuberculosis in blood brothers and sisters of tuberculous patients as compared with brothers-in-law and sisters-in-law?

28. Is there any evidence to indicate that the tendency to develop cancer and other types of tumors may be inherited? Explain.

29. What is meant by multiple allelism? Explain how multiple alleles are involved in the inheritance of blood groups.

30. Compare the inheritance of hemophilia in human beings with that of color blindness.

31. What distinctions have psychologists made between temperament, character, and intelligence?

32. Are there variations in intelligence in the general population?

33. May high correlation of academic grades between fathers and sons be accounted for on any other basis than heredity? Explain.

34. Does the study of correlation of intelligence in siblings living in orphanages tend to favor heredity or environment as the chief factor in determining intelligence?

35. What evidence did Galton find to indicate that exceptional abilities are inherited?

36. How do the data accumulated by F. A. Woods indicate the inheritance of ability?

37. What explanation may be offered to account for the decline in the numbers of eminent men coming from the so-called lower classes in Great Britain?

38. If there is a steady decline in the production of men of ability in the lower classes, what is liable to be the sociological effect of a declining birth rate in the upper classes?

39. How does the evidence from the comparative studies of identical and fraternal twins support the theory that intelligence is inherited?

40. What is the probable factorial basis for the inheritance and development of degrees of intelligence?

41. What other qualities besides intelligence are essential for achievement and success?

42. Why is it possible to study the inheritance of musical ability so successfully?

43. Does the increase in patients in mental hospitals prove that defective mentality is increasing in the United States?

44. What results may be expected in the progeny of parents each of which came from a family in which feeble-mindedness has occurred?

45. What may be said as to the possible heritability of epilepsy and insanity?

46. As a general practice would you recommend cousin marriages?

47. Review the general topic of linkage (pp. 119–176). What is sex linkage? What is autosomal linkage?

48. What three types of sex linkage are recognized in human beings? What is the physical basis of these three types? Diagram to show the chromosomal relationships. Name some characteristic of each of these three types of sex linkage.

49. Why is autosomal linkage a difficult subject to investigate in human beings?

50. Investigations indicate a crossover value of from 5 to 15 per cent, with 10 per cent as a close approximation of the amount of crossing over between hemophilia and green color blindness. Upon this basis, what is the approximate distance in units separating these genes on the sex chromosome?

51. Is the map of the **X** chromosome in human beings thought to be long or short? Why?

References

BAUR, E., E. FISCHER, and F. LENZ: *Human Heredity*, New York, The Macmillan Company, 1931.

DAVENPORT, C. B.: *How We Came By Our Bodies*, New York, Henry Holt & Company, Inc., 1936.

———: "Inheritance of Stature," *Genetics* **II**:313–398 (1917).

———, HARRISON R. HUNT, and GEORGE H. SHULL: "Should Cousins Marry?" *Eugenics* **II**:2–3 (1929).

EAST, E. M., and D. F. JONES: *Inbreeding and Outbreeding. Their Genetical and Sociological Significance*, Philadelphia, J. B. Lippincott Company, 1919.

GATES, R. R.: *Heredity in Man*, London, Constable & Co., 1929.

———: *Human Genetics*, New York, The Macmillan Company, 1946.

———: *Pedigrees of Negro Families*, Philadelphia, The Blakiston Company, 1949.

HALDANE, J. B. S.: *New Paths in Genetics*, New York and London, Harper & Brothers, 1942.

HOGBEN, LANCELOT: *Nature and Nurture*, New York, W. W. Norton & Company, Inc., 1939.

HUNT, HARRISON R.: "Intelligence as a Mendelian Character," *J. Heredity* **17**:53–58 (1926).

MACKLIN, MADGE T.: "Do the Modes of Transmission of Tumors Vary?" *J. Heredity* **30**:396–400 (1939).

———: "The Role of Heredity in Disease," *Medicine* **14**:1–75 (1935).

SCHEINFELD, AMRAM: *You and Heredity*, New York, Frederick A. Stokes Company, 1939.

SNYDER, L. H.: *Medical Genetics*, Durham, North Carolina, Duke University Press, 1941.

———: *The Principles of Heredity*, 4th ed. Boston, D. C. Heath & Company, 1951.

———, R. C. Baxter, and A. W. Knisely: "Studies in Human Inheritance XIX," *J. Heredity* **32**:22–24 (1941).

——— and DWIGHT M. PALMER: "An Idiopathic Convulsive Disorder with Deterioration," *J. Heredity* **34**:207–212 (1943).

STERN, CURT: *Principles of Human Genetics*, San Francisco, W. H. Freeman and Company, 1949.

STOCKARD, C. R.: "Human Types and Growth Reactions," *Am. J. Anat.* **XXXI**:261–288 (1922).

———: *The Physical Basis of Personality*, New York, W. W. Norton & Company, Inc., 1931.

WIENER, A. S.: "Heredity of the Rh Blood Types *IX*. Observations in a Series of 526 Cases of Disputed Parentage," *Amer. J. Human Genet.* **2**:177–197 (1950).

——— "Rh Glossary," *Laboratory Digest*, November 1950.

———: "The Rh-Hr Blood Types: Serology, Genetics, and Nomenclature," *Trans. N. Y. Acad. Sci.*, Ser. II, Vol. 13, No. 6 (1951).

———: *Studies on Individual Differences in Human Blood and Their Practical Applications*, New York, Wiener Laboratories, 1951.

———, E. B. SONN, and R. B. BELKIN: "Heredity of the Rh Blood Types," *J. Exp. Med.* **79**:235–253 (1944).

WOODS, F. A.: *Heredity in Royalty*, New York, Henry Holt & Company, Inc., 1906.

Index

(Page numbers in *bold-face* refer to illustrations.)

DATE DUE

Due